Volume 2

TECHNOLOGY

WELDING METALLURGY

CARBON AND ALLOY STEELS

by

GEORGE E. LINNERT

Supervisor, Welding Research
Research and Technology Division
Armco Steel Corporation
Middletown, Ohio

THIRD EDITION

VOLUME 2
TECHNOLOGY

Published by
AMERICAN WELDING SOCIETY

Welding Technology Series

This book is the second in the Welding Technology Series, a group of books planned by the Technical Department of the American Welding Society. Volume II of Welding Metallurgy *will be followed by* Nonferrous Welding Metallurgy *and by* Metallography of Welds. *Arrangements are being made for other selected works in the field of welding.*

Library of Congress Catalog Card Number 65-26293

Printed in the United States of America

PREFACE

The first volume of *Welding Metallurgy* dealt with those fundamentals which, in the author's opinion, provide the best path to a rational understanding of the welding of carbon and alloy steels. Development of the subject began with the essentials of welding and metallurgy, considered separately. It concluded with a study showing how the welding thermal cycle alters the microstructure of the joint and how this alteration, in turn, affects joint properties. So far, the reception accorded Volume 1 has surpassed earlier expectations. The response from many respected colleagues and other interested individuals has been most encouraging and is gratefully acknowledged.

Volume 2 of *Welding Metallurgy* is concerned with the technology of welding carbon and alloy steels. There are many avenues of choice through which joint microstructure can be altered selectively in order to obtain optimum joint properties. By *technology* is meant the various ways in which welding engineers and technicians can apply this knowledge in planning and executing actual weldments to insure satisfactory performance in their intended service. The practicing welding engineer will recognize that this is the point where the complexities of welding must be handled in detail, but where the engineering of welding frequently becomes exciting. Here is where the casual participant is likely to become bewildered by the many factors which must be considered. Often, at this point, he gladly delegates the responsibilities of joining metals to the welding-oriented individual. An excursion into the technology of welding can be a rewarding experience because of the ever present challenge to make a better, or a less costly weld, and the tremendous breadth and depth of science and engineering from which knowledge can be extracted to accomplish these objectives. For many participants, these experiences are climaxed by witnessing the assembly and use of the most fantastic engineering structures created by man! And no small measure of satisfaction should come from knowing that many of these structures could not be produced without the aid of welding.

The discussions, illustrations, and data tables of the present volume again follow a basic metallurgical approach to each subject area. In this manner, a strong skeletal understanding is provided, which the reader may easily reinforce by specialized study into whatever other aspects are deemed important. There are many additional facets of welding which may assume major importance because of either the nature of the weldment or its intended use. Supplementary studies may reach into residual stress analysis, thermal flow computations, surface phenomena, and a host of other properties and characteristics. Nevertheless, metallurgy is the best vehicle for conveying a technical description of welding as a whole, and it readily accommodates a studied elaboration in any appropriate area.

Again the writer wishes to express gratitude to the Armco Steel Corporation and to Mr. T. F. Olt, Vice President, Research and Technology, in particular, for interest shown in this book and for assistance in the preparation of illustrative material. Special thanks go to many individuals in the welding field who responded so generously to my inquiries for photomicrographs. These respondents are being sent a personal message of appreciation. While most wives are helpmates in extracurricular activities, mine has been especially patient during the long period of preparation of these volumes, and assisted me in many of the final phases of assembly. Mr. E. A. Fenton, Technical Director, American Welding Society, must be given a special note of appreciation for his encouragement during this lengthy project. He also kindly consented to make a searching review of the technical content of the text. The work of Mr. R. H. Dierkes and Mr. C. H. Willer of the AWS technical staff in handling the details of publication must be warmly acknowledged. The skill of Mr. Willer in editing and publishing was praised in the preface for Volume 1. As this project was brought to completion, his editorial ability obviously was deserving of the highest commendation.

George E. Linnert

Middletown, Ohio
March, 1966

TABLE OF CONTENTS FOR VOLUME 2

TABLE OF CONTENTS

Chapter 10

FILLER METALS FOR JOINING IRON AND STEEL

In Chapter 9 of Volume 1, a study was made of the microstructural changes that take place over the entire portion of the weld joint that is affected by the welding thermal cycle. In the present Chapter, this previous work is carried forward and attention is focused upon one particular zone, namely, the *weld metal*. This is the region of the joint that has been melted during welding, and, after coalescence has taken place, subsequently freezes to complete the weld. While the rudiments of this process may seem simple enough, a basic consideration, not often discussed in adequate detail, is the *base metal* melted and *filler metal* added to form the *weld metal*. Obviously, if the base metal and filler metal are the two components that determine the composition of the weld metal, they will be important factors in establishing the final properties of the solidified weld. The base metal commonly is a fixed component because it is presented to the welding engineer as "the material to be joined." The filler metal, however, plays a more complex role. Quite apart from the obvious purpose of filling a groove or providing a reinforcement, filler metals offer the welding engineer an area of choice which can be effectively utilized to control the final chemical composition, and, in turn, the mechanical properties of the weld. Therefore, the subject of filler metals is deserving of a careful rationalization.

A great many of the welding processes involve the deposition of filler metal. This should be evident from the repeated mention of their

use in Chapter 3. Some arc welding processes employ a consumable electrode which is deposited as filler metal, while other processes may use
a supplementary rod or wire which is melted into the joint by a heat
source, such as an arc supported by a nonconsumable electrode, or a gas
flame. Brazing and soldering make use of filler metals, even though only
a thin film of filler metal is left between the workpieces. Although filler
metals are commonly thought of as specially prepared wire-forms, they
sometimes are employed in the form of cast rods, flat strip, thin foil,
square bars, powdered metal, and even precipitated metal from aqueous
solutions or gaseous compounds.

To state that filler metals are a special category of materials would
invoke no surprise from those who are concerned with welding. The
purchasing agent recognizes their higher cost relative to equivalent base
metal cost. The design engineer is aware of special standards establishing
their various classifications. Some welders have an almost mystical faith
in the capability of certain of their pet "rods." Even the storekeeper
recognizes their special status from the care they require in storage.
While all of these points of view acknowledge their special nature, none
of them reveals what it is that makes filler metals unique. A study of
their chemical composition would show, however, that, contrary to a popular assumption, filler metals are *not* generally the same materials as the
base metals they are designed to join. But a study of composition is itself
insufficient. To appreciate the metallurgical significance of their subtle
composition variations, we must examine how *weld metal* properties are
controlled by filler metal composition and many other factors. Because,
in the final analysis, it is the weld metal upon which we depend to bond
the workpieces together.

IMPORTANT FACTS ABOUT WELD METAL

While some of the basic differences between weld metal of iron and
weld metal of steel were described in Chapter 9, it was not, then, appropriate to cover further important facts about weld metal which are vital
to an understanding of welding metallurgy, and which directly affect
decisions regarding filler metal selection.

It would be well, here, to re-examine Fig. 111 of Volume 1 and compare in this photomicrograph the microstructure of weld metal with that
of base metal. If this illustration is not available, comparison of Fig. 216
and Fig. 225 will serve. Note that even where the weld metal and the
base metal are of the same composition, differences can be observed in

their microstructures. These differences are quite marked when the weld metal is in the as-deposited condition. Where the weld metal has been reheated, such as the first bead of a two-pass weld, the differences can still be seen. Postweld heat treatment, such as normalizing, usually does not completely eradicate the microstructural differences. The unique features found in the weld metal microstructure arise from the unusual conditions under which solidification has taken place. Consequently, weld metal will display a microstructure and properties that are not exactly like those of wrought metal, or even a casting, of the same chemical composition. Sometimes certain properties of the weld metal may be regarded as inferior; sometimes they may be considered superior. It has been established that a given *base metal* type may not represent the optimum chemical composition for *weld metal*. For virtually all metals and alloys used in wrought or cast form, modification in chemical composition will improve their properties in weld metal form. This is the principal reason why welding rods and electrodes have evolved as a separate class of materials. A second reason is the influence which filler metal composition exerts upon the mechanics of deposition. The effects observed in this area of filler metal technology will be highly dependent, of course, upon the particular welding process employed. Deposition characteristics will be touched upon later as the various kinds of filler metal are reviewed.

Weld metal can be formed by simply melting the tightly abutting edges of base metal workpieces together, in which case the joint is called an *autogenous* weld, meaning the weld metal was produced entirely from the base metal. For the majority of weld joints, however, some filler metal is added during the formation of the weld metal. For a complete appraisal of the weld metal origin, we must look to three possible contributing sources: (1) the base metal, (2) filler metal, which may be a welding rod or a consumable electrode, and (3) metal carried in a flux, slag, or adjuvant material. In much of the fusion joining practiced today, the major percentage of the weld metal is derived from filler metal in the form of a consumable electrode or a supplementary rod. Not as much use is made of slag or flux as the primary source or carrier of metal for the weld deposit. The base metal which is melted and thus mixes or alloys with any deposited filler metal is a component to be considered for two reasons. First, the filler metal ordinarily is of a composition which has been carefully *designed* to produce satisfactory weld metal. If this optimum composition is adulterated with an excess of the base metal composition, the properties of the weld metal may be less than satisfactory. The percentage of base metal which represents an excess in the weld metal naturally will depend upon the steels involved and many factors concerning the weldment. Second, if the *alloy* composition of the filler metal and the base metal are quite dissimilar, it remains to be seen whether the resultant weld metal alloy composition will be satisfactory for the application. As the requirements for weld joints in alloy steels become more stringent, circumstances arise where the welding engineer must do more than merely select a classification of filler metal reputed to be compatible with the type of steel base metal to be joined. It may be necessary to specify composition requirements for the weld metal, *in situ*. Consequently, the filler metal composition can be decided upon only after the base metal composition and the percent base metal which will enter the weld metal are known. This admixture of base metal into the weld metal is called *dilution*. A simple technique for coordinating filler metal with dissimilar composition base metal at different levels of dilution to secure a particular weld metal composition will be illustrated in this chapter. The practical significance of dilution during the welding of joints in alloy steels is discussed in Chapter 15.

The homogeneity of weld metal deposits often has been questioned because of alloys being contributed by as many as three separate sources. Chemical analyses have been made of drillings from very small holes positioned on the cross-section of weld metal deposited by the shielded metal-arc process in a joint. The results showed that electromagnetic stirring of the molten weld melt had accomplished remarkable uniformity of chemical composition from side to side and from top to bottom in each bead. More recent studies, however, utilizing metallographic examination and the electron microprobe analyzer, have shown that under certain welding conditions the final weld deposit can be heterogeneous in nature to some degree. The principal conditions which encourage heterogeneity are: (1) very high weld travel speed, (2) very large additions of alloy in an adjuvant material, and a variable arc length, and (3) an arc which produces deep penetration in a central area and secondary melting. Of course, the degree of heterogeneity observed will also depend upon the amount and kind of alloys involved, their sources, and many aspects of the welding conditions. Most weld deposits, however, can be regarded as being *essentially* homogeneous both over their cross-section and along their length providing welding conditions have been held constant. Homogeneity on a microscopic scale in the weld metal structure is a basic matter that has been given scant attention. Only recently has the partitioning of elements in the dendritic structure of certain weld metals been analyzed with the electron microprobe analyzer. Information on microstructural heterogeneity may be useful in determining how the properties of weld metal can be improved.

MECHANICAL PROPERTIES OF WELD METAL

Some very helpful general remarks can be made about the mechanical properties of steel weld metals. The welding engineer has been aware for a long time that most weld metals as-deposited display an unusually high yield strength as compared with the same composition steel in the cast or in the wrought conditions. For example, low-carbon steel weld metal regularly has a yield strength of at least 50 ksi, whereas a wrought steel of this same composition would possess a yield strength of only about 30 ksi. Furthermore, the tensile strength of the weld metal is somewhat higher than its wrought or cast counterparts. These facts regarding strength often are discussed in terms of yield strength–tensile strength ratio. In low-carbon steel, weld metal has a YS–UTS ratio of about 0.75. Cast and wrought steels of this same composition ordinarily have a ratio of about 0.50; that is, the yield strength is about one-half of the tensile strength. Because of this unusual inherent strength of weld metal, it is not necessary to employ as much carbon or other alloying elements in the filler metals for many of the steels as compared to that present in the base metal. However, the higher strength of weld metal is a peculiarity deserving of study. We should determine the reasons for this difference in strength, and ascertain whether any circumstances arise where weld metal does not exhibit this strength advantage.

Surprisingly little difference is found in the strength of weld metal deposited by any of the fusion joining processes. Shielded metal-arc, submerged-arc, gas metal-arc, gas tungsten-arc, atomic-hydrogen arc, and the oxyacetylene gas welding processes have been compared, both in making single bead deposits and in making multilayer welds. In comparing processes, those which accomplish welding with lowest heat input, and therefore are characterized by more rapid heating and cooling rates, tend to produce a finer grain, acicular microstructure. In the arc welding processes, shielded metal-arc and gas metal-arc welding tend to produce the fine grain, acicular structure, and the YS–UTS ratio of their weld deposits may range as high as 0.90. Processes which involve slower rates of heating and cooling, like atomic-hydrogen arc and oxyacetylene gas welding, produce weld metal with slightly larger, less acicular grains. Consequently, the strength and the YS–UTS ratio is correspondingly lower, but usually not less than about 0.60. Fig. 121 illustrates the yield strengths exhibited by low-carbon steel weld metal (less than 0.10% carbon, silicon killed) when deposited by six commonly used fusion joining processes. Also illustrated is the grain size observed in the weld metal deposited by each of these processes. It should be noted that as the rate of cooling increases with the different processes, a finer grain size is produced and the yield

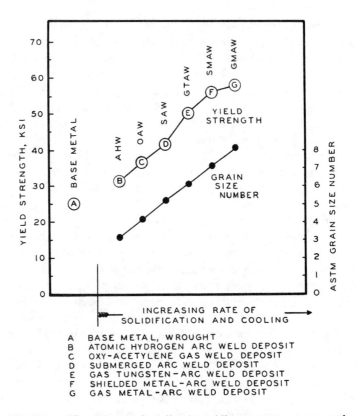

Fig. 121 — Effect of rate of cooling in welding process upon strength (and grain size) of weld metal. For weld metal containing less than 0.10% carbon, silicon killed. (After Tremlett, Baker and Wheatley)

strength is raised. Until recently, the remarkable strength of weld metal was attributed to its fine grain size. Incidently, investigators studying relationships between microstructure and properties had developed formulas for expressing the correlation found between grain size and yield strength. However, studies made on specially prepared wrought metal having a grain size equally as fine as weld metal failed to find comparable yield strength. The weld metal invariably was higher in yield strength than predicted by the formulas. It appeared that some additional feature of the microstructure of weld metal must exert a strong influence by delaying the onset of plastic flow under stress. Finally, electron microscopy showed conclusively that the very small grains of weld metal also have a substructure and an extremely large number of dislocations in the lattice. It appears, therefore, that interactions between numerous dislo-

cations in the relatively limited crystalline lattice of each small grain provide a complex mechanism that delays measurable plastic strain by slip
or twinning. Of course, the cooling rate of the weld metal also affects the
distribution of carbide particles that form in the microstructure. As would
be expected, faster cooling results in finer carbides or pearlite lamellae
and this also increases strength. Some evidence has been obtained through
careful examination of carbon replicas and electro-thinned specimens of
weld metal that extremely small, elongated areas of *retained austenite*
exist along the ferrite boundaries. While this information, at first thought,
may seem to be of little importance, it helps explain the unusual resistance
of the fine grains of weld metal to recrystallization. The retention of these
small areas of austenite, although quite surprising in view of the low-
carbon and low-alloy content, is thought to be attributable to stabilization
through plastic deformation during rapid cooling under restraint.

Reheating of weld metal by multipass deposition does little to change
the grain size and alter the dislocation density. Therefore, multipass weld
metal is virtually as strong (both UTS and YS) as single bead weld
metal. In metal-arc deposited weld metal, the small degree of recrystallization that occurs from deposition of the multiple passes tends to produce
a heterogeneous, duplex grain pattern of the original fine acicular grains
and a small number of larger equiaxed grains. Weld metal from the atomic-
hydrogen arc and the oxyacetylene gas welding processes is more
equiaxed in the as-deposited condition and undergoes even less change
during multipass welding.

When weld metal is postweld heated, no significant change occurs
in room temperature strength upon exposure to reheating temperatures
as high as 1200 F and for times as long as 5 hours. At a temperature of
about 700 F, the very small areas of retained austenite at the ferrite grain
boundaries are believed to undergo transformation to ferrite. Extremely
small carbides are precipitated in the newly formed ferrite. These areas
then appear to serve very effectively to prevent recrystallization. Hence,
the very fine ferrite grain size is preserved along with its inherent high
strength until the metal is heated to the point where austenite begins to
form (eutectoid temperature). At temperatures above 1200 F, the number
of dislocations in the lattice begin to diminish and this acts to lower the
yield strength. Temperatures about 1300 F and higher are above the
eutectoid point and cause some austenite to form. This results in the
formation of equiaxed ferrite grains when transformation occurs upon
cooling. Therefore, temperatures above 1300 F reduce dislocation density
and produce recrystallization. With microstructural changes of this kind,
the weld metal strength (and the YS–UTS ratio) will decrease to that

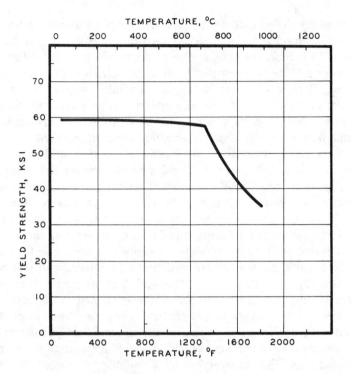

Fig. 122 — Room temperature yield strength of arc-deposited mild steel weld metal as affected by reheating to temperatures up to 1800 F (after Wheatley and Baker).

normally found in cast and wrought steel of the same composition (see Fig. 122). Annealing at 1750 F reduces the dislocation density to the low level found in annealed wrought steel. However, the grain structure of weld metal heated to this temperature, though equiaxed, still is finer than regular wrought steel and is reflected in somewhat higher strength in the weld metal. Heating to temperatures above approximately 1750 F is required to increase the grain size of the weld metal to equal that of wrought metal (see Fig. 123).

HOW WELD METAL REQUIREMENTS AFFECT FILLER METAL SELECTION

The engineering of weldments would be much less complicated if weld metal could be readily secured which possessed mechanical properties and physical characteristics matching those of the base metal. This seemingly simple objective is difficult to attain, as we now understand, because the base metal composition when fused to form weld metal invariably offers a uniquely different set of properties. In many cases, the properties of the autogenous weld would not be entirely satisfactory. Furthermore, the base metal composition may be quite unsuitable for undergoing the conditions of droplet transfer, exposure to oxidizing conditions, rapid freezing, and the many other unusual conditions to which a steel filler metal is subjected during deposition. Consequently, the welding engineer in planning practically all weldments must look for a new composition of steel which will serve as filler metal. There will be circumstances, of course, where a nonferrous filler metal will offer a better solution to the weld metal problem. However, before this search for a filler metal can be

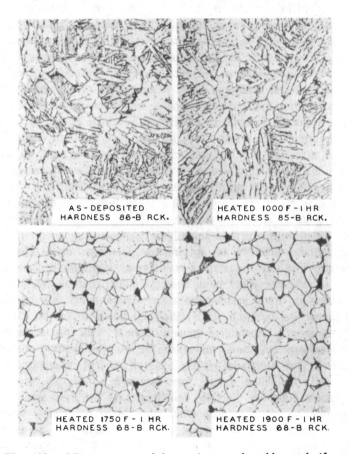

AS-DEPOSITED
HARDNESS 86-B RCK.

HEATED 1000 F-1 HR
HARDNESS 85-B RCK.

HEATED 1750 F-1 HR
HARDNESS 68-B RCK.

HEATED 1900 F-1 HR
HARDNESS 68-B RCK.

Fig. 123 — Microstructure of low-carbon steel weld metal (from an E6010 electrode) as-deposited, after heating to 1000 F, and after normalizing at two different temperature levels. Etchant: Nital.
Mag. 500X

started the engineer must know what properties are deemed important in the *weld metal,* and the required levels of test values for these properties. If the specific levels needed are not known, he should at least give some thought as to how closely the properties of the weld metal must match those of the base metal.

Strength, either ultimate tensile strength, or yield strength, usually is the first property that receives attention in considering the kind of weld metal needed. For the majority of weldments, there seldom is any argument against having the weld metal match the base metal in strength. Certainly, it would appear to be desirable to have the weld metal in a butt joint equal in strength to the base metal. There are instances, however, where a somewhat lower strength can be tolerated in the weld metal. This is often true of fillet welds where a relatively large cross-section of weld metal easily can be deposited to compensate for lower strength, and where the greater toughness and ductility which normally go with lower strength could be an attribute. Fillet welded joints often contain points of stress concentration and greater demands sometimes are made of the weld metal to exhibit toughness and ductility. It is a rare case where the weld metal is required to be substantially stronger than the base metal. In fact, weld metal of significantly higher strength is likely to be cause for concern. If the weldment containing extra strong weld metal was accidently overloaded beyond its yield point, a weld joint being subjected to transverse plastic bending might cripple or buckle in the heat-affected zone adjacent to the weld metal. If the weld joint was being forced to elongate longitudinally along with the base metal, the extra strong weld metal might have inadequate ductility to accompany the base metal through the deformation. For the majority of weldments, therefore, it is considered desirable to have the weld metal strength match that of the base metal. For this reason, many specifications for welded joints require the weld metal to meet the minimum UTS which has been set for the base metal, or at least meet a substantial percent thereof. This discussion of weld strength also provides some explanation for the classification of most steel welding rods and electrodes on the basis of strength. Furthermore, these standardized steel filler metals are designed to deposit weld metals which possess adequate ductility and toughness for most services.

Toughness is the property which appears to be next to strength in terms of importance in weld metal. Of course, there may be exceptional weldments where toughness is of primary importance. Again, we find that weld metal toughness is controlled through chemical composition, and the alloying that promotes greater toughness in base metal is not necessarily optimum for weld metal. Later in this chapter, the composition of low-alloy steel filler metals will be discussed, and special emphasis will be directed to the alloying systems which have been found to be most effective for increasing the toughness of weld metal. A particularly difficult problem is to secure weld metal that is comparable in toughness to a quenched and tempered high-strength steel base metal with the condition of the welded joint being restricted to the as-welded, or the welded and stress-relief heat treated conditions. This problem of providing weld metal with comparable toughness to a specially heat treated base metal becomes a real challenge when the weldment is to be used at cryogenic temperatures.

Many other properties can be of special importance in the weld metal depending upon the nature of the weldment and its intended service. As an example, it may be imperative that the corrosion resistance of the weld metal in atmospheric exposure equal that of the base metal. While this requirement may appear to call for the filler metal to have at least the same amount and kind of alloy content as is present in the base metal, here again we find another peculiarity of weld metal; namely, that mild steel weld metal exhibits better resistance to atmospheric corrosion than wrought mild steel. Consequently, less alloy is required in weld metal to produce corrosion resistance equal to that of a low-alloy wrought steel. Often, high-strength, low-alloy wrought steels which have been selected for their corrosion resistance are welded with unalloyed mild steel filler metal. As will be explained shortly, enough alloy is *picked up* by the weld metal to increase its corrosion resistance to an adequate level. Of course, where unusual service conditions promote corrosion, such as elevated temperature oxidation or scaling, then the weld metal probably will be required to have an alloy composition somewhat similar to the base metal in order to exhibit comparable resistance. In this case, the element chromium probably would be employed, and the amount required in the weld metal and the base metal would depend upon the nature of the environment to which the weldment will be exposed.

Other examples easily can be found of special properties needed in weld metal which must be secured through chemical composition; however, space will not permit a detailed discussion on how each is achieved. A weld metal may be required to exhibit excellent machinability, a property which often is secured in wrought steel by additions of sulfur during steelmaking. Weld metal machinability must be improved via another more complex alloying system because of the harmful effects that a high sulfur content would have upon weld metal soundness. Weld metal in an article to be coated with vitreous or porcelain enamel is expected to undergo this operation as readily as the base metal which, in many cases, is an enameling iron. The weld metal composition required will be highly dependent upon both the type of iron or steel in the base metal and the exact nature of the enameling technique. Weld metal sometimes is required to be capable of extensive, uniform tensile elongation, so that a welded article can be subjected to severe cold forming operations and not exhibit susceptibility to weld joint breakage. Although many additional examples of special requirements for weld metal can be cited, the aforementioned should serve to emphasize that when specific properties are demanded in the weld metal of a weldment, the chemical composition of the weld metal must be *designed* to provide these properties.

In the past, with strength and toughness over a relatively narrow range of temperature commonly being the only requirements, the welding engineer usually would find the standardized welding rods or electrodes satisfactory for the great majority of applications. He now finds more often that the performance demanded of weld joints calls for a more detailed study of the weld metal to be certain this portion of the weld joint possesses all the properties needed to assure satisfactory service performance. The modern engineering approach to providing weld metal best suited for a particular weldment is to formulate its composition on the basis of test data and experience with weld metal, *per se*. While the amount of such information available is only a mere shadow of that accumulated for wrought and cast steels, the data being reported in the literature grow steadily in volume and in completeness as their importance is recognized. Helpful information on weld metal composition and related properties will be offered from time to time as various types of carbon and alloy steels are discussed. Let us assume for the moment, however, that the required weld metal composition for a specific weldment has been established, and the ranges for the alloying elements are different from those of any of the readily available standard filler metals. What is the welding engineer to do — should he search for a proprietary filler metal having an analysis matching that of the desired weld metal composition? Such a move overlooks a most important step in planning a welding procedure! Namely, introducing the *base metal* composition into computations for setting the filler metal composition limits.

When weld metal composition limits are firmly fixed, the welding engineer easily can determine in a quantitative manner how the base metal will affect the filler metal composition requirements. As mentioned earlier, fusion welding invariably involves some melting of the base metal, and this impending diluent requires recognition in anticipating the weld metal composition. Ordinarily, if the welding engineer selects the edge preparation, joint geometry, penetration and weld metal area, he will be able to predetermine with sketches of the joint cross-section, or with welded test coupons the percent dilution of the weld metal by the base metal. (See Fig. 236). Of course, there can be some uncertainty about the exact amount of dilution that will occur. Also, various weld beads deposited in the joints may undergo different amounts of dilution. For example, a root bead deposited with a technique designed for deep penetration may encounter very heavy dilution, perhaps 80%; that is, the weld metal is made up of 80% base metal and only 20% filler metal. On the other hand, the final weld beads in the joint will not penetrate the base metal as extensively, and will require a greater proportion of filler metal to fill the joint and complete the weld. The dilution in such beads may be only in the order of 20% (i.e., 20% base metal and 80% filler metal). Obviously, coordination will be needed between (a) base metal composition, (b) percent dilution, and (c) weld metal composition to project the desired filler metal composition. Fig. 124 makes use of a simple diagram for illustrating the changing alloy content of weld metal as varying amounts of dilution occur with particular base metal and filler metal. Let us see how effectively this kind of diagram can delineate the minima and maxima of ranges for the alloying elements in the filler metal.

Coordination Diagram for Filler Metal Composition

A hypothetical problem is presented in Fig. 124 (A, B, C and D) to illustrate how the ideal filler metal and its composition limits can be determined for joints in a weldment. The gas tungsten-arc welding process is to be used for fabricating a weldment of 1¼%Cr–½%Mo alloy steel. The analysis of this particular heat of base metal is given in the footnote of Fig. 124. Also shown are the weld metal composition limits which experience has dictated for this (hypothetical) application. Note that carbon, manganese, chromium and molybdenum are the more important elements in the weld metal and they must be closely controlled to insure satisfactory fabricating behavior and service performance. Accordingly, the weld metal cannot be permitted to contain more than 0.15% carbon because cracking susceptibility might become a problem in welding. However, carbon is an important element in promoting strength at elevated temperatures in this alloy steel, and the application demands matching elevated temperature strength in the weld metal. For this reason, a minimum carbon content of 0.07% has been decided upon. Even so, to insure the required strength in the weld joints, the welding engineer has elected that the chromium and molybdenum contents of the weld metal shall be increased above those of the base metal to compensate for the restricted carbon content, and has specified ranges of 1.50 to 2.50% for chromium and 0.60 to 1.10% for molybdenum. The manganese content

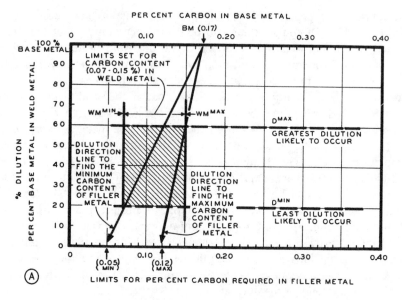

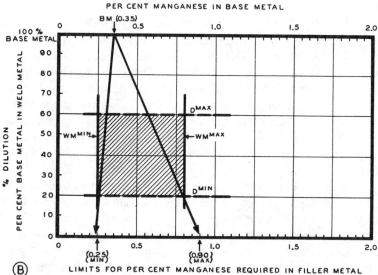

Fig. 124 (A), (B), (C) and (D) — Coordination diagram useful for determining the alloy composition limits for filler metal when a specified weld composition is desired.

Base metal analysis and percent dilution expected in the weld joints must be known, as illustrated in these diagrams for the alloying elements carbon, manganese, chromium and molybdenum. This hypothetical case concerns a 1¼ % Cr–½ % Mo steel which con-

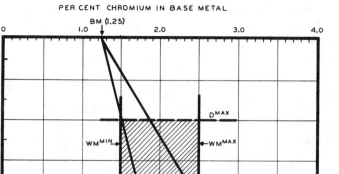

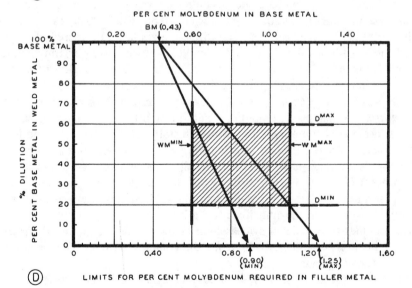

tains 0.17% C, 0.35% Mn, 1.25% Cr and 0.43% Mo. Weld metal
deposited in the joints by the GTAW process is required to contain
0.07/0.15% C, 0.25/0.80% Mn, 1.50/2.50% Cr and 0.60/1.10% Mo.
Filler metal composition limits are indicated by dilution–direction
lines which must pass through required weld composition–dilution
areas (shaded) before they intercept lower composition scale to indicate minima and maxima for alloying elements.

of the weld metal is expected to be similar to that of the base metal.

Referring to the diagrams in Fig. 124, let us imagine that the welding engineer has established from sketches of the proposed joints that the maximum dilution likely to be encountered in any of the deposited weld beads is 60%. This maximum dilution is expected in the first weld pass where complete penetration through the root of the joint is required. Of course, some base metal is expected to enter all beads deposited, but a dilution of only 20% appears to be the least which will occur in the subsequent weld beads. Therefore, each of the diagrams (A, B, C and D) in Fig. 124 have horizontal broken lines (identified as $D^{min.}$ and $D^{max.}$) depicting the 20 to 60% range on the vertical coordinate over which dilution will vary during welding. The vertical solid lines on each of the diagrams, identified as $WM^{min.}$ and $WM^{max.}$, indicate the limits within which the particular alloying element noted can be safely permitted to vary in the weld metal. It can be seen that the shaded area bounded by these lines contains all the points that satisfy the conditions for weld metal, and that all other points outside the shaded area do not. As a first step in using this diagram, the base metal content of the element in question is found on the upper horizontal scale which represents 100% base metal. This point is identified as BM. The lower horizontal scale represents zero base metal (100% filler metal). It should be obvious that a straight line drawn from point BM to any point on the lower horizontal scale will represent a "dilution-direction" line; that is, any intermediate point on this line will represent the quantity of the element to be found in the weld metal at the corresponding percent dilution. This must be true, of course, where the weld metal is composed only of base metal and filler metal and no loss of elements has occurred during welding. The next operation with the diagram is to determine the locus of dilution-direction lines extending from point BM and passing through the shaded area such that all points on these lines fall between the minimum and maximum weld metal composition limits over the anticipated dilution range. The extremes of this locus of lines have been drawn as long arrows in the diagrams of Figure 124. Thus each establishes a limit for the content of the element in question for the filler metal.

The lateral position of the shaded rectangle with respect to the point BM will greatly affect the angularity of the dilution-direction lines. It should be noted that when the dilution-direction lines traverse the shaded area, they must intersect both the D^{min} and D^{max} boundaries within the WM^{min} and WM^{max} limits. As the shaded area is shifted laterally further to the right or to the left of the point BM, the dilution-direction lines will be drawn closer together (form a more acute angle) thus indicating a narrower permissible range for the element in the filler metal. Continued lateral shifting of the shaded rectangle eventually will bring the lines into convergence as the diagonal of the rectangle, which means that only one particular level of the element in the filler metal will satisfy the prescribed welding conditions; hence, the filler metal requirement will be extremely difficult to fulfill. If the shaded rectangle is located so far to the right or to the left of the point BM that no straight line can be drawn as the diagonal of the rectangle, then no single filler metal composition will satisfy all conditions. Unless some change can be made in the parameters for dilution, or for weld metal composition, more than one filler metal will be required and these must be used to deposit specified weld beads which undergo more restricted ranges of dilution.

Let us examine a base metal–filler metal coordination diagram for details. The diagram for chromium, Fig. 124 (C), shows that dilution–direction lines can extend from point BM, which indicates the actual base metal chromium content of 1.25%, to as low as 1.90% and as high as 2.80% on the filler metal composition scale and yet pass within the specified weld metal chromium limits (1.5/2.5%) while in the 20 to 60% dilution range. Hence, the filler metal for this weldment must have a chromium content within the range of 1.90 to 2.80%, which is substantially higher than the base metal chromium content, and naturally is a little higher than the range of chromium set for the weld metal. To establish the limits for carbon, manganese and molybdenum in the filler metal, the same plotting procedure is followed as explained for chromium. On each of the diagrams, the required weld composition – dilution area has been shaded for emphasis. The element carbon must be manipulated in opposite fashion than in the case of chromium. The carbon in the base metal (0.17%) is above the range of 0.07 to 0.15% set for the weld metal. Consequently, the filler metal must offset the pickup of carbon which occurs during the 20 to 60% dilution. Fig. 124 (A) shows the desired carbon range for the filler metal to be 0.05 to 0.12%. In the case of manganese, Fig. 124 (B) shows that no particular problem should be encountered in holding the weld metal to the 0.25 to 0.80% range providing the filler metal contains approximately 0.25 to 0.90% of this element. Molybdenum, Fig. 124 (D), like chromium, also is required to be increased in the weld metal as compared with the base metal. The diagram shows that a weld metal molybdenum content of 0.60 to 1.10% can be secured if the filler metal contains 0.90 to 1.25% molybdenum. Any other elements in the weld metal, which would deserve close control to assure expected weld metal properties, could be plotted in this same manner on a coordination diagram. The thorough welding engineer probably would prepare diagrams for the elements silicon, phosphorus and sulfur just to be certain that no abnormality would develop in the weld metal composition through an oversight in filler metal selection.

The final step in the use of information from the coordination diagram is to locate welding rod or bare wire having an analysis that conforms with the projected filler metal composition ranges. Often, the desired filler metal is available as a stock material of a standard classification or a proprietary brand. This is true in the case of the low-carbon 2¼% Cr–1% Mo filler metal needed for the hypothetical weldment employed in our illustration. However, even experienced welding engineers are surprised to see how often the coordination diagram clearly indicates the need for a different type or classification of filler metal than the one which they ordinarily would have selected. If, however, no filler metal which complies with the desired composition limits is available, the welding engineer has at least two recourses. First, he can select an available filler metal which closely approaches the desired ranges for the specified alloying elements. Then, by locating the exact position for elements in this filler metal on the lower abscissa of coordination diagrams, he can quickly ascertain by means of the dilution–direction line how much deviation will occur from the required weld metal composition in any of the weld beads. Many possible changes to effect a satisfactory compromise will become apparent here. For example, the welding technique can be altered to shift the range of dilution and thus accommodate the slightly "off analysis" filler metal. Sometimes a deviation in one alloying element can be accepted, providing a compensating shift is made in the amount of another element. The second recourse which the welding engineer can take is to place a production order for the desired filler metal. Many times this is quite impracticable because of the small quantity required, or the length of time available. However, necessity is the mother of invention and more than one filler metal of special analysis has been procured as a composite material, such as a plated wire, or as two wires of dissimilar composition twisted together. Sometimes the desired filler metal composition must be pursued doggedly, but there is real compensation in its use because optimum weld metal properties are secured only when the chemical composition of the metal in the joint is within the *designed* limits.

In our hypothetical filler metal composition problem, no adjustments in alloy content were made for oxidation loss because the gas tungsten-arc welding process provides adequate shielding for the alloying elements involved. However, if a loss, or a gain of certain alloying elements would be expected as a result of the process or the procedure employed, then an adjustment should be made in the final composition limits set for the filler metal. Experience has shown the coordination diagram to be very useful in solving problems of filler metal selection with any of the arc welding processes, including shielded metal-arc, submerged arc, and gas metal-arc welding.

FILLER METALS FOR JOINING

A wide variety of metals and alloys are used as filler metal in joining operations on carbon and alloy steels. They range from the non-ferrous metals and alloys employed in soldering, brazing, and braze welding to the high-alloy steels used in welding processes. To cover all welding, brazing and soldering operations, a list of the useful filler metals would include the following:

1. Ingot iron or decarburized steel
2. Carbon steel
3. Low-alloy steel
4. High-alloy (stainless) steel
5. Nickel and nickel-base alloys
6. Copper and copper-base alloys
7. Tin and tin-base solders
8. Cobalt-base alloys

Filler metals are employed in the joining processes in a number of different forms. Probably the earliest form of filler metal was a shearing taken from the edge of thin base metal. Although shearings still are occasionally used for some operations today, we now know that this practice is questionable because base metal seldom represents the optimum filler metal composition. As welders called for more convenient forms of filler metal, material was supplied as thin cast bars, and then as smooth, round wire. From descriptions of the welding processes in Chapter 3, filler metal is also produced in the form of tubular powder-filled rods and wire, thin flat strip, pellets, and powdered metal. There are certain soldering operations in which the metal for joining is chemically precipitated from an aqueous flux solution. New brazing operations are reported in which the required filler metal is produced from a mixture of gases in a controlled atmosphere.

There is good reason, however, for starting this review of filler metals with a discussion of the two most widely used forms; namely, electrodes and welding rods. Because careless use of the terms "rods" and "wires" in place of *electrodes* and *welding rods* often causes confusion in discussions of welding procedures, it should be worthwhile to explain the correct terminology. In the AWS–ASTM classification system for filler metals, the initial letters of the designations indicate the basic process categories by which the filler metals are intended to be deposited. The letter E stands for electrode, R for welding rod, and B for brazing filler metal. Combinations of ER and RB indicate suitability for either of the process categories designated. Therefore, some filler metals cannot be identified as electrodes or welding rods until they have been put to use. This may account, in part, for the looseness with which these two terms are commonly used. Furthermore, the various shapes in which these filler metals are commonly supplied are so similar to the usual concepts of rods, wires, sticks, etc., that the ordinary use of such terms is natural and expressive. Be that as it may, some filler metals are immediately identifiable as electrodes or welding rods, and, as to those which are not, welding procedures are quite specific in regard to the process used, so that the technical language can and should be quite exact.

An electrode, in general, is a terminal that serves to conduct current to or from an element in an electrical circuit. In welding, a *filler metal electrode* serves as the terminal of an arc, the heat of which progressively melts the electrode as it is advanced to maintain an approximately constant arc length. Whenever the term *electrode* is used alone in this chapter and elsewhere, it should be clear from the context whether or not its use as a filler metal is intended. A welding rod, on the other hand, carries no current. It is advanced at a suitable rate from an external position into the heat source, which may be an arc, or a gas flame, and is melted approximately as it advances. While there should be no problem in understanding the operational difference between electrodes and welding rods, these filler metals are supplied in such great variety of forms, shapes and sizes that some attempt at further description is warranted.

Welding rod ordinarily is a *bare* rod or wire which is employed as filler metal in any fusion joining process, and which does not act as an electrode if used in an arc welding process. One exception to the bare condition is the flux-covered bronze rod which is sometimes used for braze welding. Welding rod may be either *solid* or *composite*. Solid products are made as a cast rod or as drawn wire. The solid wrought wire is available in straightened and cut lengths (usually 36"), or in coils. The cast rod is marketed in straight lengths. Solid welding rod may be used with any of the many fusion joining processes. For this reason, the chemical composition is governed by analysis requirements on the actual rod. Composite welding rod is manufactured in several different kinds of construction. The rod may be a tube filled with any desired combination of flux and powdered metal; or it may be a folded length of strip in which the folds have been filled with powdered ingredients and then closed at the surface by crimping. Composite rods are manufactured to secure an overall composition that sometimes is difficult to produce as wrought solid wire. Occasionally a number of fine, solid wires of different metals and alloys are braided together so that their overall composition fills the need for a particular alloy. Composite welding rod usually is subject to analysis requirements based upon the composition of undiluted weld metal deposited by a prescribed process and procedure. This practice is followed because the recovery of alloying elements in the weld metal deposit will depend to some extent upon their form in the composite rod.

Filler metal electrodes often called *consumable electrodes,* may be in the form of straight or coiled wire, either solid or composite. The solid electrode may be bare, lightly coated with a flux or an emissive material, or heavily covered with fluxing and slag-forming ingredients. If the solid electrode bears a coating or a covering, the heart of the electrode is the *core wire.* However, the flux may not necessarily be present as a surface covering. Sometimes the flux is included as a core material in a tubular wire or enfolded in a crimped or wrapped electrode. A braided electrode of fine wires may be impregnated with a flux. A solid core wire in coils may have a fine wire spirally wrapped on the surface and a flux covering applied after wrapping. The flux covering is then lightly brushed or sand blasted to expose a portion of the surface of the spirally wrapped wire. This wire permits electrical contact through the flux covering from the contact jaws (of a continuous type welding head) to the core wire. Another covered electrode using solid, coiled wire makes use of a wire-mesh sleeve which is imbedded in the flux (but in contact with the core wire and exposed at the surface) to pass current for welding.

Composite electrodes are those in which two or more metal components are combined mechanically. As another example of this type, a tube filled with powdered metal may be used instead of solid wire. Again, these *tubular electrodes* permit the formulation of alloys which are difficult to produce or to utilize in the form of coils of solid drawn wire. Chemical analysis determinations concerning composite electrodes are made on undiluted weld metal deposited by the electrode using the process for which the product was designed.

Knowledge of the construction and formulation of an electrode can be of considerable help in avoiding difficulties. This is particularly true in the case of composite electrodes where the components have been proportioned by the manufacturer to provide the required alloy composition in the weld deposit. In using tubular powder-filled wire, care must be taken to avoid loss of the metal powder from the core. This may occur if the electrode is bent awkwardly or crushed and the seam is opened sufficiently for the powder to sift out. If the powder is not bonded in the core, a portion may run out when the tubular electrode end is cut off. Loss of metal powder in any manner results in a weld deposit deficient in the alloying elements contained in the powder. This loss may not be detectable by the appearance of the deposit, but is likely to become apparent later. This portion of the welded joint probably will show a deficiency in mechanical properties, corrosion resistance, or whatever properties were to be gained from the missing alloy content. Covered electrodes which contain large amounts of powdered metal in the covering also must be given similar consideration. Even the method of preparing the striking end of any covered electrode can be very important. It will be recalled that a covered electrode in supporting the welding arc melts with a conical sheath (see Fig. 11). If the covering is chamfered excessively at the striking end, a smaller than normal amount of covering is melted with the initially deposited metal. If an electrode is used part way, and the welder in restriking the arc dislodges a large fragment of covering from the end, then the deposit will be deficient in alloy at the start of the bead. Whether the smaller amount of covering and its contained alloy will be significant depends, of course, upon the amount of alloy normally secured via the covering, the nature of the alloying elements, and their role in the deposit. An alloy deficiency, even in a small portion of a weld bead, can be metallurgically significant. Finally, those electrodes which contain greater amounts of easily oxidized alloying elements require more care during deposition. Electrodes which depend upon elements like chromium, molybdenum, vanadium or columbium to secure particular weld metal properties should be deposited with a short arc length, and as little weaving as possible. This technique is intended to minimize exposure of the metal droplets being transferred and the weld melt surface to any oxygen and nitrogen from the atmosphere which may have infiltrated the arc.

SPECIFICATIONS FOR WELDING RODS AND ELECTRODES

Specifications for welding rods and electrodes have been issued by a dozen or more domestic organizations, including the following:

American Welding Society
American Society for Testing and Materials
American Society of Mechanical Engineers
American Bureau of Shipping
Society of Automotive Engineers
U. S. Army Ordnance
U. S. Navy, Bureau of Ships

U. S. Federal Specifications
U. S. Navy, Bureau of Aeronautics
U. S. Coast Guard

These organizations have done much over the years to standardize the composition and construction of welding rods and electrodes, and to secure consistency in performance from lot to lot. Presently, most welding rod and electrodes for fabricating military equipment are procured against the military specifications of the "MIL—" series. Commercial users naturally turn to the specifications developed jointly by the AWS and the ASTM. The AWS-ASTM specifications, incidently, are also adopted by the ASME. Much attention has been given to having common requirements in the specifications of the military and the AWS-ASTM, but a complete merging or interchange has yet to be achieved. Space will not permit a review of all the specifications promulgated by groups concerned with welding rods and electrodes; however, those issued by AWS-ASTM are widely recognized and serve as good examples for discussion. Their specifications are quite complete, and each includes an appendix of helpful information. Rather than reproduce these specifications here, even in abbreviated form, the reader is urged to study complete copies. A list of specifications covering filler metals employed in joining steel was given in Chapter 2.

Of course, the development and standardization of filler metals is a never ending activity, and new and novel welding rods and electrodes periodically appear on the market. Those which have yet to be included in specifications, but which have achieved significant usage, are discussed after the standard classes in each kind of alloy.

Most of the AWS-ASTM specifications, it may be recalled, deal with a single kind of alloy and either the bare rod or covered electrodes. Because covered electrodes were used in much greater quantities than bare electrodes over the past twenty years, more attention was given to the preparation of specifications for the former. Recently, however, specifications have been issued by the AWS-ASTM for the bare solid and composite electrodes employed in gas metal-arc and submerged arc welding of carbon and low-alloy steels.

It is of more than passing interest to know that virtually all covered electrodes of the carbon and low-alloy steels are made from a single kind of steel core wire; namely, a low-carbon, rimmed steel. Therefore, the flux covering on an electrode is a most important factor in determining operating characteristics, and the classification of covered electrodes is determined to a large extent by the nature of the covering. The addition of deoxidizing agents and alloying elements to the deposit is accom-

Table 44 — *TYPE OF COVERINGS USED ON CARBON AND LOW-ALLOY STEEL ARC-WELDING ELECTRODES*

Electrode class	Description of covering	Positions in which satisfactory welds can be made	Kind of welding current	Penetration characteristics	Kind of slag on deposit	Weld metal soundness
E4510[a]	Sulcoat or light flux coating	F, V, OH, H	DC-SP	Moderate	Very thin	Quite porous
E4520[a]	Sulcoat or light flux coating	H, F	DC-SP	Moderate	Very thin	Quite porous
EXX10	High cellulose, sodium silicate binder	F, V, OH, H	DC-RP	Moderate	Very thin	Good
EXX10[a] iron powder	High cellulose, sodium silicate binder, 10% iron powder	F, V, OH, H	DC-RP	Moderate	Thin	Good
EXX11	High cellulose, potassium silicate binder	F, V, OH, H	AC, DC-RP	Moderate	Very thin	Good
EXX12	High titania, sodium silicate binder	F, V, OH, H	DC-SP, AC	Shallow	Moderate	Single bead good; multi-layer porous
EXX13	High titania, potassium silicate binder	F, V, OH, H	AC, DC-SP, DC-RP	Shallow	Moderate	Good

EXX14	Titania, about 20% iron powder	F, V, OH, H	DC-RP, DC-SP, AC	Moderate	Moderate	Good
EXX15	Low hydrogen, sodium silicate binder	F, V, OH, H	DC-RP	Moderate	Moderate to heavy	Excellent
EXX16	Low hydrogen, potassium, titania	F, V, OH, H	AC, DC-RP	Moderate	Moderate to heavy	Excellent
EXX18	Low hydrogen, potassium, titania, 25-40% iron powder	F, V, OH, H	AC, DC-RP	Moderate	Moderate to heavy	Excellent
EXX20	High iron oxide	H - Fillets / F	AC, DC-SP / AC, DC-SP, DC-RP	Deep	Heavy	Excellent
EXX24	Titania, 35% iron powder	H - Fillets, F	AC, DC-SP, DC-RP	Shallow	Heavy	Good
EXX27	Iron powder, iron oxide	H - Fillets / F	AC, DC-SP / AC, DC-SP, DC-RP	Moderate	Heavy	Excellent
EXX28	Low hydrogen, 50% iron powder	H - Fillets, F	AC, DC-RP	Moderate	Heavy	Excellent
EXX30[a]	High iron oxide	F	AC, DC-SP, DC-RP	Deep	Heavy	Excellent

[a] Not a recognized classification in current AWS-ASTM specifications.

plished by incorporating suitable powdered materials in the flux covering. As will be shown, a remarkably wide array of filler metal compositions is produced with electrodes which employ this covering technique. While covering formulas with respect to alloy content are held as proprietary information by the electrode manufacturer, the coverings on carbon and low-alloy steel electrodes are identified by a unique numbering system which employs four or five digits following the E prefix. The first two (and sometimes three) digits indicate the approximate minimum tensile strength expected of the weld metal in a certain condition; that is, plain steel weld metal is tested as-deposited, while the majority of the low-alloy steel weld metals are tested in the stress-relieved condition. The next to last digit in the classification number indicates the position in which the electrode is capable of making satisfactory welds. Only three numbers are employed and they indicate the following:

Electrode Classification	Capable of Producing Satisfactory Welds in the Positions Shown
EXX1X	F, V, OH, H
EXX2X	H-Fillets, F
EXX3X	F

The last digit in the classification number indicates the kind of current to be used with the electrode and the kind of covering; however, the significance of a zero as the last digit will depend to some extent on the character of the electrode covering. Table 44 lists the coverings, both standard AWS-ASTM classes and popular nonstandard kinds, which are used on carbon and low-alloy steel electrodes. Of course, not all the coverings are available on the more highly alloyed steels. For example, the EXX10 covering, which contains a high cellulose content (and therefore is hydrogen bearing), is not employed when strength above approximately 100,000 psi UTS is required. High-strength filler metals ordinarily are employed to join hardenable steels which are susceptible to cracking from hydrogen in the heat-affected zones. Furthermore, the mechanical properties of the high-strength weld metal also would be adversely affected by hydrogen picked up in the deposit from the covering.

IRON AND CARBON STEEL FILLER METALS

The number of iron and carbon steel welding rods and electrodes of different chemical analyses does not approach, of course, the great variety of alloy steel welding rods and electrodes. Nevertheless, in addition to the dozen or more flux coverings on carbon steel electrodes, several different steelmaking practices may be employed in making carbon steel welding rods, and the products differ sufficiently in welding properties to justify distinct class identification. It is well to keep in mind that the large number of electrodes and welding rods was developed by demand; that is, each is designed to best fill a particular set of needs which may involve mechanical properties, operating characteristics, weld appearance, and so forth. Because the details of electrode construction can influence the composition and properties of the weld deposit, some time will be taken here to discuss features like the kind of core wire, the nature of electrode coverings and their influence on deposit properties.

Information on covered electrodes and their deposits is presented in Tables 45, 46 and 47. Chemical composition requirements and typical deposit analyses are given in Table 45. Data on the tensile and impact strengths are not available for all deposits, but the data shown in Tables 46 and 47 provides a reasonable picture of the mechanical properties available. Both carbon and low-alloy steel electrodes are included in these tables, although for the moment we will direct our attention only to the carbon steel classifications.

Carbon Steel Covered Arc-Welding Electrodes

AWS A5.1 (ASTM A233) is a specification titled *Mild Steel Covered Arc-Welding Electrodes*. The majority of covered electrodes used in the United States are manufactured to comply with this specification even though only two modest levels of strength presently are provided. The electrodes are classified on the basis of (1) mechanical properties of deposited metal, (2) type of covering and its operating characteristics, and (3) kind of current on which the electrode is usable. The level of minimum tensile strength in the as-welded condition is the first distinguishing feature, namely, 62 ksi and 67 ksi (for the E60 series) and 72 ksi (for the E70 series). These levels of strength in the weld metal are achieved by regulation of the carbon and manganese contents. A single kind of core wire generally is employed in making all mild steel electrodes. This is a rimmed steel containing approximately 0.06 to 0.15% carbon, 0.30 to 0.60% manganese, residual amounts of phosphorus and sulphur, and, of course, very low silicon content — which is characteristic of a rimmed steel. The use of steel of this character plays an important part in the operating performance of the electrode, particularly in aiding the deposition of weld metal in the overhead position. It is believed that the expansion of gases contained in this steel at the rapidly melting tip of the electrode acts to propel minute droplets of metal away from the molten end. As these droplets of metal enter the weld pool, the deoxidizing elements

Table 45 — *CHEMICAL COMPOSITION REQUIREMENTS AND TYPICAL WELD DEPOSIT ANALYSES OF COVERED ELECTRODES FOR CARBON AND LOW-ALLOY STEEL*

PART I — SEE "MILD STEEL COVERED ARC-WELDING ELECTRODES," AWS A5.1; ASTM A233

(A) THE FOLLOWING ELECTRODES HAVE NO COMPOSITION REQUIREMENTS IN AWS-ASTM SPECIFICATIONS

AWS–ASTM classification	*Typical Weld Deposit Analyses*							
	C	Mn	S	Si	Cr	Ni	Mo	V
E4510[a]	0.05	0.25	0.02	0.01	......	......	......	......
E4520[a]	0.05	0.25	0.02	0.01	......	......	......	......
E6010	0.06	0.45	0.02	0.20	......	......	......	......
E6010[a] iron powder	0.06	0.45	0.02	0.25	......	......	......	......
E6011	0.06	0.45	0.02	0.20	......	......	......	......
E6012	0.07	0.40	0.02	0.35	......	......	......	......
E6013	0.09	0.45	0.02	0.35	......	......	......	......
E6020	0.09	0.35	0.02	0.15	......	......	......	......
E6027	0.09	0.60	0.02	0.40	......	......	......	......
E6030[a]	0.09	0.35	0.02	0.15	......	......	......	......

(B) THE FOLLOWING ELECTRODES ARE REQUIRED BY AWS-ASTM SPECIFICATIONS NOT TO EXCEED THESE WELD DEPOSIT COMPOSITIONS:

E70XX series	......	1.25*	......	0.90	0.20*	0.30*	0.30*	0.08*

* The sum total of all elements with the asterisk shall not exceed 1.50 percent.

	Typical Weld Deposit Analyses							
E7014	0.08	0.90	0.02	0.25	0.10	0.05	0.03	0.01
E7015	0.08	0.90	0.02	0.50	0.10	0.05	0.03	0.01
E7016	0.08	0.90	0.02	0.50	0.10	0.05	0.03	0.01
E7018	0.08	0.90	0.02	0.60	0.10	0.05	0.03	0.01
E7024	0.08	0.90	0.02	0.60	0.10	0.05	0.03	0.01
E7028	0.08	0.90	0.02	0.60	0.10	0.05	0.03	0.01

[a] Not a recognized classification in current AWS-ASTM specifications.

PART II — SEE "LOW-ALLOY STEEL COVERED ARC-WELDING ELECTRODES," AWS A5.5; ASTM A316.

AWS-ASTM composition requirements[b] for weld deposits are listed opposite each classification. Single values shown are maximum percentages unless specific ranges are indicated. Typical weld deposit analyses when given are listed directly below the classification.

(A) CARBON-MOLYBDENUM STEEL ELECTRODES (E70XX)

AWS–ASTM classification	C	Mn	S	Si	Cr	Ni	Mo	V
E7010-A1	0.12	0.60	0.04	0.40	......	......	0.40– 0.65	......
Typical	0.06	0.40	0.02	0.25	......	......	0.50	......

TABLE 45 — (Continued)

AWS–ASTM classification	C	Mn	S	Si	Cr	Ni	Mo	V
E7011-A1	0.12	0.60	0.04	0.40	......	......	0.40–0.65	......
Typical	0.06	0.40	0.02	0.30	......	......	0.50	......
E7015-A1	0.12	0.90	0.04	0.60	......	......	0.40–0.65	......
Typical	0.06	0.75	0.02	0.45	......	......	0.50	......
E7016-A1	0.12	0.90	0.04	0.60	......	......	0.40–0.65	......
Typical	0.06	0.80	0.02	0.40	......	......	0.50	......
E7018-A1	0.12	0.90	0.04	0.80	......	......	0.40–0.65	......
Typical	0.06	0.75	0.02	0.60	......	......	0.50	......
E7020-A1	0.12	0.60	0.04	0.40	......	......	0.40–0.65	......
Typical	0.06	0.45	0.02	0.25	......	......	0.50	......
E7027-A1	0.12	1.00	0.04	0.40	......	......	0.40–0.65	......
Typical	0.06	0.80	0.02	0.25	......	......	0.50	......

b Phosphorus content is limited to 0.03 max. percent in all cases, except where 0.030 max. percent is specifically indicated.

(B) CHROMIUM-MOLYBDENUM STEEL ELECTRODES (E80XX)

	C	Mn	S	Si	Cr	Ni	Mo	V
E8016-B1	0.12	0.90	0.04	0.60	0.40–0.65	......	0.40–0.65	......
Typical	0.10	0.75	0.02	0.40	0.50	......	0.50	......
E8018-B1	0.12	0.90	0.04	0.80	0.40–0.65	......	0.40–0.65	......
Typical	0.11	0.85	0.02	0.60	0.50	......	0.50	......
E8015-B2L	0.05	0.90	0.04	1.00	1.00–1.50	......	0.40–0.65	......
Typical	0.04	0.50	0.02	0.50	1.25	......	0.50	......
E8016-B2	0.12	0.90	0.04	0.60	1.00–1.50	......	0.40–0.65	......
Typical	0.06	0.50	0.02	0.50	1.25	......	0.55	......
E8018-B2	0.12	0.90	0.04	0.80	1.00–1.50	......	0.40–0.65	......
Typical	0.06	0.75	0.02	0.60	1.25	......	0.50	......
E8015-B4L	0.05	0.90	0.04	1.00	1.75–2.25	......	0.40–0.65	......
Typical	0.04	0.75	0.02	0.75	2.00	......	0.50	......

TABLE 45 — *(Continued)*

AWS–ASTM classification	C	Mn	S	Si	Cr	Ni	Mo	V
(C) NICKEL STEEL ELECTRODES (E80XX)								
E8016-C1	0.12	1.20	0.04	0.60	......	2.00–2.75	......	......
Typical	0.06	0.75	0.02	0.50	......	2.60	......	......
E8018-C1	0.12	1.20	0.04	0.80	......	2.00–2.75	......	......
Typical	0.06	0.75	0.02	0.60	......	2.60	......	......
E8016-C2	0.12	1.20	0.04	0.60	......	3.00–3.75	......	......
Typical	0.06	0.90	0.02	0.40	......	3.50	......	......
E8018-C2	0.12	1.20	0.04	0.80	......	3.00–3.75	......	......
Typical	0.06	0.90	0.02	0.60	......	3.50	......	......
E8016-C3 [c]	0.12	0.40–1.10	0.030	0.80	0.15	0.80–1.10	0.35	0.05
Typical	0.06	0.90	0.02	0.40	......	1.00	......	......
E8018-C3 [c]	0.12	0.40–1.10	0.030	0.80	0.15	0.80–1.10	0.35	0.05
Typical	0.06	0.90	0.02	0.70	......	1.00	......	......

[c]Classification intended to conform to military specification for similar composition. Phosphorus limited to 0.030 max. percent.

AWS–ASTM classification	C	Mn	S	Si	Cr	Ni	Mo	V
(D) CHROMIUM-MOLYBDENUM STEEL ELECTRODES (E90XX)								
E9015-B3	0.12	0.90	0.04	0.60	2.00–2.50	......	0.90–1.20	......
Typical	0.10	0.75	0.02	0.40	2.25	......	1.00	......
E9016-B3	0.12	0.90	0.04	0.60	2.00–2.50	......	0.90–1.20	......
Typical	0.10	0.75	0.02	0.50	2.25	......	1.00	......
E9018-B3	0.12	0.90	0.04	0.80	2.00–2.50	......	0.90–1.20	......
Typical	0.10	0.75	0.02	0.60	2.25	......	1.00	......
E9015-B3L	0.05	0.90	0.04	1.00	2.00–2.50	......	0.90–1.20	......
Typical	0.04	0.75	0.02	0.75	2.25	......	1.00	......

AWS–ASTM classification	C	Mn	S	Si	Cr	Ni	Mo	V
(E) MANGANESE-MOLYBDENUM STEEL ELECTRODES (E90XX, E100XX)								
E9015-D1	0.12	1.25–1.75	0.04	0.60	......	......	0.25–0.45	......
Typical	0.06	1.50	0.02	0.40	......	......	0.40	......

TABLE 45 — *(Continued)*

AWS–ASTM classification	C	Mn	S	Si	Cr	Ni	Mo	V
E9016-D1 [d]	0.12	1.25–1.75	0.04	0.60	......	......	0.25–0.45	......
Typical	0.06	1.50	0.02	0.40	......	......	0.40	......
E9018-D1	0.12	1.25–1.75	0.04	0.80	......	......	0.25–0.45	......
Typical	0.06	1.50	0.02	0.60	......	......	0.40	......
E10015-D2	0.15	1.65–2.00	0.04	0.60	......	......	0.25–0.45	......
Typical	0.12	1.85	0.02	0.40	......	......	0.40	......
E10016-D2	0.15	1.65–2.00	0.04	0.60	......	......	0.25–0.45	......
Typical	0.12	1.85	0.02	0.50	......	......	0.40	......
E10018-D2	0.15	1.65–2.00	0.04	0.80	......	......	0.25–0.45	......
Typical	0.12	1.85	0.02	0.60	......	......	0.40	......

d Not a recognized classification in current AWS-ASTM specifications.

(F) OTHER LOW-ALLOY STEEL ELECTRODES (EXXXX-G).

To meet the alloy requirements of this group, the weld deposit need have the minimum of one of the following elements:

EXXXX-G	......	1.00 min	......	0.80 min	0.30 min	0.50 min	0.20 min	0.10 min

Typical Weld Deposit Analyses

E8015-G	0.07	0.70	0.02	0.30	0.30	0.80	0.15	......
E8018-G	0.06	1.25	0.02	0.70	......	......	......	......
E9018-G	0.07	1.00	0.02	0.40	......	1.60	0.15	......
E9018-G	0.06	1.00	0.02	0.50	1.25	......	0.60	......
E10018-G	0.06	1.25	0.02	0.50	0.12	1.50	0.25	......
E10013-G	0.11	0.33	0.02	0.40	......	......	1.10	0.10
E10015-G	0.06	0.80	0.02	0.35	......	1.65	0.30	0.13
E11016-G	0.06	1.20	0.02	0.40	......	3.35	0.50	......
E11016-G	0.06	1.20	0.02	0.40	1.20	2.00	0.30	......
E11018-G	0.08	1.65	0.02	0.50	......	1.85	0.45	......
E11018-G	0.05	1.30	0.02	0.30	0.30	1.80	0.45	......
E11018-G	0.06	1.00	0.02	0.50	1.50	2.50	0.65	......
E11018-G	0.13	1.64	0.02	0.40	......	......	0.45	......
E12015-G	0.09	1.20	0.02	0.50	......	1.80	0.80	0.20
E12018-G	0.07	1.70	0.02	0.50	0.35	2.00	0.50	......
E12018-G	0.08	1.50	0.02	0.50	1.00	2.00	0.75	......

TABLE 45 — (Continued)

AWS–ASTM classification	C	Mn	S	Si	Cr	Ni	Mo	V
(G) CLASSIFICATIONS OF AWS A5.5 (ASTM A316) INTENDED TO CONFORM TO MILITARY SPECIFICATIONS FOR SIMILAR COMPOSITIONS.e								
MIL-7018 f	0.12	0.40– 1.25	0.030	0.80	0.15	0.25	0.35	0.05
MIL-8018 f	0.12	0.40– 1.10	0.030	0.80	0.15	0.80– 1.10	0.35	0.05
E9018-M	0.10	0.60– 1.25	0.030	0.80	0.15	1.40– 1.80	0.35	0.05
E10018-M	0.10	0.75– 1.70	0.030	0.60	0.35	1.40– 2.10	0.25– 0.50	0.05
E11018-M	0.10	1.30– 1.80	0.030	0.60	0.40	1.25– 2.50	0.30– 0.55	0.05
E12018-M	0.10	1.30– 2.25	0.030	0.60	0.30– 1.50	1.75– 2.25	0.30– 0.55	0.05

e Phosphorus content limited to 0.030 max. percent for these electrodes.
f Not presently an AWS-ASTM classified electrode. See military specification MIL-E-22200/1B.

(H) LOW-ALLOY STEEL COVERED ELECTRODES FOR HEAT TREATABLE WELD DEPOSITS.g								
Cr-Mo	0.10	0.55	0.02	0.45	0.50	......	1.10	......
Cr-Ni-Mo	0.20	1.50	0.02	0.50	0.50	1.25	0.25	......
4130	0.25	1.00	0.02	0.50	1.00	......	0.25	......
4140	0.40	1.00	0.02	0.50	1.00	......	0.25	......
4340	0.40	1.00	0.02	0.50	1.00	2.00	0.25	......
MIL-13018	0.10– 0.15	0.80– 1.15	0.030 max	0.30– 0.60	0.90– 1.20	1.50– 2.00	0.45– 0.75	0.02 max

g Not recognized classifications in current AWS-ASTM specification.

Table 46 — *TYPICAL RANGES FOR TENSILE PROPERTIES OF CARBON AND LOW-ALLOY STEEL WELD METAL DEPOSITED BY COVERED ELECTRODES*

PART I — MILD STEEL COVERED ELECTRODES

AWS-ASTM classification	Condition in which tested c	Tensile Properties b			
		UTS ksi	YS ksi	Elong. 2 in, %	Red. of area, %
E6010	AW	60-70	50-60	22-28	35-60
E6010 a iron powder	AW	60-70	50-62	20-28	30-60
E6011	AW	60-70	50-62	22-30	35-60
E6012	AW	60-78	50-65	17-28	20-50
E6013	AW	60-78	50-65	17-24	25-50
E6014 a	AW	60-72	50-62	17-25	30-50

TABLE 46 — *(Continued)*

AWS-ASTM classification	Condition in which tested c	Tensile Properties b			
		UTS ksi	YS ksi	Elong. 2 in, %	Red. of area, %
E6020	AW	60-70	50-58	25-30	40-60
E6024 a	AW	60-72	50-60	17-22	20-40
E6027	AW	60-68	50-55	25-35	40-75
E6028 a	AW	60-72	50-60	22-30	55-75
E6030 a	AW	60-68	50-58	25-30	40-60
E7014	AW	70-85	60-77	17-25	30-50
E7015	AW	70-76	60-62	22-35	55-75
E7016	AW	70-76	60-62	22-35	55-75
E7018	AW	70-85	60-70	22-35	55-75
	SR-1150	72	62	38	77
E7024	AW	70-85	60-75	17-22	20-40
E7028	AW	70-85	60-75	22-30	55-75
PART II — LOW-ALLOY STEEL COVERED ELECTRODES					
E7010-A1	AW	70-85	60-75	22-30	....
	SR-1150	70-80	58-65	22-35	....
E7016-A1	AW	72-85	62-75	24-35	....
	SR-1150	70-80	58-65	24-35	....
E7018A1	AW	72-85	62-75	24-35	55-75
	SR-1150	70-80	58-65	24-40	55-75
E7020-A1	AW	72-80	60-68	22-30	....
	SR-1150	70-80	58-65	22-35	....
E8015-G	AW	80-96	67-80	19-35	....
	SR-1150	80-92	67-80	19-35	....
E8016-B2	SR-1150	95	85	32	....
	SR-1350	82	67	29	....
E8016-C1	AW	82	73	30	70
E8016-C2	AW	80-100	70-90	27	68
E8016-G	AW	96	80	28	....
	SR-1150	91	77	29	....
E8018-B2	AW	90-95	79-84	24-26	62
	SR-1350	83-93	70-83	25-30	70
E8018-C2	AW	94	83	25	55
	SR-1150	85	77	32	74
E8018-C3	AW	82-90	72-79	28	73
	SR-1150	81	71	30	....
E8018-G	AW	89	80	30	73

a Not a recognized classification in current AWS-ASTM specifications.
b Pairs of values indicate approximate ranges; single values indicate approximate properties.
c AW = as welded; SR = stress relieved at temperature (F) shown; HT = heat treated at temperature shown.

TABLE 46 — (Continued)

AWS-ASTM classification	Condition in which tested c	Tensile Properties b			
		UTS ksi	YS ksi	Elong. 2 in, %	Red. of area, %
E9018-B3	AW	115-125	90-100	22	65
	SR-1350	92-115	77-100	25	70
E10018-D2	AW	105	100	22	50
	SR-1100	105	95	25	70
E11016-G	AW	115	105	20	60
E11018-G	AW	105-120	100-110	18-28	40-70
	SR-1150	110-120	100-110	18-30	40-75
E12018-G	AW	122	110	22	60

PART III — LOW-ALLOY STEEL COVERED ELECTRODES FOR HEAT-TREATABLE WELD METAL a

Cr-Ni-Mo	HT-950	160	150	16	50
4130	HT-950	170	160	12	45
4140	HT-450	250	235	10	30
4340	HT-450	270	250	10	25
MIL-13018	AW	145	120	20	....
	HT-1225	150	100	22	....

a Not recognized classifications in current AWS-ASTM specifications.
b Pairs of values indicate approximate ranges; single values indicate approximate properties.
c AW = as welded; SR = stress relieved at temperature (F) shown; HT = heat treated at temperature shown.

Table 47 — NOTCHED-BAR IMPACT PROPERTIES OF CARBON AND LOW-ALLOY STEEL WELD METAL DEPOSITED BY COVERED ELECTRODES

PART I — MILD STEEL COVERED ELECTRODES

AWS–ASTM classification	Condition in which tested c	CHARPY V-NOTCH VALUES b IN FT-LB AT VARIOUS TESTING TEMPERATURES					
		RT	0 F	−20 F	−40 F	−80 F	−100 F
E6010	AW	50-80	....	20-65	10-50	10-40	....
E6010 Iron powder a	AW	50-80	....	20-65	10-70	10-40	....
E6011	AW	50-90	50-90	25-65	10-25	10-40	....
E6012	AW	25-55	....	....	2-10	....	....
E6013	AW	30-60	....	....	5-15	....	....
E6014 a	AW	40-70	....	....	10-25	....	....
E6020	AW	40-70	....	....	10-25	....	....
E6024 a	AW	30-60	....	....	5-20	....	....
E6027	AW	40-70	....	....	10-40	....	....
E6028 a	AW	70-100	....	....	15-40	....	....

TABLE 47 — *(Continued)*

AWS–ASTM classification	Condition in which tested [c]	CHARPY V-NOTCH VALUES[b] IN FT-LB AT VARIOUS TESTING TEMPERATURES					
		RT	0 F	-20 F	-40 F	-80 F	-100 F
E6030[a]	AW	40-70	....	....	10-25	....	....
E7014	AW	40-70	....	....	10-25	....	....
E7015	AW	70-100	....	....	25-40	....	....
E7016	AW	70-120	30-100	30-100	25-40	....	....
E7018	AW	70-120	46	26	20-50	10-40	5-20
	SR-1150	122	55	35	28	....	....
E7024	AW	30-60	....	....	5-20	....	....
E7028	AW	50-100	20-75	10-50	10-40	....	....

PART II — LOW-ALLOY STEEL COVERED ELECTRODES

AWS–ASTM classification	Condition in which tested	RT	0 F	-20 F	-40 F	-80 F	-100 F
E7018-A1	AW	98	42	24	22	....	....
	SR-1150	104	50	29	24	....	....
E7018-G	AW	90-110	30-70	20-60	20-40	....	....
	SR-1150	100-120	40-70	30-50	20-40	....	....
E8016-B2	SR-1275	80-100	40-60	30-50	20-40	5-30	....
E8016-C1[d]	AW	130-170	130-150	120-140	90-120	10-40	10-30
E8018-C2	AW	100-160	50-140	....	40-80	10-60	10-50
	SR-1150	100-160	50-140	....	40-80	....	....
E8018-C3	AW	85-160	40-140	30-100	20-70	10-30	5-30
	SR-1150	75-100	40-100	....	....	....	....
E9016-B3	SR-1275	40-60	20-40	10-30	....	....	....
E9018-D1	AW	60-110	50-80	40-80	30-70	15-40	10-30
	SR-1150	....	....	....	60-68	30-50	....
E10018-D2	AW	70-90	45-65	....	30-40	....	....
	SR-1150	60-90	40-65	....	25-40	....	....
E11016-G	AW	50-80	40-60	30-60	20-50	15-40	5-40
E11018-G	AW	35-90	40-60	30-60	20-60	....	....
	SR-1150	35-90	40-60	30-60	20-60	....	....
E12018-G	AW	40-60	25-40	....	15-30	....	....

PART III — LOW-ALLOY STEEL COVERED ELECTRODES FOR HEAT-TREATABLE WELD METAL[a]

AWS–ASTM classification	Condition in which tested	RT	0 F	-20 F	-40 F	-80 F	-100 F
Cr-Ni-Mo	HT-950	80	35	30	28	....	....
4130	HT-950	50	25	....	....	....	....
4140	HT-450	15	12	....	8	....	....
4340	HT-450	15	12	....	6	....	....

[a] Not recognized classifications in current AWS-ASTM specifications.
[b] Pairs of values indicate approximate ranges; single values indicate approximate properties.
[c] AW = as welded; SR = stress relieved at temperature (F) shown; HT = heat treated at temperature shown.
[d] Charpy impact range 1–10 ft-lb at – 320 F.

(previously contained in the electrode covering, but now transferred to the weld metal) quickly take up the oxygen and change the deposit to a killed steel. Because of this desirable operating behavior, rimmed steel core wire is used even in the majority of *alloy-steel* covered welding electrodes. Of course, where the amount of alloy required in the weld deposit cannot be conveniently carried in the flux covering, the only alternative is to employ an alloy-steel core wire which contains all, or a major portion, of the needed alloy. Because alloy-steel wire usually is a killed steel, its use as the electrode core wire generally will detract from the all-position operating capability of the electrode.

If the testing requirements of the AWS–ASTM filler metal specifications are examined, it will be seen that the welding procedures are very much like those used in good shop practice, but many pertinent details are stipulated. The purpose of this close control of welding procedure is to ensure that a valid comparison can be made of results from repeated tests, or possibly from different testing facilities. In fact, every effort is made to employ similar procedures in the filler metal specifications for the different welding processes to permit direct comparison of property values obtained. In all cases, an *interpass temperature* is specified which is intended to minimize the most potent variables which affect properties, namely, interpass temperature and bead size. Also, an artificial aging treatment consisting of heating to 200 to 220 F for 48 hours is applied to the welded test plates made with all electrodes, except the low-hydrogen classifications, to accelerate the effusion of hydrogen and secure the level of ductility characteristic of the weld metal under test.

In studying the weld deposit analyses for the various classes of carbon steel electrodes in Table 45, Part I, it will be noted that small variations in composition seems to be related to the kinds of covering on each electrode. These composition variations, while not large, are sufficient to cause differences in mechanical properties, particularly when the composition changes are accompanied by different degrees of soundness (porosity) and by variations in hydrogen content. Although the tensile strength and ductility do not show marked changes, notch toughness is particularly sensitive to chemical composition and will be discussed in some detail later in this chapter. Charpy V-notch impact test properties are a recently added requirement to the AWS-ASTM Specification for certain of the mild steel arc-welding electrodes. A minimum requirement of 20 ft-lb at –20 F is expected of weld metal deposited from the E6010, E6011, E6027, E7015, E7016 and E7018 class electrodes. A minimum requirement of 20 ft-lb at 0 F is expected of the E7028 electrodes. No impact requirements are set for any of the remaining electrode classes in the AWS A5.1 specification.

E45 Series of Coated Electrodes

A thinly coated E45 series of electrodes were included as standard classes in the AWS-ASTM specification, but these were dropped in 1945 because of limited usage. Nevertheless, they present an interesting aspect of the metallurgy of electrodes, and therefore are shown in Table 45. Because the thin coating on the E45XX electrodes allows a significant loss of carbon and manganese, and does little to avoid porosity, the strength of weld metal from these electrodes may vary from 45 to 65 ksi UTS. The light coatings on these electrodes originated during the early days of arc welding when a surface film of powdered lime, sulcoat (controlled rusting), or other arc-stabilizing compounds was found to improve the operational characteristics of the electrode. However, these light coatings did little to improve the soundness and mechanical properties of the deposited weld metal, and so the more heavily coated or *covered* electrodes soon became the mainstay for the metal-arc welding process. Yet, E4510 and E4520 electrodes continue to be used to a limited extent on certain noncritical articles where electrode cost is a major consideration.

E45 series electrodes are manufactured from rimmed steel wire. No deoxidizers are contained in the electrode coatings. Therefore, the deposited metal regularly contains considerable porosity caused by the oxygen in the steel and the oxygen and nitrogen picked up from the air, and any hydrogen which may have been held in some form in the light coating. The deposit is not required to meet any particular chemical requirements, but the deposited metal is expected to have sufficient strength and ductility to display 45,000 psi min UTS and 5% min elongation in 2 inches. The E4510 and E4520 electrodes usually are operated on direct current-straight polarity.

E60 Series of Covered Electrodes

These "mild steel" electrodes are the most widely used for arc welding. Consequently, they are produced with the greatest number of electrode coverings having special operating characteristics. The following paragraphs give a brief insight into the metallurgical relationship between covering formulation and such aspects as operating behavior, weld composition, soundness, mechanical properties and deposit shape. To achieve the weld metal strengths required in the classifications of the E60 series, a weld metal carbon content of about 0.06 to 0.09% is sought along with a manganese content of about 0.30 to 0.75%. To raise the weld metal strength sufficiently to qualify for the E70XX classifications, small increases in carbon (0.08 to 0.12%) and manganese (0.40 to 1.00%) are required.

E6010 Electrodes — The heavy cellulosic covering on this electrode creates a deeply penetrating, spray-type arc, which operates with little spatter. Approximately 30% or more of alpha cellulose or similar material is employed in the covering, which burns as the electrode is deposited. Consequently, free oxygen in the arc atmosphere is consumed and the burning hydrocarbon material generates a large volume of moderately protective atmosphere composed of CO, CO_2 and H_2O gases. Although the remainder of the electrode covering is composed of titanium dioxide, magnesium silicate, sodium silicate, ferromanganese, ferrosilicon, etc., slag on the deposits is only a thin, friable layer that hardly covers the entire bead. This thin slag is easily removed from the surface of the deposit, and any traces that remain will easily remelt and float to the top of the next bead. The composition of the E6010 deposit is similar to that of the electrode core wire. However, three changes ordinarily can be expected: (1) the carbon content usually decreases a little, (2) the silicon content rises into the 0.10 to 0.25% range which deoxidizes the deposit, and (3) sufficient hydrogen is absorbed by the deposit to lead to "hydrogen effects" as discussed in Chapter 13. The hydrogen content of the weld metal is approximately 20 cc per 100 grams of metal. The oxygen content usually is in the order of 0.04%, while the nitrogen is 0.02%. The levels of these gaseous contaminants will be shown to be significantly lower with newer types of electrode coverings.

Despite the nature of the electrode covering and the chemical composition of the deposits, E6010 electrodes produce deposits which appear quite sound by radiographic examination; that is, slag entrapment and porosity are not ordinarily troublesome. Consequently, this class of electrode is widely used in welding carbon steel.

E6011 Electrodes — These electrodes are intended to be identical with the E6010 class, but permit operation with alternating current. This operating capability is accomplished by using calcium and potassium compounds in the covering formula. Often, potassium silicate is substituted for sodium silicate in an E6010 type covering to produce the E6011 electrode. Other than the better arc stabilization, there are no additional metallurgical differences which deserve comment.

E6012 Electrodes — The covering on an E6012 electrode is quite different from that on E6010. The E6012 electrode covering is commonly called the "rutile" or "slag" type. It is composed mostly of slag-forming ingredients and contains only a small proportion of gas forming ingredients, like cellulose. Consequently, the deposit receives good coverage by the welding slag. The materials employed in the covering include titania, which sometimes is in the natural mineral form — hence the name "rutile." In addition to various silicious materials like clay, asbestos, feldspar, and sodium silicate, small amounts of calcium or potassium compounds may be added to improve arc stabilization.

The E6012 electrode, because of its covering, operates with a medium penetration arc that is soft and quiet, and may produce some fine, globular spatter. A wide range of welding current is permissible with the E6012 slag covering. At low currents, the penetration is so low that gaps in a joint often can be bridged. At high currents, excellent fillet beads can be deposited rapidly. From a metallurgical standpoint, it is important to remember that deposits from an E6012 electrode are slightly higher in strength and lower in ductility than those from E6010. Also important is the fact that single layer deposits of E6012 are reasonably sound and can meet radiographic requirements for porosity. However, multilayer deposits are apt to contain considerable porosity and slag particles in the beads beyond the first layer. This unsoundness is caused by flux particles which cannot be completely removed from the deposit surface by ordinary cleaning methods.

E6013 Electrodes — The covering on this electrode represents a flux modification to permit AC operation. While many E6012 electrodes can be successfully used on AC, and even on DC-RP where desired, the E6013 electrode not only is a better AC performer, but possesses several additional advantages. The AC capability is secured, of course, by adding calcium, potassium, and other potent compounds which stabilize the arc and permit its operation under the cyclic low-current, low open-circuit voltage conditions. As a result of this modification, the arc with an E6013 electrode is noticeably softer than that of an E6012; there is less spatter; the slag is easier to remove completely; multi-pass welds are sounder, and even larger gaps in "poor fit-up" weldments can be bridged. In fact, these improved operating characteristics are so impressive that many electrode manufacturers market special varieties of E6013 intended for use on certain kinds of work; as examples, on light sheet metal, on light plate where no beveling is employed and a moderately penetrating arc is desired, and on galvanized steel where a very stable arc is desired to withstand the ill effects of zinc vapor.

E6020 Electrodes — The covering on an E6020 electrode was indicated earlier to have a high iron oxide content, possibly in the order of 30%. Various other slag-forming ingredients, like manganese compounds (asbestos), also are present in substantial amounts. Little or no gas shielding is provided by the covering. However, the slag shielding is very complete and of a nature that gas shielding is not needed. The primary purpose of this covering formulation is to provide a heavy slag layer on the weld metal and to obtain satisfactory operation at quite high currents. This enables the welder to obtain deep penetration in butt joints and fillet welds in the horizontal and flat positions. E6020 electrodes are employed most often on relatively heavy sections where deep penetration and high metal deposition rates are sought. This kind of performance has earned the popular name "hot rod" for electrodes covered with either the EXX2C or EXX30 types of flux.

Deposited weld metal from E6020 class electrodes has good soundness because generous amounts of deoxidizers, like ferromanganese, are included in the covering. Because of the consistently high quality of deposits made with the E6020 (and E6030) types of covering, they frequently are employed in welding pressure vessels. While the weld metal mechanical properties, that is, strength, ductility and notch toughness are good at room temperature, the notch toughness decreases rapidly at temperatures below about 0 F. This is to be expected of a carbon steel electrode having a covering which is not a low-hydrogen formulation.

E6027 Electrodes — This electrode is an iron powder modification of the E6020 electrode; that is, the covering formulation is the high iron oxide type and approximately 35% powdered iron is included. The addition of iron produces the usual operating characteristics; namely, smoother arc, less spatter, easier drag technique at high lineal travel speeds, increased metal deposition rates, concave fillet profile, and fine, uniform ripple on the weld bead surface. The E6027 electrode generally is regarded as a worthwhile improvement over the E6020 class from the standpoint of operating characteristics. However, no particular benefits of a metallurgical nature are gained in the weld deposit.

E6030 Electrodes — This electrode has a high iron oxide covering similar to the E6020 class. In fact, the E6020 and E6030 classes are almost identical in operating characteristics. The fine distinguishing feature is that the E6030 class may produce a welding slag that is not suitable for depositing horizontal fillet welds. Yet, the E6030 is ideally suited for flat position deposition. Because of this very limited applicability, the E6030 classification has not been retained in the AWS-ASTM specification. The E6030 covering is composed mainly of oxide compounds of iron, manganese, aluminum, magnesium, and silicon. Ferromanganese and some ferrosilicon are included as deoxidizers. The heavy covering permits this electrode to be operated on high currents; therefore, its principal use is in the rapid deposition of large amounts of metal in flat position fillet or groove joints. Weld metal from this "hot rod" generally is quite sound, and the beads normally have a smooth, concave profile with a fine, surface ripple. Little call is made for E6030 electrodes today because of the broader applicability of the E6020 class and the growing popularity of the E6027 class.

E70 Series of Covered Electrodes

These electrodes deposit weld metal that is but a small amount stronger than the E60 series. Using the same core wire as described earlier for the E60 series, the electrode manufacturer can produce an E70XX electrode by adding an increased amount of ferromanganese to his covering formulation. This addition raises both the carbon and the manganese contents the small amount needed to gain the required 72,000 psi minimum UTS, and the 60,000 psi minimum yield point.

Electrodes in the E70 series of the carbon steel variety are not widely used because the E60 series provides ample strength in the weld metal for joining mild steel. In fact, most E60XX electrodes will deposit weld metal that meets the E70 series requirements. Furthermore, the E70XX properties can be easily secured by a small inexpensive alloy addition, which gives other worthwhile benefits, as will be explained shortly when discussing low-alloy steel filler metals.

E7014 Electrodes — The covering on this electrode is similar to that on E6013 except a small addition of iron powder, possibly about 20%, is made to the covering. The amount of iron powder is less than the approximately 35% employed in the E7024 electrode covering, in order to retain all-position operating capability. The purpose of the iron powder is to improve operating characteristics and to gain certain advantages as were mentioned earlier in Chapter 8. Iron powder in the covering produces a soft stable operating arc. The covering forms a deeper, protective conical sheath at the end, which almost hides the arc. This prevents spatter, particularly at high welding currents. With high current, the penetration still is moderate and consequently large amounts of metal can be deposited rapidly in fillets and grooves. During deposition, the iron in the covering is melted and transfers into the molten weld pool to add to the volume of filler metal. Of course, some of the iron powder is oxidized and remains in the slag where it forms various ferrous compounds. Its presence promotes easier cleaning of the slag, and in some cases the solidified slag curls up and breaks free by itself.

The presence of iron powder in the flux covering is so beneficial that additions are made to a number of covering types, thus creating new classifications or special variations of existing standard classes.

E7015 Electrodes — The covering on E7015 electrodes originally was the same as employed on stainless steel electrodes. It is a heavy, "lime-type" flux, which is a misnomer for the large proportion of powdered *limestone* used in the flux formulation. This covering was selected for trial on a low-alloy steel electrode when it became apparent that hydrogen was a strong promoter of cracking and porosity in welding certain kinds of steels, and that properly prepared coverings employed on stainless steels represented "low-hydrogen" fluxes. The use of the low-hydrogen lime-type covering proved so successful, that other low-hydrogen coverings soon followed and these will be described shortly. Whereas weld deposits from the cellulosic (E6010) covered electrodes contained approximately 20 cc of hydrogen per 100 grams of metal, deposits from the mineral covered or low-hydrogen types of electrodes contain about 2 cc per 100 grams of metal. The oxygen and nitrogen contents of metal from the mineral-type electrodes also are lower because of the better protection afforded by the covering materials. Oxygen and nitrogen contents of 0.010% are usually found.

The ingredients contained in a typical E7015 electrode covering were tabulated in Chapter 8. In addition to a substantial amount of limestone, slag-forming and arc-stabilizing materials such as fluorspar, asbestos, and sodium silicate are included. A high baking temperature is an important step in removing virtually all the hydrogen (as moisture) from this covering. Like the original stainless steel covering, the present E7015 type operates properly only on DC-RP. The arc produces moderate penetration with relatively little spatter. The slag is easily removed, except perhaps from beads deposited deep in narrow grooves. While the E7015 is an all-position electrode, its operating characteristics in all positions under most conditions leave much room for improvement.

The desirable characteristics which quickly attracted considerable attention to the low-hydrogen, lime-type covering were (1) the ability to weld hardenable steels without causing underbead cracking, (2) the ability to weld high-sulfur steels without causing weld metal porosity through a sulfur-hydrogen reaction, and (3) the improvement in impact properties in the as-welded condition as compared with the properties of weld metal from E6010 and E6012 electrodes. At the present time, usage of electrodes with the EXX15 covering is decreasing because the low-hydrogen feature is also found in several other coverings which offer better operating characteristics and easier slag removal.

E7016 Electrodes — A short time after the lime-type stainless steel covering (EXX15) was found useful on steels other than the high-alloy variety, a new kind of covering had been perfected for stainless steel usage and it was only natural that this newcomer should be tried on carbon and low-alloy steel electrodes. This newer covering (EXX16) operates either on AC or on DC-RP. Its capability is achieved by incorporating substantial amounts of titania, potassium compounds, and other strong arc stabilizers in the flux covering. Again, the hydrogen content is held to a very low level by careful selection of covering ingredients and high baking temperatures. While the EXX16 covering as applied to stainless steel electrodes is called a "titania-type" flux, a similar covering on carbon or low-alloy steel is called the low-hydrogen potassium type.

The E7016 electrode operates with a smoother arc than the E7015 electrode. The solidified slag usually is much easier to remove from an E7016 deposit. The weld metal is sound, and although the E7016 does not offer as much protection for oxidizable alloying elements as does the E7015 type, the degree of protection is adequate. The mechanical properties of weld metal deposited with the EXX16 and EXX15 coverings appear to be indistinguishable.

Chemical analyses of weld metal deposited by E7016 electrodes usually show about 0.08% carbon, 0.60% manganese, residual amounts of phosphorus and sulfur, and 0.50% silicon. This is not significantly different from the weld metal of other E70XX electrodes. The improved mechanical properties of the E7016 and E7015 weld deposits must be attributed in large measure to the low-hydrogen type of covering. More information on this subject is reviewed in Chapter 13.

E7018 Electrodes — The EXX18 type of covering represents the culmination of learning from several classes developed earlier. It combines the AC arc stability of E6013, the benefits of an iron powder addition as described for E7014, and the low-hydrogen feature of the E7015 and E7016 classes. The EXX18 type of electrode covering is becoming very popular with welders because of desirable operating characteristics, and with welding engineers because of very satisfactory deposit shape and weld metal mechanical properties.

The formula for a typical covering on an E7018 electrode was given earlier in Chapter 8. Usually, about 25 to 40% iron powder is included. Sometimes small amounts of titania and potassium silicate are introduced to assist AC operation. The deposited metal may have slightly higher manganese and silicon contents than from other E70XX electrodes, but here again, the desirable mechanical properties must be credited in some measure to the low-hydrogen content of the covering.

E7024 Electrodes — This is a very heavily covered electrode which might be looked upon as having a covering formulation similar to the E6012 or E6013 classes, but which contains a large amount of powdered iron. The percentage of iron powder may range from 25 to 40%, and the weight of the covering may be equal to the weight of the core wire. The heavy covering permits the use of relatively high welding currents and deposition by the drag technique. Large beads can be deposited in the flat or horizontal positions at high metal deposition rates. However, the depth of penetration is surprisingly shallow. Consequently, this electrode is well suited for fillet welding. The fillet profile tends to have good concavity, and the surface a fine, even ripple. The soundness of the weld metal generally is good.

The presence of a large amount of iron powder in the E7024 covering produces a smooth, quiet arc, and little spatter occurs, particularly if a very close arc or drag position is held. The formation of iron oxide in the slag (from some of the iron powder) increases the fluidity and thus prevents efficient use of this electrode in the vertical or overhead positions.

E7028 Electrodes — This electrode is similar to the E7018 class, but differs in a number of important aspects. The covering on an E7028 electrode is heavier and usually contains a somewhat larger percentage of powdered iron. Often the covering contains about 50% iron powder and the weight of covering equals the core wire weight. The iron content, as might be expected, promotes a fluid slag and confines usage to the flat and horizontal positions. Furthermore, the metal transfer across the arc with the E7028 electrode is a spray type, whereas the E7018 electrode produces a globular transfer. It is important to keep in mind that the E7028 covering is a low-hydrogen formulation and the quality of deposits and the applicability of the electrode is improved in the usual way by this feature.

The standardized electrodes in the E70 series do not include all of the types of coverings offered in the E60 series. This does not mean that any particular problem would be encountered in producing an E7012 electrode, for example, if such an electrode were wanted. The E7012 electrode could be produced simply by applying the covering regularly used on the E6012 electrode, but additional ferromanganese probably would be included in the covering formula to assure the required higher strength. In general, the operating characteristics imparted by the electrode covering would remain essentially unchanged regardless of the level of strength in the weld metal being deposited. Of course, as larger additions of ferromanganese or other alloys are added to the covering as powdered metal, the electrode gradually displays the operating characteristics of the iron-powder types. Since the effects of the powdered metal additions usually are quite beneficial, electrode makers favor the use of simple, low-carbon rimmed steel core wire for making all series and classes of electrodes. The welders are inclined to develop a strong preference for an electrode with operating characteristics resulting from large additions of metal in the covering.

Iron and Steel Gas Welding Rods

AWS Specification A5.2 (ASTM A251) bears the above title. These bare welding rods are supplied in 36-in. cut lengths ranging from 1/16 to ⅜-in. diameter. Although not covered, they may be lightly copper plated to resist rusting. The current issue (1966) requires that the chemical composition of welding rod conform to the following maxima: sulfur 0.040%, phosphorus 0.040%, and aluminum 0.02%. Reasons for restricting the phosphorus and sulfur contents were indicated in Chapter 7 and are further discussed elsewhere in the text. The limitation on aluminum is intended to avoid the occurrence of aluminum oxide slag on the surface of the weld metal during melting under the oxyacetylene flame. No limits are imposed for the elements carbon, manganese and silicon. These are left to the judgment of the steelmaker, but are controlled indirectly by the strength and ductility requirements set for the weld metal as shown in Table 48. The minimum amounts of carbon and/or manganese are determined by the minimum tensile strength that must be obtained. The maxima for these elements are determined by the elongation requirement of the tension test, and a bend test. Obviously, a weld metal cannot contain an excessive amount of these hardening elements and still possess adequate ductility. The specification does not attempt to control the composition of the weld deposit because this is dependent to a large extent upon the particular technique of the welder even when following test procedures.

Three classes of welding rod are provided in AWS A5.2 as defined principally by the required minimum tensile strengths. The mechanical property requirements permit a broad range of compositions to qualify under these welding rod classifications. A survey of the gas welding rods available on the commercial market shows that at least a dozen different carbon and alloy-steel compositions are represented in this kind of filler metal. The majority of them can be classified under the three AWS designations.

RG45 gas welding rod is the lowest strength class, and is intended to cover the simplest, low-carbon steel commonly used in joining many forms of mild steel, such as plate, sheet, pipe and bars. This welding rod ordinarily is made as a rimmed steel, and the composition is very much like that of the core wire used in covered arc-welding electrodes. However, steel made for gas welding rod requires a slightly different steelmelting practice to produce a rod that melts quietly without sparking under the oxyacetylene flame and that solidifies without excessive porosity. Since it is a rimmed steel, continuation of the carbon–oxygen (rimming) reaction is bound to occur whenever the steel is remelted. However, the relatively low temperature of the weld melt under the oxyacetylene flame minimizes boiling from the

Table 48 — CHEMICAL COMPOSITION AND MECHANICAL TEST REQUIREMENTS FOR VARIOUS FORMS OF CARBON STEEL WELDING ROD OR ELECTRODES

AWS–ASTM classification	CHEMICAL COMPOSITION, PERCENT							MECHANICAL TEST REQUIREMENTS				
	C	Mn	P	S	Si	Cu	Al	Condition tested a	UTS ksi	YS ksi	Elong. % in 2	Other tests

Gas Welding Rod Per AWS 5.2 (ASTM A251)b

| RG45 | ... | ... | 0.040 Max | 0.040 Max | ... | ... | 0.02 Max | AWc | 45 Min | ... | ... | None |

Remarks — General purpose welding rod for joining low-carbon and mild steels. Usually supplied as a rimmed steel welding rod.

| RG60 | ... | ... | 0.040 Max | 0.040 Max | ... | ... | 0.02 Max | AWd | 62 Min | ... | 20e | Bend |

Remarks — Welding rods which provide medium strength, good ductility weld metal for joining carbon steels in the tensile strength range of 50 to 60 ksi. Most-often supplied as a killed steel to aid in gaining sound weld deposits.

| RG65 | ... | ... | 0.040 Max | 0.040 Max | ... | ... | 0.02 Max | AWd | 67 Min | ... | 16e | Bend |

Remarks — Often referred to as "high-strength" gas welding rods. Usually represents a high-manganese, silicon-killed steel containing approximately 0.10 to 0.20% carbon. Used in welding low-alloy steels where techniques are employed to insure alloy pickup by weld metal to secure required strength. Weldments sometimes heat treated to obtain greater strength and toughness.

Gas Metal-Arc Welding Electrodes Per AWS A5.18 (ASTM A559)

SOLID ELECTRODESf

| E60S-1 | 0.07–0.19 | 0.90–1.40 | 0.025 Max | 0.035 Max | 0.15–0.50 | ... | ... | AWj | 62 Min | 50 Min | 22 Min | None |

Remarks — Lowest silicon content. Tests made with AO gas only.n May be used with CO_2 shielding when weld quality is not critical.

| E60S-2 | 0.06 Max | 0.90–1.40 | 0.025 Max | 0.035 Max | 0.40–0.70 | ... | 0.05–0.15 | AWj | 62 Min | 50 Min | 22 Min | Impact l |

Remarks — Composition also includes 0.05–0.15 Ti and 0.02–0.12 Zr. Multiple deoxidized electrode. Capable of producing sound weld deposits in all kinds of steel (including rimmed steel). Useful for counteracting effects of rusty or scaled surfaces. May be used with any of the shielding gases.

Classification	C	Mn	P	S	Si			Condition				
E60S-3	0.07–0.19	0.90–1.40	0.025 Max	0.035 Max	0.40–0.70	...	...	AW^j	62 Min	50 Min	22 Min	Impact^m

Remarks — Most widely used solid electrode. Higher silicon (over E60S-1) permits use with any of the shielding gases. Designed for single pass welds, but also suitable for most multipass welds.

E70S-4	0.07–0.15	0.90–1.40	0.025 Max	0.035 Max	0.65–0.85	...	...	AW^j	70 Min	60 Min	20 Min	None

Remarks — Contains higher silicon than E60S-3, which improves performance where strong deoxidizing ability is needed, such as CO_2 shielding, or long arc length.

E70S-5	0.07–0.19	0.90–1.40	0.025 Max	0.035 Max	0.30–0.60	0.50–0.90	...	AW^j	70 Min	60 Min	20 Min	None

Remarks — A multiple deoxidized electrode which uses large amount of aluminum in addition to manganese and silicon. Useful for counteracting effects of rusty or scaled surfaces. Not recommended for use with shorting-arc transfer conditions.

E70S-6	0.07–0.15	1.40–1.85	0.025 Max	0.035 Max	0.80–1.15	...	...	AW^j	70 Min	60 Min	20 Min	Impact^l

Remarks — High-manganese, high silicon electrode which offers a number of advantages because of alloying, such as higher strength, good impact toughness (even with CO_2 shielding), and strong deoxidation ability.

E70S-G	No Chemical Requirements							AW^j	70 Min	60 Min	20 Min	None

Remarks — A general classification to cover those electrodes which do not qualify under any of the six preceding classes. Supplier must be consulted for details of composition, and mechanical properties other than tension test requirements.

COMPOSITE ELECTRODES^g

E70T-1^h	...	1.50 Max	...	...	0.90 Max	...	...	AW^j	70 Min	60 Min	22 Min	Impact^m

Remarks — Most widely used flux-cored electrode. For single and multiple pass welds in flat position and horizontal fillets. Requires clean surfaces. High deposition rate. Low spatter loss. Good impact properties.

E70T-2	No Chemical Requirements							AW^k	70 Min	...	...	Bend

Remarks — Similar to E70T-1 electrode except better suited for single pass welding in flat position and horizontal fillets. Stronger deoxidation to cope with rusty, scaled surfaces.

E70T-3	No Chemical Requirements							AW^k	70 Min	...	...	Bend

Remarks — Designed for use without externally applied gas shielding. Primarily for single pass, high speed welds in flat and horizontal positions. Not recommended for multiple pass welds in heavy sections.

TABLE 48 — (Continued)

AWS-ASTM classification	CHEMICAL COMPOSITION, PERCENT							MECHANICAL TEST REQUIREMENTS				
	C	Mn	P	S	Si	Cu	Al	Condition tested a	UTS ksi	YS ksi	Elong. % in 2	Other tests
E70T-4 [h]	...	1.50 Max	...	...	0.90 Max	...	1.8 Max	AW [j]	70 Min	60 Min	20 Min	None

Remarks — Designed for use without externally applied gas shielding. Suitable for single and multiple pass welds in flat and horizontal positions. Low penetrating ability. Low sensitivity to cracking.

| E70T-5 [h] | ... | 1.50 Max | ... | ... | 0.90 Max | ... | ... | AW [j] | 70 Min | 60 Min | 20 Min | Impact [1] |

Remarks — Designed for flat fillet or groove welds with or without externally applied gas shielding. Welds made under gas shield exhibit better quality. Suitable for single or multiple pass welds.

| E70T-G | No Chemical Requirements | | | | | | | AW [o] | 70 Min | 60 Min | 20 Min | None |

Remarks — A general classification to cover those electrodes which do not qualify under any of the five preceding classes. Supplier must be consulted for details of composition, and mechanical properties other than tension test requirements.

EMISSIVE ELECTRODE [f]

| E70U-1 | 0.07–0.15 | 0.80–1.40 | 0.025 Max | 0.035 Max | 0.15–0.35 | ... | ... | AW [j] | 70 Min | 60 Min | 22 Min | Impact [1] |

Remarks — Designed to operate on d-c, straight polarity under argon shielding with a spatter-free, spray-type metal transfer. Higher deposition rates than obtained with d-c, reverse polarity as used with all other gas metal-arc electrodes.

Submerged-Arc Welding Electrodes Per AWS A5.17 (ASTM A558)

LOW MANGANESE CLASSES [1]

| EL8 | 0.10 Max | 0.30–0.55 | 0.03 Max | 0.035 Max | 0.05 Max | 0.15 Max | ... | AW | ... | ... | ... | ... |

Remarks — Lowest cost electrode. Regularly made as rimmed steel with low-carbon and low-manganese.

	C	Mn	P	S	Si			AW			
EL8K	0.10 Max	0.30–0.55						AW	...	...	...

Remarks — Low-carbon killed steel.

	C	Mn	P	S	Si			AW			
EL12	0.07–0.15	0.35–0.60	0.03 Max	0.035 Max	0.05 Max	0.15 Max	...	AW	...	...	...

Remarks — Regularly made as low-manganese rimmed steel, but with somewhat higher carbon content than EL8 classification.

MEDIUM MANGANESE CLASSES[1]

	C	Mn	P	S	Si			AW			
EM5K	0.06 Max	0.90–1.40	0.03 Max	0.035 Max	0.40–0.70	0.15 Max	...	AW	...	...	...

Remarks — Low-carbon, medium-manganese, killed steel with elevated silicon content.

	C	Mn	P	S	Si			AW			
EM12	0.07–0.15	0.85–1.25	0.03 Max	0.035 Max	0.05 Max	0.15 Max	...	AW	...	...	...

Remarks — Somewhat higher carbon content than EM5K, with medium manganese, and restricted silicon which usually calls for steel to be made as rimmed steel.

	C	Mn	P	S	Si			AW			
EM12K	0.07–0.15	0.85–1.25	0.03 Max	0.035 Max	0.15–0.35	0.15 Max	...	AW	...	...	...

Remarks — Medium-manganese killed steel electrode with somewhat higher-carbon and lower-silicon than EM5K.

	C	Mn	P	S	Si			AW			
EM13K	0.07–0.19	0.90–1.40	0.03 Max	0.035 Max	0.40–0.70	0.15 Max	...	AW	...	...	...

Remarks — Similar to EM5K, but with significantly higher carbon content.

	C	Mn	P	S	Si			AW			
EM15K	0.12–0.20	0.85–1.25	0.03 Max	0.035 Max	0.15–0.35	0.15 Max	...	AW	...	...	...

Remarks — Similar to EM12K, but with slightly higher carbon range.

HIGH MANGANESE CLASS[1]

	C	Mn	P	S	Si			AW			
EH14	0.10–0.18	1.75–2.25	0.03 Max	0.035 Max	0.05 Max	0.15 Max	...	AW	...	...	...

Remarks — High-manganese electrode with elevated carbon range. Usually a killed or semi-killed steel by virtue of amount of carbon, manganese and silicon contained.

TABLE 48 — (Continued)

Submerged Arc Welding Fluxes for Use with Above Electrodes

AWS-ASTM classification	CHEMICAL COMPOSITION, PERCENT							MECHANICAL TEST REQUIREMENTS				
	C	Mn	P	S	Si	Cu	Al	Condition tested a	UTS ksi	YS ksi	Elong, % in 2	Other tests
F60								AW	60–80	45 Min	25 Min	None
F61								AW	60–80	45 Min	25 Min	Impact[m]
F62								AW	60–80	45 Min	25 Min	Impact[l]
F70								AW	70–95	50 Min	22 Min	None
F71								AW	70–95	50 Min	22 Min	Impact[m]
F72								AW	70–95	50 Min	22 Min	Impact[l]

Fluxes may be used in combination with any of the above submerged arc electrodes. Composition and method of manufacture are left to discretion of supplier, but flux when employed with a 5/32-in. electrode of specified classification must produce weld metal which conforms to requirements of specification.

a "AW" indicates as-welded condition. This is important to note because it may represent a departure from previous practice of testing in the welded-and-stress-relieved condition.

b Chemical composition requirements are for welding rod.

c As determined by a transverse tension test specimen taken from a joint in ⅜-in. thick plate (ASTM A285, Grade C, A7, or equivalent) using a stipulated welding procedure with the oxyacetylene process.

d As determined by an all-weld-metal tension test specimen prepared from weld in same plate as described in footnote (c).

e Gage length for determining elongation is 4 x diameter, which ordinarily will be 1-in. gage length on specimen required.

f Chemical composition requirements for solid and emissive electrodes are based on the as-manufactured electrode analysis.

g Chemical composition requirements for composite electrodes are based on the analysis of deposited weld metal.

h Certain elements are to be restricted to specified maxima; namely, nickel 0.30%, chromium 0.20%, molybdenum 0.30%, and vanadium 0.08%, and furthermore, the sum total of Mn, Ni, Cr, Mo and V shall not exceed 1.50%.

i Total of other elements 0.50% max.

j As determined by all-weld-metal tension test.

k As determined by transverse tension test.

l Charpy V-notch impact requirement is 20 ft.-lb. minimum at −20F.

m Charpy V-notch impact requirement is 20 ft.-lb. minimum at 0F.

n Designations for shielding gases are as follows:
AO = argon, plus 1 to 5 percent oxygen
CO₂ = carbon dioxide
None = no separate shielding gas
A = argon

o Tension test depends upon electrode intended usage; if single pass application, a transverse tension test is required. If multipass application, an all-weld-metal tension test is required.

carbon–oxygen reaction, and the slow solidification rate allows almost complete escape of the gaseous reaction products. Consequently, a reasonably sound weld bead can be expected. However! Woe unto the welder who uses this rimmed steel gas welding rod as a filler metal for a more rapid process, such as gas tungsten-arc welding: Excessive porosity will be his lot! A typical welding rod which would qualify under the RG45 classification might have the following chemical composition: carbon 0.05% manganese 0.20%, phosphorus 0.02%, sulfur 0.03%, and silicon 0.008%.

RG60 welding rod requires a minimum weld metal tensile strength of 62 ksi in the as-welding condition. Naturally, this strength demands higher carbon and/or manganese in the weld metal composition as compared with a deposit from the RG 45 class rod. Typical composition limits to meet the RG60 requirements might include carbon 0.08-0.16%, manganese 0.75-1.50%, and silicon 0.10-0.50%. Note that compositions falling within these limits would be killed steels. When the steel must contain carbon and manganese toward the high side of the ranges given for reason of strength, the rimming steel practice is not followed in steelmaking. The levels of carbon and manganese (without considering the silicon) would lower the amount of dissolved oxygen and thus reduce the rimming action. Therefore, the composition limits necessary to meet welding requirements can demand a change in steelmaking practice. If the RG60 rod is made to the low side of the carbon and manganese ranges (particularly the manganese range), then the product still can be made as a rimmed steel. Most manufacturers offer a high-manganese, silicon-killed welding rod in the RG60 class because the deoxidation ability of this composition is helpful in securing a sound deposit with a minimum of porosity. Welding rod of this classification is employed mostly for joining carbon steels in the strength range of 50 to 60 ksi, and also for joining wrought iron. Alloy steels which fall in this strength range also may be welded. The RG60 welding rod is considered a general purpose filler metal of medium strength and good ductility suitable for welding carbon steels in a wide variety of important applications, such as power plant and process piping. While RG60 welding rod is sometimes referred to as an "alloy steel" weld rod, ordinarily it would be the rather high manganese content that might properly call for this distinction.

RG65 welding rod is required to deposit weld metal which possesses a minimum UTS of 67 ksi in the as-welded condition. To effect this increase in strength over the RG60 class, either the carbon and/or manganese ranges must be raised, or other strengthening alloying elements must be added. As might be expected, a wide variety of carbon and alloy steel compositions are available as gas welding rod which meet the RG65 classification. Although the RG65 welding rods are classified on the basis of strength in the range of 65 to 75 ksi, this indicated area of application does not reveal another, most important usage. As described earlier in this Chapter, filler metal mixes with some molten base metal to form the weld metal. The coordination diagram of Fig. 124 can be used to predict the approximate weld metal composition when the analyses of the base metal and welding rod are known together with the proportions of each that make up the weld metal. Many of the applications for which RG65 welding rod is employed involve alloy steels of substantially higher tensile strength than 67 ksi. However, with a suitable welding technique, a relatively large proportion of base metal can be mixed with the lower-alloy filler metal, and the weld metal alloy content and strength can be raised appreciably. In some cases where the as-welded strength of the weld metal is not adequate, heat treatment can be applied to effect a further increase in strength. This procedure has been employed for many years in the gas welding of AISI 4130 steel tubing in the aircraft industry. Here, a gas weld in thin-wall tubing even if made with RG45 welding rod would display a tensile strength of approximately 95 ksi if the tensile breaking load was divided by the cross-sectional area of the tube. The use of RG60 welding rod for this same joint probably would increase the weld strength to the range of 100 to 125 ksi. Welding rod of the RG65 classification usually is employed, and, when the joints are heat treated after welding, a tensile strength in the order of 150 ksi is obtained.

A variety of low-alloy steel gas welding rods are marketed under trade names. The Aerospace Material Specifications (AMS) of the SAE cover a number of alloy steel gas welding rods employed in aircraft construction and maintenance. Several proprietary low-alloy steel welding rods are used in joining high strength pipe (usually small diameter) for gas and oil distribution lines. These special welding rods often are made to close composition requirements and with restricted residual element content to obtain high quality weld deposits.

Welding Rods and Covered Electrodes for Welding Cast Iron

Because of the peculiar metallurgical conditions that prevail in the joining of cast iron, the AWS-ASTM Committee on Filler Metal saw fit to write a specification covering only those welding rods and covered electrodes found especially useful for welding this seemingly simple, cast, iron-carbon alloy. AWS A5.15 (ASTM A398) includes (1) cast iron filler metals for use in gas welding and carbon-arc welding, (2) copper-base alloy filler metals for brazing and for braze welding, (3) nickel-base alloy covered electrodes for making dissimilar-metal arc welds, and (4) a low-carbon steel covered electrode for arc-welding. This specification also has a helpful appendix which touches upon the metallurgy of welding cast iron with each of the welding rods or electrodes listed. The subject of welding cast iron is discussed in the present Volume in Chapter 14.

Carbon Steel Electrodes for Gas Metal-Arc Welding

In the early development of the gas metal-arc process, welding of steel was attempted with bare wire obtained from stocks intended as filler metal for oxyacetylene, submerged arc and other welding processes. However, it quickly became apparent that electrodes would have to be manufactured specifically for the gas metal-arc process to obtain suitable deposition performance and weld metal quality. This process makes certain demands with respect to arc stability, metal transfer behavior, deposition rate, and solidification characteristics that can be satisfied only by making special types of wire tailored for use as electrodes in the gas metal-arc operation. Many different kinds of electrodes were developed and placed on the market bearing proprietary designations. In the interests of standardization, however, the AWS-ASTM Committee on Filler Metal has issued a specification, identified as AWS A5.18 (ASTM A559), to cover mild steel electrodes for gas metal-arc welding of carbon and low-alloy steels. The kinds of electrodes classified under this specification are listed in Table 48.

Gas metal-arc electrodes are available in three different forms: (1) bare solid electrodes, (2) composite electrodes, often consisting of a tube filled with either powdered metal or flux, or a mixture of both, and (3) solid electrodes coated with an emissive material. All three forms are recognized in AWS A5.18. These electrodes, in coils, or wound on spools, are used with a variety of shielding gases as described in Chapter 3. Although the gas metal-arc process is divided into three useful modes of operation; namely, (1) spray-type transfer, (2) short-circuiting type transfer and (3) pulsed-arc type transfer, the electrodes are not classified on this basis. The main feature necessary in any GMAW electrode is a substantial ability to deoxidize the weld metal. The filler metal being transferred and the weld melt are subject to somewhat unusual conditions that result in oxidation; therefore, an adequate amount of deoxidizing elements must be at hand to control these situations and avoid excessive porosity in the weld deposit. The unusual conditions favoring oxidation include the large surface area presented by the tiny metal droplets of the spray transfer mode, and the need of overcoming the possible aspiration of air into the gaseous shield surrounding the arc. Of course, many factors affect the severity of the oxidation problem. The kind of gas provided for the shielding is a most important factor. We must be concerned not only with the degree of protection afforded by the gas itself, but also the manner in which the gas affects the transfer of metal droplets.

Bare Solid Electrodes

The bare solid electrode used in gas metal-arc welding is quite different from the core wire employed in flux covered electrodes. The latter made use of a rimmed steel which was deoxidized by ingredients contained in the flux covering as it was deposited as weld metal. Bare solid electrodes for the gas metal-arc process must be a killed steel since no real opportunity presents itself to add a deoxidizer during deposition. The amount of deoxidizer contained in the wire often is sufficiently large to overcome the effects of rust or mill scale on the base metal. Therefore, the GMAW electrodes constitute a unique group of steel compositions representing different combinations of alloying elements for reasons of strength, toughness and deoxidation capability.

As shown in Table 48, standardized mild steel electrodes for gas metal-arc welding are divided into two strength categories: the E60S series which is expected to provide weld metal of 62 ksi minimum UTS and 50 ksi minimum YS, and the E70S series for which 70 ksi minimum UTS and 60 ksi minimum YS are required. Experience with deposits from covered electrodes expected to meet 60 ksi minimum UTS would indicate a required weld metal composition of approximately 0.06 to 0.12% carbon, and 0.30 to 0.90% manganese. Because some loss of carbon and manganese may occur during deposition, particularly if carbon dioxide comprises a major part of the shielding gas, GMAW electrodes usually contain a higher level of these two elements. The manganese content is held especially high because this element is not only expended as a deoxidizer, but a sufficient amount is expected to remain in the weld metal to function as a strengthening alloy addition.

If the solid electrodes are studied from the standpoint of deoxidation power, a number of different types will be observed. Some electrodes rely entirely upon their manganese and silicon contents for obtaining a properly deoxidized weld deposit. These elements may be adequate for many applications, but circumstances can arise where greater deoxidation capability is required to produce weld deposits with satisfactory soundness. Possible sources of oxygen which can promote porosity in the weld metal may be easily found. First, there is the atmosphere around the arc. Whether we must deal with oxygen in the air, or combined in a shielding gas (such as carbon dioxide), will be determined by the nature of the shielding gas, the amount supplied, and the effectiveness of its application. Rust or mill scale on the base metal is a potent source of oxygen. Finally, the steel base metal itself may contain oxygen, as indeed in the case of a rimmed steel. Therefore, the need often arises for a GMAW electrode with substantial deoxidation capacity. It might seem, at first thought, that the required capacity for deoxidation could be built into the electrode simply by including enough manganese and silicon in the steel composition to counteract the amount of oxygen expected. Although the use of these elements would be very desirable from a cost standpoint, seldom can the manganese be raised above approximately 2%, and the silicon above approximately 1¼% without encountering problems with the flowing characteristics of the molten weld metal, the bulk and fluidity of the slag formed on the molten weld, and the cracking susceptibility of the weld deposit. A more effective way of securing strong deoxidation capacity, and yet maintain satisfactory weld metal behavior, is to employ multiple deoxidizing elements and to include some which offer (1) a stronger affinity for oxygen, (2) a less voluminous oxide, and (3) a higher melting oxide to control weld metal and slag fluidity in the molten condition. There is also reason to believe that in addition to deoxidation, some nitrogen fixation may be desirable. This can be accomplished by adding strong nitride-forming elements, such as titanium and zirconium. Consequently, in any GMAW electrode, particularly those of strong deoxidation ability, it is important to properly balance the deoxidizing–denitriding elements in the general alloy content. The object of this balancing is to be certain that the weld metal can be manipulated properly in the molten condition. A minimum of slag is desired, and any slag formed must exhibit favorable flowing characteristics. Two standardized classifications of "multiple deoxidized" electrodes are listed in Table 48. The E60S-2 electrode contains small amounts of aluminum, titanium and zirconium along with fairly high manganese and silicon contents. Electrodes of the E70S-5 classification, while containing a smaller number of deoxidizing–denitriding elements, have a strong deoxidation (and denitriding) ability by virtue of the 0.50 to 0.90% aluminum which they are required to contain. Some investigators believe that the element titanium serves still another helpful function in gas metal-arc welding operations; namely, that of an arc-stabilizer. However, the formulation of alloy steel compositions for GMAW electrodes is only in its infancy, and there is much need for firmly established, quantitative data on the function of alloying elements, and trace elements in this kind of filler metal.

Chemical analyses of weld metal deposited by steel electrodes under a carbon dioxide gas shield in the gas metal-arc process show that the carbon content of the deposit may rise a point or two if the electrode contains less than 0.10%; or the deposit may decrease in carbon content if the electrode contains more than 0.10%. This tendency for weld metal deposited under CO_2 shielding to finally contain approximately 0.10% carbon suggests that this level possibly represents an equilibrium for the average welding conditions. This behavior on the part of carbon appears to be true regardless of the mode of weld deposition; that is, whether spray-arc transfer, or shorting-arc transfer. Of course, with CO_2 shielding gas, the spray-arc includes considerable globular transfer. Easily oxidized elements, however, are subject to slightly greater loss in the shorting-arc transfer. The manganese contained in the solid GMAW electrode usually is decreased by about ⅓ during deposition. Phosphorus and sulfur ordinarily are transferred without loss and without significant increase because no fluxing materials bearing these elements are involved in the process. The silicon content is reduced by about ¼ to ½ during transfer from electrode to the deposit.

The mechanical properties of carbon steel weld metal deposited by the gas metal-arc process under CO_2 shielding are not greatly different from those found in shielded metal-arc deposits. The tensile strength can be roughly estimated from the following formula:

$$\text{UTS in ksi} = 45 + 90 \text{ (Carbon Equivalent)}$$

$$\text{Carbon Equivalent} = C + \frac{Mn}{5} + \frac{P}{2} + \frac{Si}{7}$$

The elements carbon, manganese, phosphorus, and silicon are taken into consideration in this formula because these likely are the only ones present in sufficient quantity in a *carbon steel* weld metal to influence its strength. If this formula is applied to a typical weld metal with an analysis of carbon 0.10%, manganese 0.80%, phosphorus 0.02%, and silicon 0.50%, the following calculations indicate the approximate ultimate tensile strength of the weld metal:

Carbon	0.10	=	0.10
Manganese	$\frac{0.80}{5}$	=	0.16
Phosphorus	$\frac{0.02}{2}$	=	0.01
Silicon	$\frac{0.50}{7}$	=	0.07
Carbon Equivalent		=	0.34
UTS in KSI		=	45+90(0.34)
UTS		=	75,600 psi

Charpy-V impact test values from weld metal of this kind usually fall in the range of 60 to 80 ft-lb in tests conducted at room temperature. The 15 ft-lb Charpy-V transition temperature generally will occur in the range of –30 to –40 F.

Composite Electrodes

Composite electrodes for gas metal-arc welding, sometimes called "fabricated wire" or "flux-cored wire," are a relatively new form of filler metal for this process. These electrodes originally were developed for making heavy fillet welds and filling large grooved joints in the flat and horizontal positions. They were intended to fill the need of a semi-automatic or fully automatic operation in which beads could be deposited at a high rate, and where the beads were required to have a pleasing appearance because of their prominence in the weldment, as for example, in a machine base. The electrodes were expected to be capable of depositing beads of flat or concave profile, and with a minimum of spatter. It was also considered desirable that the electrodes operate satisfactorily with CO_2 shielding, or perhaps with no externally supplied shielding gas. The AWS A5.18 specification includes six standardized classifications of composite electrodes as shown in Table 48.

The composite electrodes presently available have a variety of cross-sectional configurations that somehow enclose a quantity of powdered materials. The most commonly used construction is a simple steel tube formed from strip with a longitudinal unwelded butt seam. The interior of the tube is filled with powdered materials just prior to closing the seam. Some electrodes are formed with complex convolutions of steel strip within the outer round shell. Considerable care is taken that the interior of the tube is completely and uniformly filled with the powdered materials. A lack of these materials in the core over any length of the electrode would be certain to have a marked adverse effect upon the composition and the quality of the weld deposit. Most composite electrodes are cold drawn through a die after filling and closing in order to compact the powdered materials in the core, and to obtain the relatively small diameters required for gas metal-arc welding.

The composite electrode requires new considerations in formulating the fluxing mixtures for the core. Whereas the conventional flux *covered* electrode is designed to have the covering melt at a slightly slower rate than the core wire and thus form a conical, projecting shield at the melting end (see Fig. 11, Volume 1), it would be undesirable to have the fluxing material melt at a slower rate than the metal sheath in the composite electrode. The constituents in the powdered core material include fluxing agents, arc ionizers, metals for deoxidation, such as ferrosilicon and ferromanganese, and alloying additions when required. Some CO_2 gas for shielding may be generated by a fluxing agent, such as limestone, however, most electrodes do not rely upon self-generated gas for shielding. Instead, the electrode is designed to be used with supplementary shielding gas discharged from a tube adjacent to the arc or from a nozzle around the electrode. Because of the obvious savings to be realized, increasing attention is being given to electrodes that do not require supplementary gas shielding. The core of these electrodes contains a combination of solid fluxing agents, deoxidizers, and gas-generating ingredients as inner shielding. This composite electrode therefore represents the familiar core wire and covering arrangement in reverse. The amount of fluxing materials held in the core of a composite electrode usually represents 15 to 20% of the total weight of the wire. Because of the use of composite electrodes for rapid deposition of heavy welds, the electrode must be capable of handling high welding currents without deterioration of operating properties.

The chemical requirements of AWS A5.18 for composite electrodes are not particularly restrictive, and therefore do not give a clear indication of the weld metal composition deposited by mild steel electrodes of the tubular or flux-filled variety. It should be noted that all composite electrodes are required to deposit weld metal of 70 ksi minimum UTS, there apparently being no call for electrodes of a 60 ksi minimum UTS classification. To meet the required 70 ksi UTS minimum, most electrode manufacturers aim for a weld metal carbon content in the approximate range of 0.05 to 0.12%, and a manganese content in the range of about 0.50 to 1.25%. Silicon usually is introduced as a deoxidizer to the extent of 0.20 to 0.90% mainly by the addition of powdered ferrosilicon to the core material, since this element is not likely to be present in an adequate amount in the steel strip. Some composite electrodes, particularly those designed for single pass welds in rusty or scaled steel, or those designed for deposition without externally applied shielding gas, often contain additions of stronger deoxidizers, such as aluminum. Electrodes of this character are clearly labeled to encourage their use only on single pass welds, or under the conditions for which they were designed. This cautionary advice should be heeded because the large amounts of silicon and aluminum contained as deoxidizers should be dissipated when the single bead encounters the oxide on the surface of the base metal. If an electrode of this kind is employed in making a multipass weld, the levels of silicon and aluminum retained in the later passes of weld metal may be so high as to adversely affect ductility and toughness.

Because the composite electrode manufacturing technique lends itself readily to making changes in the alloy composition of the weld deposit, many different electrodes with strength capability greater than that of the E70T-X classifications are being produced. The simplest modification for increasing the strength is to raise the manganese content. Even with the regular low carbon content, increasing the manganese content to about 1.5% will provide an UTS of 80 ksi minimum. A manganese content of about 1.75% will provide a 90 ksi minimum UTS. An addition of about 0.25% molybdenum to the latter will provide 100 ksi minimum UTS. Of course, these composition changes elevate the weld metal into the low-alloy steel category. Although no AWS-ASTM specification has been issued for alloy-steel gas metal-arc welding electrodes, some of the more popular proprietary electrodes of the alloy steel variety will be discussed later in this chapter.

Emissive Electrodes

Emissive electrodes for gas metal-arc welding are solid steel wires that have been given a very light surface coating or treatment to permit operation with direct current on straight polarity, or on alternating current. Bare solid electrodes, or composite electrodes ordinarily are operated on direct current with reverse polarity. AWS A5.18 lists a single classification (E70U-1) for an emissive electrode. The chief advantage of this specially coated product is the higher deposition rates that can be achieved with the direct current–straight polarity operation. Various elements and compounds, such as rubidium and cesium, which are good electron emitters, are employed in the surface coating. These electrodes usually are designed to be used with argon gas shielding, and, with proper current density, will produce a spatter-free, spray-type metal transfer.

Self-Shielding Bare Solid Steel Electrodes

Numerous attempts have been made to develop a bare steel wire that could be employed as a consumable electrode and deposited in the air atmosphere without having the weld metal suffer adverse effects from oxygen and nitrogen. For example, in Russia, steel electrodes containing substantial amounts of the rare earth elements cerium and lanthanum (up to 0.5%), have been proposed. In experimental welding work, these elements were shown to promote a fluid weld pool even though the major portion was lost by oxidation. However, unless the deposit also was provided with approximately 0.4% aluminum to tie up the nitrogen picked up by the molten weld metal, the ductility and toughness were quite low. The presence of the rare earth elements was reported to also stabilize the arc. Strong claims were made by the developers of these

Russian electrodes that the weld deposits would satisfy all of the requirements made by industry of an electrode for semiautomatic operation.
Furthermore, the quality of the deposits from the rare-earth aluminum-
containing electrode was stated to be equal to the weld metal from
regular, heavily covered, shielded metal-arc electrodes.

A similar report from Japan indicates that a non-shielded arc welding
electrode identified as "NKW-1" has been developed. The developer of
the electrode has not disclosed the means by which the need for shielding
by externally supplied gas or by flux is avoided. However, the composition
of the weld deposit is reported to be:

Carbon	Manganese	Silicon	Special elements
0.09	0.81	0.12	0.025 Total

The special elements as indicated above are stated to be (1) arc
stabilizers to permit low current welding operation, and (2) denitriding
and deoxidizing elements. The electrode is copper coated for rust
resistance. The electrode is especially made for welding at low current;
that is, under 180 amperes for electrodes of 1 mm size (0.039 in.), 200
amperes for 1.2 mm size (0.047 in.), and 240 amperes for 1.6 mm size
(0.063 in.). Welding tests on DC–RP indicated 90% deposition efficiency. Higher welding current resulted in the occurrence of blowholes
and porosity in the weld metal. However, weld deposits made at recommended current levels were shown to have good appearance, and the
mechanical properties reported were quite satisfactory for mild steel weld
metal.

A self-shielding, bare, solid steel electrode would find a wide, ready
market if its cost was not elevated too much by unusual alloying, and its
operating characteristics and deposit quality were something close to those
of the shielded metal-arc, and the gas metal-arc processes. However, an
electrode of this kind has yet to demonstrate completely satisfactory ability
in the hard, cold light of commercial competition.

Carbon Steel Electrodes (and Fluxes) for Submerged Arc Welding

The submerged arc process had been in use many years before the
first AWS-ASTM specification for mild steel electrodes and companion
fluxes employed in the process was issued in 1965. The writing of this
specification proved to be a difficult task for even the mild steel electrodes
and fluxes because of the multiple factors which determine the analysis
and properties of the weld metal. In this process, the weld metal is dependent not only upon the electrode used, but is also greatly influenced
by the flux, the base metal, and the welding procedure. The flux has

proved to be an effective medium not only for holding deoxidizers, slag-formers, etc., but for transferring alloying elements into the weld deposit during melting. Although certain problems can arise with alloyed fluxes, as will be explained later, nevertheless, wide use is made of powdered metal additions to the flux to control the analysis of the weld metal. The submerged arc process is noted for its ability to accomplish deep pene-tration; consequently, the base metal, through the dilution mechanics described earlier, will play an important role in establishing the weld metal analysis. Details of the welding procedure are of considerable im-portance because the travel speed, current, voltage, and other welding conditions will determine not only the extent of penetration into the base metal, but also the amount of flux melted (and metal obtained therefrom). While composition limits can be specified for any one of the materials employed in the process, it is not possible to set require-ments for the weld metal unless the remaining variables are held within relatively narrow ranges.

The writers of AWS A5.17 *Bare Mild Steel Electrodes and Fluxes for Submerged-Arc Welding,* solved the problem of setting property re-quirements for weld metal by stipulating the types of steel base metal per-missible in the welded test plates, and by prescribing a multipass welding procedure aimed at minimum dilution for preparing the test joint. Even though the submerged arc welding process is more often used as a single-pass operation, the standardized multipass test procedure was considered necessary to secure weld metal that would reflect to the greatest possible degree the qualities of the electrode–flux combination. Such a test would be more discriminating when comparing results from different electrodes and fluxes. Since this test procedure is basically the same for AWS A5.1, A5.5 and A5.18, it is also possible to compare results obtained by different processes.

In the classification system for electrodes and fluxes, a series of nine electrodes of different compositions as listed in Table 48 are provided. These electrodes may be used in any combination with the six fluxes also listed. The compositions of the fluxes are left to the discretion of the manufacturer. However, the strength and toughness to be achieved with the flux in combination with one of the electrodes are specified. Two levels of strength have been set up: (F6X—) 60 to 80 ksi UTS accompanied by 45 ksi minimum YS, and (F7X—) 70 to 95 ksi UTS along with 50 ksi minimum YS. For each level of strength, flux classifications are provided which define three levels of minimum toughness as determined by the Charpy V-notch impact test; specifically, (FX0—) has no impact test requirement, (FX1—) 20 ft-lb minimum at 0 F, and (FX2—) 20 ft-lb minimum at –20 F.

In addition to the standardized composition electrodes of AWS A5.17, many other carbon steel electrodes of different compositions are available from suppliers. A survey of all the available electrodes shows that they range from a simple low-carbon rimmed steel, to high-manganese silicon-killed steel (which technically would qualify as an alloy steel because of its manganese content). The selection of an electrode for a particular application may seem a difficult, confusing task, but only because there are so many avenues of choice. Some welding engineers prefer to employ a neutral (unalloyed) flux for all of their projects, and therefore they select an electrode which contains all of deoxidizing and alloying elements needed in the filler metal. This represents a safe, sound practice, but procurement of wire of proper composition to serve as the electrode often is difficult. Other welding engineers plan all of their projects on the basis of using the least costly electrode (low-carbon rimmed steel), and they add all required deoxidizing and alloying elements through the flux. Obviously, this practice calls for careful formulation and handling of the flux, and close control of welding conditions. Where the deposit must be thoroughly deoxidized to assure soundness and a substantial quantity of alloy must be added, the alloyed-flux technique may present difficult quality control problems. Little experience is required in submerged arc welding to see that no one practice is best, and that the welding engineer who is familiar with the many different techniques for making up combinations of materials to yield the required weld deposit can accomplish a great deal in producing better submerged arc welded joints at lower cost.

One of the newer techniques for submerged arc welding involves the use of a "cold wire", that is, a supplementary welding rod that feeds into the arc between the regular consumable electrode and the base metal. The "cold wire" filler metal can be a dissimilar alloy composition which has been calculated to shift the final composition of the weld metal to within prescribed limits. Some use is being made of composite electrodes in submerged arc welding, either as the consumable electrode, or as a supplementary welding rod. The composite electrode may be of tubular construction which is filled with powdered metals and/or flux, or it may be a twisted wire construction.

Electrodes and fluxes for submerged arc welding must be selected as a combination in order to have materials which are compatible in welding and which yield weld metal of satisfactory composition. For example, one of the objects in selecting a combination of electrode and flux is to obtain a properly deoxidized, sound weld deposit, and yet avoid excessive silicon content which may cause cracking. Keeping in mind the base metal composition and the welding procedure (in terms of dilution), a combination of electrode and flux is selected which will produce weld metal with a final silicon content of about 0.15 to 0.30%. For this application, a rimmed steel electrode would be quite satisfactory providing a high-silicon flux was employed. However, a high-silicon-killed steel electrode and a high-silicon flux might prove to be a crack-susceptible combination. Although carbon offers its usual strong potential for increasing the strength of the weld metal, the carbon content ordinarily is held rather low to avoid unnecessary reduction of toughness. Most submerged arc welding electrodes have a carbon content below about 0.20%. The most widely used electrodes have a carbon content in the range of approximately 0.07 to 0.15%. For submerged arc deposits, greater attention is given to manganese as a strengthening element. Here, care must be taken to avoid teaming a high-manganese steel electrode with a flux that contains a substantial alloy addition of manganese, unless, of course, a very high manganese content is desired in the weld deposit.

The granular fluxes used in submerged arc welding were described in Chapter 8 and the fusible minerals employed need no elaboration here. On the subject of filler metals, it is important to recognize that any metals or alloys in powdered or granular form, which have been mixed with the granular minerals, also will melt during the welding operation and will transfer into the weld melt. All of the metal or alloy added to the flux may not accomplish the transfer because a portion could be lost by oxidation. The efficiency of transfer, that is, the actual amount of the metal or alloy that enters the weld deposit from the flux will depend upon the nature of the additive, its particle size, and the welding conditions. Granulated fluxes for submerged arc welding may be acid or basic in character. Basic type fluxes usually represent more complex mixtures because materials like limestone must be used to offset the acid characteristic of the other minerals regularly employed. Acid type fluxes are the most widely used, and the mineral portion is made up chiefly of silicates. Acid fluxes can be divided into two general categories: (a) alkaline earth silicates, and (b) silicates in which manganese has replaced part or nearly all of the alkaline earth metals. Calcium aluminum silicate is often used for manufacturing the alkaline earth acid type fluxes. Many features of the granulated flux will affect its role as a carrier of deoxidizing and alloying elements. Complex reactions between the molten flux or slag and the weld metal cause changes in the carbon, manganese and silicon content of the deposit. These reactions vary with the chemical composition of the electrode, base metal and the flux, and with the welding conditions as they involve temperature, time and masses of materials. Consequently, the selection of an electrode is but one small step in establishing the composition of a submerged arc weld deposit.

LOW-ALLOY STEEL FILLER METALS

The development of low-alloy steel electrodes and welding rod is constantly spurred by the introduction of new alloy steels and the demand of users that the properties of the weld "match" those of the base metal. The problem of matching base metal properties is made more complex in the alloy steels by the addition of a factor seldom considered in carbon steels, namely, *condition* or *heat treatment*. While virtually all discussion of carbon steel filler metals was concerned with properties "as-welded," any review of low-alloy steel filler metals must make clear the condition of testing or usage; that is, whether (1) as-welded, or (2) post-weld heat treated. The latter condition may consist of one or more treatments, such as stress relieving, annealing, normalizing, or quenching and tempering. (See Chapter 12 for description of these treatments.) The welding procedure employed can be a highly influential factor in determining the weld metal properties where a low-alloy steel filler metal is employed. For this reason, the preheat temperature, as well as the inter-pass temperature is frequently noted in discussing the welding of alloy steels.

Low-Alloy Steel Covered Welding Electrodes

Standardized covered welding electrodes of low-alloy steel classes are covered by AWS A5.5 (ASTM A316). This specification covers six series of electrodes capable of producing weld metal with minimum tensile strengths of 70, 80, 90, 100, 110 and 120 ksi, respectively. These strength levels are required of the weld metals when welded in accordance with a prescribed preheat and interpass temperature range and also stress-relief heat treated at a prescribed temperature. Yield point and tensile elongation minima are required. Impact test requirements are specified as shown in Table 49. The same flux coverings as described earlier for carbon steel electrodes are employed in making low-alloy steel electrodes, except that all coverings may not be offered as standard classes in each strength series. Also, three levels of maximum moisture content are required in the flux coverings. These are 0.6% for the E70 series, 0.4% for the E80 and E90 series, and 0.2% for the E100, E110, and E120 series. A covering containing large quantities of hydrogen-bearing materials, for example, the EXX10 classification with its large amount of cellulose, would not be used on a high strength electrode because of the cracking danger associated with hydrogen pickup.

Mention was made earlier that virtually all commercial welding electrodes of the carbon and low-alloy steels employ the same kind of low-carbon, rimmed steel core. We now find that the same flux coverings are employed. Therefore, the controlling medium in the low-alloy steel electrodes must be the kind and amount of powdered alloys added to the covering. Table 45, which listed the chemical compositions of weld metals deposited by covered electrodes, indicated the various alloy systems used in securing each of the levels of strength. It is important to become

Table 49 — *IMPACT PROPERTY REQUIREMENTS*

FROM SPECIFICATIONS AWS A5.5 (ASTM A316)

AWS–ASTM classification	Condition of weld metal	Testing temperature	Minimum V-notch impact strength
E8016-C3	As-welded	–40 F	20 ft-lb
E8018-C3	As-welded	–40 F	20 ft-lb
E9018-M	As-welded	–60 F	20 ft-lb
E10018-M	As-welded	–60 F	20 ft-lb
E11018-M	As-welded	–60 F	20 ft-lb
E12018-M	As-welded	–60 F	20 ft-lb
E8016-C1	Stress-relieved	–75 F	20 ft-lb
E8018-C1	Stress-relieved	–75 F	20 ft-lb
E8016-C2	Stress-relieved	–100 F	20 ft-lb
E8018-C2	Stress-relieved	–100 F	20 ft-lb
E9015-D1	Stress-relieved	–60 F	20 ft-lb
E9018-D1	Stress-relieved	–60 F	20 ft-lb
E10015-D2	Stress-relieved	–60 F	20 ft-lb
E10016-D2	Stress-relieved	–60 F	20 ft-lb
E10018-D2	Stress-relieved	–60 F	20 ft-lb
All others			Not required

familiar with the actual weld composition from a chosen electrode. Although several alloy systems may provide the required tensile properties under the standardized test conditions, each may vary in notch toughness, or may behave quite differently under various final conditions of heat treatment. As an example, an E9018 class electrode can be made in at

least four different compositions: (1) chromium–molybdenum as in
E9018-B3, (2) manganese–molybdenum as in E9018-D1, (3) manganese–nickel–molybdenum as in E9018-M, and (4) any other alloy
combination as permitted in E9018-G. Let us assume for the sake of discussion that the latter electrode, E9018-G, was designed to deposit a weld
metal of 1.5% chromium, 0.5% molybdenum, and 0.2% vanadium. While
all three electrodes would display comparable weld metal tensile properties
in the stress-relief heat treated condition, the Cr–Mo and the Mn–Mo
weld metals likely would possess superior notched-bar toughness as compared with the Cr–Mo–V weld metal. Our discussion of low-alloy steel
electrodes, therefore, must treat the influence of alloying elements in some
detail.

Weld Metal Carbon Content

The carbon contents of low-alloy weld metals are held surprisingly
low as compared with the base metals to which they are applied. General
experience suggests that carbon is not one of the favorable alloying elements to employ for gaining high strength in weld metal. Although carbon
is the most effective hardening and strengthening element, and its effectiveness increases in the presence of most other alloying elements, higher
carbon, unfortunately, increases cracking susceptibility, and decreases
ductility and toughness. With increasing carbon content, a larger number
of carbides appear in the weld structure. The notch toughness transition
temperature rises quickly with small increases in carbon content. Most
low-alloy steel electrodes deposit weld metal with carbon in the approximate range of 0.03 to 0.07%. Of course, the carbon content of weld
metal in actual joints will be somewhat higher because of dilution with the
higher carbon base metal. Even so, the final weld metal carbon content
may be only about 0.05 to 0.10% as compared with 0.12 to 0.22% for
the base metal. It must not be concluded that lower carbon content
automatically means tougher weld metal. Some evidence has been obtained that very low carbon (less than 0.03%) low-alloy weld metals may
display undesirably low notch toughness at low temperatures. In other
words, the toughness transition temperature may be raised with very low
carbon levels. When very high strengths are desired in weld metals, that
is from about 150,000 psi UTS and higher, there appears to be no alternative in low-alloy steels but to employ higher carbon contents. Consequently, types of steel like AISI 4130, 4135, 4140, and 4340 are used
as filler metals. However, to best utilize the strength capabilities of these
weld metal compositions, they should be subjected to a post weld normalizing, or hardening and tempering heat treatment.

A high carbon content apparently increases the cracking susceptibility of weld metal because of the high solubility of this element in liquid steel and the marked tendency to segregate during solidification. The carbon level at which the cracking susceptibility becomes objectionable will depend, of course, upon the overall alloy composition of the weld metal and the conditions under which the weld metal solidifies and cools.

Influence of Manganese

Manganese is regarded as a favorable element to add to weld metals because of a number of beneficial effects which it imparts. The first helpful role which manganese plays is to preferentially combine with any sulfur present to form manganese sulfide, MnS, and thus prevent the formation of undesirable low-melting sulfides, like iron sulfide. The latter sulfide, FeS, has a melting point of only 2150 F while manganese sulfide melts at 2950 F. Approximately 1.75 parts of manganese must be added to tie up each part of sulfur. Usually a great deal more manganese is present and it is common to find the Mn–S ratio ranging from 5 to 50 in low-alloy steel. These high ratios are desirable to prevent the formation of a FeMnS complex which may introduce some hot cracking susceptibility. The beneficial effect of manganese in suppressing hot cracking has been estimated to be three times as great as any other alloying element.

Manganese contents as high as 2% in low-alloy steel weld metals appear to improve notch toughness as well as to increase strength. These benefits are quite noticeable in weld metals with strengths up to 120,000 psi UTS. Although the benefits of high manganese content have been exploited in only two standard electrodes, E90XX-D1 and E100XX-D2, the typical analyses reported for the various EXXXX-G electrode (Table 45) show that manganese in the range of 1 to 2% is now frequently utilized. Some evidence has been obtained that very high manganese contents, say about 2%, may be detrimental to notch toughness. In fact, work on weld metal deposited by the submerged arc and gas metal-arc processes indicates that deterioration may occur as the manganese content exceeds about 1.6%. As increasing amounts of manganese are added to weld metal, the ferrite grain size becomes finer and an increasing number of fine carbide particles appear in the microstructure. The marked increase in notch-toughness transition temperature which occurs at very high manganese levels seems to be associated with the formation of upper bainite in the weld microstructure.

Influence of Phosphorus and Sulfur

These elements are being viewed with disfavor by many welding metallurgists. They know full well that phosphorus and sulfur cannot be tolerated at levels above about 0.04% maximum for each element because the deposit would be quite susceptible to hot cracking, and the toughness of the weld metal might suffer as well. Most weld metal now seems to contain in the vicinity of 0.02 to 0.03% each of phosphorus and of sulfur. While this appears to be an innocuous level in low-alloy weld metals of modest strength, some work has been conducted to show benefits from lower levels of residual phosphorus and sulfur, particularly in the heat treated high-strength weld metals of higher carbon content.

Phosphorus forms low-melting eutectics with iron, manganese, chromium and nickel. During solidification, these low-melting mixtures segregate to interdendritic areas and grain boundaries. When sufficient phosphorus is present to form a significant amount of these segregates, a strong susceptibility to weld hot cracking likely would be observed. Since the effects of phosphorus and sulfur are additive in promoting hot cracking, it is necessary to consider the total amount of both elements present. Figure 125 shows the effect of phosphorus content on the cracking susceptibility of a weld metal of AISI 4340 composition. This is a Cr–Ni–Mo low-alloy

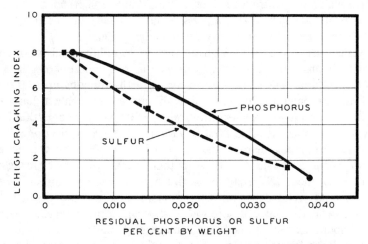

Fig. 125 — Influence of phosphorus and sulfur on cracking susceptibility of AISI 4340 weld metal. In determining the influence of phosphorus content, the sulfur content of the weld metal was held low. Also, when determining the influence of sulfur content, the phosphorus content of the weld metal was held low.

steel containing about 0.40% carbon. A number of special high-strength low-alloy filler metals are now being produced with phosphorus contents of 0.010% maximum. In addition to improved resistance to cracking, these low-phosphorus weld metals would be expected to display a slightly lower toughness transition temperature.

Sulfur also increases susceptibility of weld metal to hot cracking by formation of low-melting compounds or eutectic structures that segregate in the microstructure and provide paths of low rupture strength. Two particular compounds are notorious for promoting hot cracking in weld metal — iron sulfide and nickel sulfide. Both have low melting points and when present as a thin layer in an interdendritic area or a grain boundary, these compounds remain molten long after the surrounding metal has solidified. Fortunately, more favorable forms or compounds of sulfur can be formed by adding alloying elements like manganese or chromium. Some data has been obtained which indicates the effect of sulfur is analogous to that of phosphorus with respect to weld metal hot cracking in a high-strength low-alloy steel (Fig. 125). There is reason to also suspect that the sulfur content can affect the toughness of weld metal of this high strength variety. Consequently, weld metal with phosphorus and sulfur contents each held below about 0.010% is being used in special applications by controlling the levels of these elements both in the filler metal and the base metal.

Silicon

Small amounts of silicon are needed in most low-alloy weld metals as a deoxidizer and to aid in maintaining good fluidity in the molten weld metal. Of all the alloying elements used in low-alloy weld metals, silicon has the most noticeable effects upon electrode operating properties and the appearance of the molten weld metal. Silicon is quite important as a deoxidizer when low-carbon rimmed steel is used as the electrode core wire. Even the silica that forms when the silicon reacts with oxides or oxygen can be helpful through the fluxing action which it exerts. However, as important and helpful as the small amount of silicon may be, it is almost equally important in weld metal to avoid a very high silicon content. Silicon contents up to about 1% may be safely used to assure weld metal soundness. Beyond this amount, silicon usually increases hot cracking susceptibility. The threshold level beyond which cracking tendency increases will depend upon the alloy composition. Some low-alloy weld metals are adversely affected as the silicon exceeds about 0.75%, while others may tolerate up to 1.5% silicon.

Silicon causes cracking in weld metal by forming low-melting compounds that segregate as films in the grain boundaries and within interdendritic areas. The nature of these compounds has not been firmly established.

The notch toughness of weld metal is unfavorably affected by increasing silicon content long before the onset of cracking difficulties. Silicon in amounts exceeding about 0.60% usually exerts a detrimental effect on most weld metals, while the higher strength alloy weld may show ill effects from silicon contents exceeding about 0.35%. This knowledge is heeded in the formulation of flux coverings for electrodes of the E100 series and those higher in strength. The amount of ferrosilicon included in the covering must be limited to avoid weld metal silicon above about 0.35% if good notch toughness and a low transition temperature are to be secured. Limiting the silicon available for deoxidation purposes must be done with care if weld metal porosity is to be avoided. In fact, if the silicon is only barely enough for proper deoxidation under steady-state welding conditions, there remains the possibility that some porosity may occur at the very start of the weld as described in Chapter 13 under "Starting Porosity."

Chromium

Chromium promotes modest increases in strength in low-alloy steel weld metals and is used in amounts ranging from 0.40 to 2.50% in the EXXXX-BX chromium–molybdenum series of standard electrodes. Actually, molybdenum is the stronger partner in the alloying combination. Chromium is less effective and less consistent than molybdenum as a strengthening element. Chromium, of course, is helpful by imparting oxidation resistance to the metal. When evaluated as an individual alloying addition, chromium acts to raise the notch-toughness transition temperature. When several other alloying elements are employed in weld metal in addition to the chromium, the amount of these must be limited to avoid excessively high tensile and yield strengths, and a marked decrease in notch toughness.

Nickel

Nickel is a moderate strengthener, and consequently large amounts can be added to low-alloy steel weld metal before strength increases to an undesirably high level. Weld deposits alloyed with nickel in amounts up to 3.75% display a tensile strength of only 100 ksi when carbon is held below the usual level of about 0.07%. The ductility of the weld metal remains high. The notched-bar impact strength is improved at room temperature, and the toughness transition temperature is lower than that of unalloyed steel weld metal. Nickel appears to have a greater overall beneficial effect upon toughness transition temperature than any other substitutional alloying element. Increasing amounts of nickel appear to produce a small reduction in ferrite grain size in the weld metal, but beyond this the mechanism by which nickel effects improved toughness has not been determined. In contrast to these desirable effects of nickel in weld metal at room temperature and below, there is growing evidence that nickel leads to temper embrittlement in high strength weld metal which is subjected to long time stress-relief heat treatment, or service at elevated temperature. Consequently, the use of nickel as an alloying element often is restricted in certain Cr–Mo weld metal compositions which are designed for elevated temperature service.

Molybdenum

Molybdenum is a popular alloying element among electrode designers, and is used singly and in combination with other alloying elements. Molybdenum, of course, promotes strength by acting to increase hardenability and by taking part in the formation of alloy carbides. Many low-alloy steel weld metals designed to have good low-temperature notch toughness contain molybdenum (often in combination with manganese and nickel). The logic in the amounts of molybdenum used in various alloy-steel weld metals, however, is open to question. Laboratory work has shown that the influence of molybdenum upon notch toughness varies with different levels of this element. In general, it appears that additions up to about 0.20% will raise the transition temperature slightly. Further increase up to about 0.40% then appears to lower the transition temperature, but not below the level of molybdenum-free weld metal. Beyond 0.40% molybdenum, the transition temperature is steadily raised.

Molybdenum improves the high-temperature strength of weld metal, but for this service the addition of some chromium may be advisable to avoid graphitization during long time service. Molybdenum apparently can be added to the higher strength electrodes to the extent of 0.50% to assist in gaining the desired strength without incurring harmful effects upon the response to postweld heat treatment and upon notch toughness. However, molybdenum in excess of 0.50% has been observed to cause a more complex behavior in the postweld heat treated or stress relieved condition. Furthermore, additions of molybdenum between 1 and 2% appear to markedly raise the toughness transition temperature even in the as-welded condition.

As would be expected, molybdenum tends to suppress the formation of free ferrite in the weld metal microstructure and to increase the amount of carbide phase. As progressive additions of molybdenum are made to alloy steel weld metal, the tensile strength increases at a rate much faster than can be accounted for by the solid-solution hardening effects of molybdenum. This rate of strength increase appears to be attributable to the influence of molybdenum upon carbide size and distribution.

Copper

Copper is not as widely used as an alloying element in low-alloy steel weld metal deposited by covered electrodes as is found in wrought alloy base metals. In amounts up to about ½%, no particular influence upon strength or toughness can be observed. No information appears to be available regarding the effect of copper upon the corrosion resistance of weld metal, but presumably it is a beneficial element.

Vanadium

Some use has been made of vanadium in low-alloy steel weld metals as a strengthening element just as has been done in wrought low-alloy steel base metals. A small addition of vanadium brings about a very substantial increase in the hardness and strength of weld metal. However, vanadium now is recognized to adversely affect notch toughness and transition temperature in the as-welded condition. Furthermore, a stronger deleterious effect is found in weld metal that has been stress-relief heat treated. While a small amount of vanadium (i.e., 0.10%) can be tolerated in weld metal to be used in the as-welded condition, a postweld stress-relief treatment induces "secondary hardening" and the vanadium-containing weld metal will display noticeable embrittlement in notched-bar impact tests. In the weld metal microstructure, the addition of vanadium can be observed to produce a finer ferrite grain size.

Alloy Combinations in Weld Metal
from Covered Low-Alloy Electrodes

In examining the alloying element contents of weld deposits from electrodes conforming to AWS A5.5, questions naturally arise about the alloy systems that may have been followed in developing these electrodes. It should come as no surprise to learn that many of the alloy combinations originated many years ago when experimentation indicated they would provide improved mechanical properties for particular kinds of service. Other alloy variations were added as certain applications demanded higher levels of particular properties. Many of the new demands arose as the use of welding was extended to equipment which was required to operate at elevated temperatures, and more recently for service at very low temperatures. In general, the electrode manufacturer was given a free hand in selecting alloying elements to obtain the required properties. His success in meeting these demands is attested by the extensive and highly successful use of weldments in services ranging from cryogenic temperatures to high temperatures. However, only in the past five years has near adequate research been centered upon alloy steel weld metal to determine quantitatively the influence of individual alloying additions and the synergistic effects of multiple additions. We are just beginning to see the benefits of this research manifest itself in specifications for standard classes and in new combinations of alloying elements in weld metals.

E70 Series of Covered Electrodes

Electrodes marketed with a 70 ksi minimum UTS level represent at least three alloying systems: (1) the standardized E70XX-A1 classification, presently in A5.5, which requires the addition of approximately ½% molybdenum, (2) electrodes which would be classified as E70XX-G wherein the manufacturers increase the manganese content slightly above 1%, but make no other alloy additions, to obtain the required 70 ksi UTS, and (3) electrodes which would be classified as E70XX-G that contain additions of ½% chromium and ½% molybdenum. Therefore, in selecting an E70XX electrode, at least four compositions are presently available if consideration can be given also to the carbon steel classification in specification A5.1. There is little to be said on behalf of any particular composition in regard to room temperature tensile properties. A critical evaluation of strength at elevated temperatures or notched-bar impact toughness at very low temperatures, however, will find differences. There is some evidence to suggest that weld metal with higher strength promoted by additional manganese will display a lower toughness transition temperature. Weld metal alloyed with molybdenum, and chromium and molybdenum, would be expected to display better strength at elevated temperatures. Obviously, the engineer concerned with a critical application which makes certain demands on strength and toughness under particular temperature conditions may have to inquire about the actual composition of weld metal deposited by the electrodes selected for the job.

When welding piping for service at elevated temperatures, the E70XX-A1 electrode would be employed for joining C–Mo steel. However, much less of this carbon–½%Mo steel piping is used today because of its susceptibility to graphitization in the weld zones. The more frequently used 1Cr–½Mo steel would be joined with the E70XX-G electrode containing additions of both chromium and molybdenum.

E80 Series of Covered Electrodes

Six different standardized alloying systems or combinations of alloying elements may be employed by electrode manufacturers to obtain elec-

trodes that comply with the E80XX classification. These systems are
shown below:

E80XX-B1	½% Cr–½% Mo
E80XX-B2	1¼% Cr–½% Mo
E80XX-B4L	2% Cr–½% Mo
E80XX-C1	2½% Ni
E80XX-C2	3½% Ni
E80XX-C3	1% Ni

Other alloying systems are used by manufacturers in electrodes
designated as E80XX-G. An electrode containing 1¼% manganese, and
another containing 0.30% Cr–0.80% Ni–0.15% Mo, are shown in Table
45 to have been produced to gain the required 80 ksi UTS minimum.

These weld metal compositions were developed, of course, to not only
provide 80 ksi minimum UTS, but also to match the base metal properties
as closely as possible to withstand specific service conditions. The ½%
Cr–½% Mo electrode (E80XX-B1) was one of the first low-alloy filler
metals used for joining Cr–Mo steel piping in steam power plants and
refinery service. As a demand was felt for greater weld metal strength
at elevated temperatures, the 1¼% Cr–½% Mo (E80XX-B2) and
the 2% Cr–½% Mo (E80XX-B4L) electrodes were introduced. The
E80XX-B1 electrode has been used to join steels of the 1Cr–½Mo and
the 1¼% Cr–½Mo types. The E80XX-B2 electrode appears to offer a
better match for the 1¼Cr–½Mo steel. The E80XX-B4L electrode is
designed for joining 2Cr–½Mo steel, and may be used on the 1¼ Cr–
½Mo steel where a higher chromium content is desired in the weld
metal for reasons of elevated temperature strength or corrosion resistance.
The E80XX-B2L and E80XX-B4L classes of electrodes represent an attempt by means of lower carbon content to reduce cracking sensitivity,
and to minimize the need for close control of preheating, interpass temperature, and postweld heat treatment. The three nickel-containing electrodes (E80XX-C1, E80XX-C2, and E80XX-C3) were developed principally for welding high-strength low-alloy steels in equipment to be subjected to low temperatures in service. As indicated by the Charpy V-notch
impact values in Table 47, the nickel-containing weld metals retain good
toughness to low temperatures.

E90 Series of Covered Electrodes

Two alloy systems have been set up as standards for weld metals expected to achieve 90,000 psi UTS:

E90XX-B3	2¼% Cr–1% Mo
E90XX-D1	1½% Mn–½% Mo

The E90XX-B3 electrode containing 2¼Cr–1Mo was developed to join 2½Cr–1Mo steel piping used for elevated temperature service. An E90XX-B3L class electrode containing 0.05% maximum carbon also is available for those applications where decreased cracking sensitivity is preferred despite a small sacrifice in strength. The E90XX-D1 electrode containing manganese and molybdenum additions provides weld metal with very favorable notched-bar impact properties, particularly in the flatness of the curve correlating Charpy V-notch values with decreasing test temperature. In fact, the 20 ft-lb transition temperature has been found as low as –120 F for deposits from an E9018-D1 electrode.

Electrodes of the E90XX-G class also are produced. The alloy system favored by electrode manufacturers appears to be a 1Mn–1½Ni –0.2 Mo combination. Apparently, this is the composition offered for joining the low-alloy high-strength constructional steels.

E100 Series of Covered Electrodes

Electrodes of this series may be the standardized E100XX-D2 class which represents a 1½%Mn–½%Mo composition, or they may be the broad E100XX-G class, in which case any one of several alloy combinations as shown in Table 45 may be incorporated in the electrode. The E100XX-D2 electrode contains approximately 1.75%Mn–0.35% Mo which is similar to the alloy content of the E90XX-D1 electrode. However, the higher strength is obtained for the E100XX-D2 class by permitting higher carbon content (0.15% max) and slightly higher manganese content.

Electrodes of the E100XX class were designed principally for joining low-alloy high-strength constructional steels. It is not possible to single out particular electrode compositions as being preferred because little data has been published on the mechanical properties of E100XX weld metal. From the nature of the weld compositions deposited by the E100XX-G electrodes, the higher carbon, manganese–molybdenum weld composition does not appear as popular as lower carbon compositions. It should be noted that two of the examples contain additions of vanadium. This is the alloying element which has been observed to reduce notched-bar toughness in the stress-relieved condition. However, this detrimental effect also is dependent upon the remainder of the weld composition, particularly the carbon content. In fact, high carbon itself can lead to reduced notched-bar toughness in weld metal. Therefore, considerable care must be exercised in weighing the influence of alloying elements on weld metal properties.

E110 Series of Covered Electrodes

Because of the large scale exploitation of low-alloy constructional steels offering approximately 115 ksi UTS and 100 ksi minimum yield strength, the E110XX-G electrode has become quite popular. This is the preferred electrode for making butt joints and other weld joints requiring similar mechanical properties in the 100 ksi YS steels. Although this electrode is required to display only 97 ksi minimum YS in the stress-relieved condition, actual weld joints usually display 100 ksi or more because of dilution with higher carbon base metals. Of course, if for any reason the E110XX-G electrode is considered inadequate with respect to mechanical properties, the next higher strength class of electrode can be selected.

The E110XX class is the first low-alloy electrode discussed here for which a standardized composition is not listed in AWS A5.5. Six typical weld compositions are listed in Table 45 for E110XX-G electrodes, and it is obvious from these examples that wide differences can appear between electrodes from various manufacturers. If the first five compositions are examined, the only common feature which these electrodes possess is that they all deposit low-carbon (0.08% or lower) weld metal. The manganese content exceeds 1% in all deposits, and the silicon contents are 0.50% or lower. Beyond these elements, the alloy combinations found among these five E110XX-G electrodes include the following:

1 Mn–3 Ni–½ Mo

1½ Mn–2 Ni–½ Mo

1 Mn–½ Cr–2 Ni–½ Mo

1 Mn–1 Cr–2 Ni–½ Mo

1 Mn–1½ Cr–2½ Ni–½ Mo

The sixth E11018-G electrode listed is unusual inasmuch as the high strength is obtained with a minimum of alloy (1½ Mn–½ Mo) and a relatively high carbon content (0.13%). While this electrode may offer an advantage in cost, the carbon content is likely to adversely affect the toughness transition temperature.

Too little data have been published on the properties of deposits from the E110XX-G electrodes to make fine distinctions regarding composition. No doubt these data will be forthcoming over the next few years and ultimately standardized compositions (beyond that found in

E11018-M) will be established.

E120 Series of Covered Electrodes

The status of E120XX-G electrodes is very much like that of the E110XX-G class. That is, no alloy compositions have been standardized other than that shown for E12018-M; yet a number of alloy combinations are being employed to gain the required mechanical properties. These combinations, in fact, strongly resemble those found in E110XX-G electrodes except that small increases are made in carbon, chromium, or molybdenum to secure an additional 10 ksi in tensile and yield strengths and thus meet the requirements for the E120XX-G classification. In one electrode, an addition of vanadium has been made to secure the required strength. Even though the tensile properties required of weld metal deposited by E120XX-G electrodes are to be met in the stress-relieved condition, electrodes of this class which contain vanadium are advocated by their manufacturers to be used in the as-welded (not stress-relieved) condition.

Covered Electrodes of the EXXXX-M (Military) Classification

The requirements of Military Specification MIL-E-22200/1B are of considerable interest in a study of alloy combinations used in weld deposits. This specification covers six iron-powder, low-hydrogen, mineral covered electrodes as listed in Table 45 (see MIL-7018, MIL-8018, E9018-M, etc.). These electrodes first make use of modest additions of manganese and nickel to secure strength levels of 70, 80, and 90 ksi UTS. Vanadium is limited to 0.05% maximum, or merely the residual amount regularly present in alloy steels. To gain the 100 ksi UTS level, a further addition of 0.25 to 0.50% molybdenum is employed. To raise the UTS to the 110 ksi minimum level, the E11018-M electrode makes use of small increases in manganese, nickel and molybdenum. Only to gain the 120 ksi minimum UTS is recourse made to the use of a substantial amount of chromium. This pattern of alloying steel weld metals follows the experience outlined in the preceding paragraphs on the influence of the individual elements.

Unclassified Low-Alloy Steel Covered Electrodes

Electrode manufacturers offer low-alloy types that are not covered by the present AWS A5.5 specification. In some cases these are proprietary compositions designed to fill a specific need in fabricating low-alloy steel weldments. More often, the electrodes represent a standard AISI low-alloy steel whose composition is suitable for weld metal, and where a demand has been felt for a welding electrode of the same composition as the base metal to be joined. Again, close examination will show the latter statement is not completely true because small modifications usually have been made in the electrode composition to improve its operating characteristics or the properties of the weld metal.

Many of the unclassified or special low-alloy steel weld metals are designed to be used in the heat treated condition; often entailing hardening and tempering treatments. The heat treatment is almost as important as the weld composition in determining the final mechanical properties; therefore, it is not possible to indicate in Tables 46 and 47 the complete ranges of mechanical properties obtainable with these weld metals.

Influence of Welding Procedure on Weld Metal Properties

The mechanical properties of low-alloy steel weld metal, particularly toughness at low temperatures, are affected by a number of conditions involved in the welding procedures used with covered electrodes. The size of the electrode has an effect. The mass of the weld deposit ordinarily increases with larger electrodes, and the solidification rate and cooling rate decreases. Consequently, deposits from larger electrodes are more likely to form the softer microstructures on transformation from the austenitic state. Also, the ferrite grain size tends to be coarser, which reduces strength slightly. In addition to displaying somewhat lower strength, deposits from larger electrodes, for example, over 3/16-in. size, are inclined to produce lower notched-bar impact values. Preheating of the weld joint, and higher interpass temperature, are generally regarded as improving the ductility and notch touchness of low-alloy steel weld metal. This may be true for many steels, but certain new weld metals of the low-carbon martensitic variety may be adversely affected. The influence of preheating and interpass temperature will vary with weld metal composition, postweld heat treatment, and other features of the procedure. Even the position of welding, that is, whether the deposition is made in the flat, vertical or overhead position, will affect weld metal mechanical properties. As a general rule, weld metal deposited in the flat position by a covered electrode has noticeably better mechanical properties than deposits made in any other position. Weld metal deposited in vertical joints usually shows the greatest adverse effect from out-of-position welding. Postweld stress-relieving heat treatments, while ordinarily applied at sub-critical temperatures to reduce residual stresses and not to change mechanical properties, are quite apt to affect weld metal strength and toughness. The influence of stress-relief heat treatment in a welding procedure cannot be described in any general way because so much depends upon the actual weld metal analysis. In addition to knowing the weld composition deposited by the electrode selected, it must be remembered that some dilution will occur with melted base metal and thus the final weld analysis will be determined by at least two contributing materials. The most annoying effect of postweld heat treatment is the embrittlement which has been observed in some varieties of low-alloy steel weld metal. Even the amount of restraint which the joint offers to the cooling weld metal will affect the mechanical properties. Usually the notch toughness of the weld metal is reduced by higher restraint. This effect is attributed to strain aging of the weld metal during cooling. The adverse effect upon the level of notched-bar impact strength and transition temperature can be quite significant in highly restrained joints welded with low heat input (which consequently undergo rapid cooling).

Low-Alloy Steel Bare Filler Metal

Welding rods and bare electrodes of alloy steels to be used in the various welding processes are not presently covered by an AWS-ASTM specification. However, many alloy types have been available for some time. These steels represent proprietary compositions, standardized AISI types, and special steels manufactured to specifications issued by particular industries or branches of the government. Table 50 lists a small number of representative alloy steels used as welding rods and electrodes. Most

Table 50 — *REPRESENTATIVE LOW-ALLOY STEEL BARE WELDING ROD AND ELECTRODE FILLER METALS*

Common Designation	C	Mn	Si	Cr	Ni	Mo	V	Others
1. C–Cr	0.10	1.00	0.25	0.30	...	...	...	...
2. C–Mo	0.10	1.00	0.25	...	...	0.50	...	...
3. Cr–Mo	0.10	0.75	0.20	0.50	...	0.50	...	...
4. Cr–Ni	0.10	0.75	0.20	0.75	1.25	...	...	...
5. 4130	0.30	0.70	0.20	1.00	...	0.25	...	...
6. 4340	0.40	0.70	0.25	0.75	1.85	0.25	...	...
7. 8620	0.20	0.75	0.20	0.50	0.50	0.20	...	...
8. Cr–Ni–V	0.15	0.75	0.20	0.50	1.00	...	0.10	...
9. 502	0.10	0.50	0.20	5.00	...	0.50	...	...
10. Mn–Cr–Ni–Mo–Cu	0.15	2.00	0.05	0.50	2.75	0.50	...	Cu 0.30

APPROXIMATE CHEMICAL COMPOSITIONS

of the steels are quite low in carbon, and all are of the killed variety. These steels have been used as filler metal in gas welding, submerged arc welding, gas metal-arc welding, and gas tungsten-arc welding, and it is not possible to say that specific types of steel have been used solely with a particular process. Much research is currently underway on alloy steel filler metal to gain higher levels of strength in welds and at the same time secure better toughness, particularly lower toughness-transition temperatures. There is some evidence in early findings that the processes themselves are a factor in determining the toughness-transition temperature of the weld metal. While this may not be entirely unexpected, an examination of the metallurgy of each process is necessary to develop an explanation of the results observed in each case.

Influence of Welding Process

The 4130 Cr–Mo alloy steel filler metal listed in Table 50 has been very popular for gas welding alloy steel tubing of the same type in aircraft construction. Best weld joint properties are obtained when the weldment is postweld heat treated either by normalizing or by quenching and tempering. The oxyacetylene gas welding process has been almost completely replaced by arc welding processes in the joining of alloy steels because of (a) the problem of control of composition and unsoundness in the weld metal, and (b) the variations in mechanical properties which occur as a result of the composition changes (carbon pickup and loss of oxidizable elements).

Submerged arc welding could be performed with almost any of the filler metals listed in Table 50. Of course, the selection of an alloy filler metal is guided to a large degree by the amount and kind of alloying elements present in the base metal to be welded (assuming the dilution will be significant) and in the flux to be used. Submerged arc welding can be performed over a wide range of heat input per bead of weld metal. The beads deposited in a joint may represent small multipass deposits, or the joint may be welded by a single massive deposit. While the tensile strengths of weld metal in alloy steel made by these two different techniques often will be comparable, the notch toughness usually differs significantly. Weld metal composed of small multiple beads, which tend to have a finer grain structure, ordinarily display appreciably better notch toughness. Considering that submerged arc welding may be performed on alloy steels with electrode sizes ranging from about 1/16 up to ¼ in., current from 350 to 1000 amperes, arc voltage from 25 to 40, and travel speeds from 5 to 100 ipm, it is impractical to present a tabulation of data on mechanical properties of weld metal deposited by this process. Data on typical joints in particular types of alloy steel base metal will be discussed in Chapter 15.

The flux-covered electrodes used in the shielded metal-arc process have been reviewed in some detail earlier in this chapter. A metallurgical point deserving of thought is that the shielded arc process does not deposit weld metal with best toughness in the high strength alloy steels. Somewhat better toughness and lower transition temperature will be found in weld metal deposited by submerged arc and the gas shielded arc processes, providing weld bead size, cooling rate, other conditions which affect grain size and other features of the microstructure are comparable. The explanation for the toughness deficiency of weld metal from covered electrodes is believed to lie in the unavoidable pickup of small amounts of oxygen, nitrogen and hydrogen from the arc atmosphere and the covering materials. While silicon or other deoxidizing elements can be added to tie up the oxygen, silicon itself is now regarded as an embrittling element in high strength alloy-steel weld metal. The differences in notch toughness between weld metal deposited by the various processes are not very large with currently used types ranging up to about 120 ksi UTS. However, as more highly alloyed weld metals are employed in efforts to gain tensile strength levels well above 120 ksi, the better toughness performance (particularly lower toughness-transition temperature) of the submerged arc and the gas shielded arc processes becomes more significant.

The gas tungsten-arc process is particularly effective in producing good toughness in very high strength weld metal. In fact, weld metals possessing a minimum yield strength of 150 ksi when deposited by the gas tungsten-arc process are superior in toughness to all others. This performance is credited to the fact that the process does not add oxygen, nitrogen, hydrogen, or other impurity elements from an electrode flux covering or a slag.

The gas metal-arc process also avoids the pickup of hydrogen, but more opportunity exists for pickup of oxygen and nitrogen in the weld metal from the atmosphere than in the case of the gas tungsten-arc process. However, with proper gas shielding in the gas metal-arc process, the pickup of oxygen and nitrogen is small. Nevertheless, filler metal for gas metal-arc welding must carry an adequate amount of deoxidizing elements to maintain the steel in a completely deoxidized state when deposited in a joint. For example, in Table 50, the 502 composition (9) containing only 0.20% silicon would be likely to produce a porous deposit by gas metal-arc welding. Either higher silicon (possibly 0.40 to 0.90%) or an addition of aluminum, zirconium or titanium would be required to insure a sound deposit.

Influence of Weld Composition

Much of the information presented earlier about alloy steel weld metal from covered electrodes also applies to deposits made by other processes. However, further remarks can be made, particularly with regard to the gas tungsten-arc and gas metal-arc processes. The C–Cr steel (see Table 50, No. 1) has been a favorite for making high quality oxyacetylene welded joints in high-tensile steel pipe. The C–Mo steel (2) has been used as filler metal in the gas tungsten-arc welding of steam pressure piping for elevated temperature service. Of course, the graphitization problem with the C–Mo steels in this service has led to the greater use of the Cr–Mo steel (3). Some use is being made of a C–Mo steel bare electrode for general purpose gas metal-arc welding; however, the silicon content usually is increased to about 0.80% to insure adequate deoxidation in this process (assuming that CO_2 shielding will be employed). The 8620 filler metal (7) is a base metal composition originally developed for case carburizing applications. However, it provides a Cr–Ni–Mo steel of moderate alloy content which is suited for welding a variety of steels where approximately 100 ksi UTS and 80 ksi YS is desired in the weld deposit in the as-welded condition.

The Mn–Cr–Ni–Mo–Cu filler metal (10) represents one of a number of new alloy electrodes used for welding high strength alloy steel; that is, having a yield strength of 80 ksi or higher. These new alloy-steel filler metals must offer good notch toughness in addition to providing the required strength. They are reported to be developed in accordance with three particular guidelines: (a) the combination of principal alloying elements is patterned after the latest findings concerning notch toughness and the toughness-transition temperature, (b) certain residual elements especially phosphorus and sulfur are held to very low levels, and (c) the electrode includes carefully selected and proportioned deoxidizers to thoroughly degassify the weld metal. These three points assume greater importance as the strength of the weld metal is increased. When the tensile strength of alloy-steel weld metal exceeds about 200 ksi, a further benefit to toughness is secured by using filler metal that was produced by vacuum melting, or that was subjected to a degassing operation during manufacture. Studies of the total oxygen content of weld metal indicate a strong correlation between oxygen content and toughness-transition temperature.

HIGH-ALLOY STEEL FILLER METALS

Welding rod and electrodes of the stainless steel and heat-resisting steel types are used for joining carbon and low-alloy steels in special applications. The need for one of these *high-alloy filler* metals may arise when:

1. Carbon or low-alloy steel is joined to a stainless steel or a heat-resisting steel.

2. The unique properties of a high-alloy weld deposit or a surfacing weld are desired, for example, greater toughness, corrosion resistance, low magnetic permeability, or crack resistance.

3. Cold cracking in the base metal heat-affected zone must be prevented in every possible way.

4. The base metal is coated with a protective metal, like aluminum, and a weld metal is needed which is immune to the metallurgical effects of the coating as it is picked up by the weld deposit.

The metallurgy of high-alloy steel welding rods and electrodes is a broad, involved subject. When these steels are employed on joints in carbon and low-alloy steels the metallurgy involved in the procedure becomes even more complex. While the subject cannot be treated in detail here, it should be helpful to point out the types of welding rods and electrodes sometimes used, the considerations given to their selection, and the metallurgical principles which govern their successful use.

Covered Welding Electrodes

Corrosion-Resisting Chromium and Chromium-Nickel Steel Covered Welding Electrodes is the title of AWS A5.4 (ASTM A 298). This specification covers electrodes which deposit weld metal containing more than 4% chromium and nickel not exceeding 50%. Only two kinds of coverings have been standardized for high-alloy electrodes, (1) a covering suitable for DC–RP operation which is commonly referred to as a "lime-type," and (2) a covering for AC or DC–RP operation commonly called a "titania-type." Both coverings are suitable for welding in all positions. Electrode manufacturers offer modifications of these two standardized coverings, for example, a titania-type suitable for DC operation only in the flat and horizontal position. However, the variety of coverings on high-alloy electrodes does not equal the broad, versatile range of coverings available on carbon steel electrodes. All of the coverings employed on the high-alloy electrodes are of the low-hydrogen kind. The standardized compositions or classes included in this specification are listed in Table 51. The standard electrode coverings for all classifications are designated by the suffix –15 for the DC–RP (lime) type, and by the suffix –16 for the AC–DC (titania) type.

Table 51 — *STANDARDIZED HIGH-ALLOY STEEL COVERED WELDING ELECTRODES*

CHEMICAL COMPOSITION REQUIREMENTS IN PERCENTS FOR ALL-WELD-METAL DEPOSIT, AWS A5.4 (ASTM A298)[a]

Sulfur is limited to 0.03 max percent in all cases; phosphorus is limited to 0.04 max percent in all cases except E310, E310Cb, E310Mo and E16-8-2 for which the limit is 0.03 max percent.

AWS–ASTM classification	C	Cr	Ni	Mo	Cb + Ta	Mn	Si
E308	0.08	18.0–21.0	9.0–11.0	. . .	. . .	2.50	0.90
E308L	0.04	18.0–21.0	9.0–11.0	. . .	. . .	2.50	0.90
E309	0.15	22.0–25.0	12.0–14.0	. . .	. . .	2.50	0.90
E309Cb	0.12	22.0–25.0	12.0–14.0	. . .	0.70–1.00	2.50	0.90
E309Mo	0.12	22.0–25.0	12.0–14.0	2.00–3.00	. . .	2.50	0.90
E310	0.20	25.0–28.0	20.0–22.5	. . .	. . .	2.50	0.75
E310Cb	0.12	25.0–28.0	20.0–22.0	. . .	0.70–1.00	2.50	0.75
E310Mo	0.12	25.0–28.0	20.0–22.0	2.00–3.00	. . .	2.50	0.75
E312	0.15	28.0–32.0	8.0–10.5	. . .	. . .	2.50	0.90
E16-8-2	0.10	14.5–16.5	7.5–9.5	1.00–2.00	. . .	2.50	0.50
E316	0.08	17.0–20.0	11.0–14.0	2.00–2.50	. . .	2.50	0.90
E316L	0.04	17.0–20.0	11.0–14.0	2.00–2.50	. . .	2.50	0.90
E317	0.08	18.0–21.0	12.0–14.0	3.00–4.00	. . .	2.50	0.90
E318	0.08	17.0–20.0	11.0–14.0	2.00–2.50	6xC min, 1.00 max	2.50	0.90
E330	0.25	14.0–17.0	33.0–37.0	. . .	. . .	2.50	0.90
E347	0.08	18.0–21.0[b]	9.0–11.0	. . .	8xC min, 1.00 max	2.50	0.90
E349[c]	0.13	18.0–21.0	8.0–10.0	0.35–0.65	0.75–1.2	2.50	0.90

TABLE 51 — *(Continued)*

AWS–ASTM classification	C	Cr	Ni	Mo	Cb + Ta	Mn	Si
E410	0.12	11.0–13.5	0.60	...	...	1.00	0.90
E430	0.10	15.0–18.0	0.60	...	...	1.00	0.90
E502	0.10	4.0–6.0	0.40	0.45–0.65	...	1.00	0.90
E505	0.10	8.0–10.5	0.40	0.85–1.20	...	1.00	0.90
E7Cr	0.10	6.0–8.0	0.40	0.45–0.65	...	1.00	0.90

a Single values shown are maximum percentages except where otherwise indicated.
b Chromium may be specified as 1.9 x Ni min.
c Also titanium 0.15 max and tungsten 1.25 to 1.75.

Bare Welding Rods or Electrodes

Corrosion-Resisting Chromium and Chromium-Nickel Steel Welding Rods and Bare Electrodes is the title of AWS A5.9 (ASTM A 371). The standardized compositions are listed in Table 52.

Many other types of stainless and heat-resisting steels—proprietary, as well as standard AISI steels—also are available in the form of welding rod and electrodes. These have not been tabulated because only a limited number are justifiably used in joining carbon and low-alloy steels, even in making joints between these steels and a high-alloy steel.

Metallurgy of Dissimilar Metal Welded Joints

More metallurgical *faux pas* appear to be made in selecting a high-alloy steel filler metal for joining carbon and alloy steels to stainless or heat-resisting steels than in any other situation involving welding rod or electrode selection. Many times joints between these dissimilar steels are found to be welded with filler metal of Types 308, 347, 316 and 318. It can be said that in virtually every case the use of these particular types of welding rod or electrode is incorrect or illogical. Occasionally, selection of an improper high-alloy filler metal results in cracking during fabricating or a service failure.

The crux of the problem of improper electrode selection appears to be failure to recognize that some dilution of the high-alloy weld deposit invariably occurs by entry of the melted carbon or alloy-steel base metal. It is imperative that the amount of this dilution be taken into consideration and that, at least, an estimate be made of the final weld metal analysis.

Table 52 — *HIGH-ALLOY STEEL WELDING RODS & BARE ELECTRODES*

CHEMICAL COMPOSITION REQUIREMENTS IN PERCENTS FOR THE ROD OR ELECTRODE, AWS A5.9 (ASTM A371)

Phosphorus and sulfur are each limited to 0.03 max percent. Single values shown are maximum percentages except where otherwise specified.

AWS–ASTM classification	C	Cr	Ni	Mo	Cb + Ta	Mn	Si
ER308	0.08	19.5–22.0[a]	9.0–11.0	...	...	1.0–2.5	0.25–0.60
ER308L	0.03	19.5–22.0[a]	9.0–11.0	...	...	1.0–2.5	0.25–0.60
ER309	0.12	23.0–25.0	12.0–14.0	...	...	1.0–2.5	0.25–0.60
ER310	0.08–0.15	25.0–28.0	20.0–22.5	...	...	1.0–2.5	0.25–0.60
ER312	0.08–0.15	28.0–32.0	8.0–10.5	...	...	1.0–2.5	0.25–0.60
ER316	0.08	18.0–20.0	11.0–14.0	2.0–3.0	...	1.0–2.5	0.25–0.60
ER316L	0.03	18.0–20.0	11.0–14.0	2.0–3.0	...	1.0–2.5	0.25–0.60
ER317	0.08	18.5–20.5	13.0–15.0	3.0–4.0	...	1.0–2.5	0.25–0.60
ER318	0.08	18.0–20.0	11.0–14.0	2.0–3.0	8xC min, 1.0 max	1.0–2.5	0.25–0.60
ER321[b]	0.08	18.5–20.5	9.0–10.5	0.5	...	1.0–2.5	0.25–0.60
ER330[d]	0.15–0.25	15.0–17.0	34.0 min	...	...	1.0–2.5	0.25–0.60
ER347	0.08	19.0–21.5[a]	9.0–11.0	...	10xC min, 1.0 max	1.0–2.5	0.25–0.60
ER348	0.08	19.0–21.5[a]	9.0–11.0	...	10xC min, 1.0 max	1.0–2.5	0.25–0.60
ER349[c]	0.07–0.13	19.0–21.5	8.0–9.5	0.35–0.65	1.0–1.4	1.0–2.5	0.25–0.60
ER410	0.12	11.5–13.5	0.6	0.6	...	0.6	0.50
ER420	0.25–0.40	12.0–14.0	0.6	...	...	0.6	0.50
ER430	0.10	15.5–17.0	0.6	...	...	0.6	0.50
ER502	0.10	4.5–6.0	0.6	0.45–0.65	...	0.6	0.25–0.60

a Chromium, min = 1.9 × nickel, when so specified.
b Also titanium 9 × C min. to 1.0 max.
c Also titanium 0.10 to 0.30 and tungsten 1.25 to 1.75.
d not a recognized classification in the AWS–ASTM specification.

If the engineer planning the welding procedure takes a hard look at the properties expected of his final weld metal composition, any earlier usage of Types 308, 347, etc., as filler metal probably will prompt some misgivings. For example, let us picture an edge joint between two sheets of 3/32-in. thick carbon steel. The welding is being done manually with an electrode of ⅛-in. size in the E308 classification. It would not be unusual under these conditions for the deposit from this electrode to be diluted by approximately 35% of base metal. Consequently, the weld metal would have a final composition of about 13% chromium and 6.5% nickel. This alloy composition would be too low to maintain the tough, austenitic type of microstructure which is expected in a Type 308 weld metal. Instead, the weld structure would transform on cooling from the welding temperature to the harder, less ductile martensitic type of structure. If the carbon steel contributed a significant amount of additional carbon to the weld metal, the deposit could be quite brittle in the martensitic condition. On the other hand, if the E308 electrode is replaced with E309, then the final weld composition would contain about 16.25% chromium and 7.8% nickel. This alloy content is the bare minimum needed to maintain the tough, austenitic weld microstructure. The use of an E310 electrode would produce a weld metal containing 17.5% chromium and 13% nickel, which assures an austenitic weld structure. Of course, if the extent of dilution increases, even the E309 and E310 electrodes may be too lean to provide a final weld deposit with approximately 16% minimum chromium and 7% minimum nickel.

Conversely, if the welding can be performed with less than 35% dilution, then a lower alloy content electrode will serve. When the base metal is carbon steel, Type 308 filler metal will tolerate no more than about 22% dilution before significant martensite transformation occurs in the weld metal structure. This level of dilution is easily exceeded in arc welding operations. Hence, Type 308 filler metal or any high-alloy steel filler metal of equivalent alloy content ordinarily would be a doubtful choice.

NICKEL AND NICKEL-BASE ALLOYS

Nickel alloys are defined as those alloys containing more than 50% nickel. Approximately two dozen covered electrodes and bare filler metals have been standardized by AWS-ASTM. A number of proprietary alloys also are used as filler metals. At least a half dozen of the nickel and nickel-alloy welding rods and electrodes are used in joining carbon and alloy steels, particularly in making dissimilar metal joints with these steels.

The system of electrode and welding rod classification presently employed by AWS-ASTM for nickel and nickel alloys was adopted in 1964. It differs from the system used prior to that date, and users should be aware of the difference. As shown in Table 53, the new system follows the standard pattern of other AWS-ASTM filler metal specifications by employing a prefix to indicate bare welding rod (R), bare filler metal for welding rod or electrode usage (ER), and electrodes (E). The symbol *Ni* is used to identify the filler metals as nickel-base alloys and the additional chemical symbols indicate principal alloying elements present. The suffix numbers identify an individual classification within a given alloy series. For comparison, the previous designations are listed next to the new in Table 53. More importantly, the right-hand column indicates the

Table 53 — *GUIDE TO IDENTIFICATION OF NICKEL AND NICKEL-ALLOY WELDING RODS AND ELECTRODES*

Present classification AWS 5.11-64T (ASTM B295-64T)	Previous classification AWS 5.11-54T (ASTM B295-54T)	Frequently used trade designation	Welding process and application a
COVERED ELECTRODES			
ENi-1	E4N11	Nickel	SMAW of nickel, and nickel to steel.
ENiCu-1	E4N10	Monel	SMAW where dilution of weld with steel is expected.
ENiCu-2	. . . . . .	Monel	SMAW for nickel–copper alloys.
ENiCu-3	E3N14	"K" Monel	SMAW precipitation hardening nickel–copper–aluminum alloy.
ENiCu-4	E3N10	Monel	SMAW for applications where presence of Cb or Ta is undesirable.
ENiCr-1	E4N12	80Ni–20Cr	SMAW of nickel–chromium alloys and other dissimilar alloys.
ENiCrFe-1	E3N12	Inconel	SMAW of nickel–chromium–iron alloys.
ENiCrFe-2	. . . . . .	Incoweld "A"	SMAW of nickel–chromium–iron alloys and other dissimilar alloys.
ENiCrFe-3	. . . . . .	Inconel-182	SMAW of nickel–chromium–iron alloys and other dissimilar metals. Highly resistant to fissuring.
ENiMo-1	E3N1B, E4N1B	Hastelloy "B"	SMAW of nickel–molybdenum alloys.
ENiMo-2	E3N1C, E4N1C	Hastelloy "C"	SMAW of nickel–molybdenum–chromium alloys.
ENiMo-3	. . . . . .	Hastelloy "W"	SMAW of dissimilar metal combinations of nickel-base, cobalt base, and iron alloys.
. . . . . .	. . . . . .	Inconel "X"	SMAW of nickel–chromium–iron–aluminum-titanium precipitation hardening alloys.

TABLE 53 — *(Continued)*

BARE WELDING RODS AND ELECTRODES

Previous classification AWS A5.14-64T (ASTM B304-64T)	Previous classification AWS A5.14-54T (ASTM B304-54T)	Frequently used trade designation	Welding process and application [a]
RNi-2	RN41	Nickel	OAW of nickel.
ERNi-3	ERN61	Nickel	GTAW and GMAW of nickel
RNiCu-5	RN40	Monel	OAW of nickel–copper alloys.
RNiCu-6	RN43	Monel	OAW of nickel–copper alloys.
ERNiCu-7	ERN60	Monel	GTAW, GMAW and SAW of nickel–copper alloys.
ERNiCu-8	ERN64	"K" Monel	GTAW and GMAW of precipitation hardening nickel–copper–aluminum alloys.
ERNiCr-2	ERN6N	80Ni–20Cr	GTAW, GMAW and AHW of 80Ni–20Cr alloy.
ERNiCr-3	. . . . . .	Inconel-82	GTAW, GMAW, SAW and AHW of nickel–chromium–iron alloys and other dissimilar metals. Highly resistant to fissuring.
RNiCrFe-4	RN42	Inconel	OAW of nickel–chromium–iron alloys.
ERNiCrFe-5	ERN62	Inconel	GTAW, GMAW, SAW and AHW of nickel–chromium–iron alloys.
ERNiCrFe-6	. . . . . .	Inconel-92	GTAW, GMAW, SAW and AHW of nickel–chromium–iron alloys and other dissimilar metals.
ERNiCrFe-7	ERN69	Inconel "X"	GTAW, GMAW and AHW of nickel–chromium–iron–titanium precipitation hardening alloys.
ERNiMo-4	ERN7B	Hastelloy "B"	GTAW, GMAW and AHW of nickel-molybdenum alloys.
ERNiMo-5	ERN7C	Hastelloy "C"	GTAW, GMAW and AHW of nickel-molybdenum–chromium alloys.
ERNiMo-6	ERN7W	Hastelloy "W"	GTAW, GMAW and AHW of dissimilar high-alloy materials.

[a] AWS Designations for Welding Processes

SMAW	— Shielded metal-arc welding	SAW	— Submerged-arc welding
GTAW	— Gas tungsten-arc welding	AHW	— Atomic hydrogen welding
GMAW	— Gas metal-arc welding	OAW	— Oxyacetylene welding

welding processes with which the various filler metals are ordinarily used. The filler metal classification system is described in greater detail in the appendices of the specifications covering nickel and nickel-alloy welding rods and electrodes.

Porosity can be a problem in nickel and nickel-alloy weld deposits, and the cause and cure are not exactly like those for steel weld metals. Nitrogen is a very strong promoter of porosity in weld metals of the chromium-free nickel-base alloys, and this influence of nitrogen is counter-acted by additions of titanium and/or aluminum. Oxygen and carbon mon-oxide also are porosity promoters to a lesser degree, and are controlled by additions of manganese, silicon and aluminum. The chromium-containing alloys are more resistant to the damaging effects of these gases because of the strong affinity which chromium has for nitrogen, oxygen and carbon. Hydrogen is a relatively innocuous gas in nickel and nickel alloys.

The amount of gas-fixing elements added for guarding against poros-ity depends upon the overall alloy composition of the filler metal, the base metal, and the welding process to be employed. It is important for the welding engineer to appreciate that bare welding rod designated for oxyacetylene welding cannot be employed in the arc-welding processes because an insufficient amount of gas-fixing alloying elements are present in the rod. Conversely, the bare wires with large amounts of gas-fixing elements intended for use as filler metal in the arc welding processes, such as gas tungsten-arc welding, cannot be employed in oxyacetylene welding because the molten metal will form oxide films under the gas flame and exihibit very poor flowing ability. Furthermore, stripping the covering from an electrode designed for shielded metal-arc welding in order to employ the core wire as bare filler metal is almost certain to lead to difficulty with defects. Any interchange of filler metals among the welding processes must be guided by a thorough knowledge of the chemi-cal compositions of the materials involved and their behavior in the weld-ing process to be employed.

Nickel and Nickel-Alloy Covered Electrodes

Covered electrodes for shielded metal-arc welding are standardized under AWS A5.11 (ASTM B295). Table 54 summarizes the electrodes classified under the present issue of this specification. Also listed is one additional electrode which is used for welding alloys of the Inconel variety that have been modified with aluminum, titanium, columbium, and tanta-lum to induce precipitation hardening capability. Rather than repeat the chemical composition requirements for weld metal from these electrodes (which can be easily obtained from the AWS-ASTM specifications), Table 54 indicates typical chemical analyses which might be found in all-weld-metal deposits. It will be noted that even the so-called plain *nickel* weld metal (from ENi-1) contains a substantial amount of aluminum and titanium to insure freedom from porosity. The usability characteristics of covered electrodes of nickel and nickel-alloys have not yet been standard-ized as have steel electrodes.

Table 54 — *NICKEL AND NICKEL–ALLOY COVERED ELECTRODES*

TYPICAL CHEMICAL COMPOSITION OF DEPOSITED METAL (FOR DETAILS OF AWS-ASTM CLASSIFICATIONS SEE AWS 5.11-64T OR ASTM B295-64T)

AWS–ASTM classification	Trade name or example	Typical Chemical Composition, %					
		Ni	Cu	Cr	Si	Fe	Others
ENi-1	Nickel(131&141)	94	...	...	1.0	...	Al 1, Ti 2.5
ENiCu-1	Monel(140)	66	22	...	1.0	2	Cb+Ta 2
ENiCu-2	Monel	64	22	...	1.0	2	Cb+Ta 2
ENiCu-3	"K" Monel(134)	64	24	...	1.0	2	Al 3, Ti 1, Mn 4
ENiCu-4	Monel(130)	67	23	...	0.5	2	Al 1, Ti 1
ENiCr-1	80Ni–20Cr(142)	77	...	18	0.5	4	Cb+Ta 2
ENiCrFe-1	Inconel(132)	68	...	15	0.5	10	Cb+Ta 3
ENiCrFe-2	Incoweld "A"	70	...	16	0.5	6	Mn 2, Mo 2, Cb+Ta 2
ENiCrFe-3	Inconel(182)	67	...	15	0.5	6	Mn 7, Cb+Ta 2, Ti 0.5
ENiMo-1	Hastelloy B	60	...	...	1.0	6	Mo 29
ENiMo-2	Hastelloy C	54	...	15	1.0	6	Mo 16, W 4
ENiMo-3	Hastelloy W	62	...	5	1.0	6	Mo 25
......	Inconel "X"(139)	66	...	15	1.0	10	Al 0.7, Ti 2, Cb+Ta = 4xSi min

Nickel and Nickel-Alloy Bare Filler Metal

AWS A5.14 (ASTM B304) covers *Nickel and Nickel-Alloy Bare Welding Rods and Electrodes.* The standardized filler metal classifications contained in this specification are listed in Table 55. Again, typical chemical analyses are shown rather than the requirements of the specification. However, in this case, the analyses are those of the bare electrode or welding rod instead of deposited weld metal.

The selection of a nickel or nickel-alloy filler metal to join a carbon or alloy steel to a dissimilar, highly-alloyed material is a very involved subject. One rule, however, that practically always applies is that the welding is *never* done with a carbon steel or a low-alloy steel filler metal. If the use of such filler metals was attempted, the pickup of alloy from the highly-alloyed base metal would be likely to produce a weld deposit of unpredictable hardening propensity. The mechanical properties of the joint, therefore, would be unpredictable. Consequently, the welding engineer must plan to have the weld metal of *high-alloy* composition in order to insure particular mechanical properties. Table 53 indicated in a very general way the filler metals of the nickel and nickel-alloy variety which sometimes are used to make dissimilar metal weld joints. It will not be possible to elaborate here on the filler metals which should be selected for particular combinations of base metals. Certain of the nickel-alloy filler metals represent compositions recently developed to give improved performance in avoiding such defects as porosity and fissuring. Covered electrode ENiCrFe-3, and the related bare filler metal, ERNiCr-3, are establishing an excellent record for making satisfactory dissimilar metal joints between carbon and alloy steels and highly-alloyed materials, and for depositing a surfacing weld of nickel–chromium alloy on carbon steel.

The metallurgy of nickel and nickel-alloy weld metals is very complex, and little information is in the literature on the relationships between composition, microstructure, and performance of weld metal. While the elements columbium, manganese, silicon, tantalum and titanium are added as gas-fixing agents, it is reported that the proportioning of these elements is very influential in controlling hot-cracking tendencies.

Table 55 — *NICKEL AND NICKEL–ALLOY BARE WELDING RODS AND ELECTRODES*

TYPICAL CHEMICAL COMPOSITION OF BARE FILLER METAL. FOR DETAILS OF AWS-ASTM CLASSIFICATION SEE AWS 5.14-64T (ASTM B304-64T)

AWS–ASTM classification	Trade name or example	Typical Chemical Composition, %					
		Ni	Cu	Cr	Si	Fe	Others
RNi-2	Nickel(41)	99	...	...	0.5	...	Ti 0.5
ERNi-3	Nickel(61)	95	...	...	0.5	1	Al 1, Ti 2
RNiCu-5	Monel(40)	66	23	...	0.5	2	......
RNiCu-6	Monel(43)	58	38	...	1.0	1	......
ERNiCu-7	Monel(60)	66	24	...	1.0	2	Al 1, Ti 2
ERNiCu-8	"K" Monel(64)	67	27	...	1.0	2	Al 3, Ti 0.5, Mn 1.5
ERNiCr-2	80Ni–20Cr	75	...	20	0.3	2	Al 0.4, Ti 0.3
ERNiCr-3	Inconel(82)	72	...	20	0.3	2	Mn 3, Cb+Ta 2.5, Ti 0.3
RNiCrFe-4	Inconel(42)	74	...	16	0.5	8	......
ERNiCrFe-5	Inconel(62)	72	...	16	0.5	8	Cb+Ta 2
ERNiCrFe-6	Inconel(92)	70	...	16	0.2	6	Ti 3, Mn 2.5
ERNiCrFe-7	Inconel "X"(69)	70	...	16	0.5	7	Al 0.7, Ti 2, Cb+Ta 1
ERNiMo-4	Hastelloy "B"	60	...	...	1.0	6	Mo 29, V 0.4
ERNiMo-5	Hastelloy "C"	54	...	15	1.0	6	Mo 16, W 4
ERNiMo-6	Hastelloy "W"	62	...	5	1.0	6	Mo 25

When performing an arc or gas welding operation on carbon or alloy steel with nickel or a nickel-base alloy, the matter of dilution is very important. The metallurgy of this situation is quite similar to that described for carbon and alloy steels being welded with high-alloy steel filler metal. Nickel possesses a face-centered cubic crystallographic structure which is like that of gamma iron or the austenitic structure of steel. Nickel alloys, as a rule, also have a face-centered cubic structure. Of course, if the nickel-alloy is diluted substantially with iron, then the alloy may not be able to maintain the tough, soft, face-centered cubic structure and may transform to the body-centered cubic type. While this face-centered to body-centered cubic transformation is dependent upon the alloying elements in the total composition, generally if the nickel content is above about 25% the structure will remain in the face-centered cubic form. Consequently, in welding steels of almost every kind with nickel or nickel-alloy filler metals, it is important to hold dilution of the weld as low as practicable. If the weld metal is diluted excessively with iron, the following degradations occur starting with (a) decreasing subzero notch toughness, (b) lowered corrosion resistance, and (c) loss of room-temperature ductility and toughness. Corrosion resistance is controlled to a large measure by chromium content in the NiCrFe alloys. One step to compensate for dilution in this case would be to make use of a higher chromium variety of filler metal (containing about 20% Cr rather than 16%) which is available as bare welding rod and electrode.

The problem of microfissuring or hot cracking must be watched carefully in using the nickel and nickel-alloys as filler metals. This form of cracking is intergranular in nature and is greatly aggravated by certain residual elements in the weld metal. The severity of cracking may range from internal microfissures, which can be found only by bend testing or a searching metallographic examination at about 500X, to extensive hot cracking which is clearly observed on the surface with the unaided eye. Manganese-modified ENiCrFe-2, ENiCrFe-3, ERNiCr-3 and ERNiCrFe-6 are reported to have markedly increased resistance to this intergranular-type cracking defect.

COPPER AND COPPER-BASE ALLOYS

Copper and copper-base alloys are used extensively in braze welding, brazing, and surfacing the carbon and alloy steels. These operations are carried out with a great variety of alloys, and forms of electrodes and rods. A large number of these materials are standardized in AWS-ASTM specifications. Specifications are provided for copper and copper alloys as (1) arc-welding electrodes, both bare and covered, and (2) welding rods. Brazing filler metal is covered by a specification which also includes alloys of aluminum, magnesium, and nickel. These specifications employ a common system of classification and designation as outlined in Table 56.

Copper and Copper Alloy Welding Electrodes

Any form of copper or certain copper-base alloys, whether solid or stranded, whether bare or covered, when used as a consumable electrode in an arc welding process may be classified under AWS A5.6 (ASTM B225). Covered and bare electrodes used for braze-welding steels by the shielded metal-arc and gas metal-arc processes are commonly manufactured to this specification (see Table 57).

Since the introduction of the gas metal-arc process, the use of flux-covered arc welding electrodes of copper and copper alloys has steadily decreased. Generally, the deposits produced by the gas metal-arc process have better soundness and mechanical properties than those from covered electrodes.

Table 56 — GUIDE TO AWS-ASTM CLASSIFICATION OF COPPER AND COPPER-BASE ALLOY WELDING AND BRAZING FILLER METALS

Prefix	Alloy group	Sub-groups of alloys
E—Electrode	Cu—Copper and copper-base alloys	. . . . . .
R—Rod	CuSi—Silicon bronze	. . . . . .
	CuSn—Bronze	CuSn-A—Phosphor bronze
B—Brazing filler		
		CuSn-C—Phosphor bronze
	CuZn—Bronze	CuZn-A—Naval brass
		CuZn-B—Low-fuming (nickel) bronze
		CuZn-C—Low-fuming bronze
		CuZn-D—Nickel bronze
	CuNi—Copper-nickel	
	CuAl—Aluminum bronze	
	CuP—Copper-phosphorus	Five alloys now standard
	Ag—Silver (copper) brazing alloys	Twelve alloys now standard
	CuAu—Copper-gold	

Only two of the copper alloys listed in Table 57 are used to any great extent in arc-welding operations on carbon and alloy steels: These are phosphor bronze and aluminum bronze. The prosphor bronze is employed in braze welding. Joints of this kind normally have an open preparation, for example, a V-groove, and the copper-alloy electrode is deposited much in the same manner as a steel filler metal. Because of the lower melting point of the electrode alloy, rapid deposition occurs and less base metal melting takes place than would with a steel electrode. In

Table 57 — COPPER AND COPPER-BASE ALLOY BARE AND COVERED ELECTRODES USED IN CONSUMABLE-ELECTRODE ARC-WELDING PROCESSES

FOR DETAILS SEE AWS A5.6 (ASTM B 225)

AWS–ASTM classification	Common name	Chemical Composition of Electrode[a]										
		Cu	Zn	Sn	Mn	Fe	Si	Ni	P	Al	Ti	Pb
ECu	Copper	98 min	*	1.0	0.5	*	0.5	*	0.15	0.01*	...	0.02*
ECuSi	Silicon bronze	Bal.	*	1.5	1.5	0.5	2.8–4.0	*	*	0.01*	...	0.02*
ECuSn-A	Phosphor bronze	Bal.	*	4.0–6.0	*	*	*	*	0.10–0.35	0.01*	...	0.02*
ECuSn-C	Phosphor bronze	Bal.	*	7.0–9.0	*	*	*	*	0.05–0.35	0.01*	...	0.02*
ECuNi	Cupro-nickel	Bal.	*	*	1.00	0.40–0.70	0.50	29.0 min	...	...	0.50	0.02*
ECuAl-A1	Aluminum bronze	Bal.	0.20	...	...	...	0.10	...	...	6.0–9.0	...	0.02
ECuAl-A2	Aluminum bronze	Bal.	0.02	...	...	1.5	0.10	...	...	9.0–11.0	...	0.02
ECuAl-B	Aluminum bronze	Bal.	0.02	...	...	3.0–4.25	0.10	...	...	11.0–12.0	...	0.02

a Single values shown are maximum percentages except where otherwise specified.
* Total of elements marked with an asterisk (*) shall not exceed 0.50%.

fact, the welder usually avoids melting the steel base metal as much as possible since the iron which dilutes the copper alloy deposit is regarded as an undesirable residual element. Under the high temperature conditions of arc deposition, the copper alloy has no difficulty in flowing into all parts of the prepared joint and bonding to the base metal. Evidence of diffusion between the base metal and weld metal usually is much more apparent in joints braze welded with consumable electrodes than in joints made by braze welding with the gas welding torch.

Aluminum bronze is employed mostly for surfacing steel and thus provides a layer better suited for bearing, wear-resisting, and corrosion-resisting services. Here again, dilution with steel base metal is avoided as much as possible since any substantial pickup raises the strength and hardness of the surfacing weld and markedly decreases its toughness.

Copper and Copper-Base Alloy Welding Rod

Welding rod for use as filler metal in the gas, gas tungsten-arc or carbon-arc welding process has been standardized under AWS A5.7 (ASTM B 259). This specification includes almost a dozen welding rod classes as shown in Table 58. A larger number of these classes of copper and copper alloys are employed in rod form in joining steel than in consumable-electrode form because the limitations imposed by the high temperature of the direct arc are not necessarily imposed on the rod. However, each of the copper-base alloys usually requires somewhat different consideration depending upon the welding process being used to melt the welding rod. Three welding processes are often used to deposit these alloys: oxyacetylene gas welding, carbon-arc welding, and gas tungsten-arc welding. The oxyacetylene process usually requires use of a flux (often a mixture of borax and sodium fluoride). The gas flame commonly is adjusted to a slightly oxidizing mixture to deliberately form a surface oxide and prevent the loss of zinc by boiling. The silicon-bronze and phosphor-bronze alloys tend to be hot short (susceptible to hot cracking), and therefore precautions often must be taken to keep the weld pool small and the welding time at a minimum to avoid cracking. Braze welding of steel usually is done with the low-fuming bronze alloys (RCuZn-B and RCuZn-C). When applying the aluminum bronze alloys to surface steel, the oxyacetylene process has a decided disadvantage in the amount of aluminum lost by oxidation. The generation of aluminum oxide creates a very undesirable surface slag which is difficult to flux. Deposits usually display excessive oxide entrapment. Even the carbon-arc process requires specially compounded flux to deal with the aluminum oxide. Gas tungsten-arc welding produces the best results with the aluminum bronze alloys.

Table 58 — COPPER AND COPPER-BASE ALLOY WELDING RODS USED AS FILLER METAL IN VARIOUS PROCESSES

FOR DETAILS SEE AWS A5.7 (ASTM B 259)

AWS-ASTM classification	Common name	Chemical Composition of Welding Rod [a]										
		Cu	Zn	Sn	Mn	Fe	Si	Ni	P	Al	Ti	Pb
RCu	Copper	98.0 min	...	1.0	0.5	*	0.50	*	0.15	0.01*	...	0.02*
RCuSi-A	Silicon bronze	94.0 min	1.5	1.5	1.5	0.5	2.8–4.0	*	*	0.01*	...	0.02*
RCuSi-B	Silicon bronze	97.0 min	1.5	1.5	1.5	0.5	1.0–2.0	*	*	0.01*	...	0.02*
RCuSn-A	Phosphor bronze	93.5 min	*	4.0–6.0	*	*	*	*	0.10–0.35	0.01*	...	0.02*
RCuNi	Cupro-nickel	Bal.	1.0	1.20	1.25	0.40–0.70	0.25	29.0–33.0	...	...	0.50	0.02*
RBCuZn-A	Naval brass	57–61	Bal.	0.25–1.00	*	*	*	...	...	0.01*	...	0.05*
RCuZn-B	Low fuming nickel bronze	56–60	Bal.	0.75–1.10	0.01–0.50	0.25–1.25	0.04–0.15	0.2–0.8	...	0.01*	...	0.05*
RCuZn-C	Low fuming bronze	56–60	Bal.	0.75–1.10	0.01–0.50	0.25–1.25	0.04–0.15	...	...	0.01*	...	0.05*
RBCuZn-D	Nickel bronze	46–50	Bal.	...	...	...	0.04–0.25	9.0–11.0	0.25	0.01*	...	0.05*
RCuAl-A2	Aluminum bronze	Bal.	0.02	...	...	1.5	0.10	...	...	9.0–11.0	...	0.02
RCuAl-B	Aluminum bronze	Bal.	0.02	...	...	3.0–4.25	0.10	...	...	11.0–12.0	...	0.02

[a] Single values shown are maximum percentages except where otherwise specified.
*Total of elements marked with an asterisk (*) shall not exceed 0.50%.

Copper and Copper-Base Alloy Brazing Filler Metal

Brazing filler metals of seven different classes have been standardized under AWS A5.8 (ASTM B 260). This specification covers alloys of aluminum–silicon, copper–phosphorus, silver–copper, copper–gold, copper–zinc, magnesium, nickel–chromium, and silver–manganese. It would be unusual to find the aluminum–silicon, copper–phosphorus or magnesium alloys being used on carbon or alloy steels because of brittle compounds that would form as the brazing filler metal began to alloy with the base metal. A number of brazing filler metals from AWS A5.8 frequently employed in joining carbon and low-alloy steels are listed in Table 59.

Copper (BCu) is often used as a brazing filler metal when joining components of carbon or alloy steel by a controlled atmosphere furnace operation. The furnace atmosphere usually is dry hydrogen, and the furnace temperature is approximately 2050 F because of the relatively high melting point of the brazing metal (1980 F). The copper base brazing filler metals melt and flow at substantially lower temperatures (1800 F and lower) and are favored for manual torch brazing operations. The silver brazing filler metals (erroneously called silver solders) are widely used despite their higher cost because of their very satisfactory performance with virtually all of the brazing techniques. Their lower melting and flow temperatures is one of their major advantages.

The selection of a brazing filler metal is governed by a number of metallurgical aspects of the process. Most important, the molten filler metal must have (1) the ability to wet the surfaces of the base metals and form a sound metal-to-metal bond, (2) adequate fluidity at the brazing temperature to flow into the prepared joints by capillary action and insure proper distribution, and (3) sufficient composition stability when in intimate contact with the base metals to resist unfavorable composition changes. These changes can occur by dilution with the base metals, or by alloying element diffusion from the filler metal into the base metal. A surprising amount of composition change can occur during the brazing operation because of a large area of contact between the filler and base metals. Even the mechanism of melting in a brazing alloy can be an important metallurgical consideration. For example, an alloy with a wide melting range may upon slow heating undergo initial melting only in a secondary phase of the matrix. This phase, in addition to having a lower melting temperature, also must have a different composition than the matrix. Consequently, neither the matrix nor the secondary phase possesses the composition and melting points reported for the (homogeneous) alloy. Now, if the portion melting first flows out of the matrix, the latter

Table 59 — BRAZING FILLER METALS

FOR DETAILS SEE AWS A5.8 (ASTM B 260)

AWS–ASTM classification	Common name	Chemical Composition of Filler Metal[a]												
		Cu	Ag	Zn	Sn	Cd	Ni	Fe	Mn	P	Pb	Al	Si	Others*
BCu-1	Copper	99.90 min	...	...	...	...	...	...	...	0.075	0.02	0.01	...	0.10
RBCuZn-A	Naval brass	57–61	...	Bal.	0.25–1.00	...	...	*	*	...	0.05*	0.01*	*	0.50
RBCuZn-D	Nickel bronze	46–50	...	Bal.	...	...	9.0–11.0	...	...	0.25	0.05*	0.01*	0.04–0.25	0.50
BAg-1	Silver brazing alloy	14–16	44–46	14–18	...	23–25	...	...	...	...	...	...	...	0.15
BAg-1a	Silver brazing alloy	14.5–16.5	49–51	14.5–18.5	...	17–19	...	...	...	...	...	...	...	0.15
BAg-2	Silver brazing alloy	25–27	34–36	19–23	...	17–19	...	...	...	...	...	...	...	0.15
BAg-3	Silver brazing alloy	14.5–16.5	49–51	13.5–17.5	...	15–17	2.5–3.5	...	...	...	...	...	...	0.15
BAg-4	Silver brazing alloy	29–31	39–41	26–30	...	...	1.5–2.5	...	...	...	...	...	...	0.15

[a] Single values shown are maximum percentages except where otherwise specified.
*Total of elements marked with an asterisk (*) shall not exceed amount shown in last column. For silver brazing filler metals, the total of all unspecified elements shall not exceed the amount shown in last column.

may be left as a residual skull or honeycomb. This mechanism often is called *liquation*, and failure to dissolve the matrix is increased by having sufficient secondary (lower-melting) phase distributed in the alloy in the form of a continuous or interconnecting microstructure, and having strong capillary conditions to draw the initially melted alloy out of the matrix. Liquation and alloy separation is avoided in brazing by alloy formulation to obtain favorable distribution of secondary phases in the microstructure, narrow melting ranges, and by heating rapidly through the melting range to obtain complete melting before separation can occur.

In describing the brazing process in Chapter 3, it was noted that lithium can be added to brazing filler metals to act as a powerful deoxidizer and fluxing agent. A number of the silver brazing alloys are now available with a small lithium content (about 0.5%) which greatly assists wetting the base metal under controlled atmosphere furnace brazing conditions. The lithium readily scavenges any oxygen in the furnace atmosphere or oxide on the surface of the metal, and the lithium oxide thus formed acts as a flux to reduce the surface tension of the brazing metal. The lithium-containing alloys are not practicable to employ in a torch brazing operation in air because the small amount of lithium would be quickly lost and little benefit would be noted.

SURFACING WELDING RODS AND ELECTRODES

Welding rods and electrodes for surfacing are treated as a special group because they are designed specifically to provide a surface with certain useful properties. Properties like corrosion resistance, wear resistance, hot hardness, high toughness, etc., may be offered by these surfacing rods and electrodes. To achieve these properties in a surfacing weld, particularly a combination of special properties, unusual alloying systems not commonly seen in filler metals for joining, are employed. Surfacing welding rods and electrodes are recognized under AWS A5.13 (ASTM A 399). This specification recognizes both welding rods and electrodes, both bare and covered, both composite and solid kinds. The system for identification in this specification makes use of the regular E and R prefixes for electrodes and rods. However, the suffix letters are the chemical symbols for the principal elements in the composition as shown in Table 60.

Although the AWS-ASTM specification for surfacing rods and electrodes is designed to cover a broad variety of alloys, only a limited number are set forth as standardized compositions. A far greater number of welding rods and electrodes are marketed under trade designations, and in many cases, the manufacturer prefers not to reveal the composition of the product or the deposit therefrom. Instead, he attempts to describe his product in

Table 60 — *SURFACING FILLER METALS*

FOR DETAILS SEE AWS A5.13 (ASTM A 399)

Guide to alloy groups	Examples of some AWS–ASTM welding rod or electrode filler metal classifications
I FERROUS	
A. HARDENABLE ALLOYS	
1. Carbon steels	
a. Low	...
b. Medium	...
c. High	...
2. Low-alloy steels	
a. Low carbon	...
b. Medium carbon	...
c. High carbon	...
3. Medium-alloy steels	
a. Medium carbon	...
b. High carbon	R or EFe5-A
c. Cast-iron types	...
4. Medium-high alloy	
a. Low carbon	...
b. Medium carbon	...
c. High carbon	...
d. Cast-iron types	R or EFeCr-Al
5. High-speed steel	...
B. AUSTENITIC STEELS	
1. Chromium and chromium-nickel	
a. Low carbon	...
b. High carbon, low nickel	...
c. High carbon, high nickel	...
2. High manganese	EFeMn-A and -B
C. AUSTENITIC — NOT USUALLY HEAT TREATED	
1. High-chromium iron	...
2. High-alloy iron	
a. 1.7% carbon	...
b. 2.5% carbon	...
c. Very high alloy	...
II COBALT-BASE ALLOYS	
A. LOW ALLOY	...
B. HIGH ALLOY	R or ECoCr-A, -B and -C
III CARBIDES	
A. INSERTS	...
B. COMPOSITE	...
C. POWDER	...

TABLE 60 — *(Continued)*

Guide to alloy groups	Examples of some AWS–ASTM welding rod or electrode filler metal classifications
IV COPPER BASE	
A. COPPER–ZINC	RCuZn-E
B. COPPER–SILICON	RCuSi-A
C. COPPER–ALUMINUM	R or ECuAl-A2 -B, -C, -D and -E
D. COPPER–TIN	R or ECuSn-C
V NICKEL BASE	
A. NICKEL–COPPER (MONEL)	. . .
B. NICKEL–CHROMIUM (NICHROME)	R or ENiCr-A, -B and -C
C. NICKEL–CHROMIUM–TUNGSTEN– MOLYBDENUM (HASTELLOYS)	. . .

terms of the special properties found in surfacing weld. Strong competition in the marketing of surfacing filler metals is a constant spur to the search for new and improved compositions. The array of available electrodes is constantly changing; new alloys and filler-metal forms appear as older ones drop from the market. Consequently, any tabulation of the currently available surfacing filler metals and their compositions, in addition to being lengthy and repetitious, would be out of date shortly after printing. This situation, instead of instilling confusion in the reader's mind, should add to his conviction that a study of the metallurgy of alloys is the efficient way to master their welding properties. Whether the alloys are used for surfacing, or as filler metal in a joint, should not cause any serious uncertainty so long as the pertinent aspects of welding metallurgy are given proper consideration.

Carbon Steel as Surfacing Filler Metal

Because carbon is the most influential alloying element for increasing the hardness of steel, and because it is inexpensive, the manufacturers of surfacing filler metals do a brisk trade in plain carbon steels where hardness of the overlay is their criterion. The carbon content may range from 0.10 to 1.0%, and even higher, depending upon the level of hardness desired. As the hardness increases by virtue of higher carbon content, the surfacing weld naturally would be expected to display greater resistance to indentation from impact, better wear resistance, improved ability to be polished, and greater ability to hold a cutting edge. Unfortunately, these higher-carbon, harder weld metals also exhibit a number of shortcomings which must be taken into consideration before the carbon steel filler metals are claimed to be a bargain price-wise for depositing hard surfacing welds.

Cracking susceptibility of the surfacing weld, both hot cracking upon deposition and cold cracking upon cooling to room temperature, increases as higher carbon contents are employed. The actual hardness achieved by the deposit will be affected by its size, with larger (slowly cooled) beads having lower hardness. Initially deposited beads will undergo a loss in hardness from the tempering-effect of subsequently deposited beads. Ductility and toughness will decrease markedly as higher carbon contents are used. Toughness will be particularly poor at very low temperatures.

Little thought is required to picture the attributes and the shortcomings of carbon steel surfacing weld metal in terms of ferrite, pearlite and martensite. The description of the properties of these microstructural constituents, given in Chapter 9, apply equally as well here. The hardness of steel was shown to be commensurate with its carbon content — providing the microstructure was completely martensitic. The lower hardness of the larger weld beads no doubt is a result of cooling somewhat slower than the relatively high critical rate for a plain carbon steel. The lack of toughness at low temperatures should be expected in a carbon steel because the transition temperature regularly is in the vicinity of approximately 10 F. Each of these deficiencies and others can be alleviated to a remarkable degree *by the addition of alloying elements.* Therefore, the majority of steel surfacing rods and electrodes are of the alloy steel varieties.

Low and Medium Alloy Steel Surfacing Filler Metals

Surfacing electrodes of the low to medium-alloy steels often are called the *martensitic* varieties because the alloys added generally produce a martensitic weld structure almost regardless of the welding and cooling conditions. Chromium, nickel, and molybdenum are the most widely used alloying elements in these electrodes. Where further improvement is desired in special properties like abrasion resistance, additions of tungsten and vanadium may be made. Surfacing welds of alloy steel are likely to display a more uniform hardness because the alloyed martensite is more resistant to softening upon reheating. Consequently, multi-bead surfacing of alloy steel usually outperforms similar overlays of carbon steel of comparable carbon content. The formation of free carbides in the microstructure increases with higher levels of carbon and of carbide-forming elements like chromium, tungsten, and vanadium. To capitalize on the benefit of carbides in a martensitic steel matrix, the makers of surfacing filler metals have carried the addition of carbon and carbide-forming elements right up to the composition range of high-speed tool steels. The application of these hard, brittle surfacing welds calls for great care in following the prescribed welding procedure.

Austenitic Steels as Surfacing Filler Metals

The austenitic microstructure of steel is relatively soft and tough, but work hardens as it is deformed. Many surfacing rods and electrodes are designed to deposit a tough, crack-resistant, austenitic surfacing weld which subsequently develops the required hardness in service. Of course, the service conditions must involve a certain amount of impact loading or hammering to properly produce the work hardening. If the service consisted of abrasion by a fine, light material, the surfacing weld probably would wear away because it never achieved a higher level of hardness through deformation. The austenitic weld structure can be obtained cheaply through the combined efforts of high carbon and manganese (Hadfield's manganese steel), or a high-alloy steel composition similar to the Cr–Ni stainless steels. Remarkable properties can be obtained in these austenitic surfacing welds. They need not be very soft initially. The addition of substantial amounts of carbon and carbide-forming elements can produce free carbides in the otherwise austenitic structure and thereby increase the initial or as-deposited hardness. Generally, the austenitic deposits are highly regarded for their toughness, not only in the deposited condition, but even after severe work hardening. The more highly alloyed types containing large amounts of cobalt, tungsten, and molybdenum also have excellent hot hardness.

Carbides

Tungsten carbide, widely used in solid form as cutting tools, finds broad application as a surfacing filler metal for its hardness. It is not practicable to use solid rods of carbide as welding rod or consumable electrodes for this practice would destroy the desirable properties of the material. Instead, the tungsten carbide is crushed into pieces or a powder and is used to impregnate the surfacing weld on steel, or other metal such as cobalt or nickel. This is easily achieved by making a composite electrode or welding rod consisting of a steel tube filled with the powdered tungsten carbide and possibly other metals. During deposition of this composite electrode or welding rod, the particles of carbide are entrapped throughout the metal or alloy matrix. The presence of these extremely hard particles gives the surfacing weld very high abrasion resistance. The soft matrix metal may tend to wear away, but the carbide particles can be seen in relief on the surface exposed to abrasion. Here they act as minute bearing surfaces to support the load. Of course, the success of carbide impregnated metal in a given application depends upon having a sufficient quantity of the proper size particles uniformly dispersed in the surfacing weld. Sometimes bulk powdered tungsten carbide is used. The powder is spread over the base metal and anchored to the surface by heating with a suitable welding torch to the "sweating" temperature.

Other Metals and Alloys for Surfacing

Many surfacing filler metals employ nickel, cobalt or copper as the basic metal rather than iron. In some instances, the electrodes or rods are the same as described earlier for joining operations. For example, an ENiCr-1 electrode may be used to surface carbon or low-alloy steel for protection against corrosion or scaling. The metallurgy of this welding operation follows the principles set forth for any dissimilar metal welding operation. However, some of these nonferrous electrodes and welding rods are designed specifically for surfacing and the array of available compositions is almost as impressive as the ferrous alloys. One interesting metallurgical difference is observed between the array of nonferrous alloys as compared to the steels. Whereas in steels we find more than one matrix structure (i.e., martensitic, austenitic, etc.), the alloys of cobalt, copper and nickel base all have the face-centered cubic or austenite-like crystallographic structure. Consequently, somewhat different alloying techniques are employed to secure increased hardness or other special properties in the nonferrous surfacing filler metals. In addition to the familiar chromium, molybdenum and tungsten alloying elements used in steels, alloying elements like boron are added (usually in the nickel-base, chromium-containing alloys) to form hard particles in the surfacing structure.

SOLDERS

The filler metals for liquid–solid phase joining operations carried out at temperatures below about 800 F are called *solders*. The term usually brings to mind the familiar tin-base alloys, but alloys which do not contain tin also may be classed as solders. While the AWS-ASTM Committee on Filler Metal has not issued a joint specification for solders, standardization of alloys has been carried out by the ASTM and other specification-writing bodies. Tentative specifications for solder metal may be found in ASTM Designation B 32. Thirty kinds of tin–lead, tin–lead–antimony and silver–lead alloys are included in ASTM B 32. Table 61 lists a number of solders which are employed in joining carbon and alloy steels.

Table 61 — *SOLDER METALS*

FOR DETAILS SEE ASTM B 32

ASTM grade	Chemical Composition, %			Melting Range		Applications
	Tin desired	Lead nominal	Antimony maximum	Solidus, F	Liquidus, F	
70 B	70	30	0.50 max	361	378	For coating metals
60 B	60	40	0.50 max	361	374	General purpose
50 B	50	50	0.50 max	361	421	General purpose
35 B	35	65	0.50 max	361	477	Wiping solder
20 B	20	80	0.50 max	361	531	Coating, joining and filling
5 B	5	95	0.50 max	518	594	Coating and joining

No particular difficulty is encountered in soldering carbon and alloy steels when surface preparation, fluxing, and solder alloy are satisfactory. However, the strength of soldered joints in steel does not approach the base metal strength as closely as they do in copper or brass. This can be attributed to the greater dissimilarity in strength between the solder metal and the base metal, and perhaps to the very small amount of surfacing alloy that occurs as the solder wets the steels. While the small extent of alloying does not necessarily indicate a weak bond, it does not enrich the solder with alloying elements from the base metal that would increase strength.

Solder is available in wire, strip, tape, sheet, foil and powder. The wire may be solid or flux-cored.

Two important metallurgical characteristics of a solder metal are (1) its ability to "wet" the base metal, and (2) the range of temperature between the liquidus and the solidus. To establish a good bond, the solder must be able to wet the base metal. This action is greatly facilitated if the solder and the base metal have some mutual solubility and form alloys. It is not desirable to have the mutual solubility lead to the formation of brittle intermetallic compounds. Generally speaking, it is the tin in the solders listed in Table 61 that promotes wetting on steel. The principal purposes of including lead in the alloys are to increase the strength of the solder and to secure different freezing characteristics. Sometimes, a very narrow freezing range is desired so that a joint will solidify suddenly and not permit movement of the parts. This performance is obtained with the 70–30 and 60–40 alloys. If a joint is to be filled and the solder wiped or shaped while in a highly plastic-like condition, then a solder with a wide freezing range, like the 35–65 alloy, will be most satisfactory.

Suggested Reading

Filler Metals for Joining, by O. T. Barnett, Reinhold Publishing Company, New York, 1959.

"Ultra-High-Strength Weld Metal with Low-Hydrogen Electrodes," D. C. Smith, Welding Research Council Bulletin Series, No. 36, May, 1957.

"Factors Which Affect Low-Alloy Weld Metal Notch-Toughness," S. S. Sagan and H. C. Campbell, Ibid, No. 59, April, 1960.

"A Coated Electrode for Fusion Welding AISI 4340 Steel for Ultra High Strength Applications," E. E. Deesing, Ibid, No. 68, April, 1961.

"Some Factors Affecting the Notch Toughness of Steel Weld Metal," K. E. Dorschu and R. D. Stout, Welding Journal, v 40, no. 3, Research Suppl., pp 97s-105s, March 1961.

"Tensile Properties of High Purity Iron-Base Weld Metals," R. D. Stout, T. E. Torok and P. P. Podgurski, Ibid, v 42, no. 9, pp 385s-391s, September 1963.

"Interpretive Report on Weld Metal Toughness," K. Masubuchi, R. E. Monroe and D. C. Martin, Welding Research Council Bulletin Series, No. 111, January 1966.

Chapter 11

SHRINKAGE AND DISTORTION
IN WELDMENTS

A very trying practical problem which frequently arises in fabricating weldments is to be certain the finished article will conform to the required dimensions and will have all portions in proper contour. Inaccuracies in dimension or form easily develop because of the unavoidable heat effects which accompany most of our welding processes, particularly those involving localized fusion. Although these conditions are indeed unavoidable, they can be minimized, and, in many cases, one condition can be used to counteract another. If a few basic facts concerning the behavior of metal during heating and cooling while under restraint are understood, a little engineering skill can accomplish a great deal in securing weldment accuracy.

There is an apparent lack of standard terminology for discussing the subject of shrinkage and distortion with respect to welding. In literature on the subject, the terms *shrinkage, contraction* and *distortion*, for example, are often used as if they were synonymous. For purposes of explaining the problem with weldments, these terms should, perhaps, carry distinct meanings. In order to establish a concept of shrinkage and distortion control in weldments, several of these related terms will be discussed.

Although shrinkage is a term that will be used to describe the solid state phenomenon, it should be recognized that it is often used to describe the decrease in volume that occurs when a molten metal solidifies. In Chapter 5, it was mentioned that iron undergoes a volume shrinkage of 1.5% upon solidification. Weld metal shrinks upon solidification, of course, but this phenomenon has little to do with the distortion problem in weldments. During solidification, as the atoms of iron in the melt assume fixed positions in the crystal lattice of growing solid grains, the couplet of solid and liquid iron is very weak. Consequently, the weld metal cannot exert any real stress upon adjacent base metal members. Upon completion, *solidification shrinkage* has occurred in its entirety, and, although solidification shrinkage may have resulted in some dishing or deformation of the face of the weld metal, it cannot generate stresses capable of decreasing the overall size of the weldment or of pulling a portion of the weldment out of shape.

Immediately following solidification, however, the cooling weld metal continues to *contract*. This *thermal contraction* is the reverse of *thermal expansion* which occurs upon heating. It is important to note that the *contraction* of solid metal during cooling can generate stress, but that the maximum stress is limited to the yield strength of the weld metal at the particular temperature. The details of the stress-producing mechanism will be discussed shortly.

Distortion is deviation from a desired form, either permanent or temporary. Distortion occurs as a result of welding because of stresses which develop in the weldment from localized thermal expansion and contraction. However, it is entirely possible under some circumstances to completely contain these stresses internally within an undistorted weldment. Whether distortion occurs will depend upon (1) the magnitude of the welding stresses developed (by localized thermal expansion and contraction), (2) the distribution of these stresses in the weldment, and (3) the strength of the members upon which these stresses act. When the final stress resulting from welding (called the *contraction stress* or the *shrinkage stress*) is transmitted to a restraining portion of the weldment, that portion is at least strained elastically. If the stress exceeds the member's yield strength, the yielding of the structure can result in a permanent dimensional change and/or a distortion from its prewelded form. Because the dimensional changes usually amount to a decrease in size, the term *shrinkage* has been used to describe the net decrease in a particular dimension of a weldment.

The ensuing discussion of distortion and shrinkage will make frequent use of the following terms:

> *Residual Stress* — The internal stress which remains in the members of a weldment after a joining operation, having been generated by localized partial yielding during the thermal cycle of welding and the hindered contraction of these areas during cooling. Residual stresses in a weldment represent a system of opposing stresses which balance one another in the overall weldment, or in portions thereof.

Structure Stress — Stress arising from grain boundaries, crystal orientations, and phase transformations, which exists in infinitely small volumes of metal.

Reaction Stress — Internal stress which could not exist if the weldment members being joined were free to move or were isolated as free bodies without connection to other parts of the structure.

Stress Concentration — The increase in stress level which develops at abrupt changes in section as represented by sharp corners, notches, cracks and other surface or subsurface irregularities. The condition which promotes the increase in stress is called a *stress raiser*.

HEATED BAR ANALOGY

A simple condition of restraint is shown in Fig. 126(a), in which the bar of steel under consideration is clamped between the jaws of a press whose distance apart is maintained the same at all times. The press restrains the bar from expanding in much the same way as a localized, heated area on the surface of a thick plate is restrained by the remainder of the plate. Heat the bar uniformly to 1700 F. Note that this represents a temperature rise of 1625 F. If the press did not restrain the bar from expanding in length, the bar, initially 2 inches long, would be approximately 0.020 inch longer at 1700 F than at room temperature. Its diameter would likewise increase. When the press restrains the increase in length, Fig. 126(b), the diameter increases an additional amount, to make the volume of the bar at 1700 F practically the same under restraint as without restraint.

Let us analyze the behavior of a unit-length bar while it is being heated. When a 1-inch bar, Fig. 127, is heated 1 degree F it increases in length 0.0000067 inch. To compress this bar to its original length of 1.0000000 inch requires the application of a compressive load, which can be calculated from Young's Modulus. It will be recalled that this is the physical constant for metals which expresses the ratio between stress and strain below the proportional limit. Young's Modulus for steel is approximately 30,000,000 psi, which means that each pound per square inch of stress applied to a 1-inch cube in one direction changes the length in that direction by 1/30,000,000 or 0.000000033 inch. The change in length will be a decrease if the stress is compressive; an increase if the stress is tensile. Therefore, to compress the bar which we heated only 1 degree F from a length of 1.0000067 inches back to 1.0000000 inch, requires a compressive stress of 0.0000067/0.000000033, or approximately 200 psi.

Through these computations, we can show that for every degree

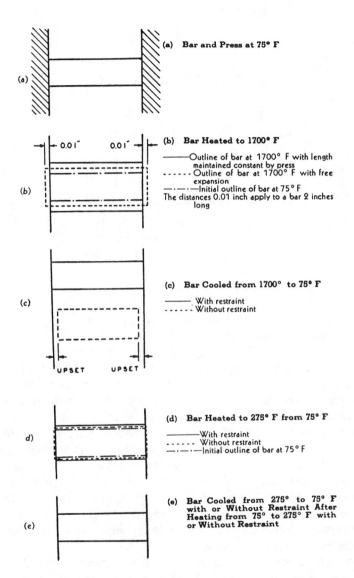

(a)

(a)   Bar and Press at 75° F

(b)

← 0.01" →   ← 0.01" →

(b)   Bar Heated to 1700° F

———— Outline of bar at 1700° F with length
            maintained constant by press
- - - - - Outline of bar at 1700° F with free
            expansion
—·—·—Initial outline of bar at 75° F
The distances 0.01 inch apply to a bar 2 inches
long

(c)

UPSET   UPSET

(c)   Bar Cooled from 1700° to 75° F

———— With restraint
- - - - - Without restraint

d)

(d)   Bar Heated to 275° F from 75° F

———— With restraint
- - - - - Without restraint
—·—·—Initial outline of bar at 75° F

(e)

(e)   Bar Cooled from 275° to 75° F
       with or Without Restraint After
       Heating from 75° to 275° F with
       or Without Restraint

Fig. 126 — Condition of a solid bar of steel upon heating and cooling.

rise in temperature of the bar restrained by the press, a compressive stress
of 200 psi is added to the steel. Of course, these simple computations
have their limitations because the coefficient of expansion and Young's
Modulus both vary with temperature. The coefficient of expansion rises
with increasing temperature, being nearly zero for steel close to absolute
zero temperature, and rising to about 8.0×10^{-6} at 800 F. Young's

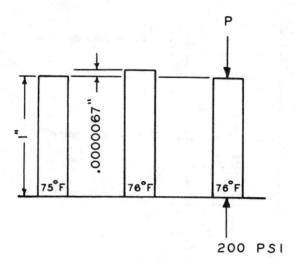

Fig. 127 — Force required to overcome thermal stress.

Modulus decreases as the temperature increases, which means that a greater amount of strain results for a given amount of stress as the temperature rises (Fig. 128). We can ignore these facts, however, and use the values employed in the computations above. At first sight it would appear that if we raised the temperature to 1700 F, the compressive stress would be 325,000 psi. Of course, such values never are attained for two reasons.

First, as we continue to compress or elongate a bar of steel, the stress continues to rise until the yield strength is reached; further elongation beyond the value corresponding to the yield strength occurs at nearly constant load, namely the yield stress. The yield strength for the restrained bar is, let us say, 40,000 psi. It is obvious that, if we raise the temperature 200 degrees F (from 75 to 275 F), the compressive stress in the bar will be 200 × 200 = 40,000 psi, the yield strength. If we continue to raise the temperature, the stress will remain at the yield value, while the steel undergoes permanent deformation.

The second reason is that at higher temperatures the yield strength of steel decreases, until at about 1200 F the yield strength vanishes altogether, Fig. 128. This is merely another way of stating that we can stretch or twist a red-hot bar of steel with a pair of tongs, whereas we can make little impression on the bar when cold.

The significance of the two reasons is made clear in Fig. 126. In Fig. 126(d) the bar has been heated from 75 to 275 F with and without restraint. At 275 F the bar under restraint has a compressive stress of

40,000 psi; it is at the yield stress but no permanent upset has occurred. Upon cooling to 75 F again, the bar returns to its original shape regardless of whether it was or was not restrained during heating and cooling. If the bar is heated above 275 F, for example to 1700 F, Fig. 126(c), it makes a great difference whether it has been restrained during heating and cooling. If it has been restrained from elongating during heating and restrained from contracting during cooling, it returns to its original dimension. If, on the other hand, it is restrained during heating, but is allowed to contract freely during cooling, the bar will be shorter and thicker than initially. The bar is said to have been permanently upset.

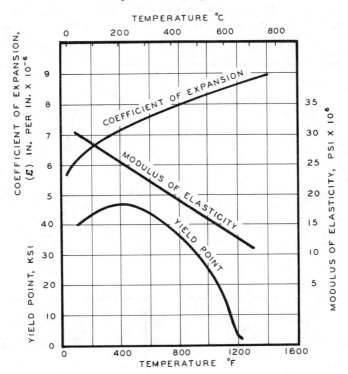

Fig. 128 — Changes in the physical and mechanical properties of steel with temperature which complicate computations on weldment shrinkage.

Curves are typical for mild steel. At the higher temperatures, the curves do not take into account the creep of steel. The shorter the time of test, the higher the yield point appears to be at the higher temperatures above 750 F. During welding, the steel is not long at the elevated temperatures; hence, the short-time yield strength is applicable.

Before proceeding further, let us plot the change in compressive stress in the bar that is heated under restraint. As shown in Fig. 129(a), as the temperature of the bar rises, the compressive stress rises. At 275 F the stress is at the yield value. If the bar is cooled to 75 F again, the stress decreases along the same path as it increased. There has been no permanent upset, and the bar is free from stress when it reaches 75 F. Had we continued to raise the temperature beyond 275 F, Fig. 129(b), the stress in the bar would have remained at the yield value at all times. At higher temperatures the yield values would have fallen to zero in accordance with Fig. 128, and at 1700 F, far from being under compressive stress, the bar would tend to sag under its own weight from the jaws of the press, as thin sheet metal sometimes sags close to a slow weld, if it is unsupported.

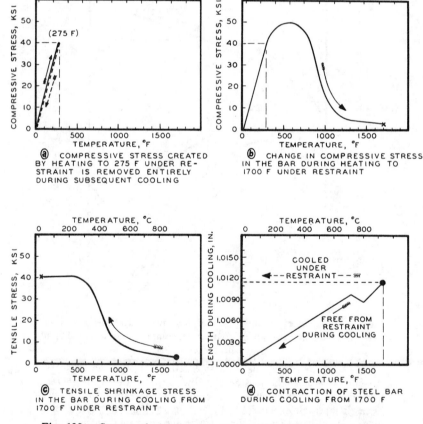

Fig. 129 — Stresses during heating and cooling of a bar; also contraction (dimensional change) during cooling from 1700 F.

We are now ready to turn to a discussion of events during cooling. Heating from 75 F to any temperature up to 275 F and cooling to 75 F again with or without restraint left the steel in its original shape without stress, Fig. 129(a). Of course, it will be appreciated that the figures 40,000 psi and 275 F have been selected for illustrative purposes and will differ for different grades of steel. Cooling under restraint after heating to higher temperatures, such as 1700 F, Fig. 129(c), creates tensile shrinkage stresses. During cooling, the bar, being clamped in the jaws of the press, cannot contract in length; instead the necessary reduction in volume occurs through abnormal reduction in diameter by a hot-working action similar to the extension (reduction in diameter) of a red-hot bar by pulling both ends. At about 1200 F the steel begins to regain elastic strength, as shown by the rise in yield strength below 1200 F, Fig. 128. Thereupon the steel becomes stressed in the reverse manner to the stress during compression.

For example, in cooling from 1000 to 999 F the steel will attempt to shrink 0.0000067 inch in length. It is withheld from this axial contraction by the press; in other words, the press must exert a tensile stress of 200 psi on the steel. Again these values are illustrative only, Young's Modulus and the coefficient of contraction being different at 1000 F than at 75 F. Further cooling brings the tensile shrinkage stress to the yield value; perhaps it may be at the yield value at all times, depending upon the shape of Fig. 128. The stress remains at the yield value thereafter. Further volumetric contraction on cooling being restrained axially, the increasing axial stress is distributed; i.e., part is stored in the growing elastic strength of the material, part is expended by permanent reduction on the cross-section (cold work at these temperatures). When the bar reaches 75 F, therefore, it has been permanently, if slightly, "elongated" and is under a tensile stress equal to the yield strength. While the bar remains in the press it has the same dimensions as it did before the heating. Upon removal from the press, the bar will contract in length and increase in diameter corresponding to complete release of the shrinkage stress. The change in length of a bar cooled without restraint from 1700 F is contrasted with the constant length of the restrained bar in Fig. 129(d).

The bar completely restrained in the press during heating and cooling illustrates qualitatively the origin of distortion and shrinkage stresses during welding, for the bar is analogous to a short length of weld metal. It is analogous to the heated zone of base metal adjacent to a weld which is heated and cooled while surrounded by cooler, more rigid base metal. It is analogous also to a flash or an upset weld between two bars held in the clamps after welding. The analogy is not exact because in these examples the temperature, and therefore the stresses, are not distributed uniformly. Because the shrinkage stresses are internal stresses which remain in the section after welding they are called *residual stresses*.

The bar analogy is useful in predicting the effect of preheating on residual stresses and distortion. If the bar is initially at 1200 F instead of 275 F, it is obvious that heating to 1700 F and cooling to 1200 F, again under restraint, can give rise to no shrinkage stresses, since all stress is expended in equally reversible deformation. Having scarcely any yield strength at 1200 F, a steel part heated to that temperature may tend to sag (distort) under its own weight. If the preheating temperature is only 275 or 375 F, the bar will be under tensile shrinkage stresses equal to the yield strength, as if it were not preheated. With preheat temperatures between about 400 and 1200 F, the restrained bar will be under tensile shrinkage stresses intermediate between the yield strength at room temperature and zero, the latter being the approximate yield value at 1200 F for a low-carbon, plain steel.

In addition to residual stresses created by changes in temperature and permanent deformation, stresses may arise from transformations in the steel. Any changes in length due to transformations that occur above 1200 F will cause no shrinkage stresses, because the yield strength is low, Fig. 128, and the expansion caused by the change from the gamma to alpha iron is accommodated, if necessary, by permanent elongation, perhaps counterbalancing the contraction due to cooling. However, if the austenite does not transform until nearly room temperature, at which the yield strength is high and creep is negligible, structure stresses may arise. Consider a needle of martensite forming in austenite, Fig. 130. The martensite must occupy a greater length than the austenite from which it transformed. It is restrained from expanding by the surrounding untransformed austenite. Consequently the martensite is under high compressive stress, whereas the adjacent austenite is under high tensile stress. The areas of different structure stresses due to transformations are on a microscopic scale, compared with the larger scale of variations of residual stresses due to upset during welding and compared with the variations on a still larger scale created by reaction stresses.

The effect of rate of heating and cooling on the distortion and stresses in the bar also can be predicted. The shorter the time at temperature, the higher the yield strength appears to be in the range 800 to 1200 F. With more rapid heating and cooling, therefore, the amount of cold work that the bar will undergo will increase compared with the amount of hot work. In welding we know that rapid cooling rates are associated, in general, with low heat inputs and narrow heat-affected zones. The narrower the heat-affected zone, for a given type of weld, the less will be the distortion.

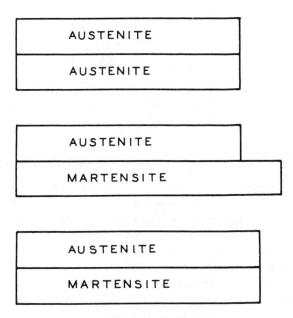

Fig. 130 — Shrinkage stresses in the vicinity of a martensite needle in austenite.

(Upper) A block of austenite, the lower half of which is ready to transform to martensite.

(Middle) The lower half of the block has transformed to martensite and its length has increased; assuming no cohesion between the austenite and the martensite needle.

(Lower) Cohesion being taken into account, both austenite and martensite expand to a compromise extent thus placing the austenite in tension and the martensite in compression.

The upset that is mentioned in Fig. 126(c) can be observed in fillet welds in thin plate, say ¼ inch, in which the temperature rises to nearly a red heat on the opposite side, Fig. 131. The barely perceptible bulge or upset shows that the metal at the bulge attempted to expand volumetrically during heating. The surrounding plate metal restrained the expansion in two directions and upset the weak hot metal in the third. During cooling the contraction was not sufficient to iron out the bulge as the material grew stronger. In any application of the bar analogy to welding distortion, it is important to remember that, in welding, restraint during heating ordinarily results in an upset which is not completely reversed during cooling.

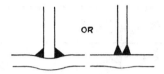

Fig. 131 — Bulging (exaggerated) of plate on the reverse side of fillet welded Tee-joint. The plate became nearly red-hot on the reverse side during welding.

DEVELOPMENT OF STRESSES IN WELDMENTS

Because shrinkage and distortion are most troublesome in weldments made by fusion joining processes, let us concentrate on the conditions which accompany all of the known methods or processes that involve a localized heat source that moves along the joint. The local rise and fall in temperature at any point along the joint as the heat source first advances toward the point, passes it and moves on, develops stresses and causes the changes in microstructure studied in preceding chapters. If the metals welded had zero coefficients of thermal expansion, no stress would develop during welding, and shrinkage and distortion would not present any problem. Actually, every metal expands and contracts when heated and cooled. Temperature changes cause a change in volume, provided the body is not restrained or prevented from changing its dimensions as the temperature changes. Instead of a change in volume, we generally speak for simplicity of a change in one dimension only. When we say that steel at room temperature has a coefficient of expansion of 6.7×10^{-6} per degree Fahrenheit, we mean that a 1-inch length increases to 1.0000067 inches if the temperature is raised 1 degree F and the body is free to expand in all directions. Since, in welding, the parts are never free to expand or contract in all directions, we must study the behavior of steel attempting to expand and contract under conditions of restraint.

We shall start by applying the bar analogy to a simple type of weld, realizing that we do not know enough about shrinkage stresses in more complicated welds to be able to predict their distribution. One general rule, nevertheless, seems to apply to nearly all types of welds made at room temperature and regardless of restraint; that is, the maximum tensile shrinkage stress is close to the yield strength. If the tensile shrinkage stresses act in two or three directions instead of in one direction, the stress at which the metal yields is raised, and the maximum tensile shrinkage stresses likewise rise to values that may be considerably above the yield strength observed in the conventional uniaxial tensile test.

The simple weld we shall study is shown in Fig. 132(a). The weld is deposited rapidly so that we can be safe in assuming that the entire welded zone is at a high temperature when the weld is completed. At the high temperature, the metal close to the weld attempts to expand in all directions. It is prevented (restrained) by adjacent cold metal, which replaces the press in the bar analogy. Being prevented from elongating, the metal close to the weld is upset, Fig. 132(b). During cooling, the upset zone attempts to contract. Again it is restrained by adjacent cold metal. As a result, the upset zone becomes stressed in tension (tensile shrinkage stresses) in the same way as the bar in Figs. 126(c) and 129(c). When the welded joint has cooled to room temperature, the weld and the upset region close to it, Fig. 132(c), are under residual tensile stresses close to the yield strength. To balance the tensile shrinkage stress at the

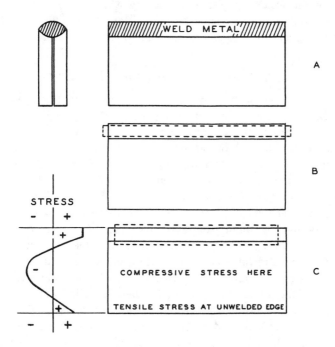

Fig. 132 — Distribution of stresses in a simple welded edge-joint.
    (a) Welded edge joint.
    (b) Welded area endeavors to expand during welding, as shown by the dotted outline, but is restrained by adjacent cooler metal, and is upset.
    (c) Welded area endeavors to contract during cooling, as shown by the dotted outline, but is restrained by adjacent cooler metal, and is elongated.

edge, equilibrium conditions demand that there must be a region of tensile shrinkage stress at the opposite unwelded edge, and a region of compressive shrinkage stress between the two tensile zones. These deductions agree in every respect with the experimental measurement of the residual stresses.

Although it is not difficult to predict the distribution and magnitude of residual stresses in a joint of the type shown in Fig. 132(a), the problem becomes more difficult with many other types of joint for the reason that the shrinkage stresses are important, not only parallel to the weld, but perpendicular to the weld as well. Consequently, we must rely heavily on experimental measurements of stresses, remembering only the general rule that the residual stresses are likely to be close to the yield strength if the majority of the welded part during welding was several hundred degrees below the temperature at which the yield strength virtually vanishes; that is, if the base metal originally was close to room temperature.

MEASUREMENT AND CALCULATION OF RESIDUAL STRESSES

One of the earliest methods of measuring residual stresses in a simple section, like a bar or a beam, involved the machining away of successive layers of metal from one surface, and noting the amount of bowing which developed. Computations of the curvature of the section could produce close estimates of the residual stresses originally present. Briefly, the removal of metal containing an internal stress would unbalance the system of opposing stresses and the section would bow or distort until a new balance of stresses was achieved. Many investigators have attempted to calculate the intensity and distribution of residual stresses at welded joints because an accurate method would be of inestimatable value in many phases of weldment design and fabrication. Distortion could be anticipated and the residual stresses counteracted in the most efficient manner. Residual stresses could be more favorably distributed, and in some cases might actually add to the useful strength of certain members of the weldment which were required to bear the higher service loads. Although the stress analyst has not shied from the complex calculations which appear necessary to even start the development of a method, his attempts have been seriously hindered by lack of detailed, accurate information on temperature distribution during the welding of a joint. Our knowledge of the actual heat input is, of course, only approximate, and this, along with the variation in thermal conductivity and changes in mechanical properties at high temperatures makes a reasonably accurate computation of residual stresses quite difficult. Only in the simpler joints, where the thermal conditions during welding have been very carefully assessed, has the analyst been able to calculate values which are in reasonable agreement with measured values. One comparatively simple system of residual stress calculation, known as Tall's "mirror method" takes into account the incremental thermal stresses which arise in the course of making a weld, and through a series of equations arrives at predicted stress values for specific boundaries. However, much additional work is needed in this field before reliable computations can be made to predict the residual stress in joints of actual weldments.

The residual stresses measured in an arc-welded butt joint between two plates are shown in Fig. 133. In this case, one measurement method known as the "subdivision method" is illustrated in Fig. 134. The residual stresses parallel to the weld are shown in Fig. 133 for the central region of the plates. In agreement with predictions, the residual stresses parallel to the butt weld at the center are tensile and are close to the yield strength.

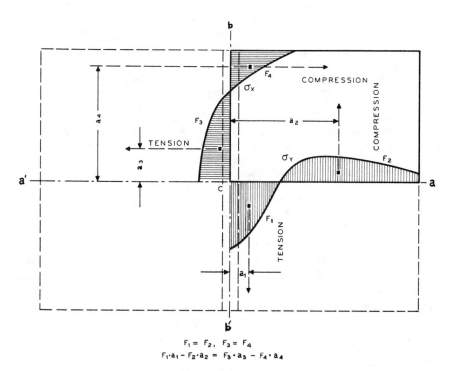

$$F_1 = F_2, \quad F_3 = F_4$$
$$F_1 \cdot a_1 - F_2 \cdot a_2 = F_3 \cdot a_3 - F_4 \cdot a_4$$

Fig. 133 — Relationship between shrinkage stresses in arc-welded plates joined without restraint. Line b – b' is centerline of weld.
(Bierett)

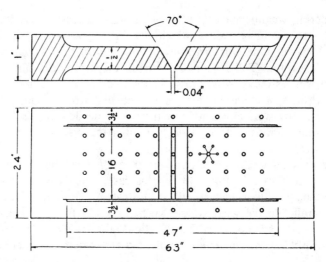

Fig. 134 — Subdivision method of measuring shrinkage stresses created by a single-vee groove weld between highly restrained plates. (Mies)

Imaginary, equal squares are ruled on the surface of the plates after welding. Gage marks (small circles) are punched at precisely known distances apart at the corners of each square. One pair of gage marks on each square may be perpendicular to the weld joint, the other may be parallel to the joint. The squares are cut from the plate after welding. If the distance between gage marks parallel to the weld increases as a result of cutting, the steel in the square was under compressive shrinkage stress parallel to the weld. If the distance decreases, the steel in the square was under tensile shrinkage stress parallel to the weld. Similar considerations govern stresses perpendicular to the weld. The changes in length are converted to stress by means of established formulas. The release of shrinkage stresses by subdivision (cutting) results in distortion.

Beyond the narrow upset zone near the weld the stress falls rapidly to zero and changes to compression as we recede from the weld. The rapid changes from tension to compression suggest stress gradients, similar to the temperature gradients described in Chapter 4. The stress gradients might be defined as a change in stress of, let us say, 10,000 psi per inch. However, we know practically nothing about the significance of stress gradients at the present time. It seems that extremely high stress gradients, for example 30,000,000 psi per inch have less effect than might be anticipated, because the change in stress must occur in the space of a single grain, which may be able to yield locally. The tensile stress parallel to the weld falls to zero at the edges of the plate perpendicular to the weld, because the atoms at the very edge of a plate cannot be stressed perpendicular to the edge, which is in contact with air.

At right angles to the weld the residual stresses are maximum at the weld. Regions some distance from the weld are stressed less highly perpendicular to the weld than the regions close to the weld. Figure 133 shows that in the center of the plate the shrinkage stress at right angles to the weld is tension; the edges are in compression to maintain equilibrium. It is always fortunate to have compressive stress at the edges of any part because the edges are the most sensitive regions from the standpoint of notch effects. The distribution of stress shown in Fig. 133 is not always observed; for back-step procedures or frequent and long interruptions to change electrodes may alter the distribution.

It should be remembered that the plates of the butt weld in Fig. 133 were under no external restraint during welding. Had the plates been clamped rigidly during welding, additional tensile stresses (the reaction stresses) would have arisen throughout the plates perpendicular to the weld. The reaction stress, Fig. 135, develops for the same reason as the tensile shrinkage stress in the bar shown in Figs. 126(c) and 129(c). When the butt-welded plates are unclamped, the reaction stresses disappear. Often, however, it is not so simple to avoid or remove reaction stresses, particularly if the weld is the last to be made in a complicated rigid structure. Under those conditions the reaction stresses rise to a maximum,

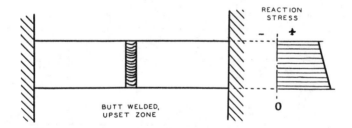

Fig. 135 — Development of reaction stress in a restrained weldment. Reaction stresses are added to the shrinkage stresses that would have appeared in the plates without restraint, provided the sum of the two does not exceed the yield strength. Otherwise permanent deformation occurs.

Fig. 136, and remain in the welded structure, other regions being under compressive stress to maintain equilibrium. Large amounts of weld metal (90 degree compared with 45 degree included angle, for instance) favor high reaction stresses; small amounts of weld metal favor low reaction stresses but may give rise to hardness and brittle martensite.

Residual stresses are found in fillet welds as well as in butt welds. Figure 137 shows the stress parallel to fillet welds joining the flange to the web of an arc-welded T-girder in the vicinity of a butt weld in the web plates. Maximum tensile stresses occur at the fillet weld, the bottom of the girder fortunately being in compression as a result of welding. When load is applied to the top of the girder, the bottom tends to be stressed in tension. The initial compressive stress prevents the appearance of tensile

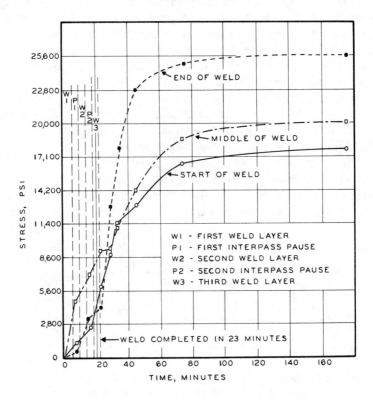

Fig. 136 — Development of reaction stress during welding and cooling a three-layer welded butt-joint made with bare metal-arc process (After Bierett). The extensometer was located perpendicular to the weld and 9⅛ inches therefrom.

stress at the bottom of the girder, which is the most critical region from the standpoint of failure, even when the applied load corresponds to a tensile stress of high order in the bottom fiber.

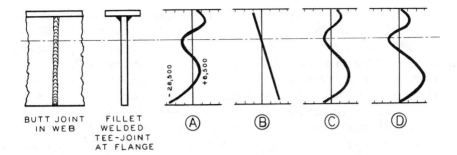

BUTT JOINT   FILLET
IN WEB   WELDED
            TEE-JOINT
            AT FLANGE

Fig. 137 — Shrinkage stress (in psi) parallel to the web to flange fillet welds of an arc-welded T-girder, and at a butt-joint in the web. (Bierett)

Flange $= 6 \times 0.59$-in.; web $= 11 \times 0.39$-in.; throat of fillet welds $= 0.16$-in.

(A) Shrinkage stress in the welded butt-joint.

(B) Bending stress produced by external load.

(C) Resulting stress produced by external load of 20,000 psi in extreme fiber.

(D) Resulting stress produced by external load of 28,500 psi in extreme fiber.

EFFECT OF RESIDUAL STRESSES UPON WELDMENT SERVICE PERFORMANCE

Since all weld joints in the as-welded condition will contain a system of internal tensile and compressive stresses that balance each other, it may seem possible that externally applied loads would add to the residual stress of like sign and would quickly overstress some local point. This is not the case because the stress system is in equilibrium. Therefore, the externally applied loading in tension cannot be additive to residual tensile stresses until the balancing compressive stresses to the system in equilibrium are overcome. Residual stresses do not decrease in intensity with time. Of course, if during service, the weldment is subjected to loading conditions which bring about a small amount of plastic strain in highly stressed areas, then the peak stress values in these areas will be reduced. In fact, it has often been proposed that a beneficial treatment for a weldment is to apply a small degree of overstress while it is held at a slightly elevated temperature (above any toughness transition range). For example, a pressure vessel might be filled with hot water and subjected to hydro-static pressure. In this way, the peak residual stresses at stress-raisers are reduced in magnitude while the steel is in a tough condition, and is able to relieve the stress concentration through plastic flow.

There is no widespread agreement on whether residual stresses adversely affect weldment performance. The satisfactory performance of in-numerable weldments in the as-welded condition (containing residual stresses) gives support to thinking that residual stresses in equilibrium have no detrimental effect upon the static load-carrying ability of the weldment. On the other hand, tests on columns, like wide-flange beams, H-shapes, and boxes, show that *welded* columns generally display some-what lower strength than do rolled columns. Residual stresses in the welded columns are believed to account for some of the difference in strength. This effect of residual stress becomes proportionately smaller as the strength of the steel in the column is increased. This influence of residual stress in built-up structurals is taken into account in many specifications govern-ing welded steel construction. The effect of residual stresses in weldments subjected to impact loading, or cyclic loading also is an area of meager knowledge.

CONTROL AND REMOVAL OF RESIDUAL STRESSES

As a general rule, residual stresses are decreased by loads (static or dynamic) sufficient to cause permanent deformation; in other words, by stresses beyond the yield strength. If, due to unfavorable structure or multi-axial stresses, the steel is incapable of undergoing permanent deformation without cracking, the residual stresses may be dissipated nearly completely by stress-relief heat treatment. The control and removal of residual stresses by heat treatment, and to a lesser extent by preheating for welding, is discussed in Chapter 12.

In Fig. 138(a) the welded plate has residual stresses similar to those for the edge weld in Fig. 132(c). For simplicity, the stresses have been divided into five zones, X in tension ($+$ S psi), Y with no stress, and Z with compressive stress ($-$ S psi). Upon stretching the plate under a high tensile load sufficient to elongate the plate by the amount A, we find that the residual stresses change, Fig. 138(b). The X zones undergo permanent deformation in elongating, while the stresses in the Z zone decrease. The stress in the Y zones rises. Observe that the stress in the X zones does not rise to any appreciable extent. When the load is removed, the X zones contract along the straight line S_1-S_2; the stress in the X zones is S_2 after contracting an amount A equal to the elongation caused by the applied load. Obviously the residual stresses have been decreased by the applied load.

Resistance-spot welds present an interesting subject for study of residual stresses and their influence upon joint behavior in mechanical testing. Although the fatigue life of spot welds subject to cyclic stress com-pares favorably with rivets, the endurance limit actually is only about

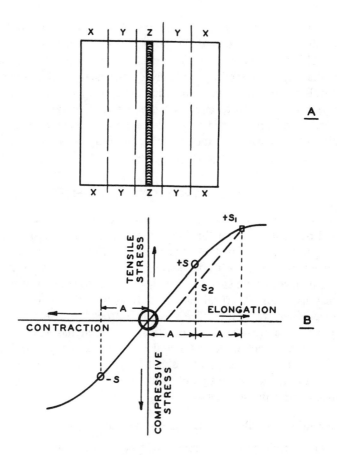

Fig. 138 — Release of residual stresses by deformation.

15% of the static tensile strength in all steels. This relatively low endurance limit is attributable to (1) concentration of applied loads by the notch effect around the weld nugget between the faying surfaces of the members, and (2) residual tensile stress throughout the weld and the peripheral area immediately surrounding the weld. It has been found possible to increase the fatigue strength of spot welds significantly by removing the residual tension stress in the peripheral area, and even further improvement can be secured if the tension stress is replaced by compression stress. This has been accomplished in several ways. Stress relief heat treatment is the simplest method and often results in a 100% improvement. Special compression treatments, applied hydrodynamically or mechanically, have increased fatigue properties by as much as 200% in mild steel. In applying the compression treatment, the spot welded assembly is held between platens to prevent as much as possible any lateral plastic flow of the spot weld. Through a suitable opening in the platen, the spot weld is subjected to a double blow by a special ring-and-tup tool. First the ring is pressed dynamically on the heat-affected zone around the spot weld to constrain this area. Then the spot weld is struck a blow by the convex tip of the tup to effect a more favorable distribution of stresses in the peripheral area. Some work also has been done with pin-point torch heating of spot welds to induce artificial compressive stresses in the area where fatigue fractures regularly initiate.

SHRINKAGE OF WELDMENTS

The overall or total dimensional decrease of a weldment member caused by contraction of the solid weld metal and the adjacent base metal during cooling is difficult to accurately predict. Yet, this information on shrinkage would be very valuable in scaling-up preweld dimensions in order to have the finished weldment conform to size tolerances. Often, a fabricator facing this problem of anticipating the amount of shrinkage in a weldment will standardize a welding procedure, weld a trial joint, and measure the shrinkage. This practical approach has many pitfalls if the fabricator does not understand and control the many variables involved. Let us examine shrinkage of welded members in different directions with respect to the weld axes, and study the techniques for measuring and controlling this physical change.

SHRINKAGE TRANSVERSE TO A BUTT WELD

The shrinkage of a member, whether a plate, sheet, bar or structural section, perpendicular to the long axis of an included weld usually is called *transverse shrinkage*. It is primarily dependent upon the cross-section of the weld metal in the joint as illustrated in Fig. 139. The larger the cross-section, the greater is the transverse shrinkage. As indicated in Fig. 139, the smaller cross-section weld area incorporated in a double-V or double-U preparation, as compared with a single-V, decreases shrinkage. One investigator of arc-welded joints found the transverse shrinkage to be approximately 10% of the average width of the weld metal section. Another investigator estimated transverse shrinkage as roughly ¼ in. per square inch of weld cross-section.

As crude as the latter method may seem, it probably is the more accurate of the two because transverse shrinkage will increase with both greater thickness and width for a given joint. On small weldments where the weld joints are small in cross-section and only one or two joints occur

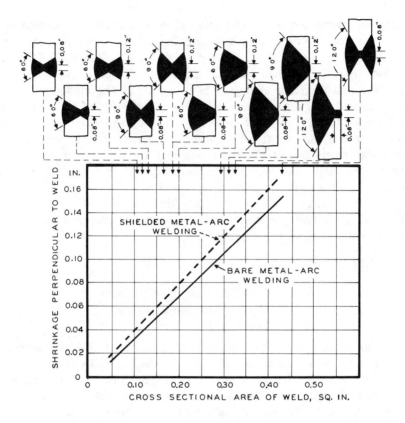

Fig. 139 — Shrinkage transverse (perpendicular) to butt-joint in metal-arc welded plate. Joints have different bevel preparations and have a root spacing of either 0.08-in. or 0.12-in. prior to welding.

in the total length of the weldment, the overall shrinkage often can be tolerated or an allowance easily made. However, in large weldments involving many joints of substantial cross-section, such as a ship or a pressure vessel, the shrinkage may amount to an inch or more. The amount of shrinkage will vary with (a) the degree of restraint on the members during welding and cooling, (b) the cross-sectional area of the weld metal, (c) the extent to which heat flows into the adjacent base metal members, and (d) the number of beads or layers employed to make up the weld cross-section and the temperature – time cycle which occurred during their deposition. Wide deviations in these variables during welding can result in considerable differences in the shrinkage from joint to joint.

Transverse shrinkage is cumulative, and close watch must be maintained on the number of butt welds made along the length of a weldment.

Where the overall length must be held within close limits, it is sometimes a practice to withhold trimming or resquaring of the last portion of an assembly until the shrinkage is checked in all but the final joint. This may be done by scribing bench marks at either side of each joint and measuring the actual shrinkage after each joint is welded. The amount by which the estimated shrinkage is in error can often be made up by a small adjustment in the size of the final portion of the assembly. Various other methods can be devised to accomplish the same result. The point is that, when the dimensions of a welded assembly are very important, careful forethought should be given to shrinkage before committing all portions of the assembly to final size.

In an effort to predict more closely the transverse shrinkage from a butt joint, the following formula has been employed to appraise welds made in steel by the shielded metal-arc process:

Transverse Shrinkage $= 0.2 \ (A_w/t) + 0.05(d)$

where

$A_w =$ cross-sectional area of weld (sq. in.)
$t =$ thickness of base metal (in.)
$d =$ root opening (in.)

This formula is particularly applicable to steel plates thicker than one inch. For plates less than one inch thick, a value of 0.18 may be substituted for the factor 0.2, inasmuch as the thinner plate is not capable of absorbing as much heat. The formula is not applicable to material less than ¼ in. thickness because buckling may be more serious than transverse shrinkage. When the widths of the plates being joined are less than 3 inches, their restraining influence will be sufficiently reduced to allow greater transverse shrinkage. In this event, the predicted shrinkage should be increased by 20%. Very short weld joints, for example, less than ten times the thickness in length, usually undergo less transverse shrinkage than predicted by the formula; perhaps 10 or 15% less.

In general, a greater degree of restraint results in less shrinkage and a higher level of residual stresses. Clamping in a fixture and tacking, therefore, tend to reduce shrinkage. Increasing the number of weld metal layers, within the limits for manual welding, will induce greater restraint in the joint during welding and will result in less shrinkage. In multilayer welding, the early layers of weld metal hinder further shrinkage as subsequent layers are deposited. However, these early layers also act as a fulcrum, so that the subsequent layers produce unwanted distortion, as will be explained shortly. Minimizing the amount of material, both weld and base metal, that goes through the weld thermal cycle acts to reduce transverse shrinkage. Obviously, this calls for welds of the smallest permissible cross-section deposited with the lowest total heat input per unit length, and the largest practicable fixture mass in contact with the base metal adjacent to the joint to act as a heat sink. Maximum conformance with these suggestions at the present time would be the application of the electron beam process at a high rate of travel speed while the base metal is clamped in a massive copper fixture. However, much can be done to minimize transverse shrinkage with any of the commonly used processes.

Welding in the flat or horizontal position, because higher travel speed is usually involved, tends to decrease shrinkage, perhaps by as much as 20%. Preheating provides more uniform heating and cooling and therefore acts to minimize shrinkage. Reductions in shrinkage as high as 20% can be effected depending upon the preheat temperature employed. Cooling between the passes or layers of a multi-layer weld increases the restraint and decreases shrinkage. Slow cooling of a weldment provides more uniform cooling and this tends to decrease the overall shrinkage by a small amount. Postheating a weldment reduces residual stresses and promotes plastic flow, but no significant change occurs in the shrinkage which took place in welding. Peening can be employed to counteract transverse shrinkage. Cold peening is more effective than hot peening. Depending upon the circumstances, peening can be applied to remove all shrinkage, to remove as little as desired, or may be carried to a degree that accomplishes an expansion at the joint. Of course, the undesirable side-effects of peening, as well as its problems of control and cost, must be considered before peening is selected as a recourse against transverse shrinkage.

The welding process will affect the amount of transverse shrinkage, and very careful analysis is required to predict whether an increase or a decrease will occur. It is not possible to generalize on a particular process. For example, gas welding may be 20 to 50% higher or lower, depending upon the relative areas being heated and cooled. If narrow plates are being welded, the application of the gas welding process would have the same effect as preheating and probably would give less shrinkage than an arc weld. On the other hand, gas welds ordinarily are made with one layer of weld metal, and the lower temperature heat source usually restricts travel speed. Consequently, the weld zone is relatively large and the shrinkage accordingly is relatively great. Automatic welding processes capable of higher travel speeds, like submerged arc welding, produce weld joints with less transverse shrinkage because of the lower heat input per unit length. Plates welded by the submerged arc process may display 50% less transverse shrinkage at the weld joint than predicted by the formula given earlier.

SHRINKAGE LONGITUDINAL TO A BUTT WELD

Shrinkage parallel to a butt weld tends to reduce the width of the plate at the weld, Fig. 140. It seems reasonable to believe that this *longitudinal shrinkage* will be proportional to the length of the weld. For example, a weld 2 feet long will shrink twice as much parallel to the weld as a similar weld only 1 foot long, whereas both will produce the same amount of shrinkage perpendicular to the weld. Longitudinal shrinkage is also a function of the cross-section of the weld and the cross-section of the colder surrounding base metal which resists the expansion and contraction forces of heated weld and base metal in and adjacent to the joint. Because the stress is not equally applied, not all of the area in the colder portion is equally effective in resisting the shrinkage and upsetting action. Therefore, it is difficult to calculate how much is effective.

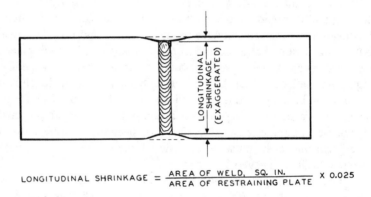

$$\text{LONGITUDINAL SHRINKAGE} = \frac{\text{AREA OF WELD, SQ. IN.}}{\text{AREA OF RESTRAINING PLATE}} \times 0.025$$

Fig. 140 — Shrinkage longitudinal to the joint in welded butt joints.

Where the area of the restraining plates is not more than 20 times the cross-sectional area of the total weld, the following formula has been employed for predicting longitudinal shrinkage:

Longitudinal Shrinkage $= 0.025 \ (A_w/A_p)$
where

    $A_w =$ area of weld (sq in.)
    $A_p =$ area of restraining plates (sq in.)

Where the area of the restraining plates is more than 20 times the area of the weld metal, the chart provided in Fig. 141 may give a closer estimation of longitudinal shrinkage. Again, proper peening can be used to counteract longitudinal shrinkage.

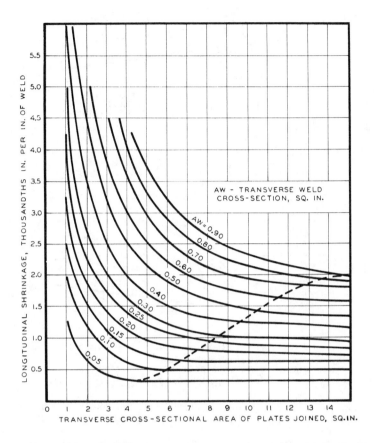

Fig. 141 — Longitudinal shrinkage of butt welds as affected by cross-sectional area of weld metal in joint (adapted by Spraragen and Ettinger from a chart by Guyot).

Each curve represents the variation of unit logitudinal shrinkage as a function of the transverse cross-sectional area of the welded assembly for a given weld cross section. The shrinkage tends to become stabilized when the sectional area of the assembly exceeds a certain value, which is indicated by the dottled line.

DISTORTION OF WELDMENTS

Distortion in weldments is an exceedingly complex subject, but the factors which tend to distort the form of a weldment are reasonably well understood. We know that the localized area along which the arc or heat source passes is the starting point of our distortion problem. It is appreciated that the temperature differential between weld zone and unaffected

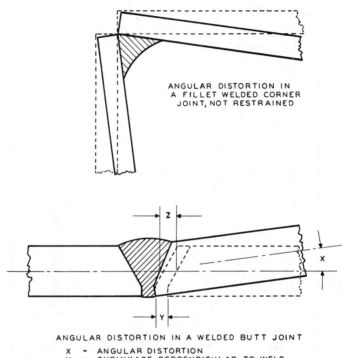

ANGULAR DISTORTION IN
A FILLET WELDED CORNER
JOINT, NOT RESTRAINED

ANGULAR DISTORTION IN A WELDED BUTT JOINT

X - ANGULAR DISTORTION
Y - SHRINKAGE PERPENDICULAR TO WELD
    WITHOUT ANGULAR DISTORTION
Z - TOTAL SHRINKAGE PERPENDICULAR TO WELD

Fig. 142 — Angular distortion of a fillet welded corner joint and a
single-V groove weld in a butt joint.

base metal is great and much localized expansion and plastic flow takes
place here. We know that restraint from external clamping and restraint
from mass in the base metal itself will have an influence upon the extent
of plastic flow. Yet these are just a few of the many mechanical engineering aspects of the physical changes in a weldment during and following the
joining operations. The relationship between the many factors involved
in a common type of welded joint is so complex that no method of analysis
has been devised which closely predicts the degree of distortion to be
expected. Of course, much study on this subject is underway, but until a
reliable method of stress and distortion analysis is developed, we shall
have to depend upon experience to guide our efforts to anticipate and
control this troublesome condition.

Distortion occurs in all weldments, but can vary widely in degree.
Attaching a small clip to a massive block of steel by electron beam welding
may be claimed to have been accomplished without distortion. Yet,

measuring instruments of great precision invariably can find a minute change in form. In the extreme opposite, distortion from welding with an oxyacetylene torch can make a thin sheet-metal cylinder look like a crumpled trash can. Engineers recognize distortion when the degree of change from welding makes the weldment form unsightly or unsuitable for its intended purpose.

Distortion can be roughly classified in three common kinds: (1) angular distortion, (2) longitudinal bowing, and (3) buckling.

ANGULAR DISTORTION

Angular distortion is the angular change in relative positions of members extending from a weld area. This kind of distortion in a fillet welded corner joint and a butt joint is illustrated in Fig. 142. When viewed as a transverse section, there is a shorter width of contracting weld metal at the root of each weld than at the face. This difference in width which must contract upon cooling is a major factor in angular distortion.

For single-bevel groove welds in butt joints and T sections unclamped during welding, angular distortion is nearly proportional to the number of beads or layers, assuming all layers are approximately the same size. That is, the greater the number of beads or layers deposited in a joint, the larger will be the angular distortion.

A formula sometimes used to roughly compute angular distortion in terms of deflection at the outer edge of flanges fillet welded to the web of plate girders is:

$$\triangle = \frac{0.02 \ W \ (w^{1.3})}{t^2}$$

Where $\triangle$ = deflection at edge of flange (in.)
W = width of flange (in.)
w = size of fillet welds (in.)
t = thickness of flange (in.)

Angular distortion in general, is decreased (1) by using the minimum amount of weld metal required to gain the desired joint strength, (2) by depositing the weld metal in the fewest possible number of layers, (3) by avoiding as much as possible the weld profile with the very narrow root and the wide face, (4) by balancing the amount of weld metal about the neutral axis of the joint, and (5) by presetting the members at a slight angle opposite to that expected to develop as a result of welding.

LONGITUDINAL BOWING

Longitudinal distortion or bowing of long members is caused by shrinkage stress which develops at some distance from the neutral axis of the member. As shown in Fig. 143, the amount of bowing distortion is determined by the magnitude of the shrinkage stress and the resistance of the member to the bending indicated by its moment of inertia. A formula used to calculate the bending resulting from longitudinal welding on a long, slim member is:

$$\triangle = \frac{0.005 \; A_w \; (L^2) \; d}{I}$$

where

$\triangle$ = resulting vertical movement (in.)

A_w = total cross-sectional area within the fusion line of all welds (sq in.)

d = distance between the center of gravity of the weld group and the neutral axis of the member (in.)

L = length of member (in.). Assumed to be welded full length

I = moment of inertia of member

Control of longitudinal distortion is done by balancing welds about the neutral axis of the member. When welds of unequal size must be made at uneven distances from the neutral axis, the opposing stresses should be balanced by first depositing welds closest to the neutral axis, and by making the welds that are further away from the neutral axis smaller in size. Prebending or cambering the member in a bow opposite to that which will develop from welding often is a practical recourse. Remember, the hot side will finally become the short side.

BUCKLING

Thin sheet often buckles during welding whereas heavy plate does not. The buckling is caused by the well-known inability of laterally unsupported sheet to resist compressive stress without buckling (column failure). Compressive shrinkage stress in regions near the weld accounts for the buckling. Wandering sequence is a corrective for distortion. Instead of making all the welds in a strict succession, welding alternately on opposite sides of a part often will reduce distortion. The distortion of the weld on the opposite side may neutralize the distortion created by the first weld. When welding is resumed on the first side, furthermore, the temperature has fallen and less of the metal will enter the plastic range during subsequent welding.

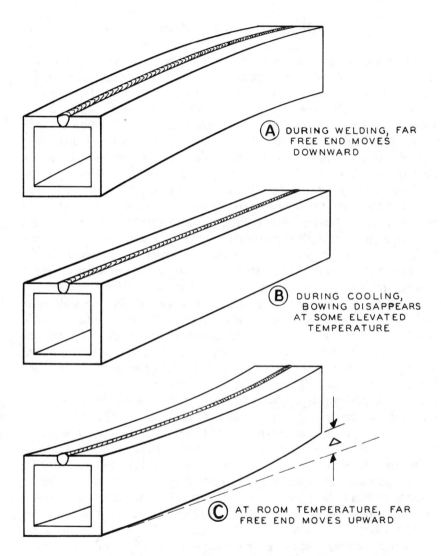

Fig. 143 — Longitudinal distortion or bowing in column member caused by welding.

(A) During welding of longitudinal butt joint on top surface, this side expands and box beam bows upward at center.

(B) During cooling, upward bow at center disappears at some elevated temperature.

(C) Upon reaching room temperature, beam bows downward at center because top side undergoes longitudinal shrinkage at weld. Approximate vertical movement of free end ($\triangle$) can be calculated from equation shown in text.

THERMAL STRAIGHTENING

Thermal straightening is deliberately applied and controlled shrinkage. It is used to shrink specific portions of plates or structural members for the purpose of reversing and correcting existing distortion. The mechanism of the straightening operation is exactly that which occurs during welding and causes distortion. A localized area of metal is usually torch heated to a high temperature. During heating, the localized area must expand, but it is constrained by the colder, stronger surrounding metal. Consequently, the heated area is easily forced to upset. This upsetting manifests itself by bulging at the heated surfaces, but the degree of bulging usually is too small to be easily detected by eye. When the localized area reaches a reasonable red heat, possibly 1600 to 1800 F, the heating must be stopped to confine the upsetting to the desired area. Incidently, some further distortion in the same unwanted direction may appear in the member at this point, but this should be ignored for the moment. Upon cooling, the heated area undergoes contraction, as would be expected.

But, because the upset due to heating is not equally reversible upon cooling, a net shrinkage results which tends to pull the surrounding metal inward. Thus the movement of the member in this direction will be greater than the movement in the opposite, unwanted direction during heating. The effect is more pronounced if the upset area is quenched shortly after heating. Obviously, the final outcome of this thermal exposure is a deliberately applied shrinkage. If the amount of metal in the localized, heated area is properly judged, or if the number of areas of shrinkage are properly estimated, the total shrinkage will produce a controlled distortion. This movement may correct a distortion which occurred earlier in welding, or by some unexpected mechanical action. The deliberate, controlled distortion may be used in lieu of a press to bend or shape a member. In many cases, an oxyacetylene torch can accomplish as much straightening or bending on large metal sections as would be done by a very large press.

When applying thermal straightening to a weldment both the location and the shape of the localized heated area are very important in determining the final movement of the member or the entire structure. Considerable skill in straightening or bending can be developed through experience. The only general rule that can be offered to guide this operation is, again – the hot side finally will be the short side. The technique employed in straightening a bowed I-beam is illustrated in Fig. 144. This operation also can be employed to straighten solid bars, tubing, and plate. Buckling can be removed from sheet by heating a localized area in the center of the

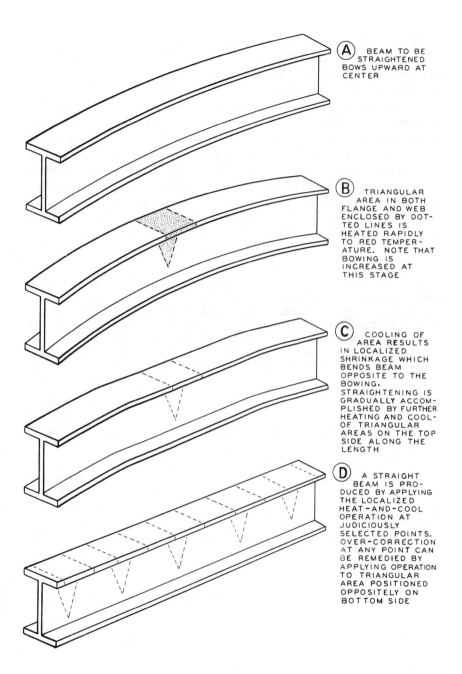

Fig. 144 — Thermal straightening applied to a bowed I-beam.

distorted panel. The edges or surrounding metal must be kept cool (use water if necessary) and are best constrained. Upon cooling, the central localized spot shrinks and draws the sheet flat.

Very thorough studies of shrinkage distortion by localized heating have been undertaken in an effort to improve this method of straightening members, or even adjusting their form to a desired shape. In this work, multiple-spot heating has been compared with line heating. It is of metallurgical interest to note that in multiple-spot heating, previously existing distortion can be relaxed by a subsequently applied spot and the resultant shrinkage or distortion is less than would be expected. While strong effort has been made to provide quantitative data for guiding thermal shrinkage, the technique of straightening or forming steel plates, bars, structural shapes, or weldments remains largely an art.

Suggested Reading

"Expansion and Contraction," by R. B. Aitchison, Journal of the American Welding Society, v 25, no. 12, pp 1195, December 1946.

"The Weld Stress Problem," Ibid, v 24, no. 6, Research Suppl. pp 313s, June 1945.

"Types and Causes of Distortion in Welded Steel and Corrective Measures," by O. W. Blodgett, Welding Journal, # v 39, no. 7, pp 692-697, July 1960.

"Analytical Investigation of Residual Stresses and Distortions Due to Welding," by K. Masubuchi, Ibid, v 39, no. 12, pp 525s-537s, December 1960.

Chapter 12

PREHEATING AND POSTHEATING

The application of supplementary heat to a joint before or after welding can be a very important part of the *welding procedure*. Elevating the temperature of the workpieces immediately before a welding or cutting operation is called *preheating*. The application of supplementary heat to a welded joint or to a weldment after welding is called *postheating*. Both preheating and postheating may be applied locally to the joint area or to the entire weldment. These treatments are employed in cutting and, particularly, in welding operations for a number of reasons, the principal ones being:

1. To avoid cold cracking in the heat-affected zones of hardenable steels

2. To increase the toughness of the weld joint and improve its ability to withstand adverse service conditions involving impact loading or low temperatures

3. To alleviate the effects of hydrogen which enters the weld metal and the base metal heat-affected zone

4. To reduce residual stresses (internal stresses from shrinkage, phase transformation, and reaction to restraint) to a desired low level

5. To minimize shrinkage and distortion

6. To produce particular mechanical or physical properties in the steel of which the weldment is constructed

Certain carbon and alloy steels to be discussed in Chapters 14 and 15 are quite sensitive to cooling rates and temperature end points on cooling. A mere hundred degrees difference in the temperature of the base

141

metal at the start of welding in some cases can determine whether the weld will be sound or will contain cracks. While for many years the question of preheating was resolved mainly on the basis of whether its benefit was judged to be needed to insure a sound joint, we no longer can treat the application of preheat from this single point of view. With some of the newer alloy steels, preheating can be harmful to the final properties of the joint if applied without regard to other thermal considerations.

For a number of reasons, both mechanical and metallurgical in nature, we must pay close attention to (a) the initial temperature of the base metal — which would be the *preheat* temperature if elevated any amount above ambient temperature, (b) the temperature of the base metal during deposition of multiple beads — which is called the *interpass* temperature, and (c) any kind of thermal cycling or treatment applied after the welding operation — which is the *postweld treatment*. The latter, incidently, might also entail treatment at subzero temperatures along with treatment at elevated or high temperatures. The welding metallurgist must be particularly vigilant on the matter of preheating and postweld treatment. Even though the metallurgical properties of the steel being welded may obviously require either or both safeguards, the welder usually regards preheat as inconvenient and uncomfortable, while the weldment manufacturer sometimes looks upon the postweld heat treatment as an unnecessary expense because the beneficial results cannot be clearly seen in the product.

PREHEATING

Preheating involves raising the temperature of the base metal above the temperature of the surroundings before welding. The entire part to be welded may be preheated or, if local preheat is called for, only the vicinity of the joint to be welded is heated. Postweld heating — that is, heating the weldment immediately after it is completed — under certain circumstances may be substituted for preheating. The requisite preheat temperatures depend upon the composition of the steel, the rigidity of the base metal members to be joined, and the welding process. Proper preheat temperatures vary from 100 to 1200 F.

Correct temperature determination is an important part of preheating technique. The temperature can be measured or estimated by many methods. Surface thermometers or thermocouples, colored chalks that change color at known temperatures, pellets that melt at known temperatures, and the boiling of water droplets are just a few of the practical methods. The best method of insuring that the preheat temperature is correct involves the use of a furnace or an oven held at the correct temperature or slightly above. Allowance sometimes should be made for cooling of the part upon removal from the furnace. Weldments of alloy steel for critical applications sometimes are preheated in a fixture equipped with electrical resistance heating elements. While the welding is performed, the heated fixture also prevents the interpass temperature from dropping too low. When the weldment is preheated in a furnace or with a torch, allowance must be made for cooling, and welding should be discontinued whenever the part cools to the minimum safe temperature. There are occasions when too high preheating may be as harmful as too low; for example, a complicated part without internal support may collapse. Excessive preheat may thwart the welder's ability to produce a sound weld. In some alloy steels, excessive preheat may promote hot cracking by increasing the amount of segregation of residual elements in the weld deposit. Some of the newer quenched and tempered alloy steels when preheated without regard for cooling rate during welding may develop unfavorable microstructures in the heat-affected zones adjacent to welds.

Preheating may be applied to a weldment for (a) the prevention of cold cracks, (b) reduction of hardness in heat-affected zones, (c) reduction of residual stresses, and (d) reduction of distortion. In comparing preheating and postweld heat treatment, we can say that postweld treatment cannot remedy cracks that occur during welding; however, it can soften hardened zones and reduce shrinkage stresses. Postweld heat treatment usually means heating the weldment to a relatively high temperature, approximately 1100 F or above after all or part of the welding is completed. Preheating, on the other hand, means heating the part to a relatively low temperature before welding is begun. Rarely is it practicable to weld joints at the temperature of heat treatment. However, joining by brazing frequently is performed in a furnace at the temperature required for heat treatment.

Regardless of other effects, it is a universal rule that preheating lowers the cooling rate after welding. For a given set of welding conditions (current, welding speed, etc.) cooling rates will be faster for a weld made without preheat than with preheat. The higher the preheating temperature, the slower will be the cooling rates after the weld is completed. Besides reducing the temperature gradient, which is a principal factor governing cooling rate, preheating lowers the thermal conductivity of iron, which at 1100 F is only half its conductivity at room temperature. Low thermal conductivity results in slow withdrawal of heat from the welded zone, and correspondingly slow cooling rates. Further, an increase in base metal temperature generally increases the superheating of the weld puddle in arc welding. As a result, beads deposited in preheated joints tend to be more fluid and to exhibit flatter or more concave surfaces than beads deposited without preheat.

Reduction in cooling rate by preheating increases the time spent by the heat-affected zone in the temperature range 1000-1200 F and therefore promotes the transformation of austenite to pearlite instead of to martensite. The preheated weld joint is less likely to have hard zones than the weld joint made without preheat.

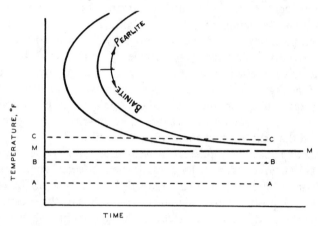

Fig. 145 — Preheat temperature in relation to the I-T curve. The dotted lines represent the different preheating temperatures.

Despite the slower cooling rate provided by preheating, the steel to be welded may yet fail to transform to pearlite during cooling. If the preheating temperature is relatively low, B in Fig. 145, contrasted with room temperature A, the heat-affected zone close to the weld may transform to martensite. It appears to be a characteristic of martensite formation in the higher-carbon steels (0.6% C or over), which we are safe in assuming applies to lower-carbon steels, that the percentage of austenite that transforms to martensite increases as the temperature decreases, assuming the critical cooling rate is being exceeded. In Fig. 145, M is the highest temperature at which austenite changes to martensite during cooling. However, at temperature M only a small percentage of austenite may change to martensite. The small percentage of martensite appears instantly as soon as M is reached in cooling, but little more martensite is formed if the temperature is held at M. Lowering the temperature to B causes further transformation of austenite to martensite, the reaction again stopping when a critical percentage of austenite has changed to martensite. During further cooling to room temperature, A, nearly all the remaining austenite changes to martensite.

PREVENTING COLD CRACKING

The dependence of the austenite–martensite transformation upon temperature partly accounts for the valuable effect of preheating at 200 to 400 F to prevent cracking in hardenable steels during welding. Hard zones may be formed even with preheat at 200–400 F, but at the preheat temperature so little austenite changes to martensite that cracks do not form. During cooling from the preheat temperature to room temperature, additional martensite forms from the retained austenite. However, the rate of cooling is slow, structure stresses and stresses due to temperature gradients are lower, and it is found by experience that cracking does not occur. An equally valuable influence of preheating in preventing cold cracking is the effect of temperature upon the solubility and diffusion rate of hydrogen in steel. The role of hydrogen in causing cold cracks and the remedial effect of preheat will be discussed in detail in Chapter 13. For the moment, we will direct attention to the influence of preheat upon phase transformation. Now, suppose that the preheat temperature C in Fig. 145 is above the highest temperature at which martensite can form. Obviously, austenite cannot change to martensite no matter what cooling rate prevails, so long as the preheat temperature is maintained. Nevertheless, any austenite that reaches the vicinity of the preheat temperature may require a long time for complete transformation to products other than martensite. For a steel containing 0.1% C, 5% Cr and 0.5% Mo, or one containing 0.4% C, 2% Ni, 1% Cr and 0.3% Mo, as examples, a week may be required for complete transformation of austenite at 950 F or 750 F, respectively. For this reason, rapid cooling from the preheat temperature sometimes is not advisable for the higher-carbon and the alloy steels. With many steels, preheating above the maximum temperature for the austenite to transform to martensite is sufficient to prevent zones of martensite next to the weld, regardless of cooling rates from the preheating temperature, provided the preheating temperature is maintained throughout the period of welding.

Before discussing the effect of preheating on residual stresses, let us consolidate the discussion to this point. We know that hard zones sometimes occur in the heat-affected areas of welded medium-carbon and high-carbon steels, and we know that if there is a hard zone, cold cracking may occur during the last stages of cooling. It seems logical to deduce that shrinkage stresses, augmented by the expansion when austenite transforms to martensite, cracks the martensitic zone, which is both hard and lacking in ductility. Preheating to a lower temperature, 200–400 F, which is adequate for the lower-carbon and low-alloy steels, may either prevent austenite from transforming to martensite by reducing the cooling rate, or may cause the austenite to change very slowly to martensite, both actions preventing cracking. Preheating to higher temperatures, 600–800 F, which often is necessary for steels containing more than 0.30% carbon, prevents the formation of martensite during welding, providing: (1) the steel is held at the preheat temperature for a sufficient period of time after welding to allow transformation to proceed to a softer structure, or (2) cooling from the preheat temperature is sufficiently slow to allow transformation to a structure other than martensite.

Because the critical cooling rate and the location of the M_s point, which are the guidelines for martensite formation, are controlled mainly by the composition of the steel, a number of methods of calculating the need for preheat using the analysis of the steel have been devised. The various formulas proposed usually consider first the carbon content and then the alloying elements which promote hardenability, and attempt to translate these factors into an "equivalent carbon content." A typical formula of this kind is given below:

$$\begin{array}{c} \text{Equivalent} \\ \text{carbon} \\ \text{content} \end{array} = \% \text{ C} + \frac{\% \text{ Mn}}{6} + \frac{\% \text{ Ni}}{15} + \frac{\% \text{ Cr}}{5} + \frac{\% \text{ Cu}}{13} + \frac{\% \text{ Mo}}{4}$$

The preheat temperatures suggested for several ranges of equivalent carbon content are:

Equivalent Carbon Content	Suggested Preheat Temperature
Up to 0.45%	Optional
0.45 to 0.60%	200 – 400 F
Above 0.60%	400 – 700 F

Of course, the need for the suggested preheat will depend upon the welding process applied. Processes which regularly involve large amounts of heat input, such as oxyacetylene welding, have no need for preheat because the temperature gradient across the heat-affected zones is not very steep. Consequently, the cooling rate in this area is relatively slow. The proponents of formulas for preheat usually have arc welding in mind, where the temperature gradients are steep and the cooling rates can be very high. The need for preheat also is dependent upon the composition of the steel. The formula given above is intended for carbon and alloy steels containing not more than 0.5% C, 1.5% Mn, 3.5% Ni, 1% Cr, 1% Cu, and 0.5% Mo.

The products other than martensite to which austenite transforms in preheated welds may be pearlite or bainite. Heat-affected zones containing pearlite, even the finest pearlite, will be capable of more deformation without cracking than zones containing martensite. All available evidence shows that a given steel exhibiting bainite is more ductile and tougher than the same steel in the martensitic condition. Bainite is about 5 to 30 Rockwell C units softer than martensite, the bainite formed at higher temperatures being softer but not necessarily more ductile than bainite formed at temperatures just above the martensite temperature M, Fig. 145. It is true that martensite, if reheated to the temperature at which bainite forms on cooling, may become as ductile or more ductile than bainite. In the welding of hardenable steels, however, it is a question of preheating or not preheating. If hard martensite forms without preheat, there is a likelihood of cracking in medium-carbon steels. No amount of postweld reheating will heal these cracks. However, if the composition of the steel is *designed* for welding, that is, containing a relatively low carbon content and a combination of alloying elements that allows transformation from austenite to bainite or martensite at a high temperature, then preheat may be undesirable. As will be explained in Chapter 15, if the cooling rate is too slow, the transformation of austenite proceeds to upper bainitic structures that have poorer notch toughness.

REDUCING RESIDUAL STRESSES

Although there is essentially no difference in the nature of stresses from external loads and residual stresses, it was mentioned briefly in Chapter 11 that external loads are not simply additive to internal (residual) stresses by superposition. Even though most works on the theory of elasticity in metals make use of the principle of superposition, this principle does not account for the distribution of stresses actually found in a weldment under load. It is strongly suspected that external loads applied to a welded structure containing residual stresses produce highly *localized* yielding, so that a small amount of localized plastic flow quickly relieves residual stresses in a general area. However, if a stress raiser is present, any external load will produce higher stresses at the tip of the flaw than in any other nearby area. This is the situation where stress distribution, rate of load application, and temperature challenge the properties of the steel. It is imperative that localized overstress at the tip of the flaw be reduced through plastic flow rather than promote a low-energy catastrophic fracture. Preheating for welding aids in promoting notch toughness in the weldment. This can be a very helpful attribute both during the welding operation, and later in service. The increased toughness is credited to a reduction in residual stresses and other factors to be discussed. To understand the action of preheat on residual stresses, let us return to the bar analogy, Figs. 126 to 129, that was found to be helpful in Chapter 11. Instead of maintaining the rigid jaws of our idealized press at room temperature, as we did in Chapter 11, we shall preheat the jaw–frame assembly as well as the bar, Fig. 146, at four temperatures: no preheat and at 200, 600, and 1200 F preheats. At all times *after* preheating, the jaws of the press shall remain the same distance apart. The bar alone will then be heated to 1700 F and cooled again under complete restraint.

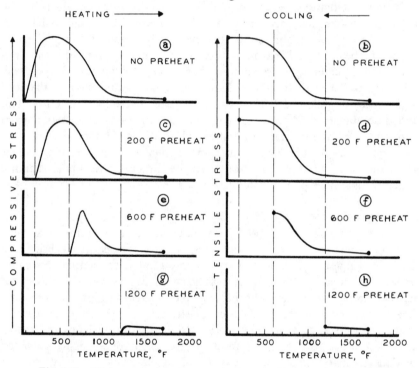

Fig. 146 — Stress-temperature curves for bars under complete restraint during heating and cooling.

During heating without preheat, the stress in the bar, Fig. 146(a), rises to the yield stress in compression as it did in Fig. 129(b), and the bar upsets while remaining at the yield stress throughout further heating. We know from Fig. 128 that the yield strength of steel determined in a test lasting a few minutes drops to nearly zero at temperatures above 1200 F. Consequently, by the time the bar in Fig. 146(a) has reached 1200 F the stress in it has dropped to nearly zero. The rate at which the bar is heated will determine to some extent the temperature at which the stress becomes zero. Rapid heating has the effect of rapidly straining the steel. At rapid rates of strain the yield stress is higher than at low rates. Since high rates of heating prevail in some processes of welding, such as spot welding, the temperature at which the stress drops to zero may be nearly 1500 F or so. Cooling rates in welding, generally speaking, are slower than heating rates. Therefore, no great effect from high strain rates, beyond the usual increase of yield strength with falling temperature, need be expected. Exception is taken, of course, to special cooling rates induced by quenching or some form of artificially retarded cooling.

Returning to Fig. 146(a), we observe that the bar is practically free from stress above 1200 F. When the bar starts to cool from 1700 F, Fig. 146(b), it promptly reaches the tensile yield stress, which is very low above 1200 F, and yields; that is, its diameter is reduced while its length remains unchanged and equal to the distance between the fixed jaws. At 1200 F and below, the yield strength rises and the shrinkage stress likewise rises. This stress is close to the yield strength at all temperatures and is at the yield strength when the bar has cooled to room temperature.

The effect of preheating press and bar to 200 F is illustrated in Figs. 146(c) and (d). Events are practically the same as with no preheat; the bar ends the cycle with the tensile shrinkage stress up to the yield strength at 200 F. Preheating to 600 F, Figs. 146(e) and (f), reduces the stress cycle on heating and cooling, since the maximum compressive stress on heating and the tensile shrinkage stress on cooling to 600 F will undoubtedly be lower than at the 200 F preheat due to the lower yield strength at 600 F.

When the press and bar are preheated to 1200 F, the stresses are extremely small at all temperatures. The bar is completely restrained during heating from 1200 to 1700 F and therefore is upset. On cooling back to 1200 F the upset is removed completely. Preheating to 1200 F, therefore, has completely prevented shrinkage stresses. But, it may be objected, do not the shrinkage stresses appear if now the bar is cooled back to room temperature? It is true that if now the bar alone is cooled to room temperature, tensile stresses would appear in it. But when both press and bar together are uniformly cooled to room temperature, they contract together, and no shrinkage stresses occur.

In the examples given in Fig. 146, the thermal response of the bar and press is analogous to that of the welded zone and the restraining portion of a weldment. Had the preheating been local instead of total (torch or induction coil preheat instead of furnace preheat), it is obvious that the cooling of the preheated region to the temperature of the rest of the part would create shrinkage stresses that could be greater or smaller than the stresses caused by welding alone, depending upon circumstances.

If shrinkage stresses must be kept at a minimum, any application of local preheat must be studied in this light.

In addition to reducing shrinkage stresses, preheating to the higher temperatures, above 600 F, reduces overall distortion (upset) appreciably and reduces the yield strength of the material. Reducing the yield strength of the material relieves shrinkage stresses which, if forced to occur solely in the highly heated zone in the immediate vicinity of the weld, might lead to hot cracks in the weld metal or in the base metal close to the weld.

Need we restrict preheating to temperatures below 1200 F? Practical problems make higher preheat temperatures uncommon in welding procedures. Temperatures in excess of 1200 F if applied locally require considerable heat input to maintain because of conduction into the surrounding colder base metal. A special heat source to provide the preheat must be arranged that will not interfere with the welding operation. If preheat above 1200 F is applied to the entire weldment, the operation virtually requires a furnace large enough to encompass the entire article, and the welder's comfort during the joining operation certainly must be considered. Also, the filler metal may reach a somewhat higher temperature than usual during deposition into the highly preheated joint and thus become too fluid for proper manipulation. Additional problems of a metallurgical nature can arise, such as the formation of heavy oxides which may interfere with the coalescence of base metal and filler metal. In general, many of the factors which enter into a welding operation favor application of the lowest acceptable preheat.

Nevertheless, high preheat temperatures exert certain effects deserving of attention and study, and there are conditions, such as in multilayer welding, under which we unwittingly make use of higher preheat temperatures. One effect of higher preheat is to widen the heat-affected zone in the base metal. As illustrated in Fig. 147, a weld joint made with no preheat (A) has heat-affected zones which can be delineated by the outermost limits of the region which was heated above the critical range (above the Ac_3 temperature, which might be approximately 1550 F for the steel in this example). If the same welding operation is performed, but with the base metal preheated to 1000 F, the width of the heat-affected zones will be increased appreciably as shown in Fig. 147 (B). Here the heat of welding is required to increase the base metal temperature only by an additional 550 degrees to bring the steel above its critical range. Obviously, a fixed welding heat input will be more effective in raising the base metal temperature a mere 550 degrees instead of the 1475 degrees as required in the case of base metal at room temperature (no preheat). Thus the heat-affected zones of the joint in preheated base metal will be wider. It may be well to point out that the depth of heat-affected zones in base metals welded with different initial temperatures will rank in the same manner regardless of the method of comparison.

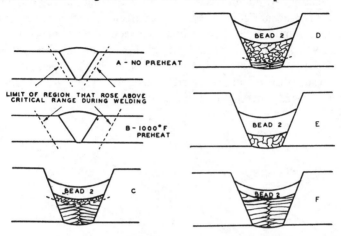

Fig. 147 — Influence of preheating on heat-affected zones.

(A) and (B) Base metal heat-affected zone is widened by preheating.
(C) Bead 1 cooled to room temperature before bead 2 was deposited. Only a small portion of bead 1 was refined by the heat of bead 2.
(D) Bead 1 was at 1000 F when bead 2 was deposited. A large part of bead 1 was refined by the heat of bead 2.
(E) After small bead 1 had cooled below the critical temperature range, large bead 2 raised it completely above the critical and refined the grains.
(F) Bead 1 never cooled below the critical before bead 2 was deposited.

In making these comparisons, some of the effects of preheat are easily measured, for example, the rate of cooling in the heat-affected zone at a fixed point. Other effects, such as residual stresses, are rather abstruse, and it may be necessary to resort to extreme simplification (as we did in Fig. 146) to analyze them. Some effects of higher preheat are rather complex, particularly if metallurgical phenomena are involved. The influence of preheat on grain size is one of these more complicated effects. Since grain size undergoes greater change in multilayer welding, which is an area where we often deal with higher preheat temperatures unsuspectingly, we will delay a discussion of the relationship between preheat and grain size until the subject of multilayer welding and interpass temperature is reviewed, and at that time make use of the additional illustrations in Fig. 147.

IMPROVEMENT IN NOTCH TOUGHNESS

Much research has been conducted in an effort to evaluate the benefits of preheating. Although we can predict with some degree of confidence the effect of preheating on cracking occurrence, the hardness of heat-affected zones, and the level of residual stresses, other benefits accompany preheating which are not well understood. For example, when arc welding mild steel with cellulosic covered electrodes, preheated specimens display superior results over nonpreheated specimens when tested for notch toughness. Several investigators have explored this area using a plate

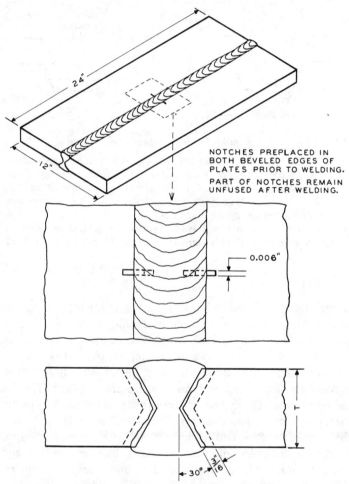

NOTCHES PREPLACED IN BOTH BEVELED EDGES OF PLATES PRIOR TO WELDING.

PART OF NOTCHES REMAIN UNFUSED AFTER WELDING.

Fig. 148 — Welded test specimen containing flaw-like notch adjacent to weld (after McGeady).

specimen of substantial size containing a notch which is placed in the beveled faces of the joint before welding. As shown in Fig. 148, the specimen after welding has a cracklike notch on each side of the weld. Test plates of this kind have been welded at various levels of preheat temperature and with various classes of electrodes. The toughness of this "weldment" has been evaluated (a) by examining the weld metal for cracking extension from the notch immediately after welding each bead, upon completion of the joint, and after holding at room temperature a week or so, (b) by making notched-bar impact tests on the weld metal and the base metal, and (c) by bending specimens longtitudinally as a beam until fracture occurred. The impact and bend testing has been performed at progressively lower temperatures to establish transition temperatures.

One investigator using this testing procedure found that nonpreheated specimens of ASTM A212 steel welded with E7010 electrodes cracked spontaneously on standing. Specimens preheated to 400 F, however, displayed a transition temperature in bending of −80 F. When E7016 electrodes were substituted in the nonpreheated specimens, a transition temperature of +20 F was observed. It was concluded that the benefits of preheating mild steels for welding were only slightly less than those of stress-relief heat treatment. No particular metallurgical change could be singled out to give major credit for the better performance of preheated test plates. However, certain findings suggested that preheating lowers the residual stresses at the tip of the flaw where cracking begins during testing. Also, preheating appears to over-age the metal at the tip of the flaw after the thermal cycle of welding has produced some strain-age hardening. These factors, stress-relief and over-aging, appear to be the principal ones involved in the mechanisms by which preheating improves notch toughness.

WELDING AT LOW AMBIENT TEMPERATURES

Before leaving the subject of preheating, attention should be turned for a moment to welding at *low* ambient temperatures. Circumstances often arise during winter when the workpieces to be joined are at a very low temperature. Naturally, the question should be examined as to whether completely satisfactory results will be obtained by applying the selected process with a regular procedure. Of course, in addition to the metallurgical effects of welding at a low ambient temperature, there are other aspects of the joining operation that can affect weld quality under these conditions: welder discomfort, equipment malfunction, and weather-effects (wind, frost, etc.) are just a few of the items that deserve consideration.

Most metallurgical difficulties which develop during welding at low ambient temperatures are caused by the increased rate of cooling of the weld metal and the heat-affected zones of the base metal. Cracking is the defect most likely to be encountered, although porosity has been observed to occur unexpectedly. Some difficulty may arise with slag entrapment because of the tendency for the molten slag on the weld pool to chill on the very cold groove faces of the joint. A further effect of the rapid cooling, even when cracking does not occur, is lower ductility and toughness in the welded joint. The extent to which ductility and toughness is lowered will depend upon the composition of the steel and the welding procedure. Many steels have sufficient latitude in toughness to offer adequate properties even when welded at a very low temperature. However, when a question exists on the capability of a steel, the practical solutions to the problems are to (1) employ a welding procedure that provides a high heat input to the joint, or (2) preheat the joint area to a safe-to-weld temperature. All considered, preheating usually is the easier to apply. However, where circumstances preclude preheating, much can be done in devising a welding procedure that compensates for a low base metal temperature. Low-hydrogen, mineral-covered electrodes often are employed, and in some cases, these alone in a regular procedure represent an adequate provision to prevent cracking. In special cases, an austenitic Cr-Ni filler metal can be deposited to ensure a sound, tough weld metal. There does not seem to be any real lower limit to the base metal temperature at which welding can be performed providing suitable precautions are embodied in the welding procedure.

MULTI-LAYER WELDING AND INTERPASS TEMPERATURE

While preheating may properly control conditions for the initial deposition of weld metal, the temperature of the weld joint and surrounding weldment members during the deposition of successive beads may be equally as important. Therefore, the permissible range of *interpass temperature* also should be stipulated. Usually the minimum of this range corresponds with the minimum preheat temperature unless a change in conditions has been brought about by the deposition of the initial bead. For example, a joint in alloy steel may be preheated to only 200 F because the initial pass or root bead is to be deposited by the gas tungsten-arc process. However, the remainder of the joint is to be completed with E7010 covered electrodes. Considering that the degree of restraint at the joint may be significantly higher during successive passes, and that the welding is not being performed with a low-hydrogen electrode, it would be well under these circumstances to specify an interpass temperature of

approximately 300 to 600 F. Of course, further consideration of the
type of alloy steel and its weldability, and the kind of joint to be made
might indicate a higher or a lower minimum interpass temperature to be
desirable.

Interpass temperature, in addition to influencing cracking susceptibility
of hardenable steels, residual stress, and distortion, also has an effect upon
grain size. This effect can be very important in many commonly used
products made of welded carbon steel. In Fig. 147(c) small bead 2 has
raised a small part of bead 1 above the critical thus refining the grain size
of that region; bead 1 had been allowed to cool to room temperature
before bead 2 was deposited. In Fig. 147(d) bead 2 was deposited soon
after bead 1; in fact, bead 1 was at 1000 F when bead 2 was deposited.
As a result, more of bead 1 was heated above the critical than in Fig.
147(c). In Fig. 147(f) bead 2 was deposited immediately after bead 1
which has not cooled down below the critical, say 1700 F. The grain size
of bead 1 therefore was not refined by being reheated above the critical.

We see that the time between beads affects the extent to which the
grain size is refined. Depositing beads one immediately after the other
may result in no grain refinement of the weld metal. Allowing previous
beads to cool to room temperature before depositing the next bead will
yield less grain refinement than depositing the next bead while the preceding one is hot but below the critical. The significance of refining sucessive
weld beads as completely as possible is reflected in notch-impact value.
Tensile values are little, if any, affected by the degree to which successive
beads are refined. High degree of grain refinement always is favorable
for high notch-impact value of weld metal, particularly at low temperatures.

Comparing bare with covered electrodes on the basis of degree
of grain refinement of weld metal, we find that bare electrodes usually
deposit at lower arc energies than covered (amp $\times$ volts; arc voltage is
usually about 18 for bare, 25-35 for covered); as a result the covered
electrode produces a wider heat-affected zone (region heated to at least
the critical) than bare electrodes. Furthermore, the slag from a covered
electrode reduces the cooling rate of the weld bead so that the beads are
at higher interpass temperatures than beads from bare electrodes when
the next bead is deposited. In addition, the bare electrode metal generally
has lower carbon and manganese contents than metal deposited by covered
electrodes. The higher critical ranges associated with the lower C and Mn
contents also favor small heat-affected zones in beads from bare electrodes,
although the high nitrogen content of bare electrode metal (0.10–0.15%
N_2) offsets the effect somewhat. Whether the difference in inclusion content between the two types of weld metal affects the critical range through

the nucleating influence of inclusions is doubtful.

It is a rule that the smaller the initial grain size the smaller is the grain size after reheating above the critical and cooling below it again. Small beads generally exhibit smaller dendrites than large beads, because the dendrites cannot grow so far in a small bead as in a large. Also, a small bead cools more rapidly, which accentuates the nucleating effect of attempting to undercool below the equilibrium freezing range. Since the small bead has smaller grains to start with, it will have finer grains, after being reheated above the critical, than the large bead. In addition, the heat-affected zone created by the second bead will extend to a greater distance through the small bead than through the large bead. However, the small bead cools more rapidly than the large and may not be at so high an interpass temperature when the second bead is deposited.

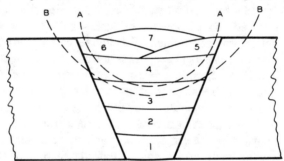

Fig. 149 — Limits of heat-affected zones produced by last bead deposited.

It is often desirable in a multi-layer weld to eliminate all coarse grain structure in the heated base metal. After the first six beads in Fig. 149 have been deposited there will be coarse grain structure in the base metal only close to beads 5 and 6, assuming that the successive beads have raised the temperature of the coarse zone created by the preceding bead above the critical range. If the size of the last bead and the temperature of the joint as a whole are such that the limit of the zone heated above the critical by bead 7 is A-A, the coarse zones from beads 5 and 6 will not be refined, and the joint will not have the highest notch-impact value. There will be coarse structure at the notch represented by the toe of the weld. Therefore, the last bead should be deposited with sufficient energy (taking into account preheat, the time interval between beads 5 and 6 and 7, and the size of the bead 7) to spread the critical zone to B-B. A common characteristic of weld metal, related to its low carbon content, is that it is not so likely to become coarse grained; i.e., develop a Widmanstätten structure. The structure of beads 5 and 6 will not be significantly coarsened by the heavy bead 7 that may be necessary to create the desired grain-refining effect.

Circumstances sometimes arise in the making of a multi-layer weld when the operation must be suspended prematurely, perhaps overnight because of problems in scheduling qualified welders. When the steel is being welded with an interpass temperature above a specified minimum, questions naturally are asked about the effects of interrupting the normal welding procedure. For example, can the weldment be permitted to cool to room temperature, or must the minimum interpass temperature be maintained? This is a difficult question to answer when the steel is one which also requires a postweld heat treatment immediately after welding. The matter of interrupted welding and heat treating procedures in the fabrication of chromium-molybdenum steel piping was studied by the AWS Committee on Piping and Tubing some time ago, and their recommendations are contained in the Committee Report identified as D10.8, *Welding of Chromium-Molybdenum Steel Piping* (Section 6). Their report defines the important metallurgical and mechanical factors to be considered in the thermal cycles when fabricating a tubular weldment of hardenable steel, and presents these general recommendations:

1. The heat cycle may be safely interrupted for the nominal chromium-molybdenum grades of less than 2.5% chromium, welded under normal conditions of fabrication and erection using low-hydrogen electrodes.

2. The heating cycle may be safely interrupted in the chromium-molybdenum grades of 2.5% or more chromium in wall thicknesses under one inch, provided they are welded under controlled procedures using low-hydrogen electrodes. In wall thicknesses one inch and over, it is recommended that these grades be completely welded and postweld heat treated before interruption or, alternatively, that the weld joint be given a short time tempering treatment at 1200 to 1300 F before interruption of the cycle.

3. For wall thickness under 1 in., where an interrupted procedure is followed, the weld deposit prior to interruption should never be less than $\frac{1}{3}$ the wall thickness or two layers, whichever is greater. For very thick pipe, a minimum, such as $\frac{3}{4}$ in. weld thickness, may be specified.

The Committee report emphasized, however, that specific job conditions deserved consideration in deciding upon the manner in which the welding would be interrupted, and that the above general recommendations should not be applied indiscriminately.

In oxygen cutting medium-carbon steels, it may be necessary to prevent cracks. Either preheating or postheating is resorted to. Instead of preheating the entire plate it is customary to precede the cutting torch by a preheating flame which preheats the line of the cut to the desired extent. The effects of preheating in this operation are identical with those discussed earlier in this section.

When postheating is resorted to, a large multi-tip torch follows directly behind the cutting torch. The postheating torch does not affect heating rates in front of the cutting torch, which often are inconsequential except for tool steels and similar materials. The postheating torch, however, prevents rapid cooling by maintaining the cut at a high temperature for some time. By increasing the heat input of the operation, postheating reduces the cooling rate and, if adequate, prevents hard zones of martensite. Any other effect of postheating is immaterial. Indeed, there is no essential difference between postheat and preheat, provided the postheating is applied before the part has cooled to room temperature; if the part has cooled, martensite may have formed with accompanying cracks, which postheating is helpless to correct.

POSTWELD HEAT TREATMENTS

Postweld heating of an entire weldment, or only a localized portion, may be done to achieve one or more of the following:

1. Relieve Stresses
2. Improve Toughness
3. Increase Strength
4. Improve Corrosion Resistance
5. Remove Cold Work

A variety of thermal treatments have been developed to accomplish these changes and have been termed (1) *stress-relief heat treatment,* (2) *annealing,* (3) *normalizing,* (4) *hardening,* (5) *quenching and tempering,* (6) *austempering, and* (7) *martempering.* The use of these terms always has been quite loose, and for this reason misunderstandings have arisen. Nevertheless, each of these terms has a fairly definite meaning as we shall soon point out. In general, the difference in the heat-treating operations are in the temperatures employed and/or the method of cooling. Temperatures for stress-relief heat treatment are below the critical range of the steel, whereas temperatures for annealing, normalizing, and hardening are always above the critical range. There is perhaps one exception to this; a softening treatment is sometimes carried out just below the critical range, and it is referred to as a *sub-critical anneal,* or a *temper-*

ing anneal. While the effects of different heat treatments are overlapping, that is, two different treatments may be used to accomplish the same purpose, each has been developed to serve a specific purpose primarily. The selection of the proper heat treatment requires the consideration of a number of factors including type of steel, conditions of stress arising from welding, microstructure in the heat-affected zones, and properties required in the material to perform satisfactorily in service.

STRESS-RELIEF HEAT TREATMENT

In the *AWS Definitions — Welding and Cutting,* stress-relief heat treatment is the uniform heating of a structure to a suitable temperature below the critical range of the base metal, followed by uniform cooling. A note also appears which states that terms such as annealing and normalizing are misnomers for this application. To be sure, shrinkage stresses, or, as they are called, residual stresses due to welding are relieved by annealing and normalizing, but these treatments involve changes in grain structure and particularly dimensional changes that may be injurious to the part. Heat treatment within the critical range is usually undesirable. Consequently, stress-relief heat treatment is performed below the critical range in most cases.

The decision to stress relieve a weldment often is guided by (or decided by) the requirements of the *ASME Boiler* and *Pressure Vessel Code.* The rules published under this code define the conditions of material, composition, thickness, and end use under which the welded vessel must be given a postweld heat treatment. The ASME rules have been adopted by many municipalities, states, foreign countries, and insurers who are concerned with public safety. Consequently, these rules have been used by many engineers for guidance in planning the fabrication of noncode weldments.

The temperatures used for stress-relief heat treatment may be in the range of 900 to 1250 F, which is below the critical range on heating of the plain-carbon and low-alloy steels joined by welding.

The time at temperature in stress relieving carbon steel is customarily one hour per inch of thickness, although longer times are required at 1000 F than at 1100 F for the same degree of stress relief. Stress relief is often required for preheated parts. With complicated structures, or with steels having a pronounced tendency toward cracking, it is often essential that the welded part be placed at once in the stress-relieving furnace without cooling from the preheat temperature.

Although the stress-relief treatment is expected only to relieve stresses, and not necessarily to produce any changes in the microstructure of the steel, the general effects of a stress-relief heat treatment are as follows:

1. Recovery
2. Relaxation
3. Tempering or drawing (removal of hard zones)
4. Recrystallization
5. Spheroidizing

The first effect is universal; the second effect is achieved when the stress-relief heat treatment is conducted at a sufficiently high temperature for an adequate length of time; the third effect is obtained only if hard zones have formed as a result of welding, and the last two effects have minor significance for welding.

Welded structures have residual stresses near the yield strength whether or not there was external restraint during welding. This fact was pointed out in Chapter 11. These stresses can cause a number of difficulties in a weldment. The likelihood that any of these difficulties will occur is dependent, of course, upon the combination of steel composition, welding process, weldment design, service conditions, etc. Relief of stresses, however, can result in the following improvements:

1. Minimized susceptibility to fracture development particularly under conditions which call for high notch toughness
2. Improved dimensional stability
3. Increased resistance to corrosion, especially stress-corrosion cracking

How important is it that residual stresses and reaction stresses be removed from weldments? Is it necessary to reduce these stresses to zero, and is this stress-free condition actually possible to achieve in a weldment? These are just a few of the questions that can be asked about this matter of stress relieving. We know from our study of the mechanical properties of metals in Chapter 6 that under conditions of multiaxial stress, high rate of loading (impact), and low temperature, metals do not easily deform (flow plastically). Instead, they tend to fracture in a brittle manner with very little deformation. Weldments contain multiaxial stresses in the vicinity of as-welded joints from the shrinkage which occurs as a result of welding. These stresses are the first major factor which should be considered when analyzing the likelihood of brittle fracture. The other factors include the inherent toughness of the steel, the occurrence of notches in the weldment design, the nature of additional stresses developed by service loads, and the temperatures at which the service loads are imposed. We have yet to develop practical formulas for calculating the quantitative importance of these factors in terms of brittle failure possibility. Therefore, the decision to relieve stresses in a weldment by heat treatment generally is based upon experience and is only guided by the data from tests which attempt to evaluate notch toughness, notch acuteness, residual stress level, and so forth.

Dimensional stability is a weldment feature which is directly affected by any stresses locked up in the structure. If a weldment, for example an engine base, is machined in the as-welded condition, the machining operation removes metal which is under residual stress, thus creating redistribution of stress and causing distortion. The machinist cannot be certain he is machining to the correct dimensions because the weldment continues to distort as he removes metal. Relief of stresses in the weldment prior to machining allows the unit to remain stable in form so that dimensions once machined remain fixed. To what low level must the stresses be relieved to achieve dimensional stability? The permissible stress level depends primarily upon the amount of metal to be removed, its location with respect to the areas of residual stress and reaction stress, and the tolerances permitted in the final dimensions. Again, no formulas for quantitative analysis have been developed and so we must depend upon experience.

Many metals and alloys are susceptible to stress-corrosion cracking. Steel is not an exception. This type of corrosion failure has been termed "caustic embrittlement" in carbon steel. A description of the conditions which promote stress-corrosion cracking was given in Chapter 6. Either a change in the nature of the corrosive environment or a reduction of the stress will eliminate stress-corrosion cracking. Often, the high-level residual stresses in the vicinity of weld joints- are responsible for exceeding the threshold of cracking conditions, and a reduction in these stresses alone by stress-relief heat treatment is sufficient to avoid the difficulty.

Often there exists cold work in a weldment of which the engineer is not aware. This condition may have been produced by some unexpected operation, like cold bending or hammering into alignment, or possibly by a more subtle action such as permanent deformation at a relatively low temperature by shrinkage stresses. Permanent deformation below 850 or 1000 F is accompanied by slip lines in the microstructure. The slip planes represent planes in the grains of steel which have moved over each other (see Chapter 6). Slip due to permanent deformation at higher temperatures occurs in the same way but the slipped planes instantaneously straighten out and lose all traces of curvature involved in the slip.

Let us imagine that the welded structure that we are about to stress relieve contains residual stresses, tensile and compressive, of all magnitudes up to the yield strength, and also has some cold-worked crystals with slip lines. Our welded structure is in a condition similar to the wheel with a shrunk-on tire in Fig. 150, which, in turn, resembles a girth weld joining a head to a drum. The tangential shrinkage stresses are tensile at the circumference, compressive toward the center. The mechanism of thermal stress relief will include the effects mentioned earlier whether the weldment is of carbon or alloy steel.

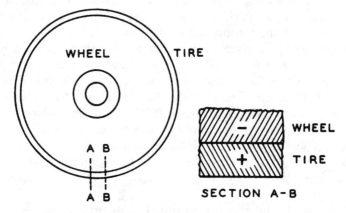

Fig. 150 — Shrinkage stresses in a shrunk-on tire. Compressive stress in the wheel, tensile stress in the tire.

Recovery

The first effect that is to be found as we start to raise the temperature for a stress-relieving treatment is recovery. The temperature is raised uniformly in order to keep all parts of the structure as nearly as possible at the same temperature at all times to prevent thermal stresses, Fig. 129(a). As the temperature is raised through the first 400 F or so, there is no observable change in grain structure, yet the shrinkage stresses decrease a little. The decrease is due to the phenomenon called recovery. It is a general rule that internal stresses in a material decrease when the temperature is raised.

The decrease in steel at 400 F is shown in Fig. 151, and cannot be due to a decrease in yield strength for it is higher in steel at 400 F (Fig. 128) than at room temperature. Recovery also causes changes in magnetic and electrical properties, suggesting that its effect on internal stresses is related to some obscure movements among the electrons and atoms of steel as its temperature is raised.

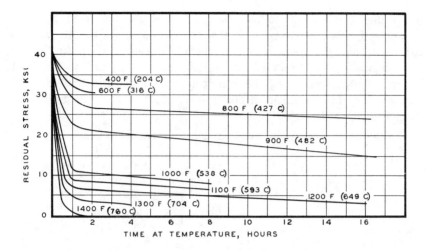

Fig. 151 — Influence of temperature and time on relieving stress.

This steel contained 0.21% carbon and 1.44% manganese. The tensile properties were: 70 ksi UTS, 35 ksi proportional limit, 36% elongation, and 73% reduction of area. Stress is relieved a small amount at 400 F, and is completely removed after some time at 1400 F. Stress is reduced first by the recovery phenomenon, and then by permanent yielding. The latter is caused first by the reduction of yield strength at elevated temperature, and second by creep under the prolonged loading at elevated temperature.

However, the release of residual stresses at the lower temperatures is not adequate and the temperature must be raised still higher. At all temperatures an increase in time at temperature reduces the stress still further, but the major release of residual stresses occurs during the first hour.

Relaxation

Upon raising the temperature of the weldment to 1200 F or higher we find that relaxation occurs and shrinkage stresses are relieved swiftly and completely, Fig. 151. The change during relaxation is shown in Fig. 152. A bar of steel is stretched to the yield stress in tension at room temperature, Fig. 152(A), upon welding it into a frame. The atoms stretch apart parallel to the load and move close together perpendicular to the stress, which indeed is the basic meaning of stress — a movement of the atoms to positions capable of withstanding load. At 1200 F, the short time yield strength is only a small fraction of the yield strength at room temperature. That is to say, the atoms no longer can withstand the stress, and return closer and closer to the equidistant positions occupied by atoms in a crystal under no stress. Now that the yield strength has fallen below the stress imposed upon the metal, the metal will flow plastically until the stress (whether compression or tension) is reduced to the yield strength of the metal at 1200 F. The center bar lengthens, and the outer bars shorten. The dimensional changes are slight and the distortions are magnified in Fig. 152(A).

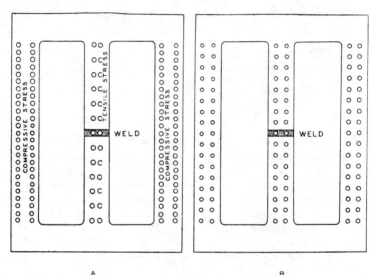

A   B

Fig. 152 — Stress-relief heat treatment removes residual stresses by permitting the atoms (open circles) to creep back to equidistant positions.

In (A) "as-welded," the atoms in the outer arms are compressed together vertically; the atoms in the inside arm are drawn apart vertically. That is, the outer arms are in compression, the inner arm in tension as a result of welding the inner arm. After stress-relief heat treatment at an adequate temperature for a sufficient time, the atoms would be neither pressed together nor drawn apart in any of the three arms as shown in (B). The residual or shrinkage stresses have been "relieved."

The stress decreases until the atoms no longer yield. While the atoms of steel can withstand stress up to the yield value indefinitely at room temperature, at 1200 F the atoms may be able to withstand considerable stress without yielding if the stress is applied and the temperature is maintained for only a short time. More precisely stated, the atoms move continuously under all stresses. The motion is so slow and minute at room temperature as to be undetectable after hundreds of years, Fig. 153, but at 1200 F the motion of the atoms is not necessarily of the type we have considered, but may involve obscure motions at the grain boundaries. Both types of motion constitute flow or creep of the metal.

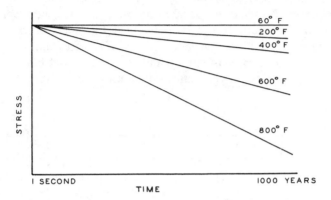

Fig. 153 — Schematic diagram (log-log plot) showing decrease in residual stress with time at different temperatures (relaxation assuming no external load).

Relaxation, therefore, is a form of creep. The distortions created by relaxation or stress relief in a welded structure are difficult to compute, but generally are far smaller than the distortions created by machining parts not stress relieved, because in machining we generally remove the most highly stressed material.

How can we favor stress relief? Resistance to relaxation or creep should be low. Figure 151 shows that the most effective method of favoring stress relief is to raise the temperature. The extent to which the temperature may be raised is governed by permissible distortion due to unsupported mass. Furthermore, it is seldom advisable to raise the temperature into the critical range. Increase in time also favors stress relief. It is a general rule that coarse grain size improves resistance to creep above 800 F, but the improvement exerts no detectable influence on stress relief at 1100 or 1200 F. The higher the initial residual stress, the higher is the stress after stress relief at a given temperature for a given time, owing to the progressive strengthening involved in the greater release of stress by strain. This strain may be looked upon as cold work during stress relief, which naturally strengthens the crystals. Since nearly all types of welds in a given steel have maximum residual stresses near the yield strength, no deduction in time of stress relief can be made solely on the basis of apparent absence of restraint during welding.

Structures that are made of steels designed to have exceptional resistance to creep at elevated temperatures will relax less rapidly than mild
steel. The creep-resistant steels, for example, 0.20% C and 0.5% Mo,
require higher temperature or longer time at temperature for a given
degree of stress relief than unalloyed steel. Figure 154 illustrates the
yield strengths of five steels which vary in alloy content from carbon
steel to high-alloy steel. It will be noted that the steels of greater alloy
content maintain a higher yield strength with increasing temperature.
Type 316, which is an austenitic stainless steel, is outstanding in this
group for retaining good yield strength even above 1200 F.

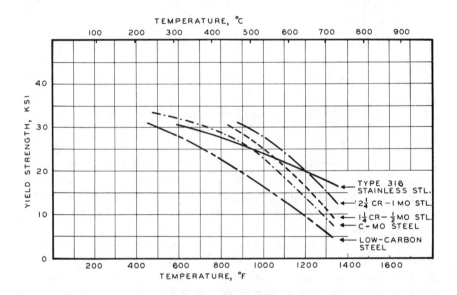

Fig. 154 — Yield strengths for five steels of varying alloy content over
a range of temperatures.

A second bead relieves the residual stresses in the underlying
bead, but creates new residual stresses. Consequently, multi-pass welds
have no lower residual stresses than single-pass welds and require stress
relief to the same extent. Besides becoming more complicated as the
thickness is increased, residual stresses in thicker parts require longer
time for relief than in thinner parts because the surface of the part is the
first to reach the temperature of the furnace. More time elapses before
the centers of thick sections reach furnace temperature than do the
centers of thin sections.

Tempering or Drawing (Softening)

Raising the temperature of quenched steel to any temperature below the critical range is called tempering or drawing. The heat-affected zone close to welds made without preheat or with insufficient preheat in medium-carbon and many other high-tensile steels cools so rapidly as to be quenched or hardened. While the quenched zone was above its critical range during welding, it consisted of austenite containing ten times as much carbon in solid solution as is soluble at room temperature. During quenching the austenite changes largely to martensite: the body-centered tetragonal crystalline form of steel. The carbon in the martensite is believed to exist as either carbon atoms or tiny crystals of iron carbide (or carbides containing alloying elements in alloy steels) which are believed to account for the great hardness of martensite compared with any other state of a steel.

When the temperature is raised, the zone containing martensite undergoes three changes:

1. Martensite changes to ferrite (body-centered *cubic* crystals) with the precipitation of fine carbide crystals from the supersaturated tetragonal crystal lattice.
2. Any austenite that has not changed to martensite during quenching changes to ferrite and carbide.
3. The minute crystals of carbides in the martensite and the larger crystals of carbide in other constituents, such as fine pearlite, increase in size.

The temperatures at which changes 1 and 2 occur are not known precisely. In plain-carbon steels with about 0.7% C change 1 occurs at 300 F, change 2 at 450 F. Small amounts of austenite can be retained on quenching plain-carbon steels of at least 0.4% C but only by carefully controlled quenching. Austenite is retained with lower carbon contents if alloying elements are present. The growth in size of carbide particles is continuous as the temperature is raised. Change 3 seems to account for the major drop in hardness on tempering; that is, the hardness of martensitic steel depends upon a fine dispersion of carbide particles on each crystal plane, which hinders slip and thus raises hardness while reducing ductility. Reheating coarsens the carbide particles and reduces their number, thus reducing hardness.

The hardness after tempering or drawing depends primarily on the tempering temperature. Time at temperature is of secondary importance. The influence of the time factor is illustrated in Fig. 155. After one minute at 1200 F, the hardness at room temperature drops from 56 to 27

Rockwell C for the quenched 0.35% C steel.

After an hour at 1200 F, the hardness has dropped to 18 C. The reduction in hardness caused by stress-relief heat treatment of a welded medium-carbon steel containing hard zones depends also upon the time of treatment. The greatest reduction in hardness as well as in residual stresses occurs in the first few minutes. For maximum effectiveness, prolonging the treatment is essential. The hardness after the first few seconds at 1200 F is nearly the same whether the steel consisted initially of martensite, bainite, or fine pearlite.

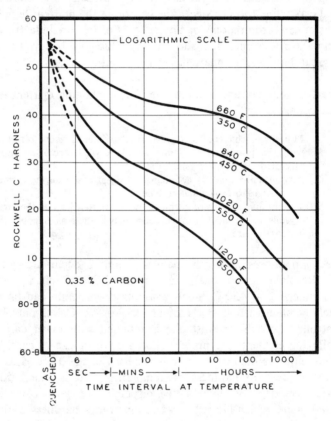

Fig. 155 — The effect of time interval at four tempering temperatures on the softening of quenched 0.35 percent carbon steel. (Bain)

Concurrent with the softening during tempering there is a rise in ductility, as revealed in the static tensile test, and a decrease in tensile strength. Notch-impact values and other measures of toughness, however, often are minimum after tempering at 400 to 700 F, rising to high values above 800 F. The reduction in notch toughness is sometimes attributed to internal stresses created by the expansion of retained austenite during its decomposition. Welded parts containing hard zones should not be heat treated at 400 to 700 F. The softening of plain-carbon steel is continuous as the tempering temperature is raised, because the main process is the agglomeration and growth of carbide particles. When carbide-forming elements are added to the steel, it may become harder instead of softer as the tempering temperature is raised in some ranges, Fig. 156. The 5% Cr–0.5% Mo steel with 0.35% C is harder after tempering at 900 F than after tempering at 700 F. The increase is called *secondary hardening* and is due to the formation of minute crystals of a second compound after the iron carbide has coalesced to a degree no longer very effective as a hardener. The minute crystals of alloy carbide form at elevated temperatures which provide the necessary opportunity for diffusion. Secondary hardening extends its influence through the alloying elements to the temperatures of stress-relief heat treatments, as Fig. 156 shows. It is to

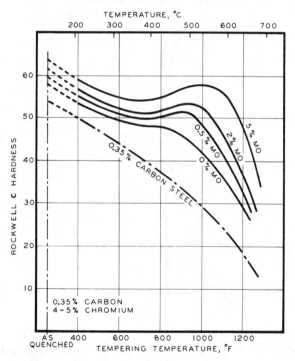

Fig. 156 — The softening, with increasing temperature, of 5% chromium steels containing 0.35% carbon and varying molybdenum contents. Lower curve (broken) represents 0.35% carbon steel without Cr or Mo.

their hardness as well as their creep resistance that are due the extra precautions in stress relieving some of the alloy steels.

Tempering is important not only in stress-relief heat treatment of welded parts containing hard zones, but in multi-layer welding of medium-carbon and other strongly hardening steels as well. In Fig. 157(a) bead 1 has created a hard zone. Bead 2 likewise has created a hard zone by raising the temperature of the base metal close to the weld above the critical range and allowing it to cool rapidly. If the heat in bead 2 is sufficient to raise the entire hard zone created by bead 1 above 500 F (but not above the critical range, of course), the zone will be considerably

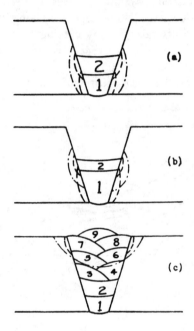

Fig. 157 — Tempering of hard zones by heat from a subsequently deposited bead.
— — — — Boundary of hard zone
— – — – — Boundary of zone heated to at least 500 F during welding

softer and devoid of untempered martensite and austenite. Whether its notch-impact strength will be raised is problematical. In general, however, it may be said that the tempered zone will be considerably tougher than the untempered zone. If bead 2 had been deposited directly after bead 1, it is possible that the potential hard zone of bead 1 would be caught before it formed. That is, the zone that would have become hard on further cooling, would be prevented from further cooling by the second bead before martensite began to form. The hard zone might then consist of bainite or fine pearlite instead of martensite, depending on the precise temperature distributions prevailing. Furthermore, the heat from bead 1 might retard the cooling rates in bead 2 and so prevent hard zones near it. Hard zones, it will be realized, are within the control of the welder to some extent.

In Fig. 157(b), bead 2 was deposited after bead 1 cooled and is too small to bring the entire hard zone of bead 1 above, say 200 to 300 F. Significant tempering has failed to occur and the hard zone is there to stay, for it is too much to expect that later beads can succeed where the second has failed. With proper welding, however, it is possible to temper the hard zones of every bead in a multi-layer weld, Fig. 157(c).

Recrystallization

Cold work or permanent deformation below the recrystallization range breaks each perfect crystal into a large number of fragments due to slip. These fragments change into new grains with undistorted crystal lattices when the temperature is raised to the recrystallization range. The appearance of the new grain among the old grains containing slip lines is known as recrystallization, as we learned in Chapter 5. The new grains appear first as minute crystals usually at the grain boundaries of the cold-worked grains. As the temperature is maintained or increased, the minute crystals grow. Eventually all the old crystals with slip lines have been absorbed by the new crystals, which are free from slip lines, and recrystallization is complete.

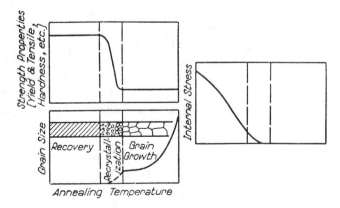

Fig. 158 — Schematic representation of recovery, recrystallization and grain growth. (Mehl and Sachs)

Recrystallization transforms the distorted fragments, which are the source of internal stresses, to new, undistorted crystals free from internal stress. Recovery, Fig. 158, partly removes residual stresses; recrystallization completes their removal. The temperature at which recrystallization occurs in a given metal is lowered by increasing the time at temperature, and by increasing the degree of prior cold work. There is no single recrystallization temperature for a given metal. For iron and steel, the lowest temperature at which recrystallization has been observed is 840 F.

No recrystallization whatever occurs, however, if there is inadequate cold work. The cold work caused by the shrinkage of parts during cooling after welding generally is too slight to cause recrystallization during stress-relief heat treatment. Stress relief occurs, therefore, through recovery and particularly relaxation, rather than through recrystallization.

Spheroidizing

The process of creating carbides having the shape of spheres in the steel is called spheroidizing. If we start with pearlite we spheroidize by converting the plates of carbides to spheres. If we start with martensite or bainite, on the other hand, in which the minute carbides are approximately spherical initially (although on account of their extreme fineness we cannot be certain of their presence, let alone their size), spheroidizing consists simply of coalescing the particles and rendering them visible under the microscope. Martensite needles do not spheroidize.

The carbide in the heat-affected zone of welded low-carbon steel usually is present as pearlite. During stress-relief heat treatment we observe that the plates become less and less and angular, the carbide particles becoming more nearly spherical, Fig. 159. The longer the time at temperature and the higher the temperature, provided the critical range is not exceeded, the larger and more nearly spherical the carbides become.

The carbide in the heat-affected zone of welded medium-carbon steel is extremely finely divided, Fig. 159(c). As the temperature rises during stress-relief heat treatment, the carbides follow the general law of small particles in a metal. Carbon from the smaller particles enters solution to precipitate again on the larger. In this way, a few large spheroidal carbide particles replace a crowd of tiny spheroidal ones. Since the coarsely spheroidized condition generally is the softest and most ductile, the spheroidizing action of stress-relief heat treatment is desirable.

When the welded part is at 1200 F, steel has an appreciable solubility for several elements, particularly nitrogen. If the part is slowly cooled from the stress-relieving temperature there is an opportunity for the complete precipitation of these elements. With rapid cooling, on the other hand, nitrogen is retained in supersaturated solution at room temperature and the steel may have low ductility. Weld metal with high nitrogen content, such as bare electrode deposits, is particularly subject to embrittlement on rapid cooling from the temperature of stress-relief heat treatment. Rapid cooling after stress relieving is undesirable in any event to avoid shrinkage stresses due to the nonuniform distribution of temperature in any rapidly cooled object.

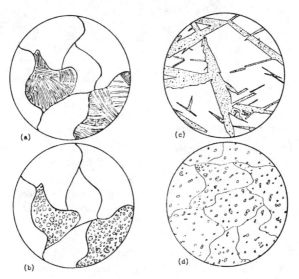

Fig. 159 — Spheroidization of carbide in pearlitic and martensitic steels.

(a) Pearlitic low-carbon steel before stress-relief heat treatment.
(b) During stress-relief heat treatment of the structure in (a) the plates of cementite in the pearlite tend to spheroidize.
(c) Needles of martensite in austenite, showing hypothetical spheroids of carbide in the needles.
(d) During stress-relief heat treatment of the structure in (c) spheroidal carbide particles tend to grow.

In these drawings, the degree of spheroidization is exaggerated. The usual stress-relief heat treatment does little more than round off the corners of the cementite plates in the pearlite.

The spheroidizing of carbide near a welded joint is a process that begins when the weld is being made, Fig. 160. The pearlite in the zone that is heated short of the critical range is more or less spheroidized depending on the length of time it has remained close to the lower temperature of the critical range. Once the pearlite is heated into the critical range the carbide in the pearlite dissolves in the austenite. In very rapid welding processes, such as spot welding, the carbide may not remain in the critical range sufficiently long to dissolve completely in the austenite. Some spheroids may be observed, therefore, even in the zone that has

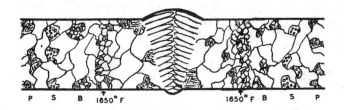

Fig. 160 — Sketch showing the zone in which pearlite tends to become spheroidized in the welding of mild steel.

B — Structure of the zone heated above the lower critical but below the upper critical temperature during welding.

S — Structure of zone heated just below the critical range during welding. The cementite in the pearlite has spheroidized.

P — Structure of the zone heated to a maximum temperature during welding that was 200 degrees F or more below the lower critical. No spheroidizing has occurred, and the structure is identical with the unwelded base metal, namely, ferrite plus pearlite.

been heated in the critical range. During stress-relief heat treatment, the spheroidization begun during welding is extended to the steel throughout the welded part. All pearlite being spheroidized to some extent by stress-relief heat treatment, the outline of the heat-affected zone in the macrostructure of a stress-relieved weld is far less sharp than in the macrostructure before heat treatment. Unlike preheating, however, stress-relief heat treatment has no effect on the width of the heat-affected zone.

Although local stress relief has the same effect in softening hard zones as placing the entire structure in the furnace, it may not always reduce residual stresses. Local stress relief is commonly used for high-pressure piping. Raising the temperature of the joint to 1200 F replaces the nonuniformly distributed shrinkage stresses in the immediate vicinity of the weld with more uniformly distributed reaction stresses. It is important that the deformation necessary during cooling of the wide heated zone be absorbed without causing cracks or endangering supports. In most structures, the severe shrinkage strains involved in local stress relief preclude its use. Instead of relieving stresses, the cycle of local heating and cooling often intensifies them.

ANNEALING

If we wish to soften a welded steel as much as possible and to create a uniformly fine-grained structure throughout, we *full-anneal* it. Annealing, or full-annealing as it is properly called, consists of heating the part 50 to 100 F above the critical temperature range; that is, the range in which ferrite changes to austenite. For 0.20% C steel the full annealing temperature is 1560 F plus 50 F = 1610 F. This temperature is held one hour for each inch of section of the heaviest parts being treated. Ordinarily, the parts are cooled in the furnace or in some substance yielding a slow rate of cooling, such as ashes. By using controlled rates of slow cooling it is possible to vary the coarseness of the lamellar pearlite formed or the degree of spheroidization.

Annealing from temperatures above the critical range is seldom applied to welded parts for the high temperatures involved would often cause excessive distortion in the welded part despite extensive means of support in the furnace. Where the shape of the weldment is self-supporting, annealing from temperatures above the critical range can be applied without distortion difficulties.

A second problem which arises in annealing because of the high temperatures and long soaking and cooling cycles is that of decarburization. The carbon is removed from the surface of the weldment by free oxygen, carbon dioxide, or water vapor in the heat-treating atmosphere. To guard against carbon removal, a low free-oxygen atmosphere is maintained by suitable adjustments. Decarburization is inappreciable at the lower temperatures employed for stress relieving.

NORMALIZING

Normalizing is a heat treatment somewhat similar to annealing and is frequently employed in treating steel, both the plate metal prior to welding and the finished weldment. Normalizing involves heating the steel approximately 100 F above its critical range to transform the structure to austenite, followed by cooling in still air. Whereas annealing with its very slow furnace cooling produces a carbide structure of coarse lamellar pearlite or spheroidized carbide, normalizing with its air-cooling treatment creates a finer lamellar pearlite in most steels which, although slightly harder, is quite satisfactory for service. A normalizing treatment may be used to (1) reduce stresses from cold working or welding, (2) remove hardened zones adjacent to the weld, (3) create a more uniform and desirable microstructure in both the weld metal and the base metal, and (4) refine (by recrystallization) any coarse structure which may have been developed in the steel through hot working or forming operations carried out at a very high temperature, perhaps above 1900 F.

HARDENING

Hardening is accomplished by heating the steel 50 to 100 F above the critical range and then cooling at a rate which exceeds the critical cooling rate of the steel. This may involve quenching in water, oil, or air, depending upon the hardenability of the particular steel being treated. Above the critical range, the structure of the steel transforms to austenite (grains of gamma iron with carbon in solid solution). When. cooled to room temperature at a rate exceeding the critical cooling rate the structure of austenite transforms to martensite, which is the hard structural condition described in Chapter 9. Hardening frequently occurs in the heat-affected zone of the base metal where it is often considered an undesirable condition. Nevertheless, we make much use of the hardening treatment in preparing cutting and forming tools, treating surfaces to improve wear resistance, and so forth.

While the "Ac_1" and "Ac_3" temperatures for many steels can be found in handbooks, it is sometimes necessary to estimate the temperature above which a steel of unusual composition must be heated to secure a completely austenitized structure preparatory to hardening. The following formula has been shown to be reasonably close in predicting this minimum austenitizing temperature:

$$A_f \text{ (deg F)} = 1570 - 323 \text{ (\% C)} - 25 \text{ (\% Mn)} + 80 \text{ (\% Si)} - 32 \text{ (\% Ni)} - 3 \text{ (\% Cr)}$$

The originator, Grange, proposed that the formula be confined to steels containing 0.3 to 0.6% C, 0 to 2% Mn, 0 to 1% Si, 0 to 3.5% Ni, 0 to 1.5% Cr, and 0 to 0.5% Mo. The actual austenitizing temperature used for a weldment should exceed the calculated temperature by at least 50 F.

Cooling to accomplish hardening often involves quenching in a liquid. This is a very important part of the treatment since cracking can result from improper quenching practice. Quenching red-hot steel in a liquid can involve three distinct stages which determine the rate of heat flow from the metal to the liquid. When a quenchant with a relatively low boiling point, like water, is employed, the red hot steel upon entry into the liquid becomes quickly surrounded by a blanket of vapor. This blanket tends to slow down the transfer of heat. As the surface of the workpiece cools to some extent the blanket decreases in thickness until finally it ruptures allowing the liquid to actually contact the steel where it may boil vigorously. Now the cooling rate is markedly increased because heat is carried away by vaporization of the water, by convection, and by radiation. When boiling stops, cooling continues at a much slower rate mainly through convection. These three stages occur during the use of almost all quenching media, but with each stage of different duration depending upon the nature of each quenchant. When salt baths are used for quenching, no vapor blanket forms upon immersion. Therefore, the first stage is virtually eliminated. Cooling starts rapidly, but does not reach a very high rate because of the absence of boiling and the smaller temperature difference between workpiece and molten quenchant. With oil quenching, the second stage is shortened because of the higher boiling point of most oils. With a brine solution, the initial vapor blanket stage is almost eliminated by the nucleating effect of the salt. Consequently, a very rapid cooling rate is experienced almost immediately. While it may seem at first glance that a bath of liquid air would be a drastic quenchant, a piece of red-hot steel will cool at a slower rate in this low-temperature liquid than the same piece in tap water. The explanation is found in the duration of the first stage of quenching. Liquified gases have low boiling points and low specific heats, and they form a long lasting vapor barrier around the hot workpiece that markedly reduces heat flow.

QUENCHING (HARDENING) AND TEMPERING

By hardening and tempering, we can generally produce the best combination of mechanical properties of which a steel is capable. The steel is first hardened in the customary fashion; that is, heated and quenched to produce a martensitic structure. Then it is tempered or drawn, which involves reheating the steel to a particular temperature somewhere below the Ac_1 (1335 F), holding for a specified length of time, and allowing to cool to room temperature. The structure produced by reheating to temperatures ranging up to 600 F is often called tempered martensite because it is not too unlike the freshly quenched structure. The structure obtained at temperatures above 600 to 900 F generally is called troostite or possibly secondary troostite. Troostite etches rapidly and appears very dark. The structure consists of a very fine aggregate of ferrite grains and cementite particles. Above 900 to 1300 F the structure that forms is called sorbite. There is no sharp point of demarkation between troostite and sorbite. In the sorbitic structure the carbide particles have grown so that the structure possesses a granular appearance. Examination under the microscope at high magnifications will reveal small globular carbides in a matrix of ferrite. As the tempering temperature is increased, the tensile strength, yield strength, and hardness of the steel will decrease, while the toughness and ductility generally increase.

AUSTEMPERING

Austempering is a heat treatment sometimes applied to relatively thin or small sections of hardenable steels for the purpose of securing a structure of bainite. By producing this structure we obtain reasonable ductility at high hardness levels without resorting to a combination treatment of hardening and tempering. Further claims are made for better properties with the bainite structure than found with a tempered martensite or troostite. Thin sections of steel are treated more easily because all portions of the steel mass must be cooled at a rate exceeding the critical cooling rate during the treatment. The first step is to heat the steel 50 to 100 F above its critical range to form a structure of austenite. Then the steel is quenched rapidly (faster than the critical cooling rate) to a temperature somewhere above the M_s point (see Fig. 119, Chapter 9) and is held at this temperature for a period of time. Thus the transformation of austenite is allowed to proceed under isothermal conditions. The cooling and isothermal treatment usually is accomplished by quenching and holding in a molten salt bath or lead pot.

A further variation of austempering is known as *ausforming*. This treatment sometimes can be applied to highly hardenable alloy steels to gain additional strength. The steel is austenitized by heating above the critical range and then cooled to the metastable austenite "bay" that exists in the I-T diagram just above the M_s temperature. Instead of allowing the steel to remain here for isothermal transformation to bainite (as in the case of austempering), the steel article is subjected to plastic deformation and then quenched to martensite. Of course, deformation by rolling or pressing is not often possible on weldments, and therefore, ausforming seldom is carried out. However, it is worthwhile to know that should the metastable austenite be deformed approximately 50 to 95%, the strength of the final martensite structure can display a 5 to 10% increase in tensile and yield strengths. The effectiveness of ausforming is determined by the amount of cold work retained by the austenite as it undergoes transformation to martensite. Consequently, greater deformation of the austenite at the lowest possible temperature (without forming bainite) produces increased strength. Tensile strengths ranging as high as 450 ksi have been achieved through ausforming.

MARTEMPERING

Martempering is a heat treatment applied to steels of high hardenability which are prone to quench cracking. During the process, the piece of steel is first austenitized by heating to a temperature 50 to 100 F above the critical range. The piece then is quenched into a molten salt bath or lead pot which is held at a temperature just above the M_s point of the steel being treated. The piece is held here until the temperature throughout the mass becomes uniform; before transformation to bainite commences, the piece is withdrawn from the bath and cooled slowly through the martensite transformation range. Martensite forms uniformly throughout the section. The likelihood of cracking is markedly reduced because stresses created by temperature gradients are virtually absent.

CARBURIZING AND DECARBURIZING TREATMENTS

Although carburizing the surface of steel to produce a high-carbon case — which can develop high hardness and great wear resistance — has been practiced for many years, only recently has much thought been given to changing the carbon content and distribution in steel employed in weldments. Briefly, carbon can be introduced into the surface of steel, and also removed from the surface, by holding the steel at a high temperature in a suitable environment. If held at a high temperature for a suitable period of time, a concentration of carbon at a surface will diffuse inward to the lower-carbon interior and eventually will establish homogeneity. In general, the higher the temperature, the more rapid the diffusion of carbon atoms through the lattice of the iron. Whether the environment carburizes (adds carbon) or decarburizes (removes carbon) depends upon the nature of the atmosphere to which the heated steel is exposed; that is, the "carbon potential" of the atmosphere. The simplest technique for carburizing steel is to heat the piece in a sealed box or retort packed with charcoal (various compounds such as barium carbonate sometimes are included to speed up the carburizing action). When heated to temperatures above approximately 1400 F, the charcoal generates carbon monoxide gas which reacts with the surface of the steel and introduces carbon. Most commercial carburizing operations are conducted at a temperature of about 1700 F, and usually make use of a prepared or generated carbon-containing gas which is introduced into the chamber of a special furnace.

Decarburizing treatments appear to hold greater usefulness for weldments. These are performed with various oxygen-containing atmospheres (wet hydrogen, carbon dioxide, etc.). Again, by controlling time and temperature, a decarburized surface layer can be produced, or the carbon can be removed from the entire cross-section as described for the "open-coil decarburized steel" mentioned in Table 6 of Chapter 2. It has been proposed that pressure vessels of welded high-strength alloy steel might well be subjected to decarburization during heat treatment to provide a thin, low-carbon surface layer on the vessel. This surface layer is believed to be able to better withstand the adverse effects of stress raisers which frequently occur at the surface of the vessel. However, this treatment has been applied only to experimental vessels to date. Of course, decarburization of a layer at the surface of the section would reduce the strength of this portion. However, if more resistant to the initiation of brittle fracture, the surface layer would provide valuable assurance against unexpected failure under high stresses.

CURRENT PRACTICES FOR PREHEATING AND POSTWELD HEAT TREATMENT

Practical procedures for preheating and postweld heat treatment of specific types of carbon and alloy steels in weldments will be discussed in Chapters 14 and 15. However, some general remarks on practices presently used in industry may be helpful at this point. Brief mention was made earlier in this chapter that various codes for welded construction often stipulate when postweld stress relief heat treatment must be employed, and less frequently, when preheat is to be applied. Codes are written by engineers who have carefully considered past experience along with findings from research, and who attempt to set forth realistic *minimum* requirements for assuring *safe* performance in service. The information provided up to this point has been of a basic nature that should be helpful when making decisions regarding preheating or postweld heat treating. Further assistance can be gained from a review of requirements contained in widely used codes and specifications. In the following summaries, it should be understood that the material presented is intended only to illustrate how the principles we have discussed are employed in the codes. Therefore, for all actual applications, reference must be made to the provisions of the applicable code as published.

ASME BOILER AND PRESSURE VESSEL CODE

Section VIII of the ASME Code provides *Rules for Construction of Unfired Pressure Vessels*. These rules (in the 1966 Edition) define the conditions under which postweld thermal treatment must be applied for stress relieving. Other methods of stress relief (peening, pre-stressing, etc.) are not recognized as an alternative to heat treatment in this Code.

Paragraph UW-40 outlines the procedures which must be used for thermal stress relief. Briefly:

1. Vessels preferably are heated as a whole in an enclosed furnace.

2. Vessels may be furnace heated in portions, provided that the overlap of the heated sections is at least 5 ft and that the portion outside the furnace is shielded so that the temperature gradient is not harmful.

3. Parts of the vessel are permitted to be heated as separate sections, but any assembly weld joints locally heated must have the width of the heated zone on each side of the weld at least two times the base metal thickness and the temperature gradients must not be harmful.

4. Vessels may be heated internally provided that the exterior is insulated and the internal pressure during treatment does not exceed 50 percent of the maximum allowable working pressure at the highest metal temperature expected during postweld heating.

5. Nozzles or attachments that require stress relief can be locally treated by heating a band around the entire circumference of the vessel. The band should be sufficiently wide to include the nozzle and extend six times the base metal thickness beyond the weld joint between the nozzle and vessel wall. Metal outside the heated band must be protected from harmful temperature gradients.

6. Joints of piping and tubing can be locally stress relieved by heating a band on each side of the circumferential joint that is not less than three times the greatest width of the weld. The portion outside the heated band must be protected from harmful temperature gradients.

The temperatures and rates of heating and cooling for stress relieving carbon and alloy steels under the ASME Code are given in Paragraph UCS-56.

Minimum holding temperatures and times are tabulated for various grades of material.

Material	Notes		Minimum holding temperature F	Minimum holding time at temperature, hours per inch of thickness (Note 2)
P-1	(1)	(3)	1100	1
P-2	(1)	(4)	1100	1
P-3	(1)	(5)	1100	1
P-4		(6)	1100	1
P-5		(7)	1250	1
P-9		(8)	1150	1
P-10**		(9)	See Note (9)	See Note (9)

**9 Percent nickel steel of Specification SA-353 only.

The notes (1 through 9 above) referred to this table provide numerous exemptions and alternatives based on the grade of material and thickness of the parts being joined. For example (Note 1), materials P1, P2, and P3 may be treated at lower temperatures provided the holding times are increased proportionately. The values in this table follow the practice in the United States of using subcritical temperature heat treatment in the order of 1100 to 1200 F for stress relieving carbon steels and carbon-molybdenum steels. A temperature range of 1200 to 1300 F frequently is used for alloy steels. The more highly alloyed steels, which possess greater strength at elevated temperatures, sometimes are heated to 1300 to 1400 F for effective stress relief. Even though these subcritical temperatures do not bring about complete elimination of residual stresses, the level of stress remaining is low and the practical objectives of the treatment are achieved without the difficulties which accompany higher temperatures.

With regard to heating and cooling, the temperature of the furnace must not exceed 600 F at the time the weldment is placed in it. Above 600 F, the rate of heating must not be greater than 400 degrees per hour divided by the maximum metal thickness, but in no case more than 400 degrees per hour. During the heating period, the permissible temperature variation throughout the weldment is 250 F within any 15-ft interval of length, and when at holding temperature, not more than 150 F. During the heating and holding periods, the furnace atmosphere must not cause excessive oxidation of the surface of the vessel. The furnace should be designed to prevent direct impingement of the flame on the work. Above 600 F, cooling is to be done in the closed furnace or a cooling chamber at a rate not greater than 500 degrees per hour divided by the maximum metal thickness, but in no case more than 500 F per hour. From 600 F, the vessel may be cooled in still air.

Vessels that are to contain lethal substances when fabricated of carbon or alloy steels are required to be postweld thermally stress relieved. (See Paragraph UW-2) Also, vessels that are to operate at temperatures below minus 20 F must be stress relieved (Paragraph UCS-67). Of course, many more details concerning exceptions and permissible deviations in these rules are contained in the original document, but the foregoing gives a quick insight into the thinking of the ASME Boiler Code Committee with regard to the importance of thermal stress relief as assurance for safe performance of pressure vessels. Incidentally, it is also necessary to consult the ASME "Cases" in which interpretations are issued on the required handling of specific types of steels. These cases may include exceptions to the original requirements. For example, Case 1308 covers a special ruling issued in reply to an inquiry on 9% nickel steel as per

SA-353 and its use in accordance with Section VIII of the Code for vessels to be operated at temperatures below – 20 F. The inquiry questioned whether postweld heat treatment of the completely fabricated vessel could be omitted if the plate material was either quenched and tempered, or double normalized and tempered, and was shown to produce certain low-temperature Charpy-V impact test values. In reply, the Committee waived the postweld heat treatment regularly called for under the rules of Section VIII, but only on welded vessels having a wall thickness of 3/16 in. minimum to 2 in. maximum, and for vessels operating at a temperature no lower than – 320 F. These special rulings (Cases) must be consulted in their complete form in order to obtain maximum allowable stresses and other important details.

AMERICAN STANDARD CODE FOR PRESSURE PIPING

Mention was made in Chapter 2 that the ASA has issued one of the few codes that include guidance on conditions for welding. The original, all-inclusive document, B31.1, which covers pressure piping for power, industrial gas and air, refinery and oil transportation, etc., as well as B31.3, the separate Code Section on Petroleum Refinery Piping, contain appendixes in which steels are grouped on the basis of hardenability characteristics. This has been done principally to reduce the number of welding procedure qualifications required, but it also facilitates suggestions concerning preheating and postweld heat treating.

Code Section B31.3 provides the following groupings of steels:

P-Number	Types of Steels
1	Carbon steels — 40 to 75 ksi minimum UTS
2	Wrought iron
3	Alloy steels with a chromium content not exceeding ¾%, and alloy steels with a total alloy content not exceeding 2%
4	Alloy steels with a chromium content between ¾ and 2%, and alloy steels with a total alloy content not exceeding 2¾%
5	Alloy steels with a total alloy content not exceeding 10%
6	High-alloy steels — martensitic
7	High-alloy steels — ferritic
8	High-alloy steels — austenitic
9	Nickel alloy steels (containing up to 5% nickel)
10	Other alloy steels (including 9% nickel steel)

On the question of preheating, the *ASA Code for Pressure Piping,*

B31.1, states that under field conditions or otherwise where the ambient temperature is less than 32 F, local preheating to a hand-hot condition is recommended for all materials listed in P-numbers 1 and 2. It also is recommended that no welding be done when surfaces are wet or covered with ice; when snow is falling on the surfaces to be welded; nor during periods of high winds, unless suitable shelter is provided for the welder and the work. This recommendation is based upon the threat of hydrogen pickup rather than accelerated cooling of the weld from these conditions. In dealing with the preheating of steels listed in the P-Number groupings, the ASA Code, B31.3, provides typical preheat temperatures as shown in Table 62. These preheat temperatures are not mandatory. Instead, the actual preheat temperature deemed necessary for the joint is to be estab-

Table 62 — *REQUIRED HARDNESS LIMITS AND TYPICAL HEAT TREAT-MENTS FOR WELDED PRESSURE PIPING AS PROVIDED BY AMERICAN STANDARD CODE SECTIONS* (a)

P-number	Type of steel	Minimum preheat temperature deg F (b)	Postweld heat treating temperature deg F (c)	Required Brinell hardness maximum (d)
1	Carbon	Ambient	1100-1200	—
2	Wrought iron	Ambient	None	—
3	Up to ¾% Cr, 2% max. total alloy	175	1100-1350	215
4	¾ to 2% Cr, 2¾% max. total alloy	300	1325-1375	215
5	10% max. total alloy	350	1325-1375	241
6	Martensitic high-alloy	400	1400-1450	241
7	Ferritic high-alloy	Ambient	None	—
8	Austenitic high-alloy	Ambient	None	—
9	Nickel up to 5%	300	1100-1200	—
10	Others (i.e., 9% nickel)	300	1050-1100	—

(a) Abstracted from Petroleum Refinery Piping Code, ASA B31.3-1966, a section of the American Standard Code for Pressure Piping.
(b) Preheat temperatures not mandatory. Their necessity is to be established by welding procedure qualification.
(c) Postweld heat treatment to be performed as necessary to obtain properties required by end-use, and to comply with hardness requirements for heat-affected base metal. Actual treatment to be established by welding procedure qualification.
(d) Hardness limitations govern regardless of welding and heat treating procedure.

lished as part of the qualifying welding procedure. The preheat temperatures suggested are roughly in agreement with the hardenability potentials of the types of steels, but an increase of 50 to 100 F over the minimum temperature suggested probably would be required for base metal thicknesses beyond about ½ inch.

The necessity for postweld heat treatment of welded joints under this ASA Code is governed by the maximum hardness permitted in the heat-affected zones of the welded base metal as shown in Table 62. Again, the actual treatment applied is established during welding procedure qualification.

Table 63 — *PREHEATING SUGGESTED FOR CARBON STEEL AND VARIOUS CHROMIUM-MOLYBDENUM STEELS WHEN WELDED IN COMBINATIONS EMPLOYED IN PRESSURE PIPING SYSTEMS*

	C-Steel	C-Mo	½ Cr — ½ Mo	1 Cr — ½ Mo	1¼ Cr — ½ Mo	2 Cr — ½ Mo	2¼ Cr — 1 Mo	5 Cr — ½ Mo	7 Cr — ½ Mo	9 Cr — 1 Mo	18-8 Stainless
C-steel	–	B	C	C	C	C	C	D	D	D	A
C-Mo	B	B	C	C	C	C	C	D	D	D	A
½ Cr — ½ Mo	C	C	C	C	C	C	C	D	D	D	E
1 Cr — ½ Mo	C	C	C	C	C	C	C	D	D	D	E
1¼ Cr — ½ Mo	C	C	C	C	C	C	C	D	D	D	E
2 Cr — ½ Mo	C	C	C	C	C	C	C	D	D	D	E
2¼ Cr — 1 Mo	C	C	C	C	C	C	C	D	D	D	E
5 Cr — ½ Mo	D	D	D	D	D	D	D	D	D	D	E
7 Cr — ½ Mo	D	D	D	D	D	D	D	D	D	D	E
9 Cr — 1 Mo	D	D	D	D	D	D	D	D	D	D	E
18-8 Stainless	A	A	E	E	E	E	E	E	E	E	–

(AWS D10.8-61, "Welding of Chromium-Molybdenum Steel Piping")

A. No preheating except that, when atmospheric temperatures are below 70 F, the weld joint should be preheated to 100 F.

B. *For butt welds,* 200 to 400 F minimum. May be lowered to 100 F minimum if the wall thickness is under ⅜ in. and the carbon content is below 0.20 percent. *For fillet welds,* no preheating required for any (throat) thickness, except that when atmospheric temperatures are below 70 F, the weld joint should be preheated to 100 F.

C. 300 to 600 F minimum. May be lowered to 200 F minimum if the wall thickness is under ¾ in.

D. 400 to 700 F minimum. May be lowered to 300 F minimum if the wall thickness is under ¾ in.

E. 200 to 500 F minimum. For chromium-molybdenum material only.

COMMITTEE REPORT D10.8-61, AMERICAN WELDING SOCIETY

A document which provides more definitive information on pre-heating and postweld heat treating carbon and alloy steels is titled "Welding of Chromium-Molybdenum Steel Piping," and is identified as AWS D10.8-61. This Committee Report points out that preheating is almost always specified for the welding of chromium-molybdenum steel base metal, even when preheating is not required for the weld metal. Table 63, (above) from AWS D10.8-61, shows the preheating conditions generally used in welding various combinations of base metal together in a piping

Table 64 — *POSTWELD HEAT TREATMENT SUGGESTED FOR CARBON STEEL AND VARIOUS CHROMIUM-MOLYBDENUM STEELS WHEN WELDED IN COMBINATIONS EMPLOYED IN PRESSURE PIPING SYSTEMS*

	C-steel	C-Mo	½ Cr — ½ Mo	1 Cr — ½ Mo	1¼ Cr — ½ Mo	2 Cr — ½ Mo	2¼ Cr — 1 Mo	5 Cr — ½ Mo	7 Cr — ½ Mo	9 Cr — 1 Mo	18-8 Stainless
C-steel	–	B	C	C	D	D	D	E	E	E	A
C-Mo	B	B	C	C	D	D	D	E	E	E	A
½ Cr — ½ Mo	C	C	C	C	D	D	D	E	E	E	A
1 Cr — ½ Mo	C	C	C	C	D	D	D	E	E	E	A
1¼ Cr — ½ Mo	D	D	D	D	D	D	D	E	E	E	A
2 Cr — ½ Mo	D	D	D	D	D	D	D	E	E	E	A
2¼ Cr — 1 Mo	D	D	D	D	D	D	D	E	E	E	A
5 Cr — ½ Mo	E	E	E	E	E	E	E	E	E	E	F
7 Cr — ½ Mo	E	E	E	E	E	E	E	E	E	E	F
9 Cr — 1 Mo	E	E	E	E	E	E	E	E	E	E	F
18-8 Stainless	A	A	A	A	A	A	A	F	F	F	–

(AWS D10.8-61, "Welding of Chromium-Molybdenum Steel Piping")

A. Postheating not usually required.

B. Postheating required where carbon content exceeds 0.20 percent or with sections over ½ in. wall thickness. Heat to 1150 to 1250 F for one hour per inch of wall thickness. No postheating required for socket-type joints.

C. 1200 to 1300 F for one hour per inch of thickness, except not required on: (1) Valves 2 in. and smaller, (2) piping or tubing with a diameter of less than 4 in. and wall thickness under ½ in. and (3) socket-type joints.

D. 1275 to 1350 F for one hour per inch of thickness, except not required on: (1) Valves 2 in. and smaller, (2) piping or tubing with a diameter of less than 4 in. and wall thickness under ½ in. and (3) socket-type joints.

E. 1300 to 1375 F for one hour per inch of thickness. Cool to preheat temperature or below before applying postheating.

F. Not required for sections up to ½ in. wall thickness. Sections over ½ in. wall thickness heated to 1300 to 1375 F for one hour per inch of thickness.

system. Of course, many aspects of a specific joint may permit a lower preheat temperature, or may demand a somewhat higher temperature. Also included in this document are suggestions on how to safely interrupt the preheating – welding – postheating cycle, and, as shown in Table 64, the procedures for postweld heat treating the combinations of carbon and alloy steels frequently employed in piping systems. Again, the procedures listed represent good practice for the majority of situations, and are not intended to be mandatory or limiting.

Table 65 — RECOMMENDATIONS OF COMMISSION X, INTERNATIONAL INSTITUTE OF WELDING, FOR HEAT TREATMENT OF WELDED ALLOY STEELS

			1.2 Mn	0.5 Mo	0.5 Mo 0.25 V	1 Cr 0.5 Mo	2.25 Cr 1 Mo	3 Cr 0.5 Mo 0.5V	5 Cr 0.5 Mo	7 Cr 0.5 Mo	9 Cr 1 Mo
A	Type of steel		1.2 Mn	0.5 Mo	0.5 Mo 0.25 V	1 Cr 0.5 Mo	2.25 Cr 1 Mo	3 Cr 0.5 Mo 0.5V	5 Cr 0.5 Mo	7 Cr 0.5 Mo	9 Cr 1 Mo
	A. S. T. M. Designation		A299	A204		A301 Grade B	A387 Grade D		A 357	A213 Grade T7	A213 Grade T9
B	Typical analysis, %	C	~0.20	max. 0.20	max. 0.15	max. 0.15	max. 0.15	~0.20	max. 0.15	max. 0.15	max. 0.15
		Mn	1.2	0.6	0.6	0.6	0.6	0.6	0.6	0.5	0.5
		Si	0.3	0.3	0.3	0.3	0.3	0.3	0.3	0.7	0.7
		Cr				1	2-2.5	3	4-6	6-8	8-10
		Ni									
		V			0.2			0.5			
		Mo		0.5	0.5	0.5	1	0.5	0.5	0.5	1
C	Examples of application, °F.		Pipe work and pressure vessels for temperatures up to					Pressure vessels containing hydrogen up to 900 °F.	Pipe work and vessels for temperatures up to		
			885°	925°	975°	1025°	1065°		1200°	1250°	1300°
			Turbine parts and chemical plant						Chemical plant		Turbine parts
D	Section ‡		Up to 5 in.					Up to 3 in.		Up to 3 in.	
E	Stress relief temperature, °F.		975-1200	1100-1300	1200-1300	1150-1350	1200-1375	1200-1375	1250-1375	1300-1375	1350-1425
	Time, min. per in. (not less than 30)		Up to 125					Up to 100		Up to 75	
	Heating, °F./min.		6	6	6	6	4.5	4.5	3	3	Slow
	Cooling, °F./min.		3	3	3	3	3	3	3	3	Slow
								Preferably immediately after welding before cooling down			
F	Technical benefits from treatment E (besides stress relief and dimensional stability)				Tempering of heat affected zone and weld deposit						
G	Preheating for thicker sections, °F.		400-750	200-400	400-575	400-575	400-575	400-575	400-575	400-575	400-660
H	Other heat treatment		Normalization is often specified: Heating to 1650-1750 °F. followed by annealing treatment E					1830 F. to 1885 F., followed by annealing treatment E			
J	Scope of treatment H				Grain refining						

Abstracted from Metal Progress Data Sheet, page 96-B, August 1956; taken from IIW Doc. X-94-55.

RECOMMENDATIONS OF COMMISSION X, INTERNATIONAL INSTITUTE OF WELDING

In concluding this discussion of current practices in preheating and postweld heat treating weldments, it should be of interest to review the viewpoint outside the USA. Table 65 contains the recommendations of Commission X (Residual Stresses and Stress Relieving) of the IIW. As should be expected, this tabulation attempts to cover conditions encountered over the broad range of joint design, welding process, and weld joint properties required. Consequently, the recommendations must be quite general in nature, and lean to the conservative side.

Suggested Reading

Principles of Heat Treatment, by M. A. Grossmann, American Society for Metals, Metals Park, Ohio, 1953.

"Effect of Preheating and Postheating on Toughness of Weld Metals," by T. N. Armstrong and W. L. Warner, The Welding Journal, v 37, no. 1, Research Suppl., pp 27s – 29s, January 1958.

"The Effect of Preheat on Brittle Fracture of Carbon Steel for Pressure Vessels," by L. J. McGeady, Ibid, v 41, no. 8, pp 355s – 367s, August 1962.

"Welding of Steel at Low Ambient Temperatures," by K. Winterton, W. P. Campbell, and M. J. Nolan, Welding Research Council Bulletin Series, No. 86, March 1963.

"Effects of Thermal Stress Relief and Stress Relieving Conditions on the Fracture of Notched and Welded Wide Plates," by A. A. Wells and F. M. Burdekin, Report B6/23/62 of the British Welding Research Association, published in Welding Research Abroad, WRC, v IX, no. 7, pp 24 – 30, August – September 1963.

Chapter 13

DIFFICULTIES AND DEFECTS

While much of the success of welding must be credited to its versatility and economy, the role played by the reliability of the processes must not be overlooked. Welded joints now can be consistently made with soundness and properties unequaled by any other means. This accomplishment is attested by the fact that only a weld will serve for the most critical joints in nuclear reactors, high-pressure steam piping, armored vehicles, aerospace ships and a host of other equally important articles. Yet, it is well known to those engaged in making weldments that this high degree of reliability or joint integrity does not come easily. Indeed, defects can, and do, occur in welded joints. It may be said that a *perfect* weld *cannot* be made. Some imperfection, perhaps only a minute slag inclusion, always can be found in any weldment. Specialists in nondestructive testing often refer to these imperfections as *discontinuities*. They define a discontinuity as any variation in the normal average properties of the material. When a discontinuity is judged damaging to the function of the material or the weldment, it is considered a *defect*. A primary object in making any weldment is, therefore, to limit the imperfections to harmless discontinuities and thus insure that it performs satisfactorily in its intended service. When defects interfere with the performance of a weldment, the malfunction may endanger life, limb or property.

What kind of difficulties can be encountered with welded joints and weldments? Experience shows that shortcomings may appear in a number of technological areas: in joint design, material suitability, weld metal structure and soundness, condition of heat treatment, and surface condition, to mention just a few. It would be desirable to touch upon every potential cause of difficulty in weldments. We therefore would have to cover almost every problem known to arise with steel. This gamut would range from decarburization to radiation embrittlement. A treatise on this scale is not possible here, so we will center attention on metallurgical-type defects peculiar to weldments and the difficulties entailed in avoiding or minimizing their occurrence.

Because most welding processes applied to carbon and alloy steels involve heating, there appears to be some logic in reviewing first those difficulties and defects which occur upon heating; second, those which occur during the manipulation or operational period; third, during the cooling period; and fourth, during service. Undoubtedly, the defect which the metallurgist or welding engineer is called upon most frequently to diagnose and correct is *cracking*. Therefore, we shall take up this subject as one of the last in Chapter 13 and treat it more thoroughly than the others.

DIFFICULTIES DURING HEATING

In Chapter 3, three basic sources of heat for welding were described. Following this description, a number of means for generating heat and transferring it from source to work were discussed because these often provided the foundation for a different process. In view of the wide variations in the rate of heating among the various processes, and the total heat input to which the base metal is subjected in each, it should be understandable that the problems which arise in heating for welding will be dependent to a great extent upon the particular welding process employed.

ARC STRIKES

A disturbance left on the surface of the base metal where a careless welder has momentarily touched an arc-welding electrode to start the arc is called an *arc strike*. What is the nature of this disturbance and why should it be singled out as a difficulty or a defect? The answer is quickly found in recent investigations of causes of failure in weldments. A number of failures by cracking initiate at abnormal structural conditions or unsoundness produced in an arc strike. Of course, the careful welder strikes the arc in the joint where the base metal will be melted by penetration as the operation progresses beyond the striking point. Or the welder may use a scrap of metal as a starting tab or a high-frequency arc starter. But let us consider for a moment the metallurgical conditions that exist when the careless welder makes an arc strike on the surface of the base metal adjacent to the weld and then quickly moves the electrode into the joint to perform the welding operation.

Because the duration of an arc strike is only about 0.2 second, the depth of heating must be very superficial. Also, the rate of cooling of this thin surface layer of metal will be extremely fast. Examination of the microstructure in this thin surface layer often shows that the steel was heated above the lower critical temperature (Ac_1). A portion of the base metal obviously was austenitized upon heating for this portion has now transformed to small areas of martensite. It is important to consider that since only a portion of the structure became austenitized, we know that the temperature did not rise above the upper critical point (Ac_3), or the time of heating was too short to accomplish solution of the iron carbide present and homogenization of the austenite. Consequently, the microscopic portions of the structure that now appear martensitic actually represent a *higher carbon martensite* than would be indicated by the average carbon content of the particular steel. We should not be surprised, therefore, to learn that small cracks sometimes initiate in these small martensitic areas caused by an arc strike. In addition to the heterogeneity of microstructure and rapid cooling, the thin, fused area of an arc strike is not properly protected from the atmosphere since the gas-generating ingredients and slag-formers in the electrode covering generally have not been heated and brought into use. Furthermore, if some of the core wire is melted and actually is deposited on the area of the arc strike during its brief duration, this metal will be lacking in deoxidizing agents and alloying elements which normally would be transferred from the electrode covering. For these reasons, arc strikes often harbor minute cracks, porosity, hard zones, and chemical heterogeneity. Despite their small scale, these conditions can trigger a major failure when they are located in an important stress field. Tests have shown that it is safer to deposit a smooth weld bead over an earlier accidental arc strike than to leave the strike and its minute defects in place. Of course, removal of the surface metal by grinding or machining also is an effective remedy for arc strikes.

STARTING POROSITY

When using the shielded metal-arc welding process with covered electrodes, certain classes of electrodes may appear prone to deposit weld metal which contains internal porosity only at the starting portion of the weld bead. The size and distribution of the porosity is illustrated in Fig. 161. This difficulty can be related to the amount of deoxidizer (usually ferrosilicon) contained in the electrode covering. It must be recalled that the core wire of covered electrodes usually is made from rimmed steel, and to secure a sound weld deposit from this core wire requires that the metal must be deoxidized. Electrodes of the high-strength alloy steel variety which are required to display good low-temperature impact values often contain carefully limited amounts of silicon because this element at high levels adversely affects the toughness transition temperature. Electrodes of the E100, E110 and E120 series frequently contain restricted ferrosilicon additions in the covering which hold the weld metal silicon contents below about 0.35%. This amount of ferrosilicon in the electrode covering generally is not adequate to properly deoxidize the first increment of core wire melted from the electrode upon starting. Although the covering and core wire which melt together soon reach proportions which result in complete deoxidation, the initially deposited metal (containing porosity) has been left behind at the starting point (Fig. 161).

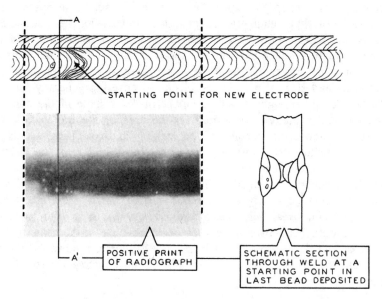

Fig. 161 — Starting porosity in weld bead deposited by E11018 covered electrode in the shielded metal-arc process.

Print made from radiograph. Restricted silicon additions commonly used in high-strength alloy steel electrode coverings often leave initially deposited metal insufficiently deoxidized.

To avoid starting porosity, the welder can make use of a scrap tab of metal to "warm up" the electrode and not include this portion in the

actual weld joint. However, this is an inconvenient practice for most production welding operations. A technique known as "back-step" starting
has been developed which can completely avoid starting porosity. The
welder, after being acquainted with the cause of this defect, is taught to
strike the arc in the joint about 1 inch *ahead* of the real starting point.
Immediately upon initiation of the arc, the electrode is moved backward
toward the real starting position taking care to deposit the initial metal
as a narrow, thin bead. Upon reaching the real starting point, the electrode
travel is reversed, and with a momentarily slower travel speed, the arc
is used to remelt the initially deposited (unsound) weld metal as the
welding operation proceeds in normal manner along the joint.

THERMAL CRACKING

When certain hard or brittle base metals, particularly castings, are
heated for welding, the use of an intense source of heat which brings
about an extremely rapid rise in temperature over a small area will cause
cracks to develop spontaneously in the metal surrounding the heated
area. The striking of an electric arc between an electrode and the surface
of a piece of white cast iron can lead to thermal cracking in the iron.
Of course, if heating is continued to the fusion temperature the cracked
portion of metal may be melted and no thermal cracking remains in the
weldment. However, metals which are prone to initiate thermal cracking
usually will allow the cracking to propagate under the stresses created
by localized heating. Therefore, melting seldom is able to overtake the
crack extensions.

INADEQUATE JOINT PENETRATION VS INCOMPLETE FUSION

The depth of weld penetration in a joint and the depth of fusion
into the faces of a joint are distinct concepts which require definition
before a deficiency in either can be understood. The three basic terms
which have been adopted by the AWS to accurately describe the extent
to which weld metal replaces base metal are *joint penetration, root penetration* and *depth of fusion.* The meaning of these terms is illustrated by
Fig. 162.

From these terms it should be immediately clear, for instance, what is
meant by *inadequate joint penetration,* regardless of whether a design
calls for *complete joint penetration* or *partial joint penetration.* Likewise
the meaning of *complete fusion* as against *incomplete fusion* should be
clear as to what surfaces are involved.

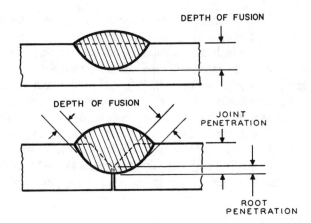

Fig. 162 — *Joint penetration* is the minimum depth a groove weld extends from its face into a joint, exclusive of reinforcement.

Root penetration is the depth a groove weld extends into the root of a joint measured on the centerline of the root cross-section.

Depth of fusion is the distance that fusion extends into the base metal from the surface melted during welding.

Joint penetration is determined by a number of factors, the most influential being the heat input per unit of base metal. Increasing the current in arc welding, for example, should result in increased joint penetration. However, other factors which have a measurable effect are travel speed, polarity and the nature of electrode flux coverings. The manner in which these affect penetration has been discussed in earlier chapters.

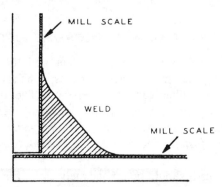

Fig. 163 — Despite unlikely appearance, no weld exists because heavy mill scale has completely prevented fusion and joint penetration.

Sometimes a surface condition such as heavy mill scale can result in zero depth of fusion. Figure 163 illustrates (in somewhat exaggerated form) how mill scale may prevent fusion and joint penetration as well. In Figure 164, inadequate root penetration is obvious. Deep back gouging will be required to open a groove sufficient to permit a weld that will achieve complete joint penetration. Figure 164 also indicates incomplete fusion.

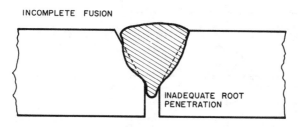

INCOMPLETE FUSION

INADEQUATE ROOT PENETRATION

Fig. 164 — Inadequate root penetration and incomplete fusion.

DILUTION

Difficulty sometimes is encountered with unwanted dilution of the weld metal by melted base metal. Dilution is the mixing or alloying of filler metal with base metal made available through penetration. The extent of dilution can be expressed as the percentage of base metal in the final weld metal; so, obviously, dilution will be determined by not only the amount of base metal melted, but also by the amount of filler metal deposited, as shown in Fig. 165. In many fusion joining operations dilution is anticipated and the filler metal composition is such that the final weld metal composition is satisfactory for its intended purpose, albeit diluted. In fact, if the base metal is an alloy steel, a lower-alloy filler metal may be employed with the knowledge that some additional alloy will be obtained in the weld metal through dilution.

The newcomer in welding often is under the impression that a dissimilar composition filler bead deposited on a base metal has a gradient composition from the top of the weld bead to the fusion line. That is, the top of the weld bead is believed representative of the filler metal composition, and the composition is assumed to gradually change to that of the base metal upon reaching the bottom of the weld bead at the fusion line. This is not the case. During deposition of filler metal into a weld pool, the stirring of the weld pool by convection currents, and by electromagnetic effects when heat is generated by means of electricity, usually is sufficient to form a homogeneous mixture or alloy within the entire boundary of the weld melt. Thus the final weld bead forms a new alloy, the composition of which is determined basically by the proportions of filler metal added and base metal melted. Each bead is uniform in

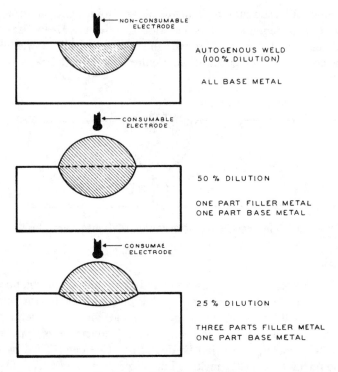

Fig. 165 — Dilution in welding.

composition from top to bottom and side-to-side, unless perhaps, the speed of deposition and solidification is too rapid for the stirring action and diffusion to accomplish homogenization, which takes place while the bead is molten. Figure 166 illustrates the degree of homogeneity which can be obtained in a properly conducted arc-welding operation when depositing a surface of austenitic Cr – Ni stainless steel weld metal on a carbon steel base. On the other hand, Fig. 167 shows the heterogeneity which can appear in weld metal deposited from the same Cr – Ni stainless steel electrode when the travel speed is too rapid for the amount of base metal which enters the weld metal.

Of course, as the amount of penetration is decreased, problems with dilution and heterogeneity diminish. While deposition of a surfacing weld without any penetration and dilution often would be desirable, this is not easily achieved with the presently available fusion processes. Minimum dilution, about 2%, can be secured with the oxyacetylene process. A skilled welder will bring the base metal surface just to the sweating temperature and then apply the filler metal to form the surfacing weld. However, deposition is comparatively slow and shielding is only fair. Unfortunately, the more

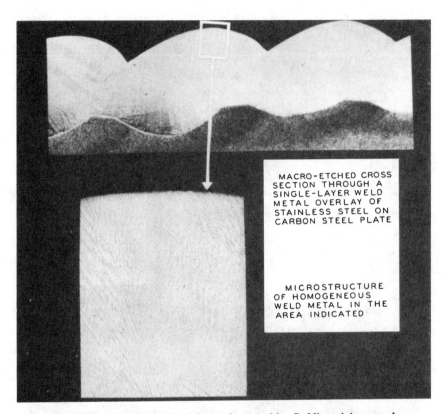

MACRO-ETCHED CROSS
SECTION THROUGH A
SINGLE-LAYER WELD
METAL OVERLAY OF
STAINLESS STEEL ON
CARBON STEEL PLATE

MICROSTRUCTURE
OF HOMOGENEOUS
WELD METAL IN THE
AREA INDICATED

Fig. 166 — Weld metal surface of austenitic Cr-Ni stainless steel deposited on carbon steel by submerged-arc welding process. Electrode wire is ER-310. Deposit analyzes 17.8% Cr and 13.2% Ni because of 33% dilution with carbon steel base metal. Note uniformity of weld metal microstructure throughout weld beads, which is indicative of composition homogeneity.

rapid arc processes entail somewhat greater penetration and dilution.

ABSORPTION OF GASES

Gases may be absorbed by heated metals, and particularly by molten metals, in a surprisingly short time. Dissolved gases seldom are desirable in metals, for besides forming objectionable compounds, their solubility usually decreases as the temperature is lowered. The state of supersaturation that results gives rise to many difficulties with blowholes, cracking, and embrittlement. The absorption of gases is one of the most important difficulties in welding, but because this phenomenon takes place in the weld pool with little or no indication, we often do not become aware of

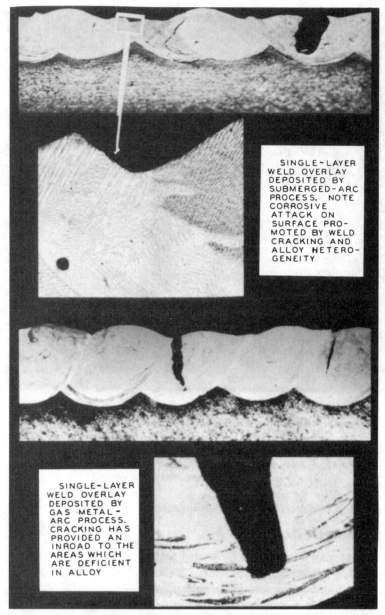

Fig. 167 — Composition heterogeneity produced by excessive travel speed. Austenitic Cr-Ni stainless steel weld surface deposited by (top) submerged-arc welding process and (bottom) gas metal-arc welding process.

its significance until too late. The gases with which we mainly are concerned are the oxygen and nitrogen in the atmosphere, and hydrogen which usually appears in the form of moisture in shielding materials.

An important fact to remember about dissolved gases in metals is that any metal exposed to any gas retains a maximum amount (saturation percentage) of the gas in solution, the amount depending in each instance on the pressure and the temperature of the gas. If the pressure of Gas A is reduced by diluting it with another gas B (replacing some of gas A with gas B), the metal evolves some of gas A but absorbs some of gas B. At first sight, it may seem impossible to free weld metal of gas by dilution, because some of gas B would be dissolved to replace any of gas A that was evolved. However, some gases are nearly insoluble in steel. In fact, only oxygen, nitrogen, and hydrogen are soluble to any appreciable extent. To reduce the oxygen, nitrogen, and hydrogen content of metal deposited in welding, we are not restricted to delaying its freezing. We may dilute the arc atmosphere around the weld puddle with gases that are practically insoluble in steel. If the atmosphere is diluted by carbon monoxide, for example, so that the atmosphere consists of 90 percent carbon monoxide, 7 percent nitrogen, 3 percent oxygen, and negligable hydrogen, there will be little oxygen, nitrogen, and hydrogen in the weld metal. This principle has brought about a new and important operation in degasifying molten metal during melting operations. By bubbling a harmless insoluble gas through the bath or melt, any dissolved gases are evolved into the bubbles and escape into the air. The contamination of weld metal is not limited to gaseous elements like oxygen or hydrogen. Sulfur, for example, may be oxidized to sulfur dioxide and this gas can be absorbed by the weld puddle. Similar absorption of impurities from the flame is observed in open-hearth steelmaking. As the percentage of sulfur in the fuel increases, the percentage of sulfur picked up by the metal bath increases.

Oxygen and Nitrogen

The oxygen in the atmosphere, in addition to forming oxides on the surface of molten metal, also dissolves in the metal to some extent as discussed in Chapter 8. Nitrogen may also be absorbed from the air. Large quantities of oxygen and nitrogen in molten metal can lead to porosity in the solid metal because of the marked decrease in solubility which occurs at the freezing point. Oxygen and nitrogen in the solid metal, which may be dissolved or held as oxides and nitrides, can result in embrittlement.

Air may reach the surface of the molten weld pool in a number of ways and introduce oxygen and nitrogen. The arc and pool may have inadequate shielding. Turbulence in a protective gaseous shield surrounding the arc may aspirate air. Poorly fitted parts may allow air to reach the unshielded underside of a weld bead. Weld metal from bare steel electrodes is contaminated to a serious degree by approximately 0.3% oxygen and 0.2% nitrogen. Weld metal deposited under proper conditions, using covered electrodes, an inert-gas atmosphere, or submerged-arc shielding, will contain substantially lower quantities of these two gases, possibly as low as 0.05% for each.

Weld metal containing oxygen and nitrogen which is able to solidify without porosity may still be adversely affected by the presence of these gases. In considering their effects, it is important to recognize whether the gas is present in the dissolved state or in the form of inclusions. Oxygen in solution tends to reduce strength, hardness, and notched-bar impact strength. This effect is particularly significant in arc deposited metal containing oxygen contents in excess of about 0.1%. When the oxygen is held in combination with iron, manganese, silicon or other elements with high oxygen affinity, as inclusions, the influence of oxygen is mainly mechanical and the number and size of the inclusions determine whether the mechanical properties are adversely affected. With an abundance of deoxidizing elements present, the residual (dissolved) oxygen content usually is very low. Thus the addition of elements like Mn, Si, Al and Ti to the weld metal is an effective way of dealing with the oxygen problem.

Nitrogen also may be contained in solution in the solid weld metal or may be present as a compound in the structure. In iron or steel, particles of iron nitride, Fe_4N, form in the structure as flattened crystals, and therefore the particles appear acicular under metallographic examination. Certain alloying elements, like chromium, titanium, and vanadium, have a much stronger affinity for nitrogen than does iron. Consequently, in alloy steels containing these elements, the alloy-nitride particles form in preference to iron nitride. The solubility of nitrogen in iron varies with temperature much in the same pattern as does hydrogen, except that the solubility limits for nitrogen are about 1/10th those for hydrogen. Because of the strong affinity between nitrogen and many metals, the amount of free or residual nitrogen in any steel must be very small. Yet, residual nitrogen can have a significant effect upon the properties of steel. Even small increases in nitrogen above the 0.05% level result in higher strength and hardness and lower ductility and toughness, particularly if the weld metal receives an aging-type heat treatment in the temperature range of 900 to 1600 F.

Nitrogen absorption in welding is minimized by use of effective gaseous and/or slag shielding. Of course, all other factors that influence the admission of air into the arc also will affect nitrogen absorption. A short arc is particularly important to hold the weld metal nitrogen content to a minimum. Any nitrogen already in the filler metal is carried into the weld deposit. For this reason, when very low nitrogen content is desired, both the welding rod or electrode and the base metal must be even lower in nitrogen. Sometimes vacuum-melted steels are employed to have an initially low nitrogen potential. In some cases, however, the addition of a very strong nitride-former, like Ti, Al or Zr, provides a more practical solution to the problem of obtaining a low content of free nitrogen in the weld metal.

Hydrogen

Hydrogen is quite soluble in molten metal and is readily picked up in the weld metal during fusion joining. The source of this gas may be any one of a dozen or more, and we have no simple, reliable indicator of the presence of hydrogen. This gas may be introduced unknowingly in the form of a compound. Water is a perfect example, and we shall point out ways that moisture (H_2O) can enter the welding operation where it is reduced or dissociated to liberate free hydrogen. Obviously, hydrogen is present in the gas-welding process where hydrogen (H_2) or acetylene (C_2H_2) is burned with oxygen (O_2) to produce heat. When using the oxyacetylene flame, we can find hydrogen, *per se,* in the inner cone of the flame where it is mixed with carbon monoxide (CO), or as the final form, water vapor (H_2O), in the outer flame where it is mixed with carbon dioxide (CO_2). The atomic-hydrogen arc process, of course, involves the use of hydrogen in both the molecular and atomic form. Water may be present in the welding operation as moisture on the groove faces (perhaps in porous rust or scale) or in a humid ambient atmosphere. Traces of hydrogen may also be found in the base metal or filler metal as a result of some prior steel processing operation.

Our greatest problems with hydrogen arise in shielded metal-arc welding where the flux covering on the electrode may often contain large amounts of hydrogen. Traces of hydrogen may be found in the ferro-alloys or other metals included in the flux. The more potent source of hydrogen in the flux covering is moisture, which may be held in the covering mechanically or in a combined form.

Mechanically held moisture may originate in the aqueous sodium or potassium silicate which is employed to bind the powdered materials together. If the electrode baking operation is not thoroughly performed, a small amount of moisture will be held in the minute voids between the flux particles. It is also possible for a thoroughly baked covering to pick up moisture if it is exposed to humid surroundings. Mechanically held moisture is not as likely to contribute hydrogen to a weld as is combined moisture. Mechanically held moisture is usually driven out of the covering by the heat at the melting end of the electrode and has little opportunity to actually enter the arc.

Combined moisture in an electrode covering is almost certain to enter the welding arc. The simplest form of combined moisture is that held by the sodium or potassium silicate binder after baking. This moisture, often referred to as "water of crystallization," will vary in amount depending upon the baking temperature and time. Combined moisture is also found in minerals employed in flux coverings: asbestos, clay, talc, and olivine being good examples. Here the moisture may be water of crystallization or "water of constitution." The latter implies that the moisture is an inherent part of the crystalline structure and is exceedingly difficult to drive off by heating.

The covering constituents which are better known as sources of hydrogen are the combustible materials like cotton, wood flour, alpha floc, and other cellulosic hydrocarbons. Large quantities of hydrogen are held in these materials either as hydrogen in chemical combination or as combined moisture.

Hydrogen, in order to dissolve in a molten weld pool, must be in the atomic form, that is, must consist of single atoms of hydrogen as compared to the molecular form where two atoms are held as a pair. Because the hydrogen atom is smaller than the interstices in the iron lattice, hydrogen in the atomic form can freely pass through the matrix structure of steel. In an arc-welding process, any hydrogen gas which enters the arc is instantly placed in the atomic form, and should molten metal be immediately adjacent to the arc, the hydrogen will dissolve in the metal until an equilibrium is attained. When the hydrogen enters the arc in the form of moisture, or perhaps we should say water vapor, it is believed that the molten steel reduces the water vapor according to the following equation:

$$H_2O + Fe \underset{\leftarrow}{\overset{\rightarrow}{}} FeO + 2H$$

Some of the hydrogen liberated by this reaction dissolves in the molten metal. Much thought has been given to the factors which determine the amount of hydrogen that will enter the molten metal. It appears that the hydrogen content of the molten weld metal will be directly dependent upon the concentration of hydrogen in the arc atmosphere inasmuch as experiments have found the amount dissolved to be very close to the solubility predicted by Fig. 168.

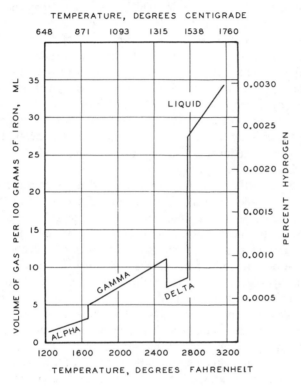

Fig. 168 — Solubility of hydrogen in iron at one atmosphere pressure.

Some experimental evidence has been obtained that the amount of hydrogen picked up in the weld pool is influenced by the mode of metal transfer from the consumable electrode to the pool. A globular metal transfer results in a lower hydrogen content than a spray transfer, presumably because the globular droplets of metal expose less surface area to the hydrogen-containing arc atmosphere than the fine spray particles for an equal quantity of metal.

The gas metal-arc welding process is not completely free of the hydrogen problem. The inert gases, argon and helium, are extremely low in hydrogen and permit virtually hydrogen-free welding conditions. Carbon dioxide ordinarily is quite low in moisture content, usually much less than 500 ppm. Even if the moisture content were twice this amount, this shielding gas would provide only 1000 ppm of molecular hydrogen in the arc. Theoretically, this atmosphere would be in equilibrium with but 1.25 ml/100 g of molten iron. The more likely source of extraneous hydrogen is the welding electrode, which can carry significant quantities on the surface in oil, grease, and drawing compounds. However, most manufacturers of this kind of electrode are aware of the need for cleanliness and it would be unusual indeed to have a surface coating on the electrode that would increase the weld metal hydrogen content to the same extent as cellulosic covered electrodes. Most gas metal-arc deposits pick up less hydrogen than 1 ml/100 g of metal. An electrode deliberately contaminated with a film of carbonaceous drawing compound contributed hydrogen only to the extent of 8 ml/100 g of metal. This pickup is likely to be objectionable only in the welding of highly hardenable steels in highly restrained joints.

Hydrogen in the solidifying weld metal can be considered in three parts: first, that which exceeds the solubility of the metal at the freezing point where the usual decrease takes place. This excess hydrogen will form gas pockets or blowholes if it is able to escape from the rapidly solidifying metal. The second part of hydrogen is that which is evolved from the solid metal at or near room temperature and which has come to be known as diffusible hydrogen. The bulk of this hydrogen is evolved within the first 24 hours after welding while the remainder escapes very slowly over the next approximately twenty days. The last part of hydrogen to be considered is a smaller amount which remains in the metal and which is called *residual* hydrogen. A portion of this residual hydrogen can be removed by rebaking at temperatures from about 300 to 900 F, but complete removal is accomplished only by vacuum fusion extraction or a carrier gas technique.

The manner in which the excess hydrogen escapes during freezing is a matter on which there is not complete agreement. Some investigators claim that hydrogen alone cannot escape to form bubbles in the melt, but that the hydrogen reacts with oxygen, carbon, sulfur, and other elements present to form insoluble gases which in turn cause bubbles in the melt. Some experimental evidence has been collected that indicates the availability of oxygen or oxides in the hydrogen-containing melt increases the onset and severity of blowholes and porosity. It is claimed that the presence of water vapor, *per se,* as might be derived from a damp electrode covering, produces blowholes and porosity more readily than the introduction of hydrogen alone in a controlled experiment. Porosity in weld metal has been found to contain methane which is believed to have formed by the following chemical reaction:

$$Fe_3C + 2H_2 \rightarrow CH_4 + 3Fe$$

Strong evidence has been obtained that hydrogen will react with sulfur and selenium in the melt to form hydrogen sulfide gas and hydrogen selenide gas which because of their extremely low solubility form bubbles in the melt.

The solubility of hydrogen in steel is not affected to any significant degree by the composition of the steel. However, changes in temperature and the crystalline structure of the steel have a marked effect upon the hydrogen solubility as can be seen from Fig. 168. Here the important fact to recognize is that *molten* iron or steel can dissolve a much larger quantity of hydrogen than they are capable of holding in the *solid* state. Note also that the solubility, in general, decreases rapidly with decreasing temperature, and that sharp changes in solubility occur at the transformation points. The face-centered cubic form of crystalline structure appears to provide a higher solubility for hydrogen. These same changes in solubility occur in steel. Determination of the hydrogen content of weld metal can be carried out by a number of techniques. The results will vary somewhat depending upon the sampling procedure employed, but there is good agreement among investigators on the trend of results. Table 66 provides typical hydrogen concentration values for weld metals deposited by arc processes with varying amounts of hydrogen in the arc atmosphere.

Table 66 — *HYDROGEN CONCENTRATIONS IN ARC ATMOSPHERE AND WELD METAL DEPOSITED BY VARIOUS PROCESSES*

Process and electrode	*Approximate Values for Low-Carbon Steel Weld Metal Hydrogen — ml/100g* [b]				
	Hydrogen [a] in arc atmosphere % by volume	Present in liquid weld metal	Diffusible hydrogen liberated during first 24 hours	Diffusible hydrogen liberated during subsequent 20 days	Residual hydrogen remaining in as-welded deposit
Metal-arc, E6010	40	28	10	3	15
Metal-arc E6012	35	15	6	2	7
Metal-arc, E6015	5	8	2	1	5
Gas tungsten-arc, (argon)	0	4[a]	1	0	3

[a] Presumably hydrogen contained in filler metal and covering if present.
[b] Hydrogen content in % by weight can be calculated by multiplying ml/100g by 0.00009: For example, 28 ml/100g equals 0.0025% by weight, or 25 ppm (parts per million by weight).

Let us now review, to the best of our knowledge, what happens to hydrogen that becomes trapped in a solid weld. Suppose molten weld metal has just been deposited by an electrode bearing a cellulosic type of covering, and that a substantial amount of hydrogen has been dissolved in the metal. If sufficient amounts of oxygen, carbon, sulfur, or selenium are present in the metal, the hydrogen might initiate one or more of the following reactions from left to right:

1. $2H + FeO \rightarrow Fe + H_2O$ (Water Vapor)
2. $4H + C \rightarrow CH_4$ (Methane)
3. $2H + S \rightarrow H_2S$ (Hydrogen Sulfide)
4. $2H + Se \rightarrow H_2Se$ (Hydrogen Selenide)

These reactions do not go to completion, but move in either direction depending upon the concentration of the various components and the equilibrium point for the reaction. In each case, the product of the reaction when moving from left to right is a gas which is practically insoluble in the metal. Consequently, the molten metal will bubble or boil, and the solid weld will very likely display porosity.

The difficulty caused by hydrogen in the molten weld metal beyond the limit of solid solubility, and through reaction with other elements to produce insoluble gases, is obvious enough. Blowholes and porosity are defects that can impair the performance of a weld. However, the difficulties produced by the diffusible hydrogen and the residual hydrogen are insidious, and can be far more damaging. The rest of the hydrogen story will be told as we discuss difficulties in the weld upon cooling, more specifically, the occurrence of blowholes and porosity, and cold cracking.

CONTAMINATION AND PICKUP

Too frequently, the base metal which we weld, or even the filler metals and adjuvant materials which we employ in welding, are contaminated on the surface with a foreign material that gives rise to a difficulty or defect. Sometimes the surface may have a coating or plating that was deliberately applied for a useful purpose, but its effect upon welding can be unfavorable. It is not entirely practicable to provide a list of contaminants and urge that all possible means be taken to avoid them. Water, for example, might be regarded as a contaminant on the surface of steel to be arc welded (because of porosity occurrence). Yet, generous amounts of water could flow over the surface of this same steel during roll resistance-spot welding, and do considerable good in connection with minimizing heating between electrode wheels and the work surfaces. However, to stimulate thinking on this subject, examine the list of common materials and chemical elements in Table 67 which are known to have played the role of contaminant in welding operations on steel. Some of these materials are readily seen on the base metal to be welded and even their source is obvious. However, some contaminants appear in the picture unexpectedly and their source often requires careful investigation. Brief examples of the sources of contaminants, their effects in welding, and countermeasures, can be given for a number of the materials and elements listed in Table 67.

Table 67 — *COMMON MATERIALS AND CHEMICAL ELEMENTS WHICH CAN BEHAVE AS CONTAMINANTS IN WELDING*

Common Materials

Aluminum coating	Oil and grease
Galvanized coating	Paint
Graphitic lubricant	Rust
Mill scale	Terne plate coating

Chemical Elements

Aluminum	Lead
Boron	Oxygen
Cadmium	Phosphorus
Carbon	Sulfur
Copper	Tin
Hydrogen	Zinc

Despite better judgement, mill scale, rust, oil, grease and paint frequently are permitted to remain on the surface where welding will be performed. It must be appreciated that any of these materials can cause porosity in the weld metal. Mill scale can cause porosity by contributing an excessive amount of oxygen to the weld metal. However, hydrogen usually is the real culprit. The mill scale often contains absorbed moisture which is released during welding. The other materials have hydrogen present in combined moisture or as hydrocarbons. Under some circumstances these materials may be volatilized or driven off by heat just before the fusion stage is reached. Hence, our warnings about grease, oil, paint, etc., causing porosity might be regarded as exaggerated. However, if the welding speed is increased (and this certainly is the trend today), the hydrogen-produced porosity suddenly may be encountered. Under these circumstances, the hydrogen-bearing material is not completely driven away by advance heating before the arc comes in contact with the contaminated area and the volatilized contaminant is swept into contact with the arc. Again, the most treacherous effects of traces of absorbed hydrogen are yet to be described.

Carbon, which can be a dangerous contaminant, is another element contained in oil, grease and paint and, of course, in graphitic lubricant. Carbon, it will be remembered, is the most influential alloying element in steel. Therefore, when weld metal is allowed to pick up varying quantities from foreign materials during welding, little imagination is needed to picture the consequences. A weld bead deposited in a groove having oil on the surfaces can increase in carbon content from 0.10% to 0.25%. This increase would raise the strength and hardness substantially, and also would decrease the ductility and toughness. If the weld metal contained alloying elements designed to impart good properties at a level of 0.10% carbon, the properties of the alloy weld metal at a level of 0.25% carbon probably would be quite unsatisfactory because of cracking susceptibility and lack of toughness.

Zinc is an element whose role ranges from a dangerous contaminant to a highly regarded protective coating — witness the enormous quantities of galvanized steel used today. Galvanized or zinc coated steels in many forms often are welded. A number of the regular welding processes are used, and generally satisfactory results are secured. Yet, experience shows that cracking difficulties appear with somewhat greater frequency in welding zinc coated steel than with bare steel, particularly in fusion joining operations. For example, in arc welding Tee joints in two pieces of zinc-coated plate, it is not uncommon to find small cracks in the fillet welds extending from the root toward the face of the bead. Close examination will show that zinc was present on the faying surfaces at the root of the joint and molten zinc penetrated the surface of the newly solidified weld bead and produced rapidly propagating intergranular cracking. This cracking appears to be promoted by *molten* zinc in contact with the hot, solid weld metal. Zinc in the vapor phase, volatilized by the heat of welding, does not seem to cause cracking. The tendency for the zinc-penetration cracking to occur is markedly influenced by stress in the weld metal. Thicker plates, or joints under restraint, are more likely to display cracking from the zinc coating at the weld root. Also, the higher the alloy content of the weld metal, the greater will be the cracking susceptibility from zinc. Remedies for this form of cracking include (a) removal of zinc from the plate surfaces in the root area, (b) use of joints designed to avoid inadequate penetration by any bead, (c) application of filler metal with a minimum alloy content, and (d) reduction of joint restraint by introduction of compressible spacers. Of course, the likelihood of cracking from zinc will depend upon the thickness of the galvanized coating. One investigation of this factor indicated that ½-inch thick steel plate with zinc coating thicknesses of 0.0005 inch or lighter (usually produced by electrogalvanizing) could be welded without cracking when depositing fillet welds with 3/16-inch E6010 electrodes in a cruciform specimen. As coating thickness increased from 0.0006 to 0.010 inch, cracking propensity steadily increased.

Because zinc boils at a relatively low temperature (1663 F), copious amounts of zinc vapor are generated during most fusion joining operations. This vapor is objectionable for several reasons. It has adverse physiological effects if inhaled by the welder. It disturbs the steady operation of the welding arc, and it causes porosity if trapped in the solidifying weld metal. Of course, the degree to which zinc is boiled off the base metal being welded, and the likelihood of entrapping vapor in the weld bead depends upon the welding process and procedure employed. The use of covered electrodes for shielded metal-arc welding which produce a light slag on the weld bead (i.e., E6010) are preferred over the more heavily covered electrodes. Submerged-arc weld deposits tend to be very porous because of the difficulty which the zinc vapor experiences trying to escape through the molten slag blanket. Although prior removal of zinc from the base metal edges to be welded is an obvious corrective for the difficulty, this seldom is economical to practice. Removal of zinc from plate edges has been tried in a number of ways. In addition to machine scarfing or scraping, zinc has been "boiled off" by using high welding currents, by welding simultaneously on each side of a Tee joint, by prior exposure to an oxyacetylene flame, and by oxygen cutting the edges to be welded. While oxygen cutting is of some help, assurance of crack-free welds is obtained only by complete removal of the zinc coating from the surfaces at the edges to be joined prior to welding. The gas shielded processes, gas tungsten-arc and gas metal-arc, offer a further means of dealing with the zinc problem. By increasing the flow of shielding gas substantially, and possibly by directing the flow at an angle to the surfaces of the workpieces, zinc vapor can be effectively removed from the area of the arc and weld pool. This technique is helpful in maintaining a stable welding arc, but does not assure freedom from cracking caused by molten zinc penetration at the root of weld beads.

Zinc also presents a problem in resistance welding. Here the copper alloy electrodes in contact with a galvanized surface pick up particles of zinc during the making of a number of welds. During the short intervals of heating, the zinc diffuses into the electrode and forms various kinds of brass which reduce the strength of the electrode alloy. Under a given set of welding conditions, the softened electrode will commence to deform or mushroom. The increase in electrode contact area acts to reduce weld nugget size at the faying surfaces of the base metal pieces. Unless the electrode is periodically redressed to proper size, or the welding current periodically increased, the weld nugget will decrease in diameter and then finally fail to form. The number of satisfactory resistance welds that can be made with galvanized steel will vary with the welding conditions. Here again, the thickness of the zinc coating also will be an influential factor. When compared with similar welding operations on bare steel, the resistance-spot or-seam welding of galvanized steel may require five times as much electrode redressing to maintain satisfactory weld nugget size. Much work has been done to develop an electrode alloy that will resist deterioration by the zinc in spot and seam welding, but to date the standard RWMA Class II electrode alloy appears to be as suitable as any new alloy proposed. One method of dealing with the electrode problem in spot welding is to turn to projection welding. Large flat-face electrodes are used to supply the current while the localized pressure is accomplished through projections embossed into one of a pair of sheet members, or machined or coined on a solid work-piece. The large, flat electrodes are water cooled and are not subject to localized heating. Therefore, they do not display rapid alloy pickup, pitting, erosion and other forms of deterioration as found on spot welding electrode tips and roller seam welding wheels.

The intergranular form of cracking from zinc penetration, as described earlier in arc-welded joints, also occurs in resistance-spot and -seam welds. Seam welds display a much greater susceptibility to this cracking than spot welds. The cracks ordinarily are microscopic in size and their presence often goes unnoticed. However, a modest pressure test of a resistance-seam welded joint will quickly disclose transverse fissures in the top and bottom (outer) faces of the weld. The cracking is far more prevalent on these outer surfaces which contact the electrodes, apparently because the copper or brass contamination picked up on the work surface from the tip or wheel accelerates the intergranular penetration. The fissures produced by penetration of the zinc and copper may propagate through the weld nugget and through the base metal in the heat-affected zone. Unfortunately, a satisfactory copper-free alloy electrode is not available for seam welding galvanized steel to alleviate this cracking mechanism.

When a knurled electrode wheel is employed in seam welding, the contacting weld surface often contains a greater number of cracks, presumably because of the stresses created in this surface by forming indentations.

Aluminum is another element which has come into wide use as a metallic coating on steel for corrosion and oxidation protection. Aluminum does not cause intergranular hot cracking as does zinc, but it exerts three distinct metallurgical effects, any one of which can cause trouble in welding. Aluminum readily forms an alloy with iron, even by diffusion at a moderate temperature, say 1000 F and above. The aluminum-iron alloy is quite brittle. When relatively small amounts of aluminum are alloyed with iron, the body-centered cubic crystallographic form (alpha iron or ferrite) tends to be stabilized. A consequence of having sufficient aluminum picked up in weld metal to form a "ferritic" steel is to have a coarse grained, brittle deposit in which the grain size cannot be refined through heat treatment. The third metallurgical trait of aluminum which can cause welding problems is its great affinity for oxygen. Unless very good protection from the atmosphere is provided, or a strong flux is employed, the surface coating of aluminum on steel will form a viscous, high-alumina slag which will interfere with the flow of molten weld metal and possibly will become entrapped in the weld deposit.

The chemical elements listed in Table 67 may be introduced in a harmful quantity by a great number of materials commonly encountered during welding. Boron can be present in fluxes as borax and may be picked up during fusion joining. Excessive boron can cause hot cracking. Copper can penetrate the grain boundaries of steel heated to a high temperature and may cause intergranular cracking. Usually, copper in molten form must come in contact with the heated steel. The higher the temperature of the steel, short of being molten, the more rapid the penetration of the copper into the grain boundaries. Circumstances favoring intergranular copper penetration easily can arise in many kinds of welding operations. When joining steel workpieces in a fixture built with copper hold-down bars, the arc may nip the edge of a copper bar and send the molten copper coursing through the grain boundaries of the base metal. A resistance welding operation in which copper penetration and cracking unexpectedly has been found to occur is illustrated in Fig. 169. During the high speed roller seam welding of steel sheet using continuous current, an arc appearently can occur between the electrode wheel and the work surface on the trailing or exit side. The arc melts tiny particles of copper alloy from the surface of the wheel which are deposited upon the heated surface of the welded seam. Rapid cooling of the wheel and work with generous amounts of water prevents deep intergranular penetration, but superficial cracking and somewhat deeper copper penetration can be clearly seen extending from the arc affected surface in Fig. 169.

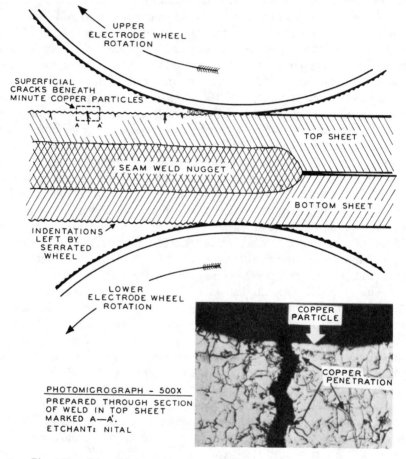

UPPER ELECTRODE WHEEL ROTATION

SUPERFICIAL CRACKS BENEATH MINUTE COPPER PARTICLES

A---A'

SEAM WELD NUGGET

TOP SHEET

BOTTOM SHEET

INDENTATIONS LEFT BY SERRATED WHEEL

LOWER ELECTRODE WHEEL ROTATION

COPPER PARTICLE

COPPER PENETRATION

PHOTOMICROGRAPH - 500X
PREPARED THROUGH SECTION OF WELD IN TOP SHEET MARKED A—A'.
ETCHANT: NITAL

Fig. 169 — Superficial cracking extending from surface of resistance seam weld in steel sheet.

Caused by arcing between wheel and work on exit side during application of continuous current. The arc transfers molten particles of copper alloy from the electrode wheel to the heat-affected work surface.

Cadmium, tin and lead are used as metallic coatings on steel and can act to cause hot cracking in fusion joining if a sufficient quantity is picked up by the weld metal. Phosphorus and sulfur may be present in various surface coatings applied for paint adherence, electrical insulation, and anti-friction purposes, but these elements when picked up by the weld metal can cause cracking and embrittlement.

DIFFICULTIES DURING MANIPULATION

In fusion joining operations on steel, the molten weld pool nearly always is covered by a thin layer of slag, which may be formed by a flux in gas welding, by the covering materials from an electrode, or by just the traces of oxide that form under a gas-shielded arc. This slag covers the weld pool except directly under the torch flame or arc, Fig. 170. Here the slag is churned into the weld melt, which is benefited thereby. Farther from the flame the slag attempts to clean the surface of the steel in advance of the weld melt and protects the molten metal from the atmosphere.

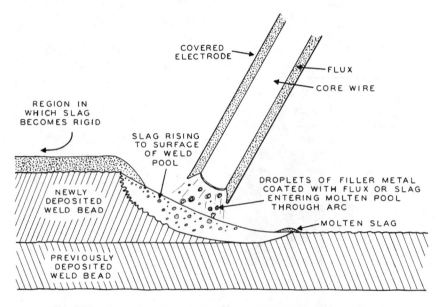

Fig. 170 — Flux is churned into the weld melt, quickly coalesces, and rises to join the fluid layer of slag. Note slag clearing the way for weld metal.

SLAG INCLUSIONS

Any particle of nonmetallic material imbedded in a body of metal, save perhaps graphite which is a microstructural constituent, may be regarded as a slag inclusion. The source of these particles need not be a slag or flux on the surface of the metal, but may also originate in the metal as the products of a deoxidation reaction. Elements like sulfur and selenium form nonmetallic inclusions; however, these are not usually referred to as slag inclusions. The shape of slag inclusions in cast metal or deposited weld metal is globular, and as such they have little effect on the mechanical properties of the metal if there are not too many large ones. Hot working, as carried out in rolling or forging, will elongate the inclusions. It is well to keep in mind, however, that inclusions bear watching, particularly if they are exposed on a stressed surface. Slag which is entrapped mechanically as a result of improper manipulation is generally the most troublesome, since the size of the inclusion is usually quite large. We might point out, however, the various ways in which slag inclusions arise. When metal-arc welding with covered electrodes, both

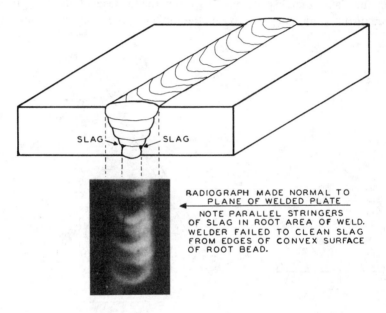

RADIOGRAPH MADE NORMAL TO PLANE OF WELDED PLATE

NOTE PARALLEL STRINGERS OF SLAG IN ROOT AREA OF WELD. WELDER FAILED TO CLEAN SLAG FROM EDGES OF CONVEX SURFACE OF ROOT BEAD.

Fig. 171 — "Wagon tracks" of slag inclusions as detected by radiographic examination.

metal and flux coverings are churned into the weld puddle or crater. If globules of flux or slag are trapped among the growing crystals at the left end of the weld melt in Fig. 170, inclusions will be found in the solid weld. In overhead welding the welder can allow only a very short time for the weld melt to freeze, otherwise there is dripping. Consequently, overhead welds tend to have more slag inclusions than flat position welds. When manganese, silicon, aluminum, and other deoxidizers are present in the weld melt, their reaction with iron oxide produces complex oxides that are insoluble in the metal and which may be molten or solid at the melt temperature. Whether the bulk of the reaction product escapes the metal and joins the slag on the surface depends upon many factors to be mentioned. The covering at the end of the electrode may chip, owing possibly to gas evolution, shock, or inversion of silica. The pieces of covering may drop into, and remain in the solidifying weld. Another source of entrapped slag is the slag on preceding beads through which the electrode has failed to fuse, particularly in undercuts and in deep furrows on each side of a weld bead having a pronounced convex shape. The latter condition has been encountered in deep grooves when the root bead or subsequent early passes have a convex shape. If a subsequent pass fails to penetrate sufficiently deep to melt out the slag that is held along each side furrow, the radiograph will disclose almost continuous lines of entrapped slag as illustrated in Fig. 171. This registry on the radiograph often has been called "wagon tracks" for a reason which is quite obvious.

Film-shaped inclusions may occur under exceptionally poor welding conditions. The film-shaped inclusions are a most serious form of defect, and can arise in the following ways. If a filler metal is added drop-by-drop and there is inadequate flux or some other form of shielding, a film of oxide forms around each drop of metal. Unless the weld melt is stirred to work the film to the surface, it will remain in the weld metal. While the oxide film may not remain unbroken around each original droplet, it easily can have sufficient continuity to detract seriously from the strength and toughness of the weld metal.

If a new weld bead is started at the end of a previously deposited bead (for example, upon changing manual, covered electrodes) without thoroughly removing the slag from the end of the first bead, the slag may become entrapped in the newly deposited layer of metal. A heavy oxide film or scale may act in a similar manner. The flowing of new metal over a scale-covered surface creates a condition known in the foundry as a *cold shut*. When weld metal spatters on the groove faces ahead and the welder hastily deposits metal over the oxide-coated globules, the films that coat the globules may remain in the weld.

The elimination of slag from the molten weld metal has been the subject of much study. To hasten the rise of slag to the surface of the melt, it might be thought sufficient to lessen the resistance to the rise of the globules. Here again, the larger the slag particle, the faster it tends to rise, but it must be remembered that whereas liquid slag particles can coalesce, solid particles cannot. The depth of the melt has little effect on the trapping of slag inclusions because the deeper melt solidifies more slowly, which allows time for the inclusions to rise. However, the hotter the melt, the more fluid it is, and the less resistance is offered to the rise of inclusions. A little reflection will show that the advantage of raising the temperature of the melt is outweighed by disadvantages. As the temperature is raised, the slag on the surface becomes more fluid (less viscous) and does not cover the metal to the proper extent. Then, too, at elevated temperatures the weld melt dissolves slag to a greater extent. Intentional overheating therefore is not a good policy.

Summarizing, the following factors chiefly affect the trapping of slag inclusions:

Viscosity of Melt — The more viscous the melt, the slower the inclusions coalesce and rise to the surface. The viscosity of the weld melt rapidly increases as the melt cools.

Temperature — The higher the temperature, the greater is the extent to which the slag dissolves in the weld metal, which, being more fluid also allows the slag to rise.

Rate of Cooling — The faster the rate of freezing, the greater is the likelihood of trapping slag inclusions.

Stirring — The greater the agitation of the bath, the greater the likelihood of trapping slag, unless the slag is worked to the surface by controlled manipulation.

Penetrators or Flat-Fractures in Flash Welded Joints

A practical example of the detrimental influence of oxide particle entrapment is found in flash welds made in ordinary low-carbon steel. For many years, manufacturers using this welding process were troubled and puzzled by small, flat facets on the fracture surfaces of welds broken in tension or bending as illustrated in Fig. 172. These flat spots became known as "penetrators" and were recognized to represent a portion of the weld which fractured prematurely. Their presence was particularly objectionable when the welded joint had to be subjected to cold forming operations during fabrication of the article. These small areas along the weld opened up as a fissure or a crack, and sometimes propagated to cause complete fracture of the weld. Although some evidence has been obtained that similar areas of premature fracture can arise from microstructural changes in "banded" steels, penetrators in low-carbon steel flash welded joints have been traced to the presence of oxide particles entrapped along the interface of the base metal pieces as shown in Fig. 172. It is suspected that the condition arises when unusually deep craters form in the flashing faces of the base metal pieces (possibly from too high a flashing voltage) and the degree of upset following the flashing stage is not sufficient to expel all of the oxide which forms in the crater areas. This crater hypothesis explains the discontinuous or localized occurrence of the penetrators.

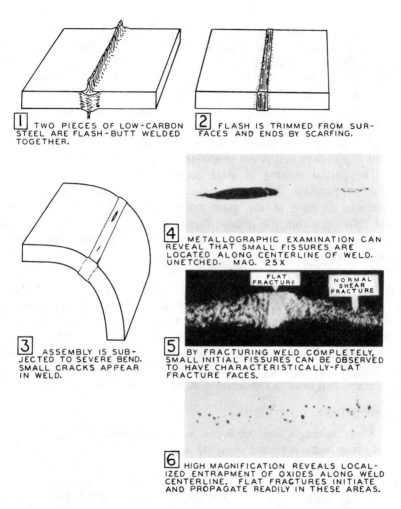

1. TWO PIECES OF LOW-CARBON STEEL ARE FLASH-BUTT WELDED TOGETHER.

2. FLASH IS TRIMMED FROM SURFACES AND ENDS BY SCARFING.

3. ASSEMBLY IS SUBJECTED TO SEVERE BEND. SMALL CRACKS APPEAR IN WELD.

4. METALLOGRAPHIC EXAMINATION CAN REVEAL THAT SMALL FISSURES ARE LOCATED ALONG CENTERLINE OF WELD. UNETCHED. MAG. 25X

5. BY FRACTURING WELD COMPLETELY, SMALL INITIAL FISSURES CAN BE OBSERVED TO HAVE CHARACTERISTICALLY-FLAT FRACTURE FACES.

6. HIGH MAGNIFICATION REVEALS LOCALIZED ENTRAPMENT OF OXIDES ALONG WELD CENTERLINE. FLAT FRACTURES INITIATE AND PROPAGATE READILY IN THESE AREAS.

Fig. 172 — "Penetrators" or flat-fractures in a flash weld joint in low-carbon steel caused by entrapped oxide particles.

BURNING

In any discussion of heating steel to 2200 F and above (white heat), the term *burning* is bound to be mentioned. By burning, one of the three following phenomena may be meant:

1. Burning in the sense of oxygen cutting.

2. The penetration of oxides through the grain boundaries of steel, rendering it brittle and fit only for remelting.

3. The partial melting of steel.

Definition 1 has been discussed in Chapter 3. The intergranular oxidation in the second definition occurs when steel is heated in an oxidizing furnace atmosphere above about 2300 F. Ordinarily the oxide does not penetrate rapidly and it may require a half-hour or more for the formation of a deep layer of grains surrounded by oxide. Under the cogging rolls or forging hammer at any temperature, steel oxidized in this way will break up. Burning in the sense of definition 2 is not likely to occur in any type of fusion joining because there is a flux over the metal and an atmosphere that is not oxidizing while the metal is at a white heat.

The partial melting of steel occurs when it is heated above the solidus temperature. No matter what the composition of the steel, it commences to melt in the grain boundaries, with isolated patches of liquid forming within the grains. Should the steel be hot worked in any way while the liquid metal is still in the grain boundaries, the steel will break up. We would expect this behavior of any alloy in the mushy stage. If the steel is cooled to a temperature at which there is no longer any liquid in the grain boundaries, it may regain its ductility. In some instances, the intergranular liquid films do not solidify into sound metal, and the grain boundaries of the steel will contain fissures or porosity. The partial melting of a metal or an alloy in this manner often is called *liquation*, and surprisingly, this intergranular melting can occur at an unexpectedly low temperature in highly alloyed materials, or when residual elements are present that tend to concentrate in or near grain boundaries.

UNDERCUTTING

When making a weld by fusion joining, particularly with the electric arc, the base metal is melted along the wall of a groove or along the surface to a point which later is called the *toe* of the weld, Fig. 173 (a). As filler metal is added, we expect the weld melt to fill the joint and replace the metal at the toe, and to form a suitable flared or filleted junction with the base metal. A number of factors in welding tend to prevent the weld melt from completely filling the area immediately adjacent to the base metal. Instead of producing a desirable junction like that shown in Fig. 173 (b), we find too often that the toe of the weld actually contains a small unfilled ditch or undercut as shown in Fig. 173 (c). Undercutting may range in size from a gross, readily seen, continuous furrow down to very small discontinuous rifts no more than a few mils in depth.

Beware to the welding engineer or welder who is inclined to slight the significance of undercutting! It has proved to be the defect with the worst record for causing mechanical failures in weldments. Undercutting creates "notch-effect" at the toe of the weld — right at the very location

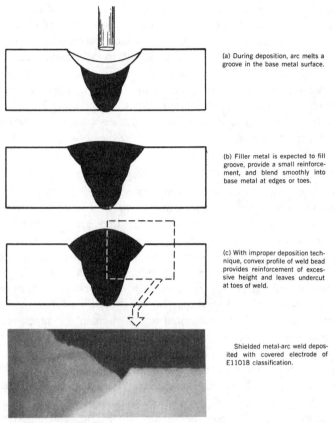

(a) During deposition, arc melts a groove in the base metal surface.

(b) Filler metal is expected to fill groove, provide a small reinforcement, and blend smoothly into base metal at edges or toes.

(c) With improper deposition technique, convex profile of weld bead provides reinforcement of excessive height and leaves undercut at toes of weld.

Shielded metal-arc weld deposited with covered electrode of E11018 classification.

Fig. 173 — Undercutting at the toe of a weld made by fusion joining.

where the regular weld reinforcement tends to cause some stress concentration because of the change in cross section of the members. If any workman were asked to devise some means of quickly breaking an article at a weld joint, he undoubtedly would make a saw-cut at the edge of the weld and then strike a blow on the adjoining member. It is difficult to understand why an undercut would be tolerated at this same crucial location, particularly if the weld joint is likely to be subjected to impact loading. An insidious role played by undercutting is to concentrate cyclic stress at the toe of the weld and thus exceed the fatigue strength of the metal. The importance of undercutting in this respect is not widely appreciated, as will be discussed shortly in describing cracking from fatigue.

Undercutting is promoted by many conditions in welding, some of which are not yet completely understood. Traveling at an excessive speed probably is the most common cause. Under these conditions the filler metal being deposited does not have sufficient time to flow to the toe and form a proper junction. Any condition which forces the weld bead to assume a marked convex contour is likely to accentuate undercutting. High viscosity slag, weld melt with a high surface tension, improper direction of arc forces as associated with electrode position are only a few of the less obvious reasons for undercut formation. Even the mode of metal transfer from a consumable electrode can affect the tendency for undercutting to occur.

SPATTER

The fine droplets of metal which are ejected from the area of a weld during fusion joining are called *spatter*. These droplets may be thrown from the weld pool, but more often they are ejaculated from the electrode or welding rod. The most profuse spatter occurs when globules of metal being transferred from a consumable electrode to the pool bridge the arc gap and create a short circuit condition. The surge of current which ordinarily occurs superheats the globule and causes it to explode in a shower of white hot spatter.

Spatter occurrence is promoted by a number of reactions in the various processes. Excessive amounts of gas being liberated from the rapidly cooling metal can cause spatter. Reactions between certain elements in the metal, for example, sulfur and gases in the atmosphere surrounding the weld melt can create spatter. Often the droplets ejected are oxidized during their brief flight and do no more than burn holes in the welder's clothing or fall upon the surface of the base metal. While these particles usually can be brushed off, it is very important to appreciate that the larger particles of spatter falling upon the base metal are capable of two unfavorable metallurgical effects. First, the particles may carry sufficient thermal energy to create a small, superficial heat-affected area, similar to that formed by an arc strike. As trivial as they may seem, droplets of spatter have been shown to cause minute hardened spots in alloy steel weldments which ultimately failed by crack initiation at one of these spots.

DIFFICULTIES DURING COOLING

The appearance of the surface of a weld bead as it is deposited and is cooling often provides a good deal of information. During welding, the metal should not become covered with a too thick layer of slag. The metal should not foam or spark. Sparks are caused by small particles of steel ejected from the weld metal as a gas bubble bursts upon reaching the surface. The small, hot drop of steel burns in the air. The solid weld should contain no cracks and no pock marks left by escaping bubbles. The rippled surface is caused by spasmodic progressive solidification of the weld metal bead. The size and shape of the ripple formations are related to the speed of welding (amount of metal deposited in a unit time), welding process and procedure, and the range of solidification of the steel.

SEGREGATION

In general, we may say that there are two kinds of segregation: first, microsegregation or coring as it was described in Chapter 7, and second, gross segregation which concerns the body of metal as a whole. Gross segregation is seldom observed in weld metal. In castings and ingots, it

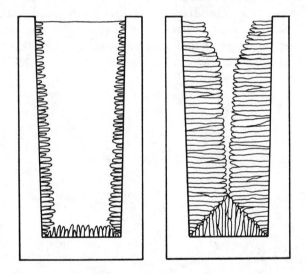

Fig. 174 — Freezing of steel in a mold. (left) freezing begun; (right) freezing nearly complete.

is a major difficuty. The first metal to freeze on the wall of an ingot mold is rich in iron. The metal crystallizes on the walls first because this is the coolest point — the surface which is abstracting heat. The remaining liquid at the center of the ingot is richer in carbon and particularly in the impurity sulfur, than the initial melt. By the time most of the ingot has solidified, the liquid, which still occupies the upper center portion of the mold, can be rather high in impurities.

The difference in composition between the center and outer portions of the solidified ingot is called segregation. In contrast with coring which may be equalized by annealing, segregation is more or less permanent. It can be eliminated to some degree only in the case of certain elements. Ingot molds, Fig. 174, must be designed so that the regions of worst segregation will be removed when the ingot is cropped before rolling. Even so, it is unusual for wrought products to be completely free from segregation. Ingots produced by (a) consumable electrode vacuum arc remelting, and (b) electroslag melting contain the least segregation, which probably can be ignored for most applications. Rimmed steel can be looked upon as the most highly segregated steel, but here the segregation is deliberate in order to secure an essentially pure iron rim.

A crude test has been used to estimate the degree of sulfur segregation in a piece of steel. A sheet of ordinary photographic paper is soaked in a 2 percent solution of sulfuric acid in water. The sensitized emulsion side of the paper is next pressed against the smooth ground, clean surface of the steel sample, rinsed in water, and fixed in hypo solution. A brown pattern formed on the paper indicates the relative distribution of sulfides. The darker and heavier the marks, the more sulfur is indicated to be present.

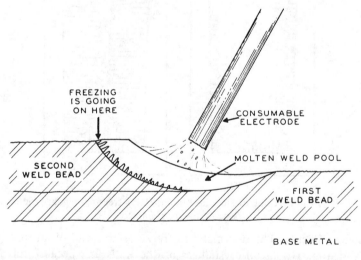

Fig. 175 — Solidification of a second bead of weld metal on the first bead.

Segregation seldom is observed in weld metal because the pool of molten metal is usually being stirred by various forces and because the solidifying crystals advance into the weld melt from one surface only, Fig. 175. New metal of constant composition is continually being added into the weld melt at the other end. However, whenever solidification proceeds from more than one surface, evidence of segregation usually can be found in the area where the solidifying fronts meet. This condition can be found in a complete penetration weld where solidification proceeds strongly from opposing sidewalls, or in a very thick surfacing weld where solidification proceeds from the top surface downward as well as from the base metal interface upward. Of course, the relatively rapid solidification rate of weld metal greatly reduces the likelihood of segregation. Nevertheless, traces of segregation, particularly of compounds of carbon, sulfur and columbium, can be found in weld metal areas which were the last to solidify. The central portion of a weld crater is a potential area of segregation, especiallly when the metal cools and solidifies at a relatively slow rate.

SOLIDIFICATION SHRINKAGE

Reverting to the diagrams of the solidification of steel in an ingot mold, we observe that the level of the liquid falls as freezing progresses, because the crystals occupy less space (are denser) than the liquid. When

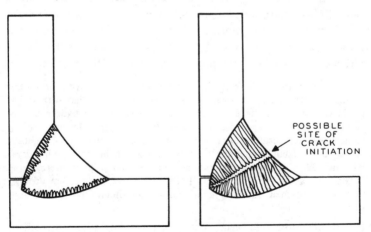

Fig. 176 — Possible source of a crack in a single-bead fillet weld. Solidification starts at both walls instead of at the root of the weld. Shrinkage at the surface centerline is analogous to pipe.

the last drop of liquid has solidified, there remains a more or less deep cavity, called a pipe, in the upper center portion of the ingot, unless special precautions are taken to prevent its formation. Pipe cavities can be distinguished from blowholes by the dendritic appearance of the pipe. The liquid has been drawn away from the solidifying crystals, exposing their dendritic structure. Upon rare occasions, wrought steel containing rolled out pipe cavities will be presented for welding. Since the welding heat tends to open the oxidized pipe cavity, the steel should not be welded.

In fillet welding, conditions may be such that solidification starts at the root or at both sides. If solidification starts at both sides, Fig. 176, there is a tendency to form a pipe cavity or crack through the throat of the weld. The root angle will be less sharp if successive layers are deposited, but the initial crack may tend to propagate through them.

BLOWHOLES AND POROSITY

Blowholes are smooth-wall, rounded openings which are sometimes observed in the surface of weld metal. They look every bit like wormholes — if one can imagine a lowly earthworm escaping from the surface of weld metal. Blowholes represent the escape point of gas from the solidifying weld metal. A trifle earlier, the gas might have escaped and the molten metal would have flowed into the escape point and obliterated the hole. A trifle later and the gas might have been trapped beneath the surface of the solidifying weld metal. Gas trapped internally forms smooth-wall, *bright,* rounded cavities which usually are referred to as *porosity.* Porosity occurs internally because the gas could not rise and escape through the surface owing to lack of time and to the viscosity of the weld melt. Blowholes and porosity arise from three effects:

1. Gases are less soluble in liquid steel at low temperatures than at high temperatures. Hydrogen, as we have learned, is a gas with which liquid steel may become saturated in fusion joining. The hydrogen may be derived from the fuel gases or the electrode covering. During cooling from a high temperature after saturation, the gas comes out of solution in the form of bubbles. If the bubbles are trapped in the growing crystals, instead of rising to the surface of the liquid melt, porosity is formed. To avoid porosity or blowholes, avoid overheating, but arrange that the weld melt solidifies continuously, not intermittently in large steps.

2. Mild steel weld metal contains carbon and oxygen in solution. When crystallization commences, the first crystals to freeze are low in carbon, according to the equilibrium diagram. The remaining liquid is enriched in carbon and a reaction occurs between carbon and dissolved oxygen to form carbon monoxide. The bubbles may create a foam, indicative of improper welding conditions. The corrective is manganese and particularly silicon, which when added to the weld melt through the filler metal, remove the dissolved oxygen from the steel as liquid oxide of manganese or solid oxide of silicon (silica).

A similar reaction occurs in the welding of steel containing un-usually high sulfur, the gas evolved being either sulfur dioxide (SO_2) or hydrogen sulfide (H_2S). To form the latter gas mentioned, the hy-drogen may be supplied by combusted fuel gas, moisture, or other hydrogen-containing compounds in an electrode covering, or the hy-drogen gas in the atomic-hydrogen welding process. A segregated steel in which the sulfur is high only in the center of the plate may also produce porous welds.

3. Many of the materials used as fluxes or constituents in elec-trode covering dissociate when heated to high temperatures, and may produce a gas. If particles of this kind of material are inadvertently mixed in the weld melt, say through faulty operation of an arc-welding electrode where pieces of the covering flake off and are covered over by the molten weld metal, they will discharge gas and may cause blowholes. Limestone in an electrode covering is a material which can act in this way.

The distribution of temperature in the weld melt should enter any discussion of blowholes. Gas is absorbed in the region of the highest temperature under the flame, Fig. 177. The gas is evolved particularly among the growing crystals because a gas is much less soluble in crystals than in liquid metal at the solidification point. Agitation of the melt tends to equalize the temperature of the weld melt and favors absorption of gases. The surface of the weld melt is always at a higher temperature than the bottom of the melt. The weld melt, therefore, tends to freeze from the bottom upward, which is favorable to the evolution of gas in

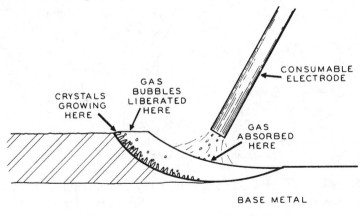

Fig. 177 — Gas bubbles may be liberated during the crystallization of the weld melt, and may be entrapped in the growing crystals. Porosity is the result.

the flat welding position. If the temperature range over which solidification occurs is large, the gas bubbles evolved have more opportunity to rise to the surface than if the range is small.

The viscosity of the weld metal also plays an important part in the escape of gas bubbles. Weld metal for overhead deposition must have a high viscosity. The high viscosity is secured by preventing the temperature of the melt from rising far above the melting range. High viscosity of weld metal entails slow rise of gas bubbles from the melt. Raising the temperature of weld metal lowers its viscosity, which favors the rise of gas bubbles. However, the high temperature favors the solution of gases, which are not evolved until the temperature has fallen to that of high viscosity. Consequently, porosity is not avoided by raising the temperature of the weld melt, except in so far as high weld temperature involves slow cooling. The larger the gas bubble, the faster it rises. Decrease in welding speed is an excellent precaution to reduce porosity.

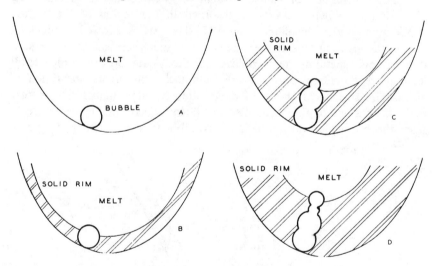

Fig. 178 — Cross section of a weld melt showing four stages in solidification, with the formation of a worm hole.

The gas holes in weld metal generally are spherical. They have detached themselves from the crystals on which they formed and have started to rise to the surface. Their rise was less rapid than the growth of the crystals. Sometimes blowholes with several constrictions (worm holes) are found. Their mode of formation is illustrated in Fig. 178. At (a) the blowhole has formed on a growing crystal, but has not detached itself perhaps because other crystals are above, or the melt is stagnant and no other bubbles are rising to create a liquid current. The crystals have grown partly around it at (b) when a new evolution of gas occurs enlarging the bubble beyond the constriction at (c). Several constrictions thus may occur, (d). High viscosity of weld metal obviously favors worm holes by discouraging the rise of bubbles. Worm holes can therefore be defined as elongated blowholes that result from progressive evolution of gas during freezing. An actual metal specimen containing several worm holes is illustrated in Fig. 179.

Fig. 179 — Worm holes in weld metal (Blomberg)

Another theory advanced to explain the formation of worm holes is that the initial cavity or gas pocket may be formed by a particular gas which may have exceeded its solubility limit, or which may be the product of a chemical reaction that is insoluble in the metal. The partial pressure of the gas in this initial pocket has no effect on other gases dissolved in the steel and soon these other gases are evolved into the cavity increasing its pressure and causing it to grow.

Users of covered electrodes for shielded metal-arc welding would do well to consider the moisture content of the flux covering if they plan to apply them to weldments which have critical requirements for weld metal porosity. In general, the cellulosic type coverings cannot be dried to very low moisture contents because the operating qualities of the electrode suffer. As shown in Chapter 8, Table 40, the covering on an E6010 electrode normally contains about 4% moisture. Under the operating conditions of this class electrode, the amount of hydrogen picked up by the weld metal ordinarily is not sufficient to cause significant porosity or blowhole formation unless large amounts of elements are present, like carbon, sulfur or selenium. These elements react with hydrogen to form gaseous compounds which have little or no solubility in the molten weld metal. However, unsound practices sometimes are found in commercial fabrication. For example, experienced welders have been known to dip E6010 electrodes into water — having found that this treatment seems to provide smoother operating characteristics for certain kinds of weld joints. The amount of internal porosity caused by the indeterminate quantity of moisture absorbed by the electrode covering is problematical, to say the least.

Low-hydrogen mineral covered electrodes also require surveillance. Although these electrodes are manufactured to meet stipulated maxima for moisture (see Chapter 10), the kind of packaging, storage conditions, and handling just prior to use is equally important in controlling the amount of hydrogen obtainable from the flux covering. Unless proper practices are followed, the moisture content easily may reach a level sufficient to cause porosity, perhaps 1 or 2% moisture. In some borderline cases, the porosity appears in the beads only in the starting area, and is difficult to distinguish from the "starting porosity" described earlier in this chapter. Briefly, the ideal practice in handling low-hydrogen electrodes just prior to use is (1) rebake at 600 to 800 F, depending on the classification, any electrodes suspected of having a moisture content above the level specified for the particular class, and (2) hold all electrodes in a heated container at 50 to 250 F degrees above ambient temperature until needed for immediate welding. Since the latter practice would require that a heated container be maintained at the welder's side, many manufacturers of weldments allow small lots of properly baked low-hydrogen electrodes to be withdrawn from a central oven. Each lot of electrodes must be used within a specified time, or they must be returned to the oven for rebaking before use. Two hours is a common period of time allowed for usage, unless environmental conditions appear to require a shorter period.

CRACKING

Cracks probably are the most feared type of defect in weldments. Because of the wide application of welding to many types of steels and joint configurations, considerable vigilance must be exercised so that cracking is anticipated and avoided, or at least detected and its removal contemplated. Cracking is an exceedingly complex subject, cracks appear in many forms, in many locations, and occur over the broadest possible range of temperature. Some cracks are readily detectable while others are not. It is not uncommon to find some uncertainty over whether a particular weldment is free of cracking. Actually, many steel weldments have very small cracks present, but because of the size of the defect and the good fracture toughness of most steels, these imperfections in the structure do not interfere with its performance in service. However, only through a rapidly growing knowledge of welding technology can cracking be kept under satisfactory control.

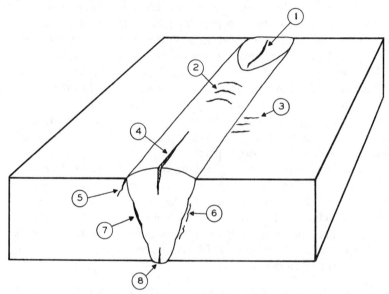

Fig. 180 — Classification of cracking according to location in a weldment

1. Weld metal crater cracking
2. Weld metal transverse cracking
3. Base metal heat-affected zone transverse cracking
4. Weld metal longitudinal cracking
5. Toe cracking
6. Underbead cracking
7. Fusion line cracking
8. Weld metal root cracking

Cracks represent the failure under stress of a metal when it is behaving in a brittle fashion — brittleness being understood to mean the inclination to fracture without deformation. It is not difficult to account for the fracture of a piece of metal that has undergone severe deformation. However, we sometimes are confronted by cases where a piece of steel has fractured or cracked with practically no sign of deformation even though conventional mechanical property tests made at room temperature may show the material to be strong and reasonably ductile. Failures like these can require considerable ingenuity to ascertain the cause of cracking.

The location of a crack in a weldment is one of the first characteristics to be carefully noted in a search for cause and cure. In general, cracking occurs in three locations: (1) weld metal, (2) fusion line, and (3) base metal heat-affected zone. As illustrated in Fig. 180, cracking in these three locations may be further identified as to the particular portion or point at which it occurs, and the orientation of the cracking with respect to the longitudinal axis of the weld. While the schematic drawing in Fig. 180 contains cracks easily seen by the unaided eye, cracking may range in size from very large *macrocracks* down to extremely small fissures or *microcracks*. The latter usually are found with the aid of a microscope (often by metallographic examination), and may be as short as a single grain in length. Microcracks may be so tight as to require special etching and staining techniques to establish that a discontinuity exists in the metal at the suspect point.

The temperature at which cracking occurs in a piece of metal plays an important part in determining the route of propagation through the microstructure. This, in turn, affects the texture of the fracture faces. Although cracking may occur at almost any level of temperature up to the point where the metal is completely molten, we usually can classify these fractures as *hot cracks* or *cold cracks* according to certain characteristics which they generally display.

CHARACTERISTICS AND OCCURRENCE OF HOT CRACKING

When cracks occur at an elevated temperature, perhaps 1000 F and above, the path of the crack through the metal generally is intergranular, that is, it travels in the boundaries between the grains instead of through the grains themselves. Also, where the crack has extended to the surface of the piece and air has been allowed to enter, the fractured surfaces when laid open for examination will be found coated with oxide. The nature of the oxide is sometimes an indication of the temperature level at which the cracking occurred, since it may range from a temper discoloration to an actual black scale. These are the identifying features of a hot crack.

Hot Cracking in Solidifying Welds

The first temperature range in which brittle behavior is exhibited by steel is the end of the solidification range. In any commercial weld melt there are alloying elements and impurities (carbon, manganese, phosphorus, molybdenum, etc.) that cause freezing to occur over a range of temperature, perhaps 50 to 75 degrees F for mild steel. As the weld melt cools and reaches the liquidus temperature, the first crystal to form contains a greater percentage of iron and therefore a lower percentage of carbon than the weld melt. Fig. 181. After the temperature has fallen 20 degrees or so, the weld is a mixture of liquid metal fairly high in carbon content and of metal crystals fairly low in carbon content. The

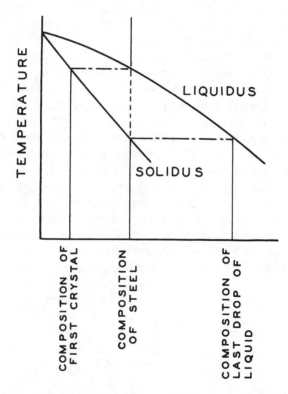

Fig. 181 — When the steel is between the liquidus and solidus, it is in the mushy stage.

weld is now in the mushy stage. At the lower end of the solidification range, although the mass may give the impression of solidity, it has no tensile strength. Not until every drop of liquid has frozen will the weld metal possess strength and ductility. The condition of the metal in the mushy stage can be likened to logs in a sawmill pond. The grains of metal resemble the logs which can be pulled about easily and separated from each other; yet once the water freezes, the logs are cemented firmly together. For this reason, if steel is vibrated, pulled, or otherwise disturbed just as the last liquid is undergoing solidification, it fails at absurdly low stresses and with scarcely any elongation. The failure, of course, takes place through the minute proportion of liquid that was to have solidified last and presumably would have formed a grain boundary. Instead, a fissure has opened without visible deformation of the metal, and if the surfaces of the cracks are examined at room temperature, they will be found temper colored or scaled. Since the liquid metal responsible for the cracking is in the spaces between the growing crystals, the fracture is intercrystalline or intergranular.

Some investigators who have studied hot cracking in weld metal question any explanation based upon the presence of liquid metal in the structure at the time of crack initiation. Instead, they have theorized on a mechanism by which cracking is initiated in the solid state. One proponent of this theory points out as one piece of evidence that hot cracks always appear to initiate at a location behind the solidification front (as interpreted from the frequent penetration of liquid metal into a crack which has propagated to the solid–liquid interface). On the other hand, the majority of investigators seem to support the liquid film theory, and have developed equally convincing, detailed explanations for the cracking mechanism. For example, one investigator points out that cracks are most likely initiated when an *almost continuous* liquid film is present between the solid crystals or dendrites. This particular distribution of liquid allows very high stresses to be built up between grains even though the nominal stress may be relatively low. If a greater amount of liquid were present, it could prevent the high localized stresses from developing.

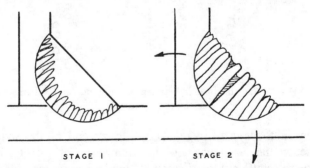

STAGE 1   STAGE 2

Fig. 182 — Two stages in the freezing of a fillet weld, showing narrow spaces partly filled with shrinking liquid (shaded). Arrows indicate the direction of shrinkage stresses, which are opposite to the direction of shrinkage distortions.

Regardless of the exact mechanism by which cracking takes place, hot cracking in weld beads may occur because the cooling of the joint results in contraction of the weld metal and base metal which imposes stress upon the weld metal. From another viewpoint, we might say that the contraction tends to move the base metal pieces apart. If the contraction cannot be tolerated by the weld metal, either through readjustment of crystals and liquid when the metal is in the mushy stage, or through deformation when the metal is completely solid, then cracking will take place. Figure 182 illustrates the early stage of solidification in a fillet weld and also the condition that might exist just prior to the development of a hot crack. When a fillet weld of this kind is cooling, the solid weld metal welded to the walls of the fillet is contracting, movement being in the direction of the arrows. Unless the plates are thin, they will promote sufficient stress to pull apart the crystals at the throat, which are separated by only thin films of liquid metal of zero tensile strength during the last moment of freezing. In this way, hot cracks may arise in welds. Weld metal which has a very wide freezing range is particularly prone to develop hot cracks because small amounts of molten metal are present in the bead for a longer period of time and generally to a lower temperature. A typical hot crack in a fillet weld is shown in Fig. 183 (a) and (b).

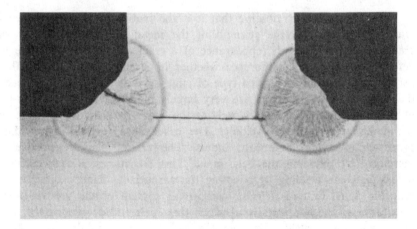

Fig. 183(a) — Hot crack in a restrained fillet weld. Bead on left of vertical member was deposited after the one on the right. Hot crack developed in the left bead because of greater degree of restraint. Specimen polished and lightly etched in nital to reveal weld metal and base metal heat-affected zones.

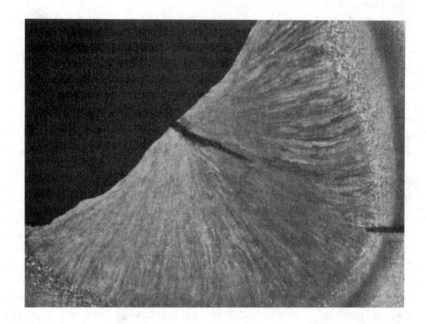

Fig. 183(b) — Enlarged view of left-hand fillet weld shown in
Fig. 183(a). Note columnar growth of grains in weld metal
structure.

It is important to observe that it is the inability to deform without cracking, rather than the strength of the metal at the temperature of cracking, that governs the appearance of a crack. If the metal is able to deform, it makes little difference whether its strength is 100 or 10,000 psi, because in welding a given type of joint, such as a butt weld in sheet, the shrinkage and distortion are very largely independent of the strength of the metal, but are related closely to the heat input, that is, the size of the flame and speed of welding. The cracks are favored by welding processes involving large heat inputs. The cracks may be prevented, therefore, by reducing the heat input. This sometimes is accomplished in oxyacetylene welding by adopting the carburizing flame technique. A reducing flame is used to raise the carbon content of the groove faces, thus lowering the temperature at which they melt and decreasing the heat input required to weld. However, the carbon pickup in the weld metal may have an undesirable influence upon its properties. A smaller size oxyacetylene flame and a smaller weld bead usually are the safer hot crack preventatives. In the arc welding processes, heat input is lowered by reducing the current and/or voltage, or by increasing the travel speed with the same power level.

Crater Cracks in Weld Metal

Craters in weld metal are prone to develop cracks because the crater cools more rapidly than the remainder of the bead, and because the crater solidifies from all sides toward the center, thus favoring shrinkage cracks. If the composition of the steel includes elements which are prone to segregate, like carbon, sulfur and columbium, these are likely to increase the susceptibility to crater cracking. In attempting to avoid a crater, the electrode should not be drawn away from the joint in a manner that will mar or produce a heat-affected zone in the base metal. By withdrawing the electrode slowly, the crater can be filled with metal, but the last droplets to be added may not receive proper protection from the atmosphere. The most satisfactory means of dealing with the crater problem is to make use of a "crater filler," a device which permits the welding power to be decreased in a controlled manner by the welder to fill the crater and extinguish the arc.

Hot Cracking in Reheated Metal

Hot cracks are not confined to weld metal, but may be found in the heat-affected zone of the base metal as well. Some highly alloyed compositions of base metal contain constituents in the microstructure which are in the nature of complex carbides or intermetallic compounds. These constituents display a wide variety of properties, considering strength, ductility and melting point. When we stop to consider that the base metal heat-affected zone in the area immediately adjacent to the weld metal reaches a temperature possibly in the range of 2100 to 2400 F during welding, it is not idle to imagine that these complex constituents at a point next to the weld fusion line might become weak or possibly even melt at some time during the welding operation. If tension stresses arise in the heat-affected zone at the time when the complex constituents are in a condition of low strength, or incipient melting, a hot crack can initiate at this point. Sometimes residual elements form these low melting or temperature sensitive compounds, for example, sulfur. Investigators have observed that the sulfide inclusions which promote hot cracking in high-strength steels may be barely perceptible in metallographic examination. Yet, susceptibility to hot cracking in the base metal heat-affected zone can be directly correlated with sulfur content.

An example of hot cracking in reheated metal is the intergranular cracking sometimes found at the edge of welds in Cr–Mo steel sheet and tubing containing approximately 0.35% C, 1.0% Cr and 0.20% Mo. The cracks are found in the base metal just adjacent to the weld metal, which usually contains a lower-carbon alloy-steel filler metal. Whenever these cracks extend to the surface of the weldment, air enters and forms a film of oxide on the crack surfaces, indicating that the cracking took place while the metal was quite hot. The color of the oxide gives a rough indication of the temperature level when the crack reached the surface. It is easy to deduce that the crack developed because the base metal was brittle and could not deform in conformity with the distortions that the remainder of the joint was undergoing. Again the question arises on the nature of the condition which developed in the grain boundaries to cause the cracking, that is, whether the boundaries were solid, but weak, or actually contained a liquid film. Many investigators believe that hot cracks in the base metal heat-affected zone are a result of fusible grain boundary segregates becoming liquid during the welding operation (liquation). The base metal adjacent to the weld initially is in a state of compression during heating and usually undergoes some upsetting. When the weld area commences to cool, the base metal heat-affected zone changes to a state of tension resulting in the separation of grain boundaries where the liquefied segregates are present in sufficient concentration to have lowered the boundary strength below the developed stress. Of course, if the segregate can resolidify and regain strength before any significant stress from cooling develops, then cracking may not occur. This matter of hot cracking in the heat-affected zones of welded alloy steels is discussed further in Chapter 15.

Hot Cracking From Low-Freezing Compounds

There is one impurity in steel that has a particularly bad reputation for causing hot cracking, namely, sulfur. Sulfur reacts with iron to form iron sulfide, FeS, which is soluble in molten steel. A few hundredths of one percent sulfur in steel as iron sulfide increases the range of temperature over which freezing occurs from 50 to 75 degrees F to possibly 800 or 1000 degrees F. The last trace of sulfur-rich liquid between the crystals does not freeze until about 1800 F. The presence of these envelopes of liquid iron sulfide around the metal crystals or grains at so low a temperature invariably results in hot cracking.

Viewed from another angle, if a steel containing iron sulfide is heated above about 1800 F, the steel commences to melt, or, more accurately, the iron sulfide contained in grain boundaries commences to melt. The result is the formation of intergranular hot cracks. Steel in this condition is called *hot short* or *red short*. A bar of steel that is not red short can be bent double over an anvil at 1800 to 2200 F without fracture. If the steel is red short, light hammer blows will crack it and split it apart. Below 1800 F and above an upper temperature that is in the vicinity of

2200 F the steel does not exhibit red shortness. Above this temperature range, the sulfide collects in globules, instead of remaining dispersed as an intergranular film. In globular form the sulfide no longer surrounds each grain and the steel can be forged without cracking.

Fortunately, there may not be need to reduce the sulfur content of steels below 0.05 percent ordinarily, because if manganese is present to the extent of 0.30 percent, manganese sulfide will be present instead of iron sulfide. This will be so because manganese has a greater affinity for sulfur than iron. There are a number of other elements which have a greater affinity for sulfur than iron, manganese being the best example. Manganese sulfide, unlike iron sulfide, does not dissolve in liquid steel. Therefore, manganese sulfide does not increase the freezing range; in fact, the manganese sulfide solidifies as globules in the liquid steel. Manganese is therefore a corrective for hot shortness. To completely combine the sulfur as manganese sulfide, at least 1¾ parts of manganese should be added to the steel for every part of sulfur. It is customary to add a larger proportion of manganese to ensure absence of hot shortness. Additional manganese is desirable to prevent oxygen in the steel from combining with some of the manganese leaving an insufficient amount to form MnS entirely. In welding, oxidation of manganese is favored by a long arc and by rusty, scaly groove faces. Once the manganese is oxidized to MnO, it cannot form MnS. Any sulfur in the weld metal then is free to form the undesirable FeS. Weld metal containing FeS is likely to crack during hot peening. Precautions are called for if high-sulfur, free machining steels are to be welded and the welds peened. The filler metal must have an abundance of manganese to combine with the sulfur picked up from the base metal, provided, of course, the large amount of manganese is not already in the base metal and accompanies the sulfur during the pickup. Figure 184 is a photomicrograph illustrating intercrystalline films of iron sulfide in weld metal. The compound iron sulfide when seen under the microscope as films or globules in steel can be identified by its yellow color, and easily distinguished from manganese sulfide which is usually grey or bluish-grey in color.

There are other elements which cause hot cracking in welds through the formation of low freezing-point compounds. While the compositions of these compounds may be a far cry from that of the aforementioned iron sulfide, the mechanism of the cracking is essentially the same. The compound segregates on cooling in the diminishing liquid between the growing crystals and by virtue of its low melting point, finally exists as an intercrystalline liquid film even after all of the metal crystals have formed. Oxygen and selenium are further examples of elements which form such troublesome compounds with iron, but here again, manganese can be used as a corrective. With increasing carbon and alloy content, the tolerance for elements which form these low melting compounds will decrease noticeably. In fact, the elements phosphorus, sulfur and silicon have a marked adverse effect upon hot cracking resistance both in the weld metal and in the base metal and test data suggests that the phosphorus and sulfur contents should be held to very low levels. The silicon appears to aid the sulfur in its hot cracking influence, so if the sulfur is very low the silicon content need not be restricted to a very low level.

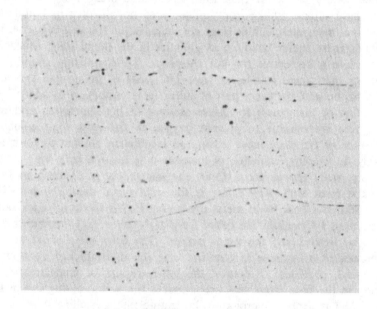

Fig. 184 — Hot short weld metal of carbon steel with films of iron sulfide in the grain boundaries. These boundaries are highly susceptible to cracking. The small globules distributed intragranularly are various kinds of oxides and manganese sulfide inclusions. Specimen unetched.

It is not possible to set specific limits for these crack-inducing elements because their potency varies with the particular alloy composition of the steel. In the higher strength low-alloy steels, carbon and phosphorus act together in a complex manner and exert a very strong influence in promoting hot cracking. With increasing carbon content, there is noticeably less tolerance for phosphorus. Nickel appears to have a slight adverse effect, while chromium and molybdenum seem beneficial.

Hot Cracking from Entrapped Slag

We seldom find hot cracking in fusion joined weld metal caused by entrapped slag because manufacturers of covered electrodes and flux-cored electrodes are careful to formulate slags which have low density and not too low a melting point. The low density favors rapid rise of the slag to the surface of the weld metal. A very low-melting slag if entrapped in the weld metal would accentuate the range in which liquid slag existed between the crystal, and over which hot cracking might occur. However, hot cracking from nonmetallic inclusions contained in base metal has been observed. Inclusions in wrought steel occur in elongated stringers. These stringers may be slag inclusions, if they consist of exogenous material entrapped during teeming, or they may be endogenous oxides developed during deoxidation or other reactions which occurred while the steel was molten. If the stringers are unusually large, as exaggerated in Fig. 185, they are called *laminations*. The most massive form of lamination arises

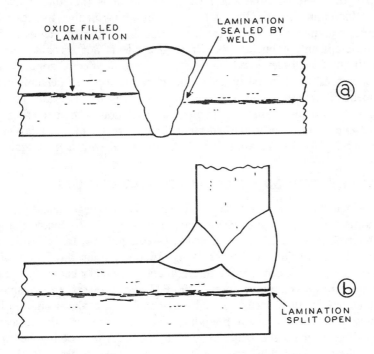

Fig. 185 — Schematic diagram of deep-etched cross sections of welds made by fusion joining in mild steel plate. Laminations in top plate (a) are shown to coagulate next to the weld and then disappear, while the lamination in the bottom plate (b) has opened up as a result of welding.

from pipe which develops in the upper part of the steel ingot during the final stages of solidification, and which, on infrequent occasions, is not completely cropped off the ingot during rolling to plate or bar. The pipe cavity usually contains some complex oxides, which are rolled out within the laminations. The heat of fusion joining is sufficient to remelt the stringers in the zone immediately adjacent to the weld, and the ends of the stringers may either coalesce, as shown in Fig. 185 (a), or they may open up as shown in Fig. 185 (b). Welding should not be performed on laminated plate because of the strong likelihood of separation along the stringers of nonmetallics. Laminated plate can be detected by the nick-break homogeneity test described in ASTM Standard A 20.

Hot Cracking From Other Causes

Weld beads that are deposited quite thin and wide, particularly fillet and root beads, often are quite susceptible to hot cracking. The weld metal is less able to resist contraction when the throat is thin than when it is thick. Increasing the rigidity of the joint by strengthening the restraining forces, or perhaps by using a steel of high tensile strength, tends to favor the development of hot cracks. Grain size affects hot cracking susceptibility both of weld metal and base metal in the heat-affected zone. As grain size increases, the amount of grain boundary surface area per unit volume of metal decreases. Therefore, compounds which segregate on grain boundaries will be present in greater concentration with increasing grain size. Hence, coarse grained weld metal or base metal may display greater susceptibility to hot cracking than the same metal with a finer grain size.

CHARACTERISTICS AND OCCURRENCE OF COLD CRACKING

When the path of a crack is intragranular (transgranular), meaning it travels across the grains with no apparent tendency to follow the grain boundaries, then the cracking most likely occurred at a fairly low temperature and is considered cold cracking. In our earlier discussion of hot cracking, we mentioned that the intergranular hot cracks generally occurred at temperatures well above about 1200 F. Hence, hot cracking is spawned by phenomena that occur at high temperatures in the vicinity of the melting point of the grain boundary material involved, or at least at temperatures where the material is quite weak. After cooling below this point, there is little tendency, ordinarily, for cracks to form in the weld joint until the temperature has fallen below about 600 F. In this low temperature range, the mechanics of fracture are quite different from those of hot cracking. The fissure-like defects that develop at the lower temperature are covered by the general term cold cracking, but there are a surprising number of basic causes for this form of cracking, with most of them imparting tell-tale features in the texture of the fracture.

An interesting observation when comparing hot cracking and cold cracking is that hot cracks always form during the welding operation, or at least before the welding heat has completely left the joint. On the other hand, cold cracks need not form immediately after the welding operation. In fact, the occurrence of cold cracking in a weldment may be delayed an hour, a day, even a week or more after the welding operation is completed. A most perplexing form of failure in weldments of high-strength alloy steel has been the spontaneous cracking of a seemingly sound weldment after it has performed satisfactorily in service for some time with the catastrophic failure occurring *without a load* on the welded section. The explanation for this kind of failure is not found in the welding procedure alone, but involves many aspects of the weldment design and the steel employed. Interested readers will find the principal factor to be the hydrogen content of the metal in the area of the failure.

Because of the many combinations of material, welding procedure, temperature, stress distribution, rate of loading, corrosive environment, and so forth that exist for actual weldments, the reason for failure by cold cracking sometimes is difficult to clearly establish. It is entirely possible to have cracking initiate as one form and then subsequently propagate through an entirely different mechanism. For example, small hot cracks can be initiated during welding and lie dormant until later circumstances provide the conditions which propagate the cracks into a complete failure. Without the triggering action of the small hot cracks, the failure possibly would not have occurred. Therefore, in analyzing cold cracking, meticulous attention must be given to the location or course of fracture, the texture of the fracture faces along their entire length, and other details of the crack appearance. In actual weldments, seldom is cold cracking promoted by a single condition. Usually a combination of conditions shape up a situation which the metal in a particular area cannot tolerate, and cracking results. Although the various crack-provoking conditions can be discussed separately, it must be appreciated that, in real cracking incidents, the difficulty more often is attributable to a combination of two or more.

The conditions which promote cold cracking can be broadly stated as (1) hardening in heat-affected areas, (2) development of residual and reaction stresses, and (3) hydrogen embrittlement. Of all the factors in these conditions, hydrogen appears omnipotent. However, this is the cracking cause about which we have the least amount of substantiated information. Because this culprit is invisible and elusive, it has challenged our best investigative techniques in studies intended to gain quantitative information on the influence of hydrogen. Nevertheless, the results gathered to date strongly suggest that hydrogen embrittlement frequently is the final element in a set of conditions that produces cracking.

Influence of Hardening in Heat-Affected Areas

The microstructure of the steel is an important factor in cold cracking. It influences both crack initiation and crack propagation. The microstructure can develop all of the elements needed to produce a cold crack, or it can provide a crack-susceptible matrix in which an additional factor, like hydrogen, can operate with destructive results. Any microstructure that possesses low ductility, and which contains internal stresses will be prone to cold cracking. Certainly, martensite fits this description, so it should be no surprise that our discussion of cold cracking first takes up the matter of hardening (martensite formation) in heat-affected areas.

There are two heat-affected areas in a weld joint in steel which may become hardened as a result of the welding operation. The first is the higher temperature portion of the heat-affected base metal which lies immediately adjacent to the weld metal. In this portion, the heat from the welding operation has raised the metal above its critical range and the crystalline structure of the iron has become face-centered cubic (austenitic). We now know that the cooling rate at the edge of a weld often is sufficiently rapid that the austenite is not given enough time to transform to ferrite and pearlite, but instead, a harder, less ductile, martensitic structure is formed. The likelihood of encountering a hardened zone like this, of course, depends upon the carbon content and the amount of alloying elements present that promote hardenability. As the carbon and alloying element contents increase, the chances of forming martensite grow stronger. Even more important, as the carbon content goes up, the martensite formed increases in hardness and decreases in ductility. The second area which may become hardened is the weld metal itself. Since this metal cools from the liquid state, naturally it passes through the gamma-to-alpha iron transformation. Whether the final structure will consist of ferrite and pearlite, or martensite, will depend upon the cooling rate of the weld and the weld metal composition, the latter being a mixture of the original filler metal and the base metal picked up by penetration. Cold cracking, which ordinarily occurs somewhere between 600 F and room temperature — roughly the martensite formation range — is sometimes found in hardened (martensitic) weld metal, but more often is located in the base metal heat-affected zones because of the higher level of carbon generally present, and the greater hardness and lower ductility which develops upon hardening. Of course, special recognition must be given to those alloy steels of *limited* carbon content which are designed (see Chapter 15) to form martensite or lower bainite in the base metal heat-affected zones *without* cracking.

When the subject of cracking was introduced, we stated that cracking was a form of failure wherein material under stress behaved in a brittle fashion. It would seem logical that to seek the cause of the crack we should attempt to find two pieces of information: first, the mechanism by which stress was applied to the material at the point where its failure initiated, and second, the reason why the metal behaved in a brittle fashion. Returning now to our weld joint we might ask; what caused stresses to rise? Obviously, shrinkage stresses are part of the answer. However, we must not lose sight of the fact that where an austenite-to-martensite transformation takes place, an expansion in volume takes place which undoubtedly adds to the stress. We may, at first thought, believe that the expansion would be helpful since it might relieve some of the shrinkage stress. This seldom is the case because the expansion occurs in three directions and is hindered by the surrounding contracting metal. Briefly, the localized hardening adds to the complexity of the stress pattern and easily can create multiaxial residual stresses. Next, we should ask, why does the metal behave in a brittle fashion? Again the answer is obvious; the martensite or hardened structure has only limited ductility even under the most favorable conditions of stress as can be seen in the diagram for materials tested in simple tension in Fig. 186.

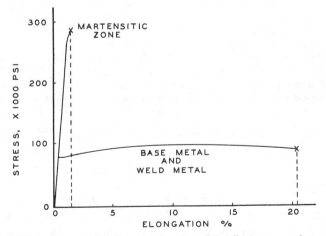

Fig. 186 — Stress-strain diagram showing a ductile base metal (and weld metal) and a brittle heat-affected zone (X indicates fracture)

Cracking may occur spontaneously in an area after hardening transformation has taken place and the metal can no longer deform properly to accommodate residual stresses. It also is possible that the stresses will not rise to the threshold of cracking as the weldment cools to room temperature, and so the hardened zone remains free of cracks. This can be a dangerous condition under some circumstances. If the residual stresses remain in the welded joint and a stress raiser is present which interferes with plastic flow, the additional stress applied in service may complement the residual stress and produce a crack. Rarely are welded parts which contain hardened (martensitic) zones required or designed to undergo severe deformation in service. Rather, they are expected to resist occasional overload without sudden, brittle failure. The danger associated with hard zones in a weld joint in service is illustrated in Fig. 187. When a crack initiates in a hard zone, it tends to propagate rapidly through the hardened material. This is understandable inasmuch as impact tests have told us that highly hardened structures ordinarily have poor fracture toughness. Hardened zones of this character should be removed by post-weld heat treatment, at least by stress relief heat treatment, which will lower the residual stresses to a safe level and reduce the hardness somewhat. Other alternatives would be (1) preheating to retard cooling rate and thus prevent the formation of martensite, (2) selecting a steel of lower

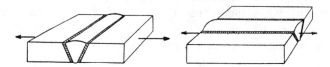

Fig. 187 — Single-layer butt weld made with a mild steel electrode in high-tensile medium-carbon steel (shaded area is martensitic heat-affected zone). (Left) When stressed transversely, as shown by arrows, the weld metal and unaffected base metal deform without causing cracks in the martensitic zone. (Right) When stressed longitudinally the martensitic zone is forced to deform and soon cracks.

hardenability to avoid the formation of martensite under the cooling conditions of the welding procedure, or (3) selecting a steel with lower carbon content which reduces the hardness and increases the toughness of any martensite that forms.

All martensitic structures are not equally susceptible to cold cracking. Furthermore, their cracking propensity oftentimes does not correlate well with their hardness or ductility. This irregular behavior has spurred a number of investigators to study in detail the microstructures of base metal heat-affected zones at weld joints in attempts to explain the degree of cracking susceptibility. Even though only limited work has been carried out to date in this area, the consensus is that microstructures vary in their sensitivity to hydrogen embrittlement, and this characteristic may

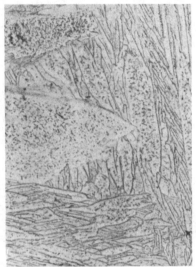

OPTICAL PHOTOMICROGRAPH   500X   ELECTRON TRANSMISSION MICROGRAPH
                                                     20,000 X

Fig. 188-A — Regular needle-like or acicular martensite structure as found in base metal heat-affected zones. Left: photomicrograph, mag. 500X. Right: electron transmission micrograph, mag. 10,000X. Both photos reduced 50%. (Watkinson, Baker and Tremlett)

Steel of the following composition was austenitized at 1742 F for 30 minutes and cooled in a blast of argon gas to simulate the cooling conditions found in the heat-affected zone of a 1-inch thick C.T.S. test plate: C 0.13, Mn 0.84, Si 0.28, Cr 0.91, Ni 1.00, Mo 0.40%.

overshadow the influence of hardness and ductility upon cracking tendency. Briefly, the base metal heat-affected zones of steels in general are believed to increase in susceptibility to cold cracking as the microstructure is varied from the unhardened ferrite and pearlite type to the various hardened types. Listed below, in order of increasing propensity to cold cracking, are six microstructures commonly found in the heat-affected zones of welded joints:

1. Ferrite and carbides (i.e., pearlite)

2. Bainite

3. Bainite mixed with martensite

4. Martensite

5. Martensite with some ferrite and bainite

6. Martensite with internal twinning

Martensite with internal twinning only recently has been recognized as a distinctive type as contrasted with the familiar acicular structure made up of laths or needles, as shown in Fig. 188-A. Twinned martensite, shown in Fig. 188-B, consists of flattened or plate-like grains which are

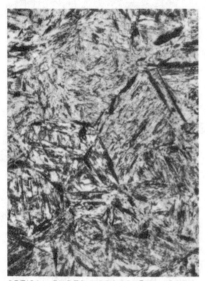

OPTICAL PHOTOMICROGRAPH   500X   ELECTRON TRANSMISSION MICROGRAPH
                                              10,000 X

Fig. 188-B — Twinned martensite composed of plate-like grains with twins of approximately 100 A width and spacing. Left: photomicrograph, mag. 500X. Right: electron transmission micrograph, mag. 20,000X. Both photos reduced 50%. (Watkinson, Baker and Tremlett)

Steel of the following composition was austenitized at 1742 F for 30 minutes and cooled in a blast of argon gas to simulate the cooling conditions found in the heat-affected zone of a 1-inch thick C.T.S. test plate: C 0.34, Mn 0.66, Si 0.29, Cr 0.88, Ni 3.23, Mo 0.34.

twinned on a fine scale. These internal twins have an average width and spacing of only about 100 A, and require electron transmission microscopy for resolution. This type of martensite is prone to form in steels of higher carbon content. Evidence of twinning in a few martensite grains can be found starting at about 0.15% carbon. As the carbon content is increased, the number of twinned grains increases until at high levels, perhaps about 0.8% carbon, twinning is present virtually in all grains. At the present time, the transformation mechanism that accounts for this feature in the morphology of martensite has not been firmly established. However, the markedly greater susceptibility of internally twinned martensite to hydrogen embrittlement has been confirmed by several investigators working independently. And indeed, the general experience in welding the higher carbon air hardening steels is that a low-hydrogen welding process constitutes a vital part of the welding procedure.

Influence of Residual and Reaction Stresses

Cracking can be caused by residual and reaction stresses; particularly if they are multiaxial stresses, and are developed in metal which possesses limited ductility and toughness. Relatively thin base metal sections can develop high biaxial stresses during welding, while relatively thick sections can develop high triaxial stress. It rarely happens that the stress in the direction of the thickness is high in thin metal sections. Since the stress in the direction of the thickness, Fig. 189, must be zero at both surfaces of the plate it can become high near the center only if the plate is thick.

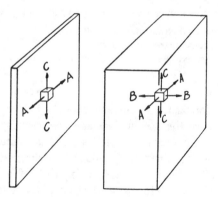

Fig. 189 — Stress perpendicular to the surface can be high ordinarily only in thick plates.

In the thin plate at the left there can be practically no stress perpendicular to the surface. In the center of the thick plate at the right it is possible for high-tensile stresses to act in three directions at right angles. The tiny cubes represent elementary particles in the plate. The arrows represent the direction of stress.

A common example of the conditions under which triaxial stress may occur is shown in Fig. 190. The heavy-wall pipe connects the two rigid receivers 1 and 2. Tensile shrinkage stresses produced by the cooling weld act in two directions, while the tangential stress due to internal pressure acts in the third direction. Since the pipe and weld are subjected to triaxial stress, which will favor a brittle cold crack under sudden overload, stress relief heat treatment frequently is applied to weldments of this kind.

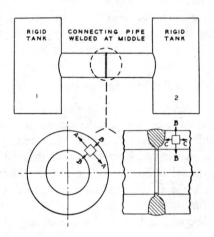

Fig. 190 — Stresses in a weld in a pipe connecting two rigid tanks.

A — Stress due to internal pressure in the pipe
B — Residual tensile stress due to welding
C — Reaction stress due to restraint during welding

Cracking at Notches

Notches are dangerous in metals when high levels of internal stress are developed because the notches act as stress raisers, meaning points of stress concentration. Moreover, notches tend to create a condition of multiaxial stress, as explained in Chapter 6 in discussing the mechanical properties of metals. The unit stress at the root of a notch increases as the notch grows sharper. However, the most severe state of multiaxial stresses exists in the metal below the terminus of the notch. The position of this maximum multiaxiality moves deeper into the section as the notch sharpness decreases. This fact explains why cracks usually initiate at a number of related points on a microscopic scale in the metal just below the notch, and upon linking up, propagate progressively both toward the notch terminus and deeper into the section. The crack represents the ultimate in notch acuity. The crack, upon reaching a critical size for the prevailing conditions, will propagate as a running fracture without significant deformation of the metal on either side of the fracture; although many times a very small portion of metal along the surface will fail in shear. This portion of the fracture is called the *shear lip*. Metal which fractures in this manner is considered "brittle." The brittleness likely to be exhibited at notches is especially important for welding.

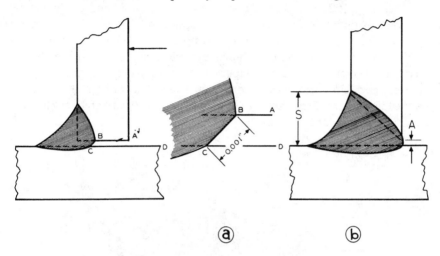

Fig. 191 — Stress concentration at a notch in the root of a fillet weld.
    (a) The drawing at center shows the character of the notch at BC (the root of the fillet weld) at high magnification.
    (b) Forty-degree single bevel-groove weld in a tee joint avoiding excessive stress concentration at the root.
S — Size of fillet; A — Root opening

In Fig. 191 a notch is bounded by the edges of the plates AB and CD, and by the root of the weld, which for simplicity is represented as a straight line 0.001 inch long. When the leg of the T is bent in the direction shown by the arrow on the face of the plate, the surface of the fillet weld is compressed, but the root is placed under tensile stress. It is easy to see that a motion of the leg of the T sufficient to move the end of the plate AB 0.001 inch will force the root of the fillet to yield 0.001 inch, that is, 100 per cent elongation. Is it surprising if the metal fails? To avoid the notch, the type of joint should be changed to that shown in the drawing (b) of Fig. 191. Cold cracks can initiate prematurely at notches because of high stress concentration and stress multiaxiality.

Notches can appear in a variety of forms in real weld joints. Inadequate root penetration is only one of the more flagrant forms. Heavy reinforcement of butt joints, though well intended, can act as a stress raiser by the abrupt change in section which occurs at the toe of the weld. Of course, the degree of stress concentration depends upon the (a) height of the reinforcement, (b) the re-entrant angle at which the weld profile approaches the base metal, and (c) whether any undercutting is present. Undercutting at the toe of an excessively convex reinforcement, as illustrated in Fig. 192, is a particularly severe stress raiser, and easily can be the point of initiation for a cold crack. An added reason why cold cracks often originate at this point again brings up the matter of hydrogen. Ordinarily, undercutting is centered upon the edge of the heat-affected base metal into which the greatest amount of hydrogen diffuses; providing, of course, the weld metal has become supersaturated with hydrogen from the welding atmosphere. Let us see now why hydrogen threatens to produce a cold crack at this point.

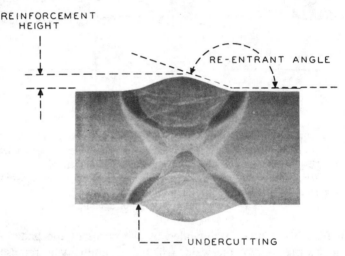

Fig. 192 — Three principal features of a butt weld which affect stress concentration at the toe of the weld. Re-entrant angle should approach 180° as closely as possible. Reinforcement height should be held to a minimum. Base metal undercutting should be virtually non-existent.

Influence of Hydrogen

Embrittlement in steel generally is caused by the presence of any one of a number of residual elements in an amount beyond a certain critical level. This critical amount may be present throughout the steel, or, to the consternation of the welding engineer, it may be concentrated in small areas by action of temperature gradients, or localized stresses from welding. The elements that promote embrittlement in steel may be either interstitial or substitutional with respect to solution in the iron lattice, or they may be present as a compound. The interstitial elements are carbon, nitrogen, hydrogen, oxygen and boron. These elements have as a common characteristic the ability to diffuse relatively rapidly through the iron lattice, as compared with the substitutional alloying elements. However, the most powerful promoter of embrittlement is *hydrogen,* and this element can diffuse through the iron lattice many times the rate of the next fastest element when the hydrogen is in the atomic form. The radius of the H proton is of the order of 10^{-13} cm, while the iron atom (and the H_2 molecule) is of the order of 10^{-8} cm.

Appreciation of the powerful influence of hydrogen embrittlement in causing cold cracking has been advanced both by the cracking incidents which have occurred with highly hardenable steels, and by the remarkable success achieved in welding these same steels with the "low-hydrogen" welding processes. The latter experience lends considerable support to the suspicion that transformation products and stresses from welding by themselves seldom are completely responsible for cold cracking. Embrittlement by hydrogen is not a new phenomenon; it has been experienced in the wire industry for years where steel absorbs hydrogen during acid pickling for scale removal. The higher carbon types of steel, such as used for spring wire, are particularly susceptible to hydrogen embrittlement. The usual method of removing this embrittlement from wire has been the application of a baking operation for at least several hours at a temperature of about 400 or 500 F. Because wire represents a relatively slender section, that is, the amount of surface area is large for the mass, the baking treatment is very effective in aiding the escape of hydrogen from the steel.

What is meant by "hydrogen embrittlement"? We can describe an embrittled metal as one in which evidence of abnormally low ductility is displayed for the existing structure and hardness. For example, if we should heat treat a medium-carbon steel and obtain a structure of martensite, we might possibly find the following combination of properties: hardness 500 BHN, UTS 250 ksi, and tensile elongation 5% in 2 inches. This material would be classed as *brittle,* yet we would not consider it *embrittled* because approximately 5% elongation is the measure of ducility which we have come to know as inherent in a martensitic structure of this composition. However, if our tensile test displayed practically no elongation; say perhaps only 0.5% in 2 inches, then we would class the material as embrittled for this is an abnormally low value even for medium-carbon steel in this structural condition. Examples of embrittlement are often found where a steel which normally displays 25 or 30% tensile elongation in 2 inches will produce only 2 or 3% in a test specimen. It is a peculiar fact that materials which are embrittled, besides displaying abnormally low ductility, seldom show an increase in hardness or tensile strength. More often, an erratic drop in tensile strength is observed. Obviously, a steel which is abnormally brittle will have difficulty in deforming or adjusting itself to residual stresses from welding, and will be more susceptible to cracking. However, hydrogen embrittlement can exert its influence in more devious fashion. It is entirely possible to have a steel display normal properties in a number of regularly-conducted mechanical tests, and yet have the steel succumb to hydrogen embrittlement merely while sustaining a static tensile load of less than yield point value. This alarming behavior is being called *delayed, brittle failure,* and is deserving of serious consideration when employing high-strength steels in a weldment.

Hydrogen Pickup, Diffusion and Effusion

Let us imagine that a joint is being arc-welded with a covered electrode of the E6010 classification, and the weld metal in the pool under the arc is steadily dissolving hydrogen gas until it reaches a level of about 30 ml/100g. As the temperature of the molten metal falls, part of the hydrogen will escape by bubbling out of the melt or by reacting with other elements (oxygen, carbon, etc. as discussed earlier) to produce bubbles of gas having extremely low solubility. Actually, the fall in temperature is so rapid that evolution of hydrogen cannot occur quickly enough to maintain equilibrium conditions and therefore the greater part of the hydrogen is trapped in the solidified weld, thus forming a solid solution (interstitially) of atomic hydrogen in steel. Naturally, as the temperature of the solid metal falls, the state of the solid solution becomes one of greater supersaturation. While in the atomic form, hydrogen is capable of moving or diffusing through the crystalline structure or lattice of the solid steel and it seeks every possible route of escape to relieve the supersaturated condition. The rate of diffusion markedly decreases with the falling temperature.

The first avenue of escape which we believe the hydrogen takes is diffusion into any internal cavity in the weld metal. By cavity we imply gas pockets, voids around nonmetallic inclusions, or even discontinuities of a very small order in the crystalline structure of the metal. Upon diffusing into an internal cavity in the steel, a portion of the hydrogen gas is presumed to change from the atomic form to the molecular form (H_2). Diffusion into the cavity will continue until the pressure of the molecular hydrogen is equal to the square of the pressure of the dissolved atomic hydrogen in the metal lattice. Therefore, considerable pressure may be built up in the cavity before equilibrium is attained. The molecular form of hydrogen is not only insoluble in the steel, but is incapable of diffusing through the lattice. Therefore, the molecular hydrogen is trapped under high pressure in the cavities.

A second way in which the hydrogen attempts to relieve the condition of supersaturation in the weld metal is to diffuse to the outer surface of the weld where it can effuse into the air. At room temperature, hydrogen will effuse from the weld metal at an appreciable rate if it is present in a supersaturated concentration. This has been demonstrated by submerging a weld bead freshly deposited by a cellulosic covered electrode in a bath of oil. Fine streams of minute bubbles will be seen rising from the weld metal, and they will continue to rise from the surface of the weld for many days. If the bubbles are collected, analyses will show the gas to be hydrogen. This is the hydrogen which has been termed *diffusible hydrogen.*

A third escape route for the hydrogen (this is of greatest concern to the welding engineer) is into the heated base metal adjacent to the weld. The base metal is not likely to contain more than a trace of hydrogen before being welded. When heated, the solubility for the gas is increased, and consequently the heated zone of base metal provides an excellent sponge or receptacle to receive some of the excess hydrogen from the weld metal. However, this increased solubility for hydrogen is only a fleeting condition because of the rapid thermal cycle of welding, and as soon as the base metal heat-affected zone begins to cool a condition of supersaturation develops in this area also!

The remainder of hydrogen gas in the weld metal is, of course, held in solution in the atomic form. The amount present depends, naturally, upon the success of the hydrogen in: (1) reacting with oxygen, carbon, sulfur and selenium to form gaseous compounds; (2) diffusing into cavities where it changes to molecular hydrogen; (3) entering voids filled with oxide inclusions where hydrogen may react to form water vapor; (4) being absorbed by the heated zones of the base metal; and (5) effusing into the air. Ordinarily, the weld metal cools so rapidly that about half of the amount picked up when in the molten condition is finally retained in the solid weld metal at room temperature to create a state of supersaturation. Of course, the amount retained will vary with the interpass temperature, size of the weld beads, and many other factors which affect the five escape mechanisms mentioned above. Inasmuch as the solid solubility of hydrogen in iron or steel at room temperature is extremely low, relatively little hydrogen need diffuse into the base metal heat-affected zone to create a state of supersaturation in this location. Ordinarily, wrought steel made by regular melting practice will have a hydrogen content in the order of 3 to 5 ml/100g. This level is somewhat lower than present in the ingot because the hydrogen is given frequent opportunity to escape during heating for hot working operations, and possibly heat treatment. Again, the amount of hydrogen contained in the final steel section will depend upon production procedures. Conceivably, a steel which had a low hydrogen content in ingot form probably could increase in hydrogen content under certain circumstances involving heating practices and pickling operations. Nevertheless, the base metal heat-affected zone adjacent to a hydrogen-bearing weld metal will pick up hydrogen, probably increasing to a level almost equal to the amount in the weld metal, and will retain a substantial portion of this gas during cooling to room temperature. Incidently, the quantitative determination of the hydrogen content of iron or steel is a very, very difficult task, particularly in localized areas like weld metal, or the base metal heat-affected zones. The sampling procedure is just as demanding as the analytical method. For example, when a sample is selected for hydrogen analysis, it must be refrigerated to a very low temperature until the chemist can start his analytical procedure in order to avoid loss of hydrogen by effusion during the interim period. The samples cannot be subjected to unnecessary cutting or other preparatory steps at room temperature. Some investigators have adopted a practice of storing samples in a bath of liquid nitrogen until the moment the hydrogen determination is started. Difficulties with hydrogen determination keep us in a state of uncertainty about details of hydrogen pickup. From data obtained thus far, it is believed that any hydrogen-containing compound will dissociate in the arc, and that some of the hydrogen will be picked up in the molten weld metal. However, the introduction of hydrogen into the arc as water vapor appears to result in a greater hydrogen pickup than if hydrogen gas was introduced. The introduction of a hydrocarbon (e.g., propane) also does not appear to result in as great a saturation of the weld metal with hydrogen as when moisture is involved. In general, the correlation between the diffusible and residual hydrogen contents of the weld metal and the hydrogen originally present in filler metals, base metal and the arc atmosphere is not very good — presumably because of sampling and analytical difficulties.

There are additional reasons why the distribution of hydrogen will be nonuniform in a steel weldment, both on a macro-scale and on a micro-scale. Naturally, the pickup of hydrogen from the arc atmosphere during a welding operation results in a high level of hydrogen in the weld metal. The hydrogen content of the base metal heat-affected zone increases because of diffusion from the weld metal during the heating portion of the welding thermal cycle. However, as the weldment ages at room temperature, the hydrogen concentration near the surface of all portions decreases by effusion of hydrogen into the air. Also, because austenite has a higher solubility for hydrogen, any areas of retained austenite (or areas which remained austenitic to a lower temperature before transformation) will contain a higher level of hydrogen.

Mechanism of Hydrogen Embrittlement

Many investigators have attempted to establish the mechanism by which hydrogen embrittles steel and promotes cracking. While much progress has been made in this direction, which allows us to take reasonable precautions to avoid unexpected cracking in weldments, we cannot be positive that the hydrogen problem is under complete control until the exact mechanics of the embrittling action are known. Sifting the mass of literature on this subject reveals that at least a half-dozen strong theories have been developed to explain the mechanics of hydrogen embrittlement and the characteristics of the affected metal.

One of the first theories became known as the *planar pressure theory*. It proposed that hydrogen dissolved in the crystalline structure of solid steel, but by exceeding its very low solubility limit it would seek to escape from the lattice by precipitating into voids of any shape and size. Because the structure of iron and steel was strongly suspected to contain numerous grain boundary imperfections, sub-microscopic rifts, and voids associated with nonmetallic inclusions, some of the hydrogen was believed to precipitate into these spaces despite their extremely small size. Upon precipitating, the hydrogen changed to the molecular form, and because of the square-root relationship between the pressure of the dissolved atomic hydrogen and the pressure of the precipitated molecular hydrogen, tremendous pressures were believed to build up in these voids or rifts. For example, a hydrogen content of 11 ml/100g was calculated to develop a pressure of about 200,000 psi. It was believed that the pressure exerted throughout the microstructure was sufficient to build up a triaxial stress state that resulted in a high susceptibility to premature failure. Another theory proposed that the hydrogen upon precipitating from the lattice is absorbed on the surface of the internal lattice imperfections and microcracks. By this mechanism, the surface energy would be reduced and lower stresses could extend the submicroscopic rifts into major cracks.

Both of the theories mentioned have been supported by the soundly demonstrated fact that hydrogen in the atomic lattice of steel would evaporate at all surfaces, including internal voids of any kind. This evaporation would continue until the opposing pressure of molecular hydrogen formed in the void reached equilibrium. Therefore, it appeared that hydrogen embrittlement appeared to be nothing more than a mechanism of internal precipitation along imperfections where free energy was available, except that the precipitate was a gas which could cause no precipitation "hardening." Instead, a weakness was induced by the precipitation.

These theories were advanced, however, before delayed, brittle fracture from hydrogen embrittlement was recognized, and the planar-pressure theory, and related hypotheses, are inadequate to explain many details of delayed, brittle fracture. For example, sometimes, baking the hydrogen embrittled steel will completely remove the embrittlement; sometimes, it will not bring about complete recovery. If the embrittlement was caused by high pressure molecular hydrogen trapped in microscopic voids, it is difficult to explain the mechanism by which this pressure would be relieved by baking. The degree of dissociation of the molecular hydrogen to the atomic form (which would be capable of re-adsorption, diffusion and escape) is insignificant at baking temperatures. Continued work has shown that the hydrogen occluded in internal voids probably is non-damaging, and that the embrittlement seems to stem from the hydrogen in solution in the crystalline lattice.

At the present time, the most widely accepted theory appears to provide an explanation for most of the principal characteristics of hydrogen embrittlement. It is based upon the concept of *stress-induced diffusion* of hydrogen. The theory starts from the situation where hydrogen is present in the crystalline structure of the metal. The average amount of hydrogen contained need not be so excessive as to represent a condition of high supersaturation. In fact, as little hydrogen as 1 ml/100g can be sufficient to embrittle a very high strength steel, and indeed, this has been verified experimentally. The hydrogen is believed to cause embrittlement and cracking in three distinct stages: (1) incubation, (2) slow crack growth, and (3) rapid crack growth with propagation sometimes continuing even through areas of relatively low hydrogen content. During the incubation period, the hydrogen is believed to migrate under the driving force of a stress gradient. The hydrogen tends to concentrate in regions of triaxial stress where it is assumed to lower the cohesive strength of the metal. It is suspected that the hydrogen concentration in the triaxial stress region in front of an imperfection, a microcrack, or a surface notch, rather than the molecular hydrogen pressure within the crack or void, is the factor which portends embrittlement. When the hydrogen concentration in the highly stressed region reaches some critical level, a crack will be nucleated. This initial crack propagates until it is arrested by the higher fracture strength of the metal outside the region of high triaxial stress. However, as soon as the crack stops, triaxial stresses develop at the terminus and the diffusion of hydrogen again commences to this region. Whereupon this cycle of (a) hydrogen concentration by diffusion, (b) crack initiation, and (c) crack propagation is repeated as often as conditions dictate. Interrupted crack growth in hydrogen embrittled steel has been observed experimentally. Eventually the steel fractures cataclysmically when the crack (formed by slow, interrupted growth) reaches a critical size and propagates as a running crack through the remaining section.

The degree of embrittlement produced by hydrogen is dependent upon the strength of the steel. In general, the likelihood that a given amount of hydrogen will produce significant embrittlement increases with higher strength. Ultra high strength steels can be seriously embrittled by very small amounts of hydrogen, perhaps as little as 1 ml/100g when the UTS is in the order of 300 ksi. The real determining property appears to be the yield strength, since this limits the, level of stress which can be developed in a site. This, in turn, establishes the driving force for the diffusion of hydrogen and the criticality of the stress field into which the hydrogen precipitates and the crack initiates.

Embrittlement is dependent upon temperature because this factor controls the diffusion rate of the hydrogen. The embrittlement mechanism operates most effectively over the temperature range of about −150 to 200 F. At very low temperatures, the hydrogen cannot diffuse at a rate sufficiently rapid to build up the critical cracking concentration. At elevated temperatures, increased diffusion rate allows the hydrogen opportunity to escape from the lattice by effusion at the surface of the section. Most studies have suggested that the average hydrogen concentration seldom is sufficiently high to cause immediate embrittlement that initiates and propagates a major crack. It appears that crack formation must await the build-up of hydrogen in the localized stressed areas until the concentration reaches a crack-initiating level. Therefore, the rate of crack propagation will be dependent upon the rate of diffusion of the hydrogen to the stressed sites. Hence, temperature is very important. Although little good can be accomplished in welding with the knowledge that diffusion ceases at cryogenic temperatures, much practical use will be shown for the increased diffusion rates at slightly elevated temperatures.

Embrittlement is affected by strain rate. As the strain rate exceeds about 10 in./in./min. the embrittling mechanism becomes inoperative because the hydrogen cannot diffuse sufficiently fast to exert its adverse effect. This explains why impact tests frequently do not reveal the presence of a hydrogen content capable of producing embrittlement. The strain rate during fracture being too rapid for the hydrogen embrittlement to develop. With other forms of embrittlement (as caused by carbon, phosphorus, etc.), toughness is decreased by increased strain rate or speed of loading. Whether a steel under a given set of conditions will fail in a delayed, brittle manner from hydrogen embrittlement can be determined only by a sustained load test. Even the results of tensile tests can be misleading, since the specimens can display normal ductility and yet the steel can fail in a brittle manner after a period of time under a sustained load.

Obviously, the hydrogen content of the steel is an important factor in the hydrogen embrittlement mechanism. The manner in which the hydrogen gets into the steel is of no importance. Normally, the critical amount of hydrogen needed to produce embrittlement is not present in the areas where the failure initiates. Hydrogen moves into these areas as a result of a stress gradient. Of course, if the steel is hydrogen-free, this form of embrittlement cannot contribute to a failure. The lower the hydrogen content of the steel, the less likelihood of hydrogen reaching a critical concentration in a stressed site.

Section size appears to have an effect upon susceptibility to hydrogen embrittlement. Of course, many factors tend to develop in an unfavorable manner insofar as toughness is concerned in a heavy section of steel; grain size usually is larger, residual stresses become higher and more complex, heterogeneity in composition is more apparent, and anisotropy in mechanical properties is not uncommon. However, in addition to these factors, thicker sections have reduced surface area to mass, and hydrogen must diffuse greater distances to reach the surface before effusion can relieve the supersaturation. Therefore, hydrogen removal from large masses is quite slow. The baking time probably should be increased by the square of the diameter or thickness to remove hydrogen.

Cracking from Hydrogen

In actual cold cracking in weldments, hydrogen usually plays the role of a powerful contributing factor. The cracking in a hydrogen-embrittled joint may occur immediately upon cooling below a temperature of about 200 F, or it is more likely to be delayed for a period of time. If the crack occurs after the weld joint has cooled to a temperature equal to the surrounding base metal (no temperature gradient remaining as a result of welding), then the fracture would be considered delayed cracking. Delayed cracking can occur over a wide range of imposed stress, but there appears to be an upper critical stress above which cracking occurs without delay, and a lower critical stress level below which hydrogen does not damage the metal and failure does not occur under a sustained static load. Over the intermediate range of stress, brittle fracture occurs after a period of time which becomes shorter with the higher stress. The delay may range from less than an hour to many days.

While spontaneous cold cracking possibly may be caused solely by transformation hardening, or by stress development from externally applied loads in extreme situations, delayed cracking appears to result from the combined effects of (1) the presence of hydrogen, (2) gradient stresses, and (3) a microstructure which is susceptible to hydrogen embrittlement. Cracking is most likely to be promoted by hydrogen when the microstructure is martensitic. With this structure and a quantity of hydrogen present, fracture can occur at applied stresses far below the normal cohesive strength. In general, the stress required to produce failure is progressively lower as the hydrogen content increases. The toughness transition temperature of the steel also appears to be raised with increasing hydrogen content. The great susceptibility of martensite to hydrogen-assisted cracking is believed partly due to the high intensity of short range stresses (structural stresses) in this microstructure. Bainite, for example, displays markedly lower susceptibility to cracking from hydrogen, and while this structure will have a hardness level approaching that of martensite in the same composition, the short range structure stresses are significantly lower in bainite. Twinned martensite, as described earlier and illustrated in Fig. 188-B, apparently displays a very high susceptibility to hydrogen embrittlement because of the presence of extremely high short range stresses as indicated by the twinning.

A mixture of ferrite and a high-carbon martensite or bainite also is quite susceptible to hydrogen embrittlement. This microstructure would be produced by a cooling rate during transformation from austenite that is just slightly faster than the critical cooling rate for the steel. Therefore, any localized weld area containing this mixed structure is apt to be the first to display cold cracking. Because weld joints present a range of cooling rates in the heat-affected zones, there is certain to be a narrow region at some variable distance in the heat-affected zone where this crack-sensitive structure is produced.

Even the microstructure of the steel *prior* to welding can affect susceptibility to hydrogen embrittlement and cracking if the weld heat-affected microstructure is heterogeneous. However, there is a sharp difference of opinion as to whether cracking susceptibility is increased or decreased by some of the microstructural features to be discussed. If the prior microstructure is heterogeneous, by virtue of containing massive carbide particles from spheroidizing, or free ferrite from annealing, this micostructural condition can result in some degree of heterogeneity in the weld-heat affected zones. Massive carbides in the structure before welding will tend to produce carbon-rich areas in the austenite. Despite the solubility of this phase for carbon or carbide, the austenite cannot become homogeneous because of the very short time involved. These carbon-rich areas in the austenite, upon transformation to martensite become harder, and have less ductility. Even more important, the higher carbon content markedly increases the susceptibility of the martensite to hydrogen embrittlement. Consequently, heat-affected zones will be found to increase in cracking tendency because of these localized areas of very high crack initiation propensity. On the other hand, some investigators report that steels having an annealed structure in which massive carbides do not go into solution easily under the heat-effect of welding, will behave like a lower-carbon steel during welding and will be less sensitive to cracking than the same steel containing smaller carbides. Both claims appear to have some basis for fact, so it is likely that the particular combination of conditions involved in each weldment will determine whether cracking propensity would be increased or decreased by microstructural heterogeneity. It would be prudent to anticipate that the cracking tendency might increase if the structure of the steel prior to welding were very heterogeneous.

Another feature of the microstructure which appears quite important, but on which little information is available, is the retention of austenite in rapidly cooled structures. It is a well known fact that alloy steels frequently cool to rather low temperatures before all of the austenite transforms to martensite. Some highly alloyed steels actually retain small amounts of austenite in the martensitic structure at room temperature, and require subzero treatment to encourage the retained austenite to undergo transformation. Considering that austenite has an appreciably higher solubility for hydrogen, this phase obviously acts as a reservoir for some of the damaging gas and holds it while the metal cools. If the retained austenite transforms at a temperature above approximately 300 F, the hydrogen may have an opportunity to escape. However, if the austenite is retained to a much lower temperature and then finally transforms, the contained hydrogen now supersaturates the newly formed martensite and has no opportunity to escape. These circumstances contribute significantly to cracking, and unfortunately the thermal cycle in the heat-affected zone along with the microstructural changes that occur are not favorable for avoiding the effects of hydrogen. To illustrate this remark, picture the atoms of hydrogen in a newly deposited weld bead diffusing toward the freshly austenitized zone of base metal to escape supersaturation. The base metal readily absorbs some hydrogen because its newly formed austenitic structure has a much higher solubility for the gas than the residual amount customarily present in the wrought steel. As cooling commences, supersaturation develops both in the weld metal and base metal. However, the weld metal, because of its lower carbon content, probably transforms from austenite to the familiar acicular ferrite and carbide structure before transformation occurs in the base metal heat-affected zone. The state of supersaturation in the weld metal now is greatly increased as a result of transformation. The temperature of the joint still is elevated, so the hydrogen has some opportunity to diffuse at a relatively rapid rate. Some of this hydrogen undoubtedly is forced into the still austenitic base metal heat-affected zone. Consequently, there is good reason to suspect that a concentration of hydrogen builds up in the heat-affected zone immediately adjacent to the weld. It is regrettable that transformation to martensite starts at the surface (where the temperature is lower during cooling) and progresses inward because this is directly opposite to the direction in which the hydrogen would like to diffuse and escape.

There is no doubt that hydrogen will take advantage of any notch or stress raiser present in a weldment and commence its embrittling action in the most highly stressed area near the terminus. Ordinarily there is an incubation period while the hydrogen diffuses and finally reaches a critical concentration for the particular steel and the level of imposed stress. When sufficient hydrogen has concentrated in this region, a crack is initiated. Whether this crack propagates to macrocrack size, or proceeds slowly and irregularly as a series of microcrack initiations will depend upon the diffusion rate of the hydrogen and many other circumstances. An important aspect of notches or stress raisers is the presence of blocked dislocation arrays in the highly stressed area near the terminus. These arrays are suspected to act as crack-embryos in the hydrogen embrittlement failure mechanism. Many investigators make use of carefully notched specimens to create a localized triaxial stress field of controlled intensity. In this way, the origin of a failure can be detected and studied. In actual weldments, notches or stress raisers usually spell earlier failure from hydrogen embrittlement because they provide the ideal site for crack initiation.

Cracking in the Base Metal Heat-Affected Zone

The greatest problem with cracking induced by hydrogen arises in the heat-affected zone of hardenable steel base metal. Cracking in this particular location is called *underbead cracking* if present as internal, longitudinal, intragranular fissures just a short distance away from the weld

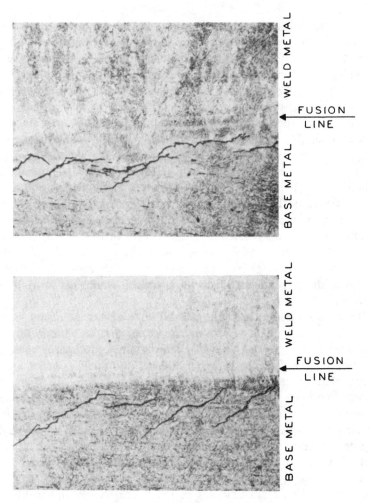

Fig. 193 — Examples of "underbead cracking" in the heat-affected zone of hardenable steels welded by the shielded metal-arc process using hydrogen-bearing covered electrodes. Etchant: Nital Mag. 100X.

The pattern of cracking beneath the weld in the base metal may vary depending upon the many factors which influence the exact initiation sites and the direction of propagation.

fusion line as illustrated in Fig. 193. However, under particular conditions of residual stress distribution, location of stress raisers, and applied load to the weldment, it would not be unusual to find the cracking following some other path. Sometimes the cracking will initiate in the heat-affected zone and propagate across the base metal section if the applied load on the weldment fosters this path of fracture. A further explanation for this behavior is the marked decrease in critical crack size for self-propagation which occurs when an appreciable quantity of hydrogen is present.

Mention was made earlier that mixed structures of ferrite in a matrix of martensite or bainite seem to display a high susceptibility to hydrogen embrittlement and cracking. A structure of this kind would be expected to occur in the heat-affected zone at a greater distance from the fusion line with increasing hardenability in the steel. This has proved to be the case in making cracking tests on steels having widely different hardenability. Steel with high hardenability, for example, AISI 4140, displays

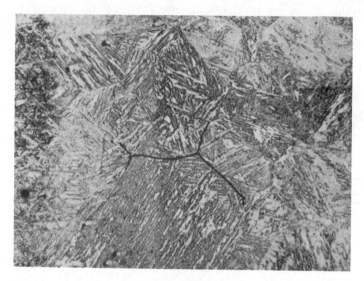

Fig. 194 — Heat-affected zone cracking in Cr-Ni-Mo alloy steel base metal (0.20% Carbon) showing initiation of defect in boundary between areas of martensite and bainitic ferrite. Mag. 200X (Berry and Allan)

underbead cracking at a location deep in the heat-affected zone. It is important to mention that steels which do not exceed approximately 300 BHN in the martensitic condition (because of too low a carbon content) appear to be immune to hydrogen-induced brittle cracking. As will be shown in Chapter 14, such a steel probably would contain less than about 0.10% carbon. Constructional steels of the carbon and alloy varieties usually exceed this level, hence, our concern about cracking from hydrogen embrittlement. However, special alloy steels of the precipitation hardening variety sometimes contain less than 0.10% carbon, and, as will be described in Chapter 15, they appear to have remarkable resistance to hydrogen-induced cracking.

Considerable effort has been put into metallographic studies of heat-affected zone microstructures to ascertain the exact location of crack initiation and thus help explain cracking propensity. Figure 194 shows the first stage of cracking in a base metal heat-affected zone. This section represents a bead-on-plate specimen welded by the gas metal-arc process using a shield of argon gas to which was deliberately added a small quantity of hydrogen. The microcrack obviously has developed between areas of martensite and the more ductile bainitic ferrite. A possible explanation for this microcrack location, which in effect "unzips" the dislocations which coalesce along the boundaries between the mixed structures, is given in Fig. 195.

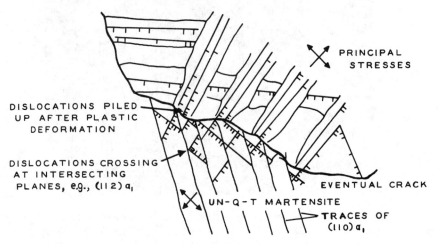

Fig. 195 — Schematic concept of cold crack initiation in a mixed microstructure. (Berry and Allan)

Sequence of Events

1. Plastic flow in bainitic ferrite (or possibly Q.T. martensite) pile-up occurs.
2. Un-Q-T martensite attempts to relieve stress due to pile-up in bainitic ferrite.
3. Dislocations in martensite move in several intersecting systems (i.e., work-hardening occurs rapidly). No further relief of stress.
4. Fracture starts on or near lath boundary (possibly by coalescence of edge dislocations in bainitic ferrite) and follows such boundaries in an "unzipping" motion.

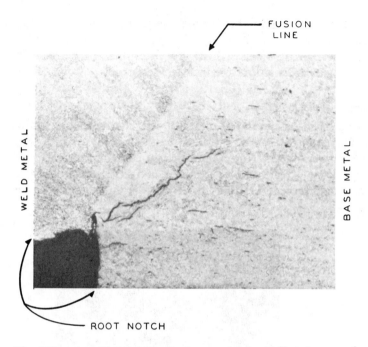

Fig. 196 — A microcrack in the base metal heat-affected zone of hydrogen embrittled HY-80 alloy steel. Note initiation in region of triaxial stress just above root notch, and the discontinuous nature of the microcracking. Mag. 100X (Interrante and Stout)

To illustrate how well actual cold cracking from hydrogen embrittlement conforms with current theory, Fig. 196 is a photomicrograph of the root area of a weld which contains microcracking in the heat-affected zone of the base metal. The welding was performed by the gas metal-arc process, but 5% hydrogen and 10% water vapor were added to the argon gas shield to produce delayed cold cracking. The stress or degree of restraint on this joint was calculated to be just above the critical stress or cracking threshold for this hydrogen embrittled joint. The weld joint contains a root notch which undoubtedly is acting as a stress raiser. Note that the microcracking is not an extension from the terminus of the root notch, but has initiated in the region of maximum triaxial stress a very small distance from the notch terminus. Note also, that the cracking is discontinuous, as predicted by the hydrogen embrittlement theory. Electron microscopy also has been used to study fracture in hydrogen embrittled steel. At magnifications in the order of 27,000X, replicas of the fractured surfaces show a marked difference in the texture of hydrogen embrittled steel as compared with low-hydrogen (tough) steel. It is possible to see tiny voids at the sub-grain boundaries, apparently produced by the hydrogen embrittlement. Electron microfractography seems to be a useful tool for ascertaining whether hydrogen embrittlement played some part in producing a particular fracture in a steel section.

Cracking of Weld Metal

Weld metal has given less difficulty with cold cracking than has base metal. This probably can be explained by the general use of lower carbon contents in weld metal. However, hydrogen can embrittle the weld metal to a significant extent, and, as a matter of fact, there probably is more cold cracking present in weld metal than most welding engineers are aware.

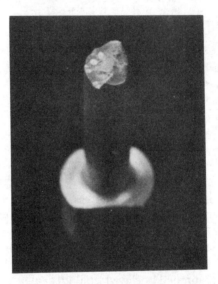

Fig. 197 — "Fisheyes" in the fracture of an all-weld-metal tensile specimen of carbon steel deposited by an electrode with a hydrogen-containing covering.

One form of hydrogen-induced cold cracking which occurs in weld metal has been long recognized. These defects are called "fisheyes." As shown in Fig. 197, fisheyes appear as small white spots on the grey fractured faces of broken specimens of weld metal. The fisheye usually surrounds some kind of discontinuity in the metal, such as a gas pocket or a nonmetallic inclusion, which accounts for the appearance of a pupil in the fisheye. Our present state of knowledge of fisheyes needs reinforcement at a number of points, but the behavior and appearance of the defect can be explained using the hydrogen embrittlement theory given earlier. Fisheyes do not represent an area in the weld metal which was cracked prior to the fracture of the metal in a bend or tensile test. Instead, each of these tiny areas are a portion of metal which has prematurely failed in a brittle manner during the test, and if a large number of fisheye sites are present they can promote premature failure of the weld metal section as a whole. Apparently, when atomic hydrogen precipitates in a pocket or void to form molecular hydrogen, the pressure can be sufficiently great to cause straining in the crystalline lattice immediately surrounding the cavity. This means, of course, that a multiaxial stress field with dislocations and rifts is created in the lattice surrounding the cavity. However, the stress field probably is not as severe as that near the terminus of a sharp notch or crack. Nevertheless, this localized stress induces additional hydrogen to diffuse into the area, thus bringing the state of hydrogen embrittlement somewhere near the microcracking threshold. When the weld metal is loaded and strained relatively slowly in the tension or bend test, more hydrogen diffuses into the embrittled sites surrounding the cavities and these localized areas of metal fail prematurely with a flat, brittle fracture. Too little time is available during the execution of the conventional bend or tension test for the regular mechanism of hydrogen-induced microcracking to repeat itself at the extremity of the newly-formed crack. Therefore, the fisheye is confined in size to the initial microcrack associated with the cavity. The remainder of the weld metal fractures later with greater evidence of ductility in the fracture texture. Consequently, the fisheyes easily can be seen on the fracture face.

The conditions which lead to the formation of fisheyes in weld metal fracture faces can be eliminated simply by heating the metal at some temperature over the range of 200 to 1300 F. Longer times are required at the lower temperatures, just as we found necessary in other cases where the hydrogen was expected to diffuse and escape from the metal into the atmosphere. Of course, if the specimen is broken very quickly, for example, by conducting the test as impact-tension, then the size and number of the fisheyes will decrease substantially. Also, the length of time which elapses between the deposition of the weld metal and the tension testing will affect the size and number of fisheyes. Weld metal tested as soon as possible after deposition may show many fisheyes in the fracture and have a low elongation value. However, if testing is delayed to allow a substantial amount of diffusible hydrogen to escape from the specimen, the elongation value from this specimen will be higher and the fisheyes will be noticeably reduced in size and number.

Although fisheyes have been long recognized as a weld metal defect, it was not until about 1950 that mild steel weld metal was found to contain microcracks in the as-welded condition; that is, cracks which were present in the metal prior to straining by an applied load. These fissures, as illustrated in Fig. 198, apparently had escaped detection by investigators earlier because of their extremely small size, which averages only about 0.0005 inch in length. However, careful metallographic examination at about 250X using electropolishing techniques will reveal their presence in weld metal which has been deposited under a hydrogen-containing arc atmosphere, and particularly if the weld metal has been rapidly cooled through the lower portion of the cooling range; that is, from about 300 F down to room temperature. It is the consensus of investigators that hydrogen dissolved in the weld metal plays the leading role in the formation of microcracks, inasmuch as the defects do not appear in weld metal of the same composition from the same filler metal source, but deposited under low-hydrogen conditions. As an example, E6010 weld metal ordinarily will contain microcracks to some extent, but E6015 weld metal will be free of the defect.

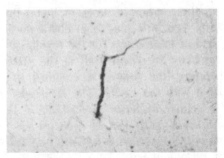

Fig. 198 — Microcracking in mild steel weld metal deposited by an E6010 arc welding electrode. Rapid cooling through the low temperature portion of the weld thermal cycle greatly increases the number of sites at which these minute defects appear. Specimen etched very lightly in nital. Mag. 1000X

Studies of the occurrence of microcracking have shown that the cooling cycle after welding determines the severity or number of microcracks that appear in the hydrogen-containing weld metal. It appears that rapid cooling in the upper portion of the thermal cycle after welding (water quenching immediately after deposition of the bead) provides immunity to microcracking which is not affected by the rate of cooling in the low temperature range. Also, bead-on-plate specimens made with an E6010 electrode on ASTM A 285 steel have shown that isothermal treatment immediately after welding over the range of 1700 F down to

200 F produces significant changes in microcracking occurrence when the specimen is subsequently water-quenched to bring it to room temperature. Surprisingly, a brief isothermal exposure (approximately one minute) in this temperature range increases the susceptibility to microcrack formation. After each isothermal treatment, the specimens are water quenched to accentuate any susceptibility to microcracking. Increasing time of isothermal treatment over the temperature range of 1700 to 200 F gradually accomplishes immunity to microcracking, with the exception of specimens isothermally treated at about 875 F. Holding as long as 18 hours has proved insufficient to provide immunity to microcracking (when quickly cooled through the low temperature portion of the thermal cycle to room temperature). At temperatures over the range of 1000 to 1300 F, and the range of 800 down to 200 F, virtually complete immunity to microcracking was provided by isothermal exposure for 50 minutes or less. There appears to be no relationship between microcracking and the hardness of the weld metal, inasmuch as variations in hardness with the various isothermal treatments did not correlate with cracking severity. It has been hypothesized that the weld metal microcracking phenomenon is determined by that hydrogen which is retained in austenite. The cooling cycle of the weld is suspected to control the following "hydrogen-retained austenite" cracking mechanism: (1) a dangerously large quantity of hydrogen must be contained in the weld metal, (2) during the transformation of austenite upon cooling, there is a tendency for hydrogen to become concentrated in the remaining austenite, (3) the increase in hydrogen content acts to stabilize the austenitic phase thus permitting it to cool to lower temperatures before transformation occurs, and (4) the circumstances under which the last portions of hydrogen-laden austenite transforms determine whether microcracking takes place. If transformation of the hydrogen-laden austenite occurs at a sufficiently high temperature the diffusivity of hydrogen is likely to avoid serious hydrogen embrittlement and the toughness of the transformation product is able to resist the formation of cracks. If, on the other hand, transformation occurs at a relatively low temperature, the degree of hydrogen embrittlement and the likelihood of a lower fracture-toughness in the structure results in the initiation of cracks on a microscopic scale at many retained austenite decomposition sites.

The presence of a large number of microcracks in mild steel weld metal has been shown to detract from mechanical properties. Laboratory specimens prepared from weld metal which has been rapidly cooled (water quenched) through the range of 300 F down to room temperature, and which contains many microcracks, display lower tensile ductility values and lower fatigue strength. Tensile and yield strengths are not as sensitive to the presence of microcracks.

Interface Cracking in Dissimilar Weld Joints

Another form of cold cracking caused by hydrogen occurs in joints made in carbon and alloy steels welded with austenitic stainless steel electrodes. Electrodes of this kind may be used for a number of reasons; one being that austenitic filler metal under most circumstances will avoid the formation of underbead cracks in the base metal heat-affected zones of hardenable steels. This remarkable property of austenitic weld metal is attributed to its substantially higher solid-solubility for hydrogen gas, which probably withholds much of the hydrogen that ordinarily would diffuse into the heat-affected zone from a carbon or low alloy steel weld metal as it undergoes the austenite-to-ferrite transformation.

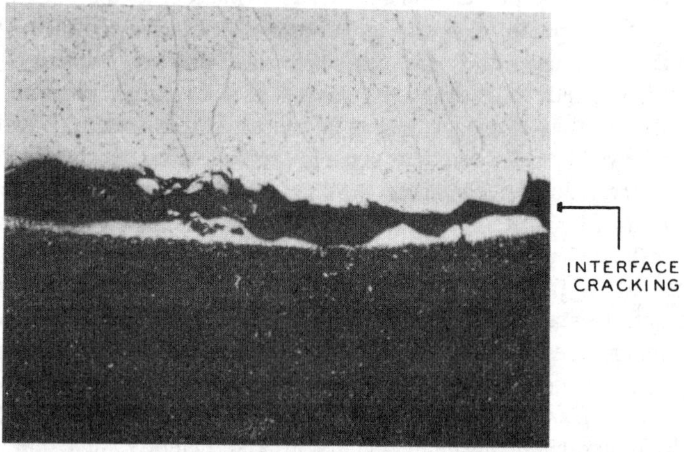

WELD METAL

INTERFACE CRACKING

BASE METAL

Fig. 199 — Interface cracking in a weld joint made with an austenitic 20 Cr – 10 Ni stainless steel (E308-15) electrode in a 0.30% carbon-containing Cr-Ni-Mo alloy steel. The electrode covering contained a high moisture content which resulted in a large pickup of hydrogen in the weld metal and subsequent hydrogen embrittlement of the weld-base metal diffusion zone. Mag. 250X

While austenitic weld metal does not appear to become crack-sensitive when hydrogen is introduced, and the base metal remains crack-free, *interface cracking* as illustrated in Fig. 199 can appear in the diffusion zone regularly found between the dissimilar weld metal and base metal. When welding a carbon or an alloy steel, this zone ranges in microstructure from a high-alloy martensite at the base metal side of the diffusion zone, to a high-alloy austenite at the weld metal side. The zone usually forms, for the most part, in the solid, but very hot base metal immediately adjacent to the fusion line. Alloying elements, like chromium and nickel, which are at a high level in the weld metal diffuse into the base metal, but penetrate only about 0.003 inch. At the innermost boundary of penetration, the diffused alloying elements are present only in a low concentration, but they still can impart hardenability to the steel in this area, hence the martensite along the base metal side of the zone. Of course, as the diffusion zone is traversed toward the weld metal, the composition becomes richer in alloy, and at some point, the total alloy content is sufficient to stabilize the austenitic form of microstructure at room temperature, just as is present in the weld metal. It is the martensitic portion of this diffusion zone, as might be expected, in which cold cracking is likely to occur if a substantial hydrogen content has been picked up by the weld metal and high residual and reaction stresses are present. Again, these stresses may be intensified by short-range structural stresses arising from the transformation of austenite to martensite, by the presence of stress raisers, and by high restraint upon the joint. Laboratory tests have shown that despite the dissimilar alloy composition that forms in the weld-base metal diffusion zone and the presence of high stresses from restraint, the diffusion zone will not cold crack if the weld metal hydrogen content is low. For example, the joint in Fig. 200 was welded under conditions identical to those which existed for the cracked weld joint in Fig. 199; however, an electrode which contained less than 0.20% moisture (as determined in accordance with AWS A5.5) was employed. Incidently, susceptibility to interface cracking will decrease as the total alloy content of the weld metal is increased. For example, an E310 stainless steel electrode (25 Cr–20 Ni Composition) will provide a joint which is substantially more resistant to interface cold cracking, even when a high moisture content is present in the electrode covering. The reason for this increased cracking resistance has not been established, but it appears possible that the higher alloy content of the diffusion zone imparts microstructural features that lend immunity to embrittlement from hydrogen. With a higher total alloy content in the weld metal, the steeper composition gradient between weld and base metals reduces the width of the martensitic portion of the diffusion zone. Although freedom from interface cracking can be assured by using an austenitic electrode having a very high alloy content, it is more economical to provide this assurance by use of electrodes having a controlled moisture content in their coverings. Of course, the deposited weld metal must be able to tolerate the dilution which takes place as a result of penetration into the base metal.

WELD METAL

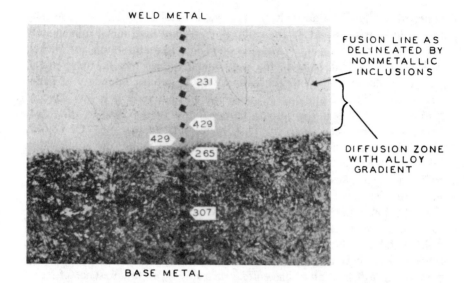

FUSION LINE AS
DELINEATED BY
NONMETALLIC
INCLUSIONS

231

429

429

265

307

DIFFUSION ZONE
WITH ALLOY
GRADIENT

BASE METAL

Fig. 200 — Interface of a weld joint made with an austenitic 20 Cr – 10 Ni stainless steel (E308-15) electrode bearing a controlled "low-hydrogen" covering (0.20% maximum moisture content) in the same Cr-Ni-Mo alloy steel illustrated in Fig. 199. The indentations were made using an Eberbach Microhardness Tester. Mag. 250X

For reasons explained in Chapter 10, the Cr–Ni–Mo alloy steel illustrated in Figs. 199 and 200 more often is welded with stainless steel electrodes of the E307, E309, E312 and E310 classes.

Avoiding Difficulty from Hydrogen

An accounting has been given of how hydrogen can be picked up by weld metal and thus allow a significant quantity to diffuse into the heated base metal adjacent to the weld. We must remember, of course, that even when a low-hydrogen, or a hydrogen-free welding process is employed, the filler metal and the base metal may already contain some hydrogen unless they were produced by one of the vacuum melting or pouring methods. Regardless of the source of hydrogen, its presence in the weld metal or base metal becomes especially dangerous if the microstructure in either of these areas becomes martensitic and the hardness exceeds approximately 300 BHN. The danger increases rapidly as the carbon content and the hardness of the martensite increases. Martensitic base metal heat-affected zones have been pointed out as an area particularly deserving of close attention in guarding against the occurrence of cold cracking. All the blame for underbead cold cracking cannot be placed upon hydrogen alone. Upon analyzing the stresses which arise in the heat-affected zone of a hardenable steel, we found that they could be described as (1) reaction stresses from restraint of the welded base metal members, (2) residual stresses from the unequal contraction of the base metal and weld metal sections — sometimes referred to as "long-range stresses," and (3) transformation or structure stresses resulting from the volumetric expansion as austenite transformed into martensite — sometimes referred to as "short-range stresses." These stresses, of course, are multiaxial, which means that the hardened steel will be given little opportunity to utilize its limited ductility to accommodate the stresses. These stresses by themselves can be sufficiently high to cause cracking, but if on top of these three kinds of stresses we impose the effect of hydrogen, the likelihood of cracking is increased manyfold. Yet, if any of the three kinds of stress are absent or reduced to a minimum, the hydrogen possibly will be ineffective in causing cracking. We have not reached a point where the factors responsible for cold cracking can be evaluated closely, but the significant factors ranked in accordance with their apparent importance appear to be: first, the degree of hardening and the nature of the microstructure in the heat-affected zone, inasmuch as cracking will not occur in an unhardened steel; second, the quantity of hydrogen which enters or is present to embrittle the heat-affected zone; third, the presence of stress raisers which are quick to produce sites of high triaxial stress where hydrogen can concentrate; and fourth, the severity of the stresses which arise in the joint from shrinkage and restraint.

The control of embrittlement and cracking induced by hydrogen can take but three general courses:

1. *"Low-Hydrogen" Welding Processes*
   Steps can be taken to insure that little or no hydrogen in any form comes in contact with the molten weld pool, and thereby avoid an increase in hydrogen content of the weld metal, or the base metal heat-affected zone.

2. *Degassing During Welding*
   The welding operation can be performed en vacuo (e.g., electron beam welding process). During the operation, dissolved gases in the weld metal and in the base metal heat-affected zones are reduced to a very low level.

3. *Control of Hydrogen Embrittlement Through Welding Procedure*
   The use of a welding process that entails hydrogen pickup is continued, but the welding procedure is planned to alleviate the embrittling effect of hydrogen.

Many of the regularly used arc-welding processes can be operated in a manner so that they qualify as a low-hydrogen, and in some cases a hydrogen-free joining method. Shielded metal-arc welding, the most widely used process, is often performed with covered electrodes of the E6010 and E6012 classes because of their highly desirable operating characteristics. While there is little likelihood of the copious amounts of hydrogen from these electrodes causing difficulty in the welding of carbon steels containing less than about 0.30% carbon, the joining of steels of higher carbon content, or of alloy steels (containing more than about 0.10% carbon) usually will call for countermeasures against the influence of hydrogen. Even the addition of manganese to a level of about 1.25% in a carbon steel containing approximately 0.30% carbon might call for precautions against hydrogen when welding heavy sections. The reasoning behind this apprehension is simple — such a steel in heavy sections would tend to form martensite in the base metal heat-affected zones unless welding was conducted with a high, controlled heat input to secure relatively slow cooling rates. It is not difficult to decide when countermeasures are needed against hydrogen if proper consideration is given to the principal features of the anticipated microstructure and residual stresses as discussed earlier.

Covered electrodes of the "low-hydrogen" classes have not swept into popularity with welders because the operating characteristics are quite different from the earlier standardized classes which employ cellulose in their coverings. However, by using deposition techniques developed specifically for the low-hydrogen classes, sound deposits with proper contour and appearance can be made and the properties and freedom from hydrogen-induced defects are well worth the effort. Of course, precautions must be taken to be certain the electrodes are being deposited with the lowest possible hydrogen content present in the arc atmosphere. Covered electrodes can be purchased to maximum moisture limitations, but the supply of electrodes must be handled in a manner that avoids additional moisture being present at the time they are used. Holding electrodes (and submerged-arc fluxes) in an oven for several hours at 250 F until needed for use has become a common practice to assure low-hydrogen conditions.

Because covered electrodes of the low-hydrogen variety cannot be made with no moisture content (some water of crystallization must be left in the silicate binder to prevent extreme fragility), welding engineers sometimes turn to the submerged-arc, gas metal-arc, or gas tungsten-arc processes for "hydrogen-free" welding conditions. Welding with a gaseous shield of *welding grade* argon, helium or carbon dioxide does not add any significant amount of hydrogen-bearing compounds into the weld metal.

Submerged-arc welding fluxes of many kinds are virtually hydrogen-free as manufactured, and if not, they can be baked to drive out the remaining traces of moisture. The gas shielded processes have proved so convenient for controlling the arc atmosphere that in addition to their use in fabricating operations to obtain hydrogen-free conditions, laboratory investigators recently have turned to making small additions of hydrogen or water vapor to the gas shielding stream to obtain quantitative data on the deleterious influence of hydrogen.

Any welding process conducted in a vacuum, of the fusion type, or at least involving substantial heating, will not only avoid hydrogen pickup, but may rid the weld metal and the heat-affected zone of the base metal of some, or all of its residual hydrogen. For example, when welding with the electron beam process the molten metal is very effectively degassed by the vacuum in the welding chamber; that is, providing the depth of of the penetration hole drilled by the beam allows escape of the gas from the molten metal. When the weld metal solidifies and heat flows into the adjacent base metal, residual hydrogen in the heat-affected base metal will tend to diffuse into the weld area because of the lower concentration here. This is the reverse of the situation when electrodes which produce a hydrogen-containing arc atmosphere are used to deposit the weld metal.

The low-hydrogen, or hydrogen-free welding processes are not a panacea, because in joining the very hardenable steels (i.e., AISI 4150, 4340, 502) cracking still may occur in the heat-affected zones. In certain cases, the residual hydrogen in the filler metal and the base metal can cause sufficient embrittlement in the martensitic heat-affected zones to produce cold cracking. Limited work with steels produced by vacuum melting processes, or degassed by vacuum pouring techniques shows improved ability on the part of these materials when welded by a hydrogen-free process. Finally, we must not overlook the fact that even with hydrogen virtually absent from the base metal heat-affected zone, a *high-carbon* martensite can succumb to cold cracking sheerly from the extremely high localized stresses which develop in this area.

Preheating and postheating would appear to be natural recourses for dealing with hydrogen when this factor is considered a danger to the soundness of the weld joint. Cracking tests on both carbon and alloy steels have shown that postheating *immediately* after the welding operation at temperatures often used for preheating (200 to 600 F) is effective in avoiding cracking from hydrogen embrittlement. The time required at temperature depends upon the size of the sections welded because the length of the diffusion path over which the hydrogen must escape is the controlling factor. Raising the temperature modestly will markedly reduce the time required at temperature. Treatment at about 375 F for 24 hours seems to represent an optimum time and temperature for reducing the average hydrogen level. Since the solubility for hydrogen increases rapidly with rising temperature, treatments to remove hydrogen must be a compromise between increased diffusion rate and the greater solubility prevailing at the elevated temperature. Of course, preheating and postheating temperatures also control hydrogen embrittlement indirectly through the microstructure which they encourage; that is, preheating not only provides greater opportunity for the hydrogen to effuse from the weld joint area, but it also helps temper any martensite that forms, or helps produce microstructures other than martensite which have a lower susceptibility to hydrogen embrittlement. For this reason, the welding engineer may elect to use a preheat temperature above the 375 F level where hydrogen solubility and diffusion rate were the only considerations. Finally, immediate postheating at too low a temperature, or for too short a period of time may pose more of a threat to the weld joint than will no postheat treatment. Tests have shown that postheating at about 150 F, or at 200 F for only 10 minutes actually brings on the cracking from hydrogen embrittlement in a *shorter* period of time than if the same kind of joint received no postweld treatment.

DIFFICULTIES OF A METALLURGICAL NATURE

Certain difficulties arise from conditions which cannot be described as occurring during a particular period in the making of a weld. In some instances, they stem from conditions or characteristics present in the base metal prior to welding.

DIRECTIONALITY (ANISOTROPY) IN BASE METAL

Wrought steels sometimes display markedly different mechanical properties depending upon the orientation of the test specimen with respect to the longitudinal axis (principal forging or rolling direction) of the steel section. As an example, tensile specimens prepared parallel to the rolling direction of a steel plate or bar may exhibit 25% elongation over a 2-inch gage length, whereas specimens prepared normal (transverse) to this axis may display only 15% elongation. For this reason, mechanical properties often are indicated to be values from "longitudinal" or from "transverse" test specimens. If special sub-size specimens are made through the thickness of the plate or bar (often referred to as the short-transverse direction), they may display even less ductility. If the capability of the steel for plastic flow is especially poor in a certain direction, the tensile strength may be lowered somewhat, but seldom is the yield strength affected. Impact values also may be lower when specimens are prepared in the transverse direction. The degree of directionality or anisotropy in mechanical properties will depend upon many factors. The processing of the steel section is very important as witnessed by the fact that plate often is cross-rolled to a controlled extent to equalize the mechanical properties as much as is practicable in the longitudinal and transverse directions. Looking at the composition and microstructure of the steel, we find that homogeneity of chemical composition, cleanliness, and the nature of the microstructure are major factors in determining directionality.

Steels of some types may show a tendency for alloying elements or residual elements to be segregated in the ingot structure. These segregations, depending upon the elements involved and the degree of concentration, may develop into a banded condition during hot working of the ingot to a finished section, and the composition banding may be reflected in the uniformity of the microstructure. This condition may be revealed by microstructural constituents arranging themselves in long strings in the direction of rolling, or by heavier attack on distinct bands during deep etching. In mild steel, pearlite grains sometimes arrange themselves in bands with similar bands of ferrite grains on either side, as shown in Fig. 201. Phosphorus sometimes segregates in bands, which will cause less deep etching in areas containing lower phosphorus and consequently appear like ghosts (white) against a dark, deeply etched back-

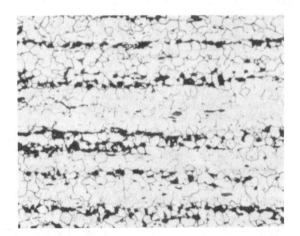

Fig. 201 — Banding of pearlite grains in mild steel. Mag 100X. Dark patches are pearlite grains, their lamellar structure being unresolved at this magnification.

ground indicating high phosphorus. Banding may or may not be eliminated by further hot working, or by heat treating depending upon the alloying elements or residual elements that are segregated. This condition easily can be a serious matter in welding because the segregated bands may develop defects that ordinarily would not occur if the steel was of uniform composition and structure. Steels of moderate hardenability containing bands of manganese segregation have been shown to display high susceptibility to weld heat-affected zone cold cracking along these areas, because these bands or areas actually represent a more highly alloyed steel and consequently possess greater hardenability.

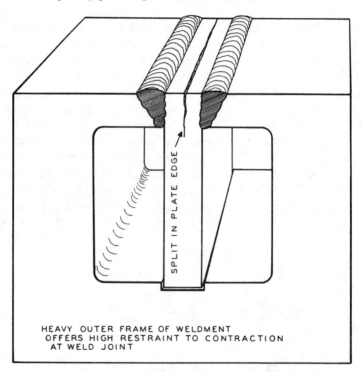

SPLIT IN PLATE EDGE

HEAVY OUTER FRAME OF WELDMENT
OFFERS HIGH RESTRAINT TO CONTRACTION
AT WELD JOINT

Fig. 202 — Splitting of a plate edge as a result of severe stress development through the short-transverse direction.

The elongated nonmetallic inclusions in wrought steel also tend to impart directionality to the sections. Wrought iron is an extreme example. Free-machining steels containing sulfur, selenium, or tellurium have many tiny nonmetallics in the steel matrix. These nonmetallics, in addition to aiding machinability, also make the steel directional. However, free-machining steels still are very satisfactory for many applications if consideration is given to their anisotropy. Steels made by the vacuum, consumable-electrode melting process generally display very little directionality because of their freedom from ingot segregation and excellent cleanliness. Of course, if a steel section contains major inclusions, such as the nonmetallics in a lamination (rolled out pipe from the ingot), then the section may be delaminated or split by residual weld stress after cooling to room temperature. Sometimes steel is severely stressed through the short-transverse direction, as illustrated in Fig. 202, so that plate with even a small degree of anisotropy will be prone to crack. The joint illustrated should be avoided whenever possible through weldment design. When inescapable, extending the vertical plate in Fig. 202 several inches beyond the joints will avoid the splitting problem during welding. The excess plate can be trimmed off after completion of welding, but some stress relief may be necessary to insure positively against crack development.

COARSE GRAIN IN STEEL

The highly desirable characteristic of iron and most steels to undergo a reversible allotropic transformation during heating to a high temperature and cooling has been pointed out in several chapters. The grain refinement which accompanies these transformations also has been described. The very fine grain size of arc-deposited weld metal, which is produced by rapid cooling, has been described in some detail. The impression may have been given that no particular problem exists in avoiding an undesirably coarse grain structure in steel weldments. This is quite true with most welding processes and with most carbon and alloy steels. Even though high temperatures are involved in welding and brazing operations, both rapid cooling and allotropic transformations usually act to produce a relatively fine grain structure. Circumstances do arise, however, where high temperatures and slow cooling produce coarse grain weld metal and base metal heat-affected zone structures. The electroslag welding process presents this problem in the joining of thick sections. Submerged-arc welded joints touch upon this difficulty when heavy beads are deposited. The problem of coarse grain also arises in most fusion joined steels which have been alloyed in a manner that the allotropic transformations do not occur. The high silicon content electrical steels, to be described in Chapter 15, always maintain a ferritic (bcc) crystalline structure. and consequently are not capable of grain refinement simply by heating and cooling. Steels of this character present a problem in controlling grain size in weld metal and in the base metal heat-affected zone.

Because coarse grain, in general, begets poor toughness and crack-ing susceptibility, welding engineers sometimes want to refine the grain size of certain weld joints, particularly that of the weld metal. To this end, they have tried seeding the weld metal with artificial nuclei, and with various forms of mechanical agitation of the molten weld pool. Many attempts have been made to secure finer grain size in weld metal by intro-ducing vibration, stirring, or turbulence in the molten weld pool and thus effect the solidification of smaller grains. The mechanism by which these various forms of agitation produce smaller grains has not been clearly established, but a number of hypotheses have been proposed.

Vibration of the weld pool is believed to create pressure waves within the molten metal which fragments more-delicate dendrites as they grow. Naturally, these fragments act as nuclei for new grains, thus increasing the number of grains which finally appear in a given mass of solid metal. Early experiments were conducted with mechanical, or electromagnetic vibrators. These relatively low-frequency vibratory devices were applied in many ways: to the entire fixture or weldment, to a local area of the weld adjacent to the molten pool, to the electrode or to a filler metal, and to a non-consumable ceramic or water-cooled copper probe which extended into the molten weld pool. More recently, ultrasonic vibration has been employed by connecting the driver of a transducer to the weld or the weld pool by one of the aforementioned techniques.

Stirring of the weld pool can be accomplished by applying electro-magnetic force through means of coils placed around or adjacent to the weld joint. Stirring or turbulence is believed to mix high-melting embryos of the cooling metal into the lower-melting remaining liquid where they may act as nuclei and secure earlier grain formation over a narrower solidification range. Stirring also may produce a shear gradient at the face of the freezing front and thus encourage the formation of additional nuclei. High energy input of ultrasonic vibration into molten metal can cause cavitation (rapid formation and collapse of evacuated bubbles) which fragments dendrites or even grains. Such vigorous vibration, how-ever, may cause the molten metal to splash out of the pool. In this event, porosity in the solidified metal is a distinct possibility.

Experiments in laboratories have produced some spectacular results in demonstrating that mechanical energy of the proper kind, effectively directed to the solidifying metal, and carefully controlled in intensity can produce grain refinement. However, none of the effective laboratory methods have proved practicable for use in commercial welding operations to date. For example, the introduction of ultrasonic vibration into the molten pool during the making of an electroslag weld appeared to be a relatively simple matter, and certainly any grain refinement would be well worth the effort. It appeared simple enough to insert a probe through a hole in one of the water-cooled copper shoes as illustrated in Fig. 203, so that the end contacted the molten metal. By attaching the driver from

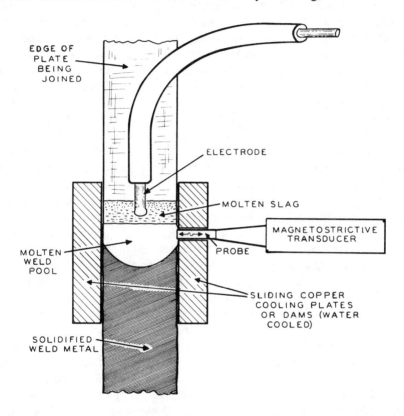

Fig. 203 — Proposed technique for introducing ultrasonic vibration into the weld pool of an electroslag operation to accomplish grain refinement. (After Erokhin and Silin)

a transducer to the outer end of the probe, ultrasonic energy can be transmitted into the weld metal. Unfortunately, grain refinement accomplished with this device has been found not uniform along the length of a joint, and inconsistent over the cross section of the weld. Further work is needed to determine the factors which affect the degree and uniformity of grain refinement, and to control these factors during the application of a convenient, practical device.

DIFFICULTIES WITH WELDMENTS IN SERVICE

Of the tremendous number of weldments put into service, only an extremely small percentage give difficulty. Even in the case of the almost infamous *welded* Liberty ships built during World War II, less than 3% of the 3,000 ships suffered a major break or failure in the hull. Furthermore, less than 10 broke in two — a failure rate lower than 0.3%. Newspaper publicity can blow these stories of failure far out of proportion. Studies of service failures in weldments of many kinds have shown that the most frequent causes of unsatisfactory performance are poor workmanship and poor weldment design. Although difficulties caused by metallurgical phenomena are in the minority, this area of weldment technology is worthy of review if it will prevent but one further failure where life, limb, or property are endangered. Also, it is not difficult to show how design and workmanship faults go hand-in-hand with certain undesirable metallurgical conditions and create circumstances which ultimately lead to weldment failure. Finally, this excellent record of performance by weldments will be maintained or improved only by careful study of difficulties. In addition to avoiding outright repetition, we must be alert to note trends in failures or difficulties. To give just two simple examples: the greater tendency for weldments exposed to very low temperatures to develop more fractures, and the seemingly unpredictable behavior of very heavy weldments made from very thick plate of carbon steel. Trends like these, when detected, often prompt widespread effort to probe for reasons, and ultimately a major advancement is made in the suitability of weldments of particular kinds or for particular services.

The kind of failure most feared in a weldment is a cataclysmic fracture completely through major load-carrying members which is preceded by no warning, such as bending, stretching, or buckling. When these, or other forms of plastic distortion occur, many signals, both visible and audible, usually provide ample warning of the impending failure. However, weldments occasionally do fracture in a sudden manner with little or no real warning and without exhibiting significant plastic deformation. This "brittle" behavior often is not only unexpected, but may be downright puzzling to the engineers concerned with the weldment if they previously had conducted mechanical tests on laboratory specimens of the steel employed and had secured normal property values for strength, ductility and notched-bar impact toughness. Careful analysis of the laboratory mechanical property test results, and even more painstaking scrutiny of the actual weldment and the service conditions may be required to explain brittle failure.

At least four different mechanisms which produce brittle failure are deserving of study from a weldment standpoint. They are: (1) fatigue, (2) hydrogen embrittlement, (3) stress-corrosion cracking, and (4) running fracture from a crack of critical size. All of these mechanisms have been touched upon earlier in this book, at least to the extent of discussing the fundamental facts regarding these mechanisms. Now we can supplement these facts with the intricacies of their occurrence in weldments. It will be important to note that, in general, more than one of the mechanisms can operate in producing a brittle failure, either operating simultaneously, or in sequence. Also, each of the mechanisms is sensitive to temperature, but not in the same way. This aspect must be watched closely because elevated temperature might serve to alleviate hydrogen embrittlement, yet it would accelerate stress-corrosion cracking. As might be expected, the nature of stresses present, their intensity, axiality and rate of application also influence these failure mechanisms.

FATIGUE

The failure of metals under repeated cycles of stress was covered in Chapter 6 under the mechanical properties of metals. This failure mechanism is discussed first because of all the metal articles which must be removed from service for reason of some form of mechanical failure, more display fatigue fractures than any other terminal condition. Furthermore, weldments which fail by fatigue represent a somewhat greater percentile than those failed articles which did not contain weld joints. This high incidence of fatigue fractures in weldments has been investigated at length, and many reasons for the occurrence of the fractures have been firmly established. Unfortunately, the findings on this subject have been given scant attention by too many of the people involved in the design and production of weldments. Fabricators who have only recently turned to assembly by welding particularly are prone to manufacture articles which display susceptibility to fatigue — not necessarily because the joints are poor or defective. Instead, the novice fabricators become so charmed with the ease by which components can be joined together that they lose sight of even the rudiments of good engineering design. Too often, they consider assembly complete as soon as the last weld bead is deposited. Too late, they learn that machining or grinding sometimes is a vital part of finishing a satisfactory weld joint.

Weldments give more difficulty with fatigue failure for the same reason that the incidence of brittle fracture is high — namely, concentration of residual stresses and service loads at stress-raisers, to the extent that the endurance limit is exceeded. The stress raiser may be a defect of some kind in the weld joint, or, as is more often the case, the external change in section at the weld joint presents a geometrical notch which effectively concentrates stress. What are the defects that act as stress-raisers and contribute to fatigue? Obviously, cracks are the most dangerous since they may have a stress concentration factor (Kt) as high as 18. Almost as dangerous are slag inclusions along the fusion line since they frequently taper at the ends to crack-like proportions. Porosity also lowers fatigue strength, particularly if the voids are near the surface of the weld. The first 5% of porosity reduces the fatigue strength a great deal. Additional porosity causes a less rapid drop, but then the static strength starts to drop.

Weld bead shape (external profile) is the most important variable affecting the fatigue strength of a sound weld joint. The fatigue crack in an ordinary (not machined) weld joint invariably occurs at the toe of the weld as illustrated much earlier in Fig. 4 when the applied cyclic stress is normal to the long axis of the weld. This is true both of butt welds bearing a bead reinforcement and of fillet welds. If the stress is applied parallel to the long axis of the weld, the failure will initiate in some location along the weld at which stress concentration is the highest. This point may be located in a weld bead crater, or merely at a location where the weld bead ripple changes markedly and accentuates undercutting at the toe. The toe of a convex weld bead is an obvious point of stress concentration, of course, because of the abrupt change in section of the weldment members at this point. The height of the weld reinforcement and the re-entrant angle (θ) between the weld bead and the surface of the base metal, as illustrated in Fig. 204, ordinarily determine the degree of stress concentration which develops at the toe. However, if undercutting is present at the toe (and this is almost commonplace), the concentration is certain to be greatly localized and intensified. If the weld is sound and has strength equal to the base metal, complete removal of the reinforcement and undercutting by machining, grinding and polishing will substantially increase the fatigue strength of the weld joint area, often to a level equal to that of the base metal.

The geometrical notch effect of the weld external profile does not explain all of the degradation in fatigue strength which may be found at a weld joint. Even when the weld profile is removed to avoid mechanical stress concentration, some steels will suffer from a metallurgical notch effect. Both residual stresses and microstructural changes have been blamed for this effect. Since coarse grain size has been shown by investigators to lower the endurance limit of steel, the grain-coarsened zone which occurs in the base metal of many steels immediately adjacent to the edge of the weld naturally is suspected to play a role. If the steel has been

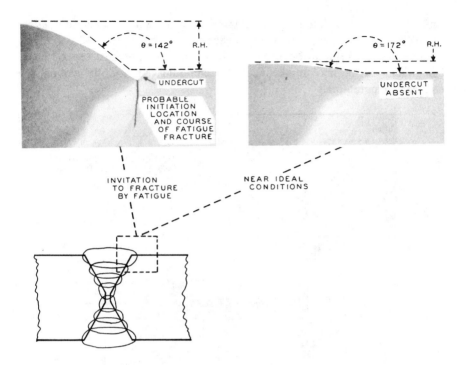

Fig. 204 — Three principal features of a welded joint which determine resistance to fatigue failure because of the manner in which
they affect stress concentration at the toe region.

Re-entrant angle (Θ) should approach 180° as nearly as possible.
Reinforcement height (R.H.) should be held to a minimum. Undercutting of base metal at toe should be virtually nonexistent.

strengthened by cold work, the heat-effect of welding will reduce the
strength (by the processes described in Chapter 12). With hardenable
steels, the influence of welding will depend upon the difference in properties between the base metal prior to welding and the heat-affected zones
after welding. Certain steels, such as the quenched and tempered high-
strength alloy steels often show no significant loss of fatigue strength
purely from the heat-effect of welding. This is attributed to the ability of
these steels to reform a favorable microstructure (bainite) in the austenitized portion of the heat-affected zone and to resist loss of strength
through tempering in the more remote areas of the heat-affected zone.
When dealing with highly alloyed hardenable steels, retained austenite
in the microstructure is one factor which adversely affects endurance limit.
Under cyclic stress, the retained austenite is transformed to untempered

martensite and the latter structure is believed to exert a deleterious effect upon endurance limit. Retained austenite can be eliminated from the microstructure prior to being placed in service by applying a special heat treatment which may involve double tempering, or possibly cooling to subzero temperatures.

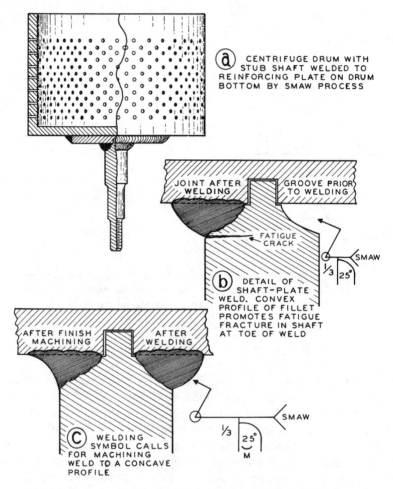

Fig. 205 — Cause and cure of fatigue fracture in welded shaft and centrifuge drum assembly.

Fatigue fractures can develop in welded pressure vessels, piping systems, bridges and any other weldment subjected to cyclic stress. Many typical examples are documented in the literature. Rotating machine parts are especially vulnerable to this form of failure. As illustrated in Fig. 205, a shaft is to be welded to a centrifuge drum which later will be operated at a high rotational speed. Let us picture the joint between shaft and drum being made with a strong-looking convex-profile weld, Fig. 205 (a). Despite this imposing looking weld, a fatigue fracture as shown in Fig. 205 (b) easily might develop because many times the rotating equipment is not in absolute balance and cyclic stresses are imposed on the outer fibers of the shaft and weld joint. An abrupt change in section, as exists at the edge of the circumferential weld, can raise the peak stresses above the endurance limit of the steel. If any doubt exists on the ability of the welder to produce a concave-profile weld to avoid stress concentration, then the welded joint should be machined to a uniform radius fillet as shown in Fig. 205 (c). Shafting reclaimed by welding (built up by surfacing welds) appears to suffer a higher incidence of fatigue failure than any other kind of weldment, even when the surface has been machined as smooth as a new shaft of homogeneous wrought steel. These failures usually can be. traced to some form of weld defect in the surfacing weld — which, of course, constitutes the more highly stressed outer fibers under torsional load.

Many aspects of fatigue must be taken into consideration when appraising a weldment for resistance to this form of failure. While the endurance limit for a steel as determined by tests on polished specimens is of interest, the performance of the weldment with its unpolished surfaces, stress-raiser defects, geometrical and metallurgical notches, etc. is certain to be governed by a lower fatigue strength. The loading conditions on the weld joints also must be considered. A weldment subjected to a dead load stress (zero to tension) will be able to sustain many more cycles of a maximum stress than when subjected to a complete reversal of stress (tension to compression). This fact was illustrated earlier by the fatigue chart in Fig. 60. When the performance of welded joints with regular reinforcement in place is plotted on a similar fatigue chart, the results are significantly poorer. Consequently, many weldments subjected to cyclic stress on which the weld reinforcement cannot be removed and the surface ground or polished, are designed on the basis of a safe fatigue life rather than an infinite life. To do otherwise would be uneconomical because the allowable load would be greatly restricted by a very low actual fatigue limit for the structure. However, by gaining an understanding of the factors that influence fatigue fracture development, and guided by fatigue test data most weldments can be designed and fabricated so that failure by fatigue is a remote possibility.

Sometimes the material in a weldment is required to sustain a limited number of cycles of very high stress; that is, well above the endurance limit and also above the yield point. Often this high stress occurs locally in the vicinity of a stress raiser. Naturally, the stress causes some plastic strain. The ability of the material to sustain repeated plastic strain, albeit in a very small localized area, is being referred to as *plastic endurance*. Much investigative work is currently underway to determine the effects of strain in large membrane areas, as well as localized strain in the vicinity of a stress raiser. An important observation already has come out of these studies concerning the comparative behavior of steels ranging from low-strength carbon steels to high-strength alloy steels. Surprisingly, the low-cycle plastic fatigue strength does not appear to vary with tensile or yield strength. Apparently, as yield strength increases, the reduction in strain range by strain redistribution becomes progressively less. Consequently, the plastic straining in a high strength steel takes place in a much smaller volume of metal at the terminus of a stress raiser, and because high-strength steel has less capacity for plastic deformation, the net result is that high-strength steels may not necessarily display higher plastic endurance.

A subtle aspect of cyclic stresses and fatigue crack development is the subordinate role played in spontaneous brittle fracture. Fatigue can cause the initiation and development of a small crack which, because of the stress level and frequency of application, is destined to grow at a very, very, slow rate; perhaps, too slow to cause complete failure of the weldment within its expected service life. Possibly the most damage the crack might cause would be a leak in a vessel, which could be detected and repaired. Such a crack may initiate at a point where unexpected bending moments apply undue strain, or where discontinuities or defects are present. It is entirely possible, however, to have these fatigue-developed cracks grow to a size which represents the critical size for promoting a brittle fracture — providing, of course, that conditions of temperature, stress, and material toughness are disposed to produce a brittle fracture. As will be explained shortly, the number of stress cycles applied may be considered too few to produce a fatigue failure. Yet, limited cyclic stress, as might be applied in repeated, periodic high pressure testing of a vessel, could lead indirectly to failure by propagating a small defect (which might have been declared of tolerable size during nondestructive testing when the weldment was fabricated).

General precautions to be observed in avoiding fatigue failure in dynamically stressed weldments include (1) securing complete weld penetration in all joints to eliminate internal unfused areas, (2) avoiding all external stress raisers in both design and workmanship, (3) relegating welded joints to locations where fatigue conditions are least severe, (4) providing a gradual transition where changes in section occur, and (5) minimizing unnecessary cyclic stresses from imbalance in rotating weld-ments. It cannot be emphasized too strongly that further important con-siderations may arise in all facets of weldment production, from material procurement to quality control and final inspection. This is particularly true in utilizing the high-strength steels where refined design, excellent workmanship, and careful nondestructive testing should be the rule.

HYDROGEN EMBRITTLEMENT

Embrittlement of the weld metal and heat-affected zone of the base metal by hydrogen picked up during fusion joining was discussed at length earlier in this chapter. This is not the only source of hydrogen which must be guarded against in weldments. Hydrogen can enter the lattice structure of the steel through corrosive attack, metallic plating operations, pickling operations, and exposure to hydrogen under high pressure at elevated temperatures. As an example of the treachery of hydrogen embrittlement, consider a high strength pressure vessel made of a vacuum-melted medium-carbon alloy steel. The vessel has been carefully assembled by welding using a hydrogen-free process and has been postweld heat treated to secure the highest possible level of strength with adequate toughness to assure against brittle failure under the anticipated service conditions. Let us assume that the fabricator elects to include a hydrostatic proof pressure test as part of his nondestructive testing procedure. Upon successful com-pletion of the hydrostatic test, let us picture that a small amount of water is allowed to remain in the drained vessel for several days and that some light rusting and pitting occurs in the wet areas. Rusting represents corro-sive attack and in the process of corroding, a small amount of atomic hydrogen can enter the steel as it is liberated during the chemical re-action. This hydrogen can cause embrittlement and microcracking if the susceptibility of the steel is high, an area of triaxial stress is in the vicinity of the corroded surface, and other circumstances are such that embrittle-ment from hydrogen is encouraged. While this example may seem farfetched to the novice, actual cases of brittle failure have been traced to this cause.

STRESS-CORROSION CRACKING

Stress-corrosion cracking in steel most often occurs as so-called "caustic embrittlement." This form of cracking takes place when hot, concentrated caustic solution is in contact with steel under a high level of tension stress. Caustic cracking frequently occurred in early riveted boilers because the caustic used to adjust the alkalinity of the water would concentrate in the crevices of the riveted seams. Cold work in the plate metal around the rivet holes often supplied the residual stress required to produce the attack. Virtually all metals and alloys are susceptible to stress-corrosion cracking, but their likelihood of developing this form of failure varies widely with the environment. Stress-corrosion cracking can be avoided in steel weldments by:

1. reducing the concentration of caustic in the solution which contacts the steel,

2. preventing the solution from reaching highly stressed areas,

3. eliminating free caustic from boiler water, and

4. inhibiting the reaction between the steel and any free caustic in the water.

Sulfates, nitrates and phosphates of sodium have been used as inhibitors. Sodium nitrate has given some difficulty because nitrates also induce stress-corrosion cracking under certain conditions. Treatment with sodium phosphate appears to be most effective. Again, it is important to recognize that stress-corrosion cracking if present only to a very small extent presents a form of microcracking which can develop into a catastrophic running fracture if circumstances foster brittle failure.

BRITTLE FRACTURE IN WELDMENTS

When a metal article develops a major crack that suddenly runs completely through a section with seemingly little or no effort, the failure is commonly termed a *brittle fracture*. In Chapter 6, the mechanics of brittle or running crack formation in metals was described in some detail. The brittle fracture problem in weldments is an imposing one, and on occasions has led to the collapse of an entire bridge, the bursting of large rocket motor casings, and the mile-by-mile destruction of gas transmission pipe lines, to mention just a few of the more spectacular instances.

An outstanding characteristic which invariably can be seen in articles which fail by brittle fracture is the almost complete lack of plastic deformation or ductility associated with the crack. If sections on opposite sides of the crack are placed together, no difficulty will be experienced in re-creating the article — save for the fine, tightly-fitting crack which cleaved the section. Any observer would be forced to admit that the metal must have been *brittle* to behave in this manner.

What is brittleness? For many years, engineering instructors were content to give practical demonstrations of brittleness, and its opposite, toughness, in constructional materials by bending ⅛-inch diameter round rods of soft rubber, lead, soft steel and glass. The glass rod would snap during any attempt to force bending; it behaved in brittle fashion. The soft rubber could be bent double, but would spring back to its original shape; it was elastic. The lead rod could be bent double easily and remained bent; it was weak and ductile. Likewise, the soft steel rod could be bent double and remained bent, but it required more force to bend than did the lead. Compared with lead, the soft steel was strong as well as ductile. Yet, the three materials that could be bent easily at room temperature can be made to break in a brittle fashion under some condition, while the glass rod if bent at a red heat, does not snap, but behaves like taffy. Although we have no difficulty in stating that, in bending at room temperature, glass is brittle and lead is not brittle, it is more difficult to decide whether different steels are brittle. After these simple bending demonstrations, the instructor often turned to the plastic elongation exhibited by materials in a tensile test. In the tensile test with load in one direction, an elongation at fracture of 20 percent in 2 inches is characteristic of ductile weld metal; 5 percent would be brittle. Yet, bridge wire with 5 percent elongation is ductile, while with 2 percent elongation it would be classed as brittle. Reduction of area of the tensile specimen cross-section at the fracture is not of much more assistance in trying to assess brittleness. We see that there is no absolute value of tensile ductility below which all materials can be said to be brittle and above which they can be said to be not brittle. For purposes of discussion, however, we can say that a material is brittle if it breaks without appreciable deformation, Fig. 206.

Another criterion which has been watched in the past as a guide for avoiding brittle metal is its yield strength-to-tensile strength ratio. As an extreme first example, gray cast iron has a yield strength which is coincident with its tensile strength. It fractures upon reaching the point where plastic deformation ordinarily would occur in iron. Consequently, the yield-tensile ratio of gray cast iron is 1.0. Carbon steels of moderate strength ordinarily have a yield-tensile ratio in the range of about 0.50 to 0.70. It was noted many years ago by observers that abnormally low toughness in carbon steels was accompanied by high yield-tensile ratio; that is, above 0.70 or 0.80. This would mean that the yield strength was unusually high, for example, as a result of strain aging, or that the steel fractured at an abnormally low tensile strength. In either event, the high yield-tensile ratio was accompanied by lower-than-normal tensile elongation. Often, other mechanical tests, such as notched-bar impact, indicated low notch toughness. However, in the higher strength steels,

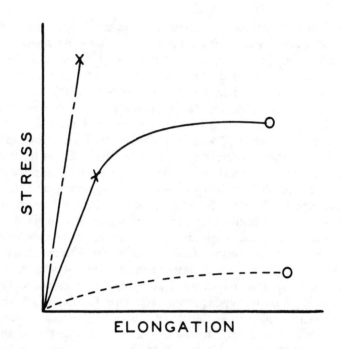

Fig. 206 — Stress-strain diagrams in the tensile test.

    If fracture occurs at X before the specimen has elongated permanently to any appreciable extent, it is said to be in the "brittle" condition. Metal deforming considerably before fracture at O is said to be ductile, regardless of the magnitude of stress at fracture.

particularly those which are hardened and tempered, the yield-tensile ratio often is found in the range of 0.80 to 0.95, and this does not signify brittleness. As a matter of fact, some steels if improperly heat treated will have a lower yield-tensile ratio, perhaps in the 0.50 to 0.70 range, and yet will display poor fracture toughness in various tests. Therefore, the yield-tensile ratio will not serve as a criterion for judging the possibility of brittle behavior by a steel — particularly in the higher strength steels where the brittle fracture problem is more complex.

    As described in Chapter 6, the antithesis of brittleness is *toughness,* and although we presently are wallowing in a mass of literature describing many types of tests and experiments to evaluate toughness (see Chapter 16), there is good reason to feel that real progress has been made recently in understanding the fundamental mechanics of brittle fracture. As our grasp of the fundamentals improves, we should be able to concentrate on the most informative tests, simplify their execution, and devise systems for more accurately predicting the behavior of real weldments from laboratory test data.

Mechanics of Brittle Failure in Weldments

To date, examinations of brittle failures in weldments show that in the great majority of cases the fracture initiated at a design fault, a flaw, or a pre-existing crack. As the usual course of events, the fault or defect existed in the weldment at the time of fabrication. In many cases, the defect was enlarged by microcrack extension either through momentary over-stress or through hydrogen embrittlement. Nevertheless, the defect or crack remained in the weldment as a minor imperfection and gave no reason to call for removal or repair — until service conditions changed which suddenly made the defect or crack *critical* with respect to further propagation. As soon as critical conditions occur, the small defect propagates at speeds of 1,500 feet per second or greater. Seldom does the metal spontaneously initiate a crack in a defect-free section and immediately develop a running fracture. Of course, it might be argued that the perfect weldment cannot be made (indeed, this was postulated in the opening paragraph of this chapter); therefore, a weldment exposed to adverse conditions will always contain some fault or flaw to serve as an initiator for the brittle fracture. On the basis of this reasoning, the problem of avoiding brittle fracture appears to be one of (a) being able to weigh all of the factors which establish the critical size defect, and (b) being constantly aware of all defects, their form and size, in the weldment. In this way, as service conditions are changed in a manner that lowers the fracture toughness of the metal, a reappraisal could be made to see if any defects of critical size are present. This statement of the problem possibly has been simplified to the point of absurdity. The task of being able to state quantitatively both the critical crack toughness of the metal in a given weldment, and the exact population and measurements of defects in the weldment is highly complicated. At present, we do not have means of assessing quantitatively many of the factors which influence fracture toughness, to say nothing of the limitations of presently available nondestructive methods of locating and measuring internal defects.

Possibly no other form of weldment dramatizes the need for a system to control brittle fracture to the nth degree as do the high-strength, thin-wall casings used for rocket motors. Consider for a moment the fact that certain alloy steel casings heat treated to a yield strength range of 250 to 300 ksi may have a calculated critical crack length of only 0.010 inches at room temperature. Obviously, no detail of weldment fabrication, inspection, or handling in service is unimportant in this application. For example, if the casing is subjected to service stresses at a temperature of 45 F instead of room temperature, will the fracture toughness of the material be lessened so that the critical crack length becomes impossibly small? Would even a "jewelry-quality" casing be in danger of brittle fracture at the lower operating temperature? This can be ascertained only by conducting a fracture toughness test at the lowest anticipated operating temperature, inasmuch as we are unable at present to predict the change in fracture toughness with lowered temperature. But this is only one troublesome aspect of predicting the behavior of a full size weldment under actual service conditions on the basis of data obtained from laboratory test specimens. There are many other features of the full size weldment that are extremely difficult, if not impossible, to simulate in a laboratory test specimen. To meet the challenge of this situation, metallurgists and welding engineers have responded with a rash of fracture-toughness tests which employ widely different specimen designs and test procedures. Many hours have been spent trying to correlate the results from these tests with full size weldments. Of course, this can be attempted only when a full size weldment also is tested to destruction under simulated service conditions, which may have to be carried to extremes.

A recently developed method of fracture toughness evaluation which has attracted considerable attention is known as *linear-elastic fracture mechanics*. An organized effort to advance this method is being guided by an ad hoc committee of ASTM because of the great need for fracture toughness measurement of sheet and thin plate of the very high strength steels. Standard notched-bar impact tests cannot be conducted on these thin sections, and subsize specimens appear quite inadequate. This method of fracture mechanics analysis is described in more detail in Chapter 16, but must be mentioned here because it holds strong promise of being the long awaited professional tool for guarding against brittle failure. Briefly, several different designs of laboratory tensile specimens, usually from sheet or thin plate, which contain some form of very sharp notch or pre-placed crack, may be employed. Essentially, the test specimen must be so severely notched that it fails in a brittle manner at a stress below the nominal yield point. When subjected to gradual tensile loading, some slow, progressive crack growth may occur. However, at some point in the loading, the onset of running fracture occurs — very much like the yield point in conventional tensile testing. It is necessary to determine the exact point at which rapid fracture started, both with respect to the extent of slow-crack size and the stress on the specimen. Equations have been developed which allow the engineer to first solve for a single crack-stress-field parameter, usually identified as K, which is the stress normal to the crack plane a specified short distance ahead of the crack border. From the crack size and the stress at the time of initiation of the running crack, the K value at the point of instability is determined and this second value is identified as K_c, the *critical plane-stress* at the leading edge of the crack necessary for running propagation. The K_c value will decrease with increasing thickness of the material being tested because of the greater elastic constraint upon yielding in the metal near the crack border. To establish a direct relationship between the laboratory notched or cracked specimens and the strength of a weldment containing a crack, the fracture toughness should be computed in a form that is, as nearly as possible, independent of the crack size and the test piece dimensions. Therefore, to secure a limiting value which applies to a section of infinite thickness, further calculations are made to obtain the *plane-strain* critical stress of the material. This fracture toughness value is identified as K_{Ic}. The Roman numeral subscript I designates the opening mode of crack extension. Of course, this extrapolation to K_{Ic} for a thick section must be used with discretion because anisotropy and other characteristics peculiar to heavy sections may tend to lower the actual K_{Ic} value. Brittle steels may have a K_{Ic} value as low as 50. Very tough steels may reach as high as 135. (These values are in units of 1,000 psi $\sqrt{\text{in.}}$ as explained in Chapter 16). This method of fracture toughness evaluation is not easily applied to the lower-strength carbon and alloy structural steels because they are strain-rate sensitive and tend to develop a large plastic zone beyond the crack terminus which amounts to "crack blunting." Consequently, the running crack required for K_c calculation may not be obtainable below the yield stress unless the test is conducted at very low temperature or at a very high strain rate.

Temperature, as would be expected, is a very important factor in determining the K_c or K_{Ic} values for a metal. Naturally, these indexes of fracture toughness decrease with lower temperature. Therefore, it is necessary to determine K_c and K_{Ic} at the lowest temperature expected to be encountered in service. Because some metals exhibit a sharp drop in fracture toughness over a narrow temperature range (fracture toughness transition), it is desirable to have information on K_c or K_{Ic} over the whole range of possible service temperatures. As an example of temperature dependence, an alloy steel containing 0.43% C, 1.5% Si, 2.0% Cr, 0.5% Mo, and 0.05% V was heat treated to a yield strength of 195 ksi. At a test temperature of 90 F, the K_c value for the steel was 187. At 70 F, K_c dropped to 173, a decrease of 7½% over the 20 degree temperature drop. Yet, the yield strength changed only about 1% over this same 20 degree temperature range. The lowered fracture toughness as indicated by K_c values would mean that a significantly smaller crack could prove critical at a service temperature of 70 F than at 90 F. Values for K_c and K_{Ic} are regarded as fundamental measures of fracture toughness and technically aggressive organizations already are using these data to guide the manufacture of critical weldments from the higher strength steels.

Cracks in weldments from which brittle failures initiate may be described generally as (1) through-the-thickness cracks, (2) surface cracks, and (3) internal cracks. The crack size required for the onset of rapid propagation (brittle fracture) at a given stress level is called the *critical crack size*. This critical size depends upon the values of K_c and K_{Ic} for the material. Which toughness factor controls the critical size depends largely upon the kind of crack, but is also a function of the "toughness" of the material. Surface cracks and internal cracks usually have a high degree of elastic constraint at the leading edge of the crack, and plane-strain (K_{Ic}) conditions predominate. Through-the-thickness cracks in thin sheet usually involve plane stress (K_c) conditions.

As loads are applied to the weldment containing a preexisting crack, the value of K at the crack leading edge increases linearly with the value of the nominal tensile stress component normal to the crack plane. If the crack does not exceed the critical size at the operating stress level, the weldment will sustain the first load application. However, with subsequent load applications and time under load, the crack will grow in size. At first, the crack extension process is self-limiting — it will not continue unless the nominal stress continues to increase. This is a function of the plastic deformation which occurs in the vicinity of the advancing crack front. In effect, the plastic strain increases the strength of the metal and raises its resistance to further extension of the crack. In the initial stages of this slow crack propagation, each small increment of higher stress which causes the crack to extend further also increases the area of the plastically strained zone, and therefore increases the resistance to crack extension. Not only is the crack extension limited for each small unit increment of higher stress, but the process moves toward crack stabilization under most ordinary conditions of service loading. However, if the applied stress does continue to rise, a greater amount of crack extension will occur per unit of increased stress, and eventually the process ceases to be self-limiting. Hence, the process moves toward crack extension without further increase in stress. The ultimate situation is rapid or unstable crack growth; that is, a running crack.

The stress at which slow crack growth commences has not been defined. The extent of slow crack growth is less the more brittle the material; in other words, the onset of a running crack occurs earlier. The limit of extreme brittleness is found where the start of slow crack propagation and the onset of a running crack coincide. Consequently, there is less uncertainty in the determination of K_c for a more brittle material. Investigators are continuing efforts to predict slow crack growth, but slow crack propagation, particularly through the thickness of tougher materials, is too complicated for analysis. Yet, this is a preface to brittle fracture which we eventually also must be able to predict.

In summary then, we know that *seemingly* sound weldments are "conditioned" for potential brittle failure by the slow growth of minor cracks. Brittle fracture manifests itself by the occurrence of a set of circumstances which makes a given crack "critical" in size. From a fundamental standpoint, the slow growth of cracks is governed by the stress-plastic strain process just described. However, unexpected crack growth toward critical size can be fostered in a weldment by: (1) concentration of residual and reaction stresses in the vicinity of a crack associated with a weld joint, (2) concentration of service loading because of weldment design, (3) cyclic service stress of sufficient intensity which propagates the crack as a fatigue fracture, (4) hydrogen embrittlement which extends the crack by the stress-gradient-diffusion microcracking mechanism, and (5) stress-corrosion cracking. Regardless of the mechanism of slow crack extension, with the advent of critical crack size — brittle failure occurs. The environmentally-promoted slow crack growth stage may take only seconds to reach a critical condition, or it may take years, if ever, depending upon many aspects of the weldment and service conditions.

Study of Brittle Failure by Fractography

When brittle failures do occur in metal sections, the surface of the fracture can be very informative — assuming the engineer is interested in ascertaining the cause to benefit from the experience. Observation of the topography of the fracture with the aid of a low-power glass or microscope has been long recognized as a useful procedure. One of the earliest findings, which continues to be of immense help in locating the origin of a fracture, was the detection of *chevron pattern* on the fracture surface. The origin frequently is found "bracketed" by the oppositely-positioned chevrons in the fracture on either side as illustrated in Fig. 207. Further examination of the fracture surface in the area of origin usually will disclose the reason for initiation. Often, obvious defects, such as notches, corrosion pits, nonmetallic inclusions, blowholes, or hot cracks (temper colored) can be found. However, finding the initiator does not necessarily tell *why* the weldment failed. The whole story will require determination of the mode of fracture *after* initiation.

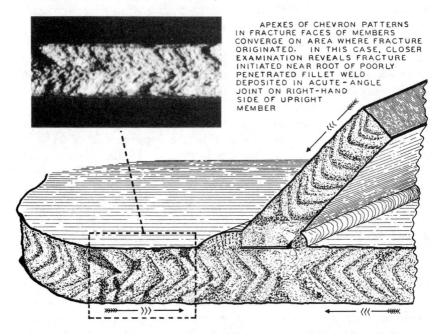

APEXES OF CHEVRON PATTERNS IN FRACTURE FACES OF MEMBERS CONVERGE ON AREA WHERE FRACTURE ORIGINATED. IN THIS CASE, CLOSER EXAMINATION REVEALS FRACTURE INITIATED NEAR ROOT OF POORLY PENETRATED FILLET WELD DEPOSITED IN ACUTE-ANGLE JOINT ON RIGHT-HAND SIDE OF UPRIGHT MEMBER

Fig. 207 — Chevron pattern frequently observed on the surface of brittle fractures will indicate the direction of origin. Apex of chevrons point toward fracture source.

The electron microscope has proved to be a most useful tool in the study of fracture surfaces. Electron microfractography can provide evidence on the cracking mechanism at all locations along the fracture path from origin to terminus. Actually, replicas of the fracture surfaces are examined, but these can be quickly and accurately prepared using simple replicating techniques. The higher magnification capability, better resolution, and greater depth of focus of the electron microscope (as compared with the light microscope) are all extremely helpful in gathering evidence needed to conclusively diagnose fracture mode. It is not unusual in a failure analysis study to find several mechanisms involved in a complete fracture. Instances have been found where a corrosion pit spawned traces of stress-corrosion cracking, which then propagated a short distance by fatigue, and after reaching a critical size developed into a running (brittle) fracture. The electron microscope already has proved superior in establishing the cracking mechanism at critical locations. It also is adept at indicating the direction from which the fracture originated, and to observe microcracks formed ahead of a crack front.

Presently, an experienced electron microscopist can differentiate fracture by cleavage, shear, fatigue, intergranular separation (by stress-corrosion or by hydrogen-induced mechanics), and ductile tensile mechanics. His efforts are especially rewarding when identifying fatigue fracture where the striations or beach-marks normal to the direction of crack propagation are too fine or indistinct to be seen under the light microscope. It is interesting to note that these striations of fatigue appear to be grooves developed during propagation. They seem to be a direct consequence of the successive rounding (because of plastic flow) and sharpening (at the minimum stress) during each stress cycle. The initiation of the fatigue crack is believed to develop through the process of slip — and indeed, close examination of the initiation area usually reveals striations which are positioned parallel to the direction of propagation. In examining fractures generated through hydrogen embrittlement, it appears possible to point out the original sites of hydrogen precipitation (believed to be voids at subgrain boundaries), the area of limited microcrack formation, and finally the running or cleavage fracture.

Electron microscopy holds considerable promise for guiding efforts to increase the fracture toughness of metals because it comes closest to revealing the path of fracture in the most intimate detail of the microstructure. For example, in examining an alloy steel which displayed an abnormally low K_{Ic} value, the electron microscope revealed that this particular material contained an unusual distribution of extremely small particles on the fracture surfaces. These were established to be nitrides and sulfides which developed during heat treatment.

Avoiding Brittle Failure in Weldments

After digesting a large portion of the information available on fracture-mechanics, the welding engineer probably will feel enlightened on how metals fail suddenly in a brittle manner, but it will be not altogether surprising if he is perplexed about how to apply this information to real weldments. Certainly, none of the present methods of fracture toughness testing provide values that can be applied directly as limits for design or as allowables for service conditions. Our best test measurements still represent qualitative indexes, and their use is a matter of engineering judgement. Despite the inadequacies of currently used methods of toughness evaluation, most popular systems, like notched-bar impact testing, NDT testing, and the more sophisticated linear-elastic fracture mechanics analysis of notched or precracked tension tests, can be very helpful in engineering a fracture-safe weldment. Let us review some of the major steps in the planning and manufacture of a weldment where fracture toughness can be given consideration.

Although the welding engineer may not have been concerned with the procurement of steel heretofore, the time has arrived to begin his surveilance at this early point. Since the failure of any weldment is commonly charged to the fact that it was "welded," the whipping boy may as well be certain that poor selection of a steel type has not put him at a disadvantage right from the start. Sometimes he is chided with remarks that the weldment will be constructed of "regular, dependable mild steel", and that the toughness of this kind of material should give no cause for concern. On the contrary, experience has shown that even weldments of low-carbon steel require forethought about toughness if the article is to see service below room temperature, if the sections employed are quite thick, if the residual and reaction stresses are likely to be high, and if service loads are applied suddenly or cyclically. In short, the welding engineer should be as knowledgable as possible on the toughness of various types of steel under varying conditions of temperature and strain rate. He must appreciate the difference between a non-deoxidized steel of uncontrolled grain size and an inherently fine-grain, killed steel. He must know how the properties of steels change with their condition or heat treatment, and particularly the manner in which toughness varies with condition. While the need for evaluating the fracture toughness of weldments in the heat-affected areas of the weld joints has been stressed, toughness of the steel before welding also is important. Seldom will the toughness of the weld heat-affected areas be any better than that of the unaffected material. If dealing with a heat-treated, high-strength steel, it is sometimes advantageous to not treat for maximum strength since the toughness may be poorest at this level. By making some sacrifice in strength for a gain in toughness through modification of heat treatment, the weldment may prove stronger (by virtue of being tougher) at the lower level of strength and hardness. It should not be considered blasphemy to question the heat treater on the procedure which he intends to follow in quenching and tempering a hardenable steel. Instances have come to light where failure to agitate the oil bath properly during a quenching operation has resulted in a significantly lower level of fracture toughness; even though no abnormality could be seen in the conventional tensile strength and ductility values. Therefore, it is important to check not only the temperatures employed in heat treating, but the cooling practices as well.

In present commercial practice with widely used carbon and alloy steels, many welding engineers have selected arbitrarily a Charpy-V impact value of 15 ft-lbs at the lowest temperature expected in service as the minimum energy absorption capability which they will tolerate in the steel. Because this test incorporates multiaxial stresses, low temperature, and high strain rate, they feel that a 15 ft-lb capability is a practical indication of the steel's ability to withstand a reasonable amount of notch-effect from weldment design, questionable workmanship, and to sustain impact loading. Furthermore, if the weldment is subjected to overstress, they would expect deformation and a tough, shear-type fracture instead of a sudden, brittle failure. The 15 ft-lb criterion is included as a requirement in a number of codes and specifications for steel to be used in low temperature service.

If steel is already on hand for a critical weldment and is found to be merely a hot rolled steel, perhaps also of unfavorable composition; it is quite possible that an improvement can be made in properties by heat treatment of the raw material or the finished weldment. Here, the welding engineer earns his salary and respect by judging when an improvement in fracture toughness is vitally needed, and how to accomplish this at minimum cost.

The design of any weldment should be examined critically for details not in accord with sound welding engineering principles. The overall design and the location of joints should take into consideration that welding in some cases will result in significantly poorer properties than found in a simple section of the base metal. The weldment may be handicapped with lowered fatigue strength as caused by weld bead geometry, decreased toughness as produced by microstructural changes in heat-affected zones, or lowered corrosion resistance in certain media as caused by residual stresses in the vicinity of the weld joints. Because these, and other shortcomings of welding, vary in occurrence and severity with different steels and welding processes, it is the responsibility of the welding engineer to state in what manner and to what degree welding will change the properties of a particular steel at a welded joint. He also should point out the best procedure under the circumstances for making and finishing the weld, and should assist as much as possible in making allowances for welding effects through suggestions on overall design. He should look carefully at the allowable stresses followed in design to be certain that fatigue strength has not been ignored where loading will be cyclic or dynamic. Also, the size of the weldment should be given consideration. Experience has shown that large weldments rigidly constructed of heavy members are more susceptible to brittle fracture than small weldments made of light members. Most of the cases of catastrophic failure in weldments by brittle fracture have been in bridges, ships, penstocks, pressure vessels, and other massive structures. Of course, it is the thicker steel sections and more massive structures in which anisotropy, residual stresses, undetected defects, material heterogeneity and other conditions that detrimentally affect fracture toughness are likely to be at their worst. An investigation of *size-effect* was conducted some years ago in connection with ship construction. Hatch-corner specimens were constructed in sizes ranging from ¼ scale to full size, and were tested for susceptibility to brittle failure. The full size hatch-corner failed at about one-half the stress level as compared with the ¼ scale specimen. A ½ scale specimen failed at an intermediate strength. Because these specimens were virtually identical with respect to weld soundness, geometry, etc., it was felt that the intensity of residual stresses influenced the results. As a general rule, a smaller possibility of error exists in predicting the behavior of a weldment when test results are taken from specimens approaching in scale and construction those of the real weldment. Of course, the objections to full-size testing are many, but they can be summed up simply as being too expensive and time consuming.

The preparation of base metal edges for joining deserves as much attention as the welding operation. Some welders have illusions of prowess and believe they can produce a satisfactory weld in almost any prepared joint sheerly through their skill in manipulating the welding process. The truth of the matter is that inaccuracies in joint preparation, such as a too thick abutting root face, can lead to a defective weld (unfused root area in this example) as readily as improper welding technique. Even the processes used in preparatory work should not go unchallenged. The widely used oxy-gas cutting operation produces a heat-affected zone on the plate edge, the depth and hardness of which is dependent upon the heat input and cooling rate. If steel of substantial hardenability is being fabricated, cold forming operations on plate with oxygen cut edges may produce superficial cracks in these edges. If a bending or rolling operation is conducted when the plate is chilled, the superficial edge cracks have been known to propagate (as a running crack) through the entire plate section. The welding engineer may have to insist upon some grinding to remove nicked and gouged areas that can act as a stress raiser, and possibly a tempering treatment (applied either by torch or furnace) after the oxygen cutting operation. Inspection of plate edges prior to welding for cracks, laminations, etc., is effort well spent. The spectacular brittle failure of a large gas storage sphere some years ago developed from a crack which occurred in the edge of a plate during cold shearing, and remained undetected during and after welding. Because of the location of this crack, the quantity of gas being held, and a sudden drop in temperature, the crack suddenly represented critical size and a catastrophic run-

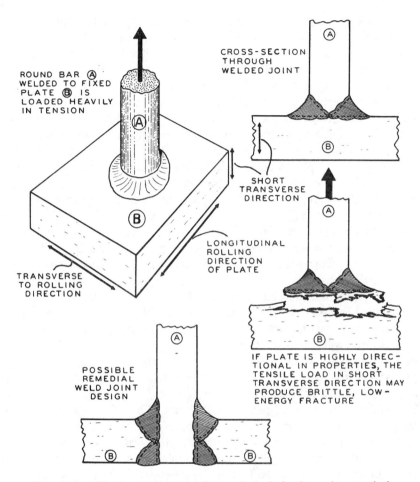

ROUND BAR Ⓐ WELDED TO FIXED PLATE Ⓑ IS LOADED HEAVILY IN TENSION

CROSS-SECTION THROUGH WELDED JOINT

SHORT TRANSVERSE DIRECTION

LONGITUDINAL ROLLING DIRECTION OF PLATE

TRANSVERSE TO ROLLING DIRECTION

POSSIBLE REMEDIAL WELD JOINT DESIGN

IF PLATE IS HIGHLY DIREC-TIONAL IN PROPERTIES, THE TENSILE LOAD IN SHORT TRANSVERSE DIRECTION MAY PRODUCE BRITTLE, LOW-ENERGY FRACTURE

Fig. 208 — (Top) attachment of a principal load-carrying vertical member (A) to the surface of a plate (B) may require consideration of fracture toughness through the short-transverse direction. When resistance to crack propagation in this direction is low, brittle fracture will be a serious threat unless a design change is made, possibly as shown in illustration at bottom.

ning fracture developed. The crack, which originally was present in a sheared edge, was now adjacent to a weld joint where residual stresses also could aid in promoting the fracture. This costly failure could have been prevented by any one of a number of precautions: more searching nondestructive testing, application of a steel with greater fracture toughness, or stress relief heat treatment, to mention just a few.

With regard to precautions which can be taken in the welding operation itself to avoid brittle fracture, it must be appreciated that both the shortcomings and the adroitness of the processes can lead to difficulty if not carefully watched. On one hand, the metallurgical effects of welding can involve hardening, grain growth, quench aging, gas absorption, and residual stress development; all of which can detract from the properties of the metal sections in the weld joint area. On the other hand, all of the metallurgical effects may be tolerable, but the ease with which the sections can be assembled by welding sometimes leads to a configuration which has a very unfavorable arrangement of "timbre" (directionality or anisotropy). For example, appendages may be attached to the surface of a main member, which might be a structural beam, or the shell of a pressure vessel as shown in Fig. 208 (top). If the vertical appendage (A) is expected to carry a high load, the stress through the thickness of the horizontal member (B) may not be safely below the brittle fracture threshold for the *short transverse direction*. A number of changes in joint design usually can be suggested to circumvent this problem, such as that shown in Fig. 208 (bottom).

Although the welding engineer should make every effort within economical and practicable bounds to have a weldment defect-free, experience shows that it is better for him to proceed on the assumption that (1) defects will occur in the weld joints, and (2) some defects will escape detection and be present in the weldment as it enters service. This philosophy may come as a shock, but experience shows that the cost of attaining and maintaining "zero-defects" status is extremely high, and can be justified only in very special applications. When the welding engineer tempers his deliberations with the foregone conclusion that defects of a maximum size as determined by nondestructive testing limitations will be present, he is forced to give brittle fracture the attention it deserves. By virtue of this philosophy, he is more likely to be dilligent over the entire course of weldment manufacturing operations in mustering all practicable assurances against brittle failure. The welding operation, *per se,* always has been looked upon as the welding engineer's prime responsibility, and unquestionably here is where he should strive for perfection — singlehanded, if need be. However, his knowledge of the properties, characteristics and shortcomings of welded joints can be invaluable in properly planning postweld operations.

The question of postweld stress relief heat treatment frequently arises in the course of weldment planning. In Chapter 11, residual stresses from welding were described as an enigma. Apparently, they had no significant detrimental effect upon the service performance of a weldment if brittle fracture conditions did not materialize. In other words, if a weldment were forced to undergo structural failure and the destruction took place as a *ductile* fracture, the presence or absence of residual stresses would not make any appreciable difference. However, residual stresses can contribute significantly to the occurrence of a brittle failure. No stretch of imagination is needed to see the effect of residual stress when the plasticity of steel is restricted for reason of temperature, strain rate or stress multiaxiality. Experience with large welded structures, such as ships, bridges and pressure vessels, has shown that catastrophic brittle failure can occur even in sub-assemblies which are at rest on the shop floor with no external load applied on them. Often, the fracture is associated with a sharp drop in temperature, and the point of initiation is a notch, crack, or major stress raiser. Considering that residual stresses of a tensile nature probably are at a maximum in the very area where welding defects are most likely to occur, and that these stresses commonly have a high degree of triaxiality, it is understandable that the welding engineer will favor stress relief heat treatment where possible. After all, brittle failures occur at relatively low stress levels, and if a condition which restricts plastic flow is present, the residual stresses may not require superposition of an external load to produce fracture stress intensity in a localized area. In general, the desirability for stress relieving a weldment will hinge upon the fracture toughness of the steel employed, the thickness of the members, the rigidity and complexity of design, the degree of embrittlement expected at weld joints, and ad infinitum. When all possible facts are at hand for weighing, the decision on whether to stress relieve a weldment still must be largely engineering judgment. When postweld stress relief heat treatment is not possible or practicable, the welding engineer may wish to resort to other recourses if assurance against brittle fracture is imperative. Consideration can be given to preheating, localized low-temperature heating, mechanical stress relief, or localized "crackstoppers." The latter may consist of sections of very notch-tough steel inserted strategically in the weldment. Sometimes an adequate crackstopper section can be merely an austenitic high-alloy steel weld metal employed in making the joint.

Inspection of the completed weldment is extremely important in avoiding brittle failure in service, and for many obvious reasons the welding engineer should have a hand in selecting the nondestructive testing methods and setting the limits for discontinuities. Sometimes the nondestructive testing procedures include steps which deserve greater consideration than given heretofore, particularly those involving proof loading. If a weldment, such as a pressure vessel, having been declared free of *defects* by nondestructive examination, is subjected to a given stress level during proof pressure testing and does not fail, this automatically sets a limit on the size of any flaw that can be present *at the temperature of testing.* It is within the realm of possibility that a discontinuity in the vessel has undergone some slow growth under the proof stress, but has stabilized itself through plastic flow. This raises some vital questions: (1) Will the new discontinuity size constitute a "defect" under the limits of the nondestructive test requirements? (2) Will the new discontinuity-or-defect represent a *critical crack length* if the vessel is exposed to a substantially lower temperature in service? (3) If the weldment or vessel is to be subjected to similar periodic proof loading during its service life will the discontinuities-or-defects undergo slow growth by fatigue and ultimately reach critical crack size? As the welding engineer ponders these and other questions which are suggested through the latest concept of brittle fracture mechanics, he undoubtedly will reconsider some of the assumptions about previously used practices which have bred a certain amount of complacency. The re-examination by nondestructive testing methods *after* proof loadings certainly appears to be one practice worthy of consideration. Also, any proof-loading procedure should include adequate safeguards against catastrophic failure if gas pressurization is employed, and protective steps against even superficial corrosive attack if a hydrostatic technique is used. Sometimes, light oil, rather than water, provides a safer pressurization medium.

GRAPHITIZATION

Because of the thermal cycle of arc welds, joints in carbon and certain low-alloy steels subjected to long-time service in the 850–1100 F temperature range are susceptible to the metallurgical change called *graphitization.* This is the breakdown of carbides in the steel to small patches of graphite and iron. It is not widely appreciated that all the familiar microstructures of carbon and low-alloy steels, like pearlite, spherodized carbides in ferrite, etc., actually are metastable conditions. The true equilibrium structure is graphite in iron, yet this condition normally is not achieved in carbon and alloy steels.

In 1943, a failure in a steam power plant brought out the fact that the strength of welded joints could be drastically reduced by the development of graphite in chain-like pools through the cross section of the base metal. This unexpected formation of graphite was found at the outermost edge of the heat-affected areas where the base metal had been heated to the Ac_1 temperature during welding. The pools of graphite appeared to form most readily from the coarse carbide particles which tended to coalesce in this region. The time required to produce the graphite was quite long, perhaps in the order of 10,000 hours. It is important to recognize that the thermal cycle of welding, and possibly other aspects of a welded joint, for example, the residual stresses, made weldments prone to this unusual difficulty in elevated temperature service.

If the graphite pools occurred at random, they would be of no more significance than any nonmetallic inclusion of equal size. However, the chain-like or film-like arrangement of graphite particles not only reduces strength, but also embrittles the joint by inducing a high susceptibility to fracture through this area.

Welded carbon steels deoxidized with aluminum display the greatest susceptibility to graphitization. While molybdenum tends to retard graphitization, the C–Mo low-alloy steels widely used as tubing in constructing 950 F steam power plants were the first to suffer this difficulty in long-time service. Graphite formation occurs very slowly at the lower end of the 859 to 1125 F range and increases in rate at the higher temperatures. The practical remedy for graphitization proved to be the use of more alloy. Chromium was found to form a more stabile carbide which resisted the breakdown to graphite. This finding is one of the reasons for the rapid introduction of the Cr–Mo steels into steam power plants and other long-time, elevated-temperature services. Stress-relief heat treatment of welded joints in carbon steels and C–Mo low-alloy steels at about 1300 F also will reduce the graphitization tendency. For some time, normalizing was advocated as a heat treatment for welded joints which had just started to form graphite pools. It was reasoned that the austenite formed during heating would dissolve the graphite and permit formation of a cementitic microstructure during transformation upon cooling. However, the dissolution of the graphite in the austenite leaves microscopic voids where the graphite pool originally formed. Therefore, this heat treatment is of questionable value as a solution to the graphitization problem.

Suggested Reading

The Brittle Fracture of Steel, by W. D. Biggs, Pitman Publishing Company, New York, 1960.

Fatigue of Welded Steel Structures, prepared by W. H. Munse and edited by La Motte Grover, Welding Research Council, New York, 1964.

"Cracking in High-Strength Steel Weldments — A Critical Review," by P.A. Kammer, K. Masubuchi, and R. E. Monroe, Defense Metals Information Center, Battelle Memorial Institute, DMIC Report 197, Feb. 7, 1964.

"Hydrogren-Induced, Delayed, Brittle Failures of High-Strength Steels," by A. R. Elsea and E. E. Fletcher, Ibid, DMIC Report ˙96, January 20, 1964.

"The Prevention of Pipe Failures," by Helmut Thielsch, Heating, Piping and Air Conditioning, v 34, no. 8, pp 98-103, August 1962; Ibid, no. 9, pp 152-158, September 1962; Ibid, no. 10, pp 120-126, October 1962; Ibid, no. 12, pp 131-140, December 1962; Ibid, v 35, no. 2, pp 115-119, February 1963; Ibid, no. 3, pp 106-109, March 1963.

"Flash Welding — Process Variables and Weld Properties," by Warren Savage, Welding Research Suppl., Welding Journal, v 41, no. 3, pp 109s-119s, March 1962.

"Graphitization of Steel in Petroleum Refining Equipment, and The Effect of Graphitization of Steel on Stress-Rupture Properties," by J. G. Wilson, Welding Research Council Bulletin Series, No. 32, January 1957.

"Radiation Effects on Mechanical Properties of Structural Metals, and Their Influence Upon Pressure Vessel Design, Fabrication, Operation, and Surveillance," a bulletin of four papers authored by R. G. Berggren; L. R. Weissert and D. K. Davies; D. W. McLaughlin; and L. E. Steele and J. R. Hawthorne, Welding Research Council Bulletin Series, No. 87, April 1963.

"Weld Flaw Evaluation," by S. T. Carpenter and R. F. Linsenmeyer, Welding Research Council Bulletin Series, No. 42, September 1958.

"Thermal Fatigue — A Critical Review," by T. C. Yen, Welding Research Council Bulletin Series, No. 72, October 1961.

Defects & Failures in Pressure Vessels & Piping, by Helmut Thielsch, Reinhold Publishing Corporation, New York, 1965.

Chapter 14

WELDING CARBON STEEL

Carbon steel is trade jargon for a large array of ferrous products which range from one-coat enameling steel (which is virtually carbon-free and almost qualifies as iron) to cast iron (which contains about 3% carbon and technically is not a steel). Included in this broad array are low-carbon, deep drawing steels for auto bodies, mild steel for structural use, medium carbon steels for pressure vessels and machinery, high-carbon steels for abrasion resistance, and very high carbon steels for springs and cutting tools. While this brief description emphasizes the range of carbon content to be encountered, these products require a much closer examination of chemical composition to understand why they serve so well in particular kinds of applications and their behavior in welding.

Carbon steels were defined in Chapter 2 as alloys of iron and carbon in which the manganese content did not exceed 1.65% and the silicon and copper contents did not exceed 0.60% each. Furthermore, specified limits were not to be set for any other alloying elements. Even so, *carbon steels* sometimes contain additions of elements like aluminum or titanium for purposes of deoxidation, or to secure a fine McQuaid-Ehn (austenitic) grain size. Small amounts of needling agents containing boron or vanadium may be added to increase hardening capability. Grain size inhibitors like columbium or nitrogen may be added to increase strength, particularly yield strength. Carbon steels may be rephosphorized to levels somewhat above the usual residual level to achieve a modest increase in strength. Sulfur or lead may be added to improve machinability. Obviously, the "carbon steels" encountered in welding are more than simple iron-carbon alloys with restricted manganese, silicon and copper contents. We shall see shortly that subtle aspects of the chemical composition of carbon steel can have a profound influence upon a welding operation. A small addition of an element to improve a particular quality or property may unexpectedly appear as a hinderance, or as a help, in the steel's weldability. Although we shall find that carbon is the element wielding the greatest influence over the welding behavior of carbon steel, we also shall see that the remainder of the composition deserves as close study as might be given an alloy steel.

Success in welding carbon steels is determined to a large degree by familiarity with the microstructural characteristics of each particular type and our ability to avoid the development of an unsuitable structure in or adjacent to the weld joint. Chapter 9, which dealt with simple welds in iron and steel, was concluded by stressing the importance of cooling rate on the final structure of a given steel in its heat-affected zone adjacent to the weld deposit. With increasing carbon content, faster rates of cooling tend to produce a martensitic structure whose properties are not desirable for weld joints. Microstructural changes involving transformations of austenite, ferrite and martensite are a most important part of welding carbon steels and must be given attention before dealing with any other metallurgical aspect.

COOLING RATES IN WELDS

From the discussion in Chapter 4, we should recall that the fastest cooling rates occur in the metal which has been heated to the highest temperature during welding. If we had no prior knowledge, we should conclude that, since the fastest rates of cooling have the greatest effect upon the steel, the weld metal itself should be the center of discussion. This is not so, however; for the weld metal of most carbon steels has so low a carbon content that it does not change its properties to any great extent under the most rapid cooling likely to occur in welding. Besides, in multi-layer welding the next bead always refines the preceding bead. Instead of the weld metal, therefore, we will examine primarily the base metal in the immediate vicinity of the weld, for it is the metal closest to the weld that cools rapidly and is most likely to exhibit important changes in the structure and properties as a result of welding.

COOLING RATES IN TERMS OF QUENCHING MEDIA

Quenching is rapid cooling by immersion in liquids or gases or by contact with metal. The term is applied commonly to the heat treating operation in which a medium-carbon or high-carbon steel is heated 100 degrees F above the upper critical (Ac_3) and after removal from the furnace is immersed in a quenching medium at room temperature or thereabout. Immersing the steel in cold brine is known as brine quenching, in oil as oil quenching, in air as air quenching. The steel cools extremely fast in brine quenching, slower in oil quenching, and still slower in air quenching.

During brine quenching of a thin section of steel, say ¼-in. diameter, the austenite is supercooled to 200 to 400 F, then changes to martensite, and appears to our microscope at room temperature as martensite. The steel is said to be fully hardened. The maximum hardness that can be obtained in any carbon steel by a full hardening treatment like this is governed by the carbon content. Oil quenching usually is too slow to fully harden plain carbon steel. Brine quenching cools a thin piece of steel at the rate of over 900 degrees F per second while the steel is in the temperature range of 800–1200 F in which the austenite transforms most rapidly. In other words, the steel remains in the range less than ½ second, which is insufficient time for the first transformed crystal to appear. The austenite continues to cool until at 200–400 F it is changed to martensite. During oil quenching, on the other hand, the rate of cooling of a thin bar of steel in the temperature range of 800–1200 F is only about 100 degrees F per second. The steel remains in the range about 4 seconds, which is sufficient to permit the austenite to change partly or wholly to fine pearlite. Of course, when this transformation starts, heat is evolved which tends to reduce the cooling rate still further.

Air quenching is usually so slow that the steel transforms entirely to pearlite during cooling in the range 1200–1100 F. Of course, a wire cools faster in air than a 1-inch plate, but in all our discussion we must remember that the surface of a part cools more rapidly than the interior, and that thin sections of uniformly heated metal cool more rapidly than thick. Consequently, air cooling may harden a wire, yet it may produce a soft pearlite in a 2-inch thick plate. Indeed, air cooling of steel ¼ inch and thicker from 100 degrees F above the critical range is the customary means of creating a strong, ductile structure in steel, and was described in Chapter 12 as normalizing.

In welding, the rate of cooling after the weld melt has passed by is governed by contact with adjacent steel rather than by immersion in air. In Chapter 4 on Temperature Changes in Welding, we found that as we moved back along the bead, away from the melt, the weld became cooler. The temperature fell as heat was absorbed from the hot regions in and near the weld by the cold regions farther away. Note that the heat is absorbed by brine, oil, or air in heat treating, whereas in welding, experience shows that the major portion of the heat is absorbed by the steel adjacent to the weld rather than by the air.

THE WELD DURING COOLING

The effects of a large variety of heat treatments can be found in a weld depending upon the mass in the joint, its initial temperature, the welding process, and so forth. It may be well to refresh our memories on a few points brought out in Chapter 4 on Temperature Changes in Welding and Chapter 12 on Preheating, in regard to the weld during cooling. Remember now, the charts illustrating temperature distribution in a weld represent a quasi-stationary condition, or the temperature distribution that we would find if the operation were stopped for an instant. Because the welding operation is always moving, the true thermal history of the weld is very involved. For the present, the simplified explanations which we brought out will suffice.

The maximum temperatures to which portions of the plate are heated will range from that of molten metal down to that of unheated metal. The rate of cooling which these portions will undergo depends mainly on the temperature gradient that exists between the heated and cooler portions. However, since heat input and metal mass are also quite important, the actual cooling may vary from very fast rates (as we may normally find in brine quenching) to very slow rates (as we find in air cooling). Also, the cooling cycle of a weld may be arrested at some point above room temperature because of deliberately applied postheat. Thus the cooling conditions in the weld may approach that of an isothermal treatment. Finally, it is not unusual to find portions of the weld being reheated to some temperature by a subsequent weld bead or an adjacent weld joint. By now there should be no question as to why we find an extensive array of structures in weld joints.

Characteristic Cooling Rates for Welds

Much work has been conducted to establish the cooling curves for the heat-affected zones of metal-arc welds having given masses and welded with a variety of heat inputs at various initial base metal temperatures. Cooling curves were first established by means of electrical analogy on a Heat-Mass-Flow Analyzer. These results were later confirmed by making actual welds and measuring the temperature changes through a thermocouple imbedded in the metal in the heat-affected zone. A characteristic cooling curve was found for each given joint design, thickness, heat input, and initial temperature. The data from this work have been published in the form of charts, tables, and formulas from which it is possible to calculate the cooling rate for the heat-affected zone of any weld when given the joint design, plate thickness, heat input, and initial temperature. The validity of these data was confirmed in a most interesting manner. Another group of investigators determined the cooling rate in the heat-affected zones of a wide variety of welds simply by first making a hardness determination at a point in the zone immediately adjacent to the fusion line. Then a piece of the base metal was machined into a Jominy End-Quench Hardenability Specimen and end-quenched from 2100 F (the effective temperature believed attained by the heat-affected zone). A point was located on the Jominy bar where the bar hardness equaled the hardness found in the heat-affected zone. The assumption was made that a steel cooled at a given rate from the same austenitizing temperature will always produce the same hardness regardless of its form— whether a hardenability specimen or a weld heat-affected zone. Therefore, if the hardness of our weld heat-affected zone could be located at a particular point on the Jominy bar, then the cooling rate of the heat-affected zone could be learned by noting the cooling rate of the Jominy bar at that particular point. Reasonably good agreement was found between cooling rates established for welds by the thermocouple measurement method and the method of matching the hardness of the heat-affected zone with a point on a hardenability specimen of known cooling characteristics.

The ultimate aim of this work was, of course, to gather quantitative information on the influence of mass, heat input, and preheating so that these variables might be controlled to attain any desired cooling rate in the weld heat-affected zone. By predetermining the cooling rate, we would also be preselecting the structure and hardness of the heat-affected zone. In Chapter 16 on Welding Tests, a more complete description is given of a system which has been offered as a "Guide to the Weldability of Steels." The system incorporates the method of correlating heat-affected zone hardness and Jominy bar hardness. However, it may be well to mention a few of the more important facts which have been uncovered pertaining to the cooling rates in welds. The cooling of the heat-affected zone is determined largely by the volume of base metal within a 3-inch radius of the weld. The base metal outside of this radius is too far removed to be influential in determining the rate at which heat is withdrawn from the relatively narrow heat-affected zone, at least during the early important stages of cooling. Special attention must be given to the start and finish of a weld where the cooling rate may be faster or slower than along the length of the weld depending upon whether the end or start reaches the very edge of the plate or is removed from the edge. The effect of pre-heating is, of course, to reduce the temperature gradient between the heat-affected zone and the unaffected base metal and consequently reduce the cooling rate. If a value of 1.00 is assigned the cooling rate of a plate welded at 75 F, then the ratio of similar values for other initial plate temperatures like 32 F, 200 F, and 400 F would be 1.10, 0.85, and 0.67, respectively. The heat input can be estimated by calculating the number of Joules per inch (voltage $\times$ amperage $\times$ seconds per inch travel speed). A number of factors which at first glance would seem to be important in connection with heat input from the welding arc and deposited metal were actually found to be of secondary order. The absorption of energy liberated by the welding arc is only slightly better when the operation is performed deep in a groove between the plates as compared with depo-sition of a bead on the surface. Only a slight influence on the cooling rate appears to be exerted by the electrode size, core wire composition, type of flux covering, kind of current (a-c or d-c), and polarity on direct current.

STRUCTURES IN WELDS

When a weld is made, the metal closest to the weld is heated with extraordinary rapidity. The base metal at the fusion line, of course, reaches the vicinity of its melting point. A portion further back exceeds the critical temperature range and the ferrite and carbide change to austenite. It has been determined that in metal-arc welds, the portion of the base metal heat-affected zone immediately adjacent to the fusion line reaches an effective temperature of approximately 2100 F. This temperature has been ascertained by comparing the grain size of a weld heat-affected zone with the grain size of a series of base metal specimens which had been heated to progressively higher temperatures. This is important information for we know that a steel specimen heated to 2100 F may form quite coarse grains. Also, the cooling rate of this zone will be somewhat slower as it passes the crucial temperature level of 1100 F than if the maximum temperature reached was only slightly above the critical range, say per-haps 1800 F. Nevertheless, we know that the heat-affected zone may cool at widely varying rates depending upon the mass of base metal, heat input, and temperature gradient. In any event, we must not lose sight of the fact that the metal in the heat-affected zone may not respond to a particular cooling rate in the manner indicated by an I–T curve or a hardenability test specimen; particularly if the test data were taken from specimens cooled from temperatures a hundred degrees or so above the critical range. It appears that an austenitizing temperature of 2100 F and a soaking time of 30 minutes are needed to simulate metal in the weld heat-affected zone.

AUSTENITE GRAIN SIZE

Before entering a description of the structures that form in welds upon cooling, a few remarks appear in order concerning the grains of austenite from which the final structures germinate. Various steels may differ in the rate at which their austenite grains grow after the temperature rises above the critical range. One steel may display a tendency to grow quite coarse austenite grains at a temperature not too far above the critical range, perhaps at 1500 F. Another steel may retain a fine austenite grain size until it reaches substantially higher temperatures, say 1800 F. The austenite grain size, besides affecting the size of the pearlite grains which may form upon cooling, also affects the critical cooling rate of the steel. A coarse austenite grain size shows greater tendency to undercool than fine grain size. Stated in another manner, coarse grain size promotes hardenability. Why? A complete explanation is not yet at hand. Perhaps the greater reluctance of the coarse grain steel to transform can be attributed partly to the fewer grain boundaries at which the transformation initiates.

The foregoing fact regarding austenite grain size no doubt will bring a few questions to mind. We immediately wonder where the coarsening temperature lies for steels which tend to retain a fine grain size; how the grain size is determined; and how the grain size may be controlled. Quality steels are usually rated for inherent austenite grain size by the McQuaid-Ehn grain size test. A small specimen of steel is carburized to develop a hypereutectoid case. The temperature is usually 1700 F, which is just above the temperatures normally employed for heat-treating operations, and the carburizing time is eight hours. Upon very slow furnace cooling, a network of cementite remains around the pearlite boundaries to clearly reveal the grain size. The size may be rated under the metallographic microscope, with the aid of the chart in ASTM Specification E112, as ranging from 1 to 4 (coarse grained), or 5 to 8 (fine grained). The inherent austenite grain size is established by melting practice. Steels of the fine-grained type are commonly produced by adding a quantity of aluminum over the amount needed to deoxidize the steel. It is a peculiar characteristic of fine-grained steels that when the grain-coarsening temperature is exceeded, the austenite grains rapidly grow to sizes equal to, or even greater than, the sizes of grains in an inherently coarse-grained steel at the same temperature. Therefore, we see little difference between the behavior of fine-grained and coarse-grained steel in the base metal heat-affected zone immediately adjacent to the weld, for here the effective temperature of 2100 F exceeds the coarsening temperature of both types of steel. However, a difference in grain size will be noted in the heated-affected zone further away from the weld.

Often it is important to know the critical range, that is, the temperature range bracketed by the Ac_1 and the Ac_3 points. Available tables of critical ranges may not include those for the type steel at hand. Formulas have been proposed for calculating the critical points from the composition of the steel. When determined isothermally, these points may be called the Ae_1 and the Ae_3; meaning that the critical point has been established under *equilibrium* conditions. However, because the temperature level of these points will vary with heating rate, one investigator has proposed that they be identified as A_s (start of austenitization) and A_f (last trace of ferrite to transform to austenite). From data on many different steel compositions, it was found that phosphorus and sulfur have a very small effect and can be ignored. Molybdenum also had no significant effect. The following formulas were proposed:

$$A_s \text{ (degree F)} = 1333 - 25\ (\%\ Mn) + 40\ (\%\ Si) - 26\ (\%\ Ni) + 42\ (\%\ Cr)$$

Note that determination of the lower critical temperature, A_s, does not require consideration of the carbon content, which is in accordance with the iron-iron carbide equilibrium diagram shown earlier in Fig. 87.

$$A_f \text{ (degree F)} = 1570 - 323\ (\%C) - 25\ (\%\ Mn) + 80\ (\%\ Si) - 32\ (\%\ Ni) - 3\ (\%\ Cr)$$

These formulas are believed to predict the critical temperatures within ±5%, which is sufficiently accurate for planning most heat treating operations. The developer of these formulas, Grange, believed they could be applied to steels having a composition within the following ranges: 0.3/0.6 %C, 0/2 %Mn, 0/1 %Si, 0/3.5 %Ni, 0/1.5 %Cr and 0/0.5 %Mo.

LAMELLAR PEARLITE

When the austenite in the heat-affected zone is cooled very slowly, we know that no change occurs in it until the temperature has fallen to the critical range. Upon reaching the upper critical, ferrite crystals form in the grain boundaries of the austenite. As the temperature continues to fall, the ferrite crystals grow until, at the lower critical, the remainder

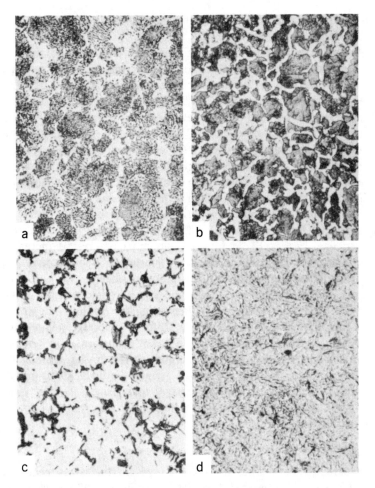

Fig. 209 — Microstructure of plain-carbon steel containing 0.50 percent carbon after cooling at increasing rates from above the critical range. Etchant: Picral. Mag. 500X

- (a) (upper left) Slow furnace cool, coarse pearlite and ferrite grains. Hardness 187 Bhn
- (b) (upper right) Air cool, medium pearlite and ferrite boundaries. Hardness 255 Bhn
- (c) (lower left) Oil quench, very fine pearlite in matrix of martensite. Hardness 429 Bhn
- (d) (lower right) Brine quench, martensite. Hardness 601 Bhn

of the austenite changes to pearlite. The corresponding structure for a 0.50 percent plain-carbon steel is shown in Fig. 209 (a). The upper and lower criticals are the temperatures given by the Ar_3 and Ar_1 lines in the iron-iron carbide diagram shown in Fig. 87.

As the cooling rate of the austenitized heat-affected zone is increased, we know that the iron–carbon diagram can no longer be depended upon for all we wish to know about the structure of our 0.5% C steel. Let us examine the structures of heat-affected zones cooled at rates equivalent to air, oil, and brine quenching. The corresponding structures are shown in Figs. 209 (b), 209 (c), and 209 (d). According to general principles, the increase in cooling rate will lower the temperature range of transformation. The number of crystals that form during transformation increases as the critical range temperatures are lowered. Thus, in Fig. 209 (b) the grains are smaller than in Fig. 209 (a) because the cooling rate was more rapid and the transformation occurred at a lower temperature. A further increase in the rate of cooling will further refine the grain size, Fig. 209 (c), for as the number of crystals increases, the size of each must decrease. A larger proportion of the structure appears to be occupied by the pearlite in Fig. 209 (b) than in 209 (a). Furthermore, the distance between the carbide plates of the pearlite is smaller in Fig. 209 (b) than in 209 (a). Increasing the cooling rate of a steel such as our 0.50% C material below 1390 F (the AR_3 temperature on slow cooling) results, therefore, in a lower transformation temperature range, a smaller grain size, a lesser amount of free ferrite, a smaller interlamellar spacing in the pearlite, and a greater hardness. This trend continues until the speed of cooling exceeds the critical cooling rate and then a structure composed wholly of martensite like that shown in Fig. 209 (d) is formed.

MARTENSITE

Experience shows that the cooling rates in the zones heated above the critical range during welding may be rapid enough to cause undercooling of the austenite below 1100 F and to form martensite. To express this experience in metallurgical terms, we say that the cooling rates in the heat-affected zones of welds may exceed the *critical* cooling rate of the steel and when this happens, naturally, martensite is formed. All in all, the rate at which different regions of a weld cool through the temperature range from the critical to below 1000 F varies with the plate thickness, welding process, and other variables. A thin bead deposited between thick plates is particularly likely to create martensite in the heat-affected zone. Martensite is also favored by the large grain size of austenite in the zone adjacent to the weld melt. As another example, full hardening, meaning that the structure is entirely martensitic and devoid of pearlite, may occur in the heat-affected zone of a spot weld in high-carbon steel sheets because of a very rapid cooling rate. Partial hardening, corresponding with a mixed structure of martensite and pearlite, like that shown in Fig. 209 (c), may be created in the heat-affected zone of a heavy bead deposited on a thin plate for here there is little likelihood of exceeding the critical cooling rate by a sufficient margin to entirely prevent the appearance of lamellar pearlite.

STRUCTURAL CHANGES IN THE HEAT-AFFECTED ZONE

Transformation diagrams have been helpful in predicting the structures in welds. To use this tool, we must first determine cooling curves for portions of metal in which we are interested. These portions might be (1) the point in the heat-affected zone immediately adjacent to the weld bead where we know that fast cooling takes place, (2) a point further back in the heat-affected zone where a medium cooling rate prevails, and (3) a point a still greater distance away from the weld bead, but where the metal is heated just slightly above the critical range during welding. These cooling curves are not difficult to measure and in some cases can even be calculated. We might first apply our cooling curves to an I–T diagram, although we hasten to add that the C-curve has been determined under isothermal transformation conditions as described earlier and the position of the curve will be shifted when continuous cooling conditions are in force. We can gain a better understanding of our cooling curves by taking the viewpoint that a curve can be subdivided into a large number of steps, Fig. 210 (a). Even though we know the steel is cooling continuously, the steel is assumed to remain at a series of temperatures for lengths of time sufficient so that the dotted curve approximates closely to the actual curve. The time occupied at each of the selected temperatures then is compared with the time required for the austenite to start changing to other products at those temperatures, Fig. 210(b). For a given cooling rate it is possible to calculate the temperature at which the austenite starts and completes its transformation. The faster the cooling rate, the lower will be the temperature of transformation; we say that the critical temperature has been lowered.

Studying the curves in Fig. 210 (b), we see that the cooling curve for the point in the base metal farthest from the weld bead, the point where slow cooling took place, intersected the transformation curve at a fairly high temperature where we would logically expect lamellar pearlite to form. The base metal at the intermediate point, where medium cooling took place, displays a cooling curve which intersects the transformation curve at a somewhat lower temperature, just above the nose of the C-curve.

The structure of the metal at this point would therefore be a very fine lamellar pearlite. Continuing our inspection of Fig. 210 (b), we observe

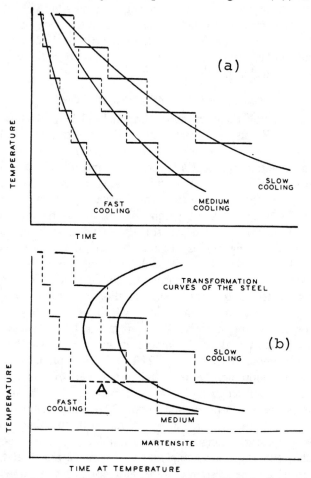

Fig. 210 (a) and (b) — The times at the horizontals in (a) are expressed as a percentage of the total time for austenite to transform at each temperature for the purpose of plotting in (b)

Thus, the time represented by the horizontals at 1100 F in (a) may be 2 seconds, which may be 10 percent of the time required to start the transformation of austenite. When the sum of the percentages calculated at the different horizontals in (a) equals 100 percent, the austenite has begun to transform. The fast cooling would have exceeded the critical cooling rate of the steel, but if the fast cooling had been arrested at A, martensite would not have formed.

that the curve labeled *fast cooling* has never intersected the transformation curve. The austenite represented by this curve will not transform to ferrite and pearlite, but will change instead to martensite as the metal cools through the martensite formation range.

CCT Diagrams

A number of investigators have spent considerable time developing *continuous cooling transformation* diagrams to predict more closely the microstructure which would form in the base metal heat-affected zone upon cooling from the welding temperature. One team of laboratory workers, using a number of selected steels, heated many specimens to 2460 F and cooled them at various rates representing a wide variety of welding conditions. Various pieces of apparatus and techniques were employed to determine the start of transformation to a particular microstructure during cooling. The relationship between the critical cooling times derived from these determinations and the chemical composition of the steel were carefully studied. Hardness and bend tests were performed on small specimens cooled at the various rates. It was believed by the investigators that the *critical cooling time* (identified as C_F) obtained from a plotted CCT diagram could be helpful as an index to the ductility and toughness of the heat-affected base metal. A nomograph, as shown in Fig. 211, was developed to predict the cooling time in seconds from 1472 to 932 F when the heat input and plate thickness were known. Summaries were provided to show the probable hardness which would be developed in the heat-affected zone of a specific carbon steel with different cooling rates. The relationship between cooling time and hardness for a steel containing 0.17% carbon is shown in Fig. 212. These data enabled the investigators to plot CCT diagrams, an example of which is shown in Fig. 213 for the 0.17% carbon steel previously employed in Fig. 212. A comparison of the CCT diagram with an I–T diagram (see Figures 119 and 120, Chapter 9) will show much similarity in the microstructural phases present at certain temperature levels. The CCT diagram shows the steel in the austenitic condition above the A_3 temperature. Four important cooling curves have been plotted on the CCT diagram to mark boundary conditions. These curves will illustrate how the base metal heat-affected zone immediately adjacent to the fusion line will differ in microstructure and in hardness as varying lengths of time are taken in cooling from the high austentitizing temperature (2460 F) through the temperature range of 1472 to 932 F. Note that time is measured on the abscissa with a logarithmic scale, which accounts for the increased slope of the curves as

HEAT INPUT COOLING TIME PLATE THICKNESS

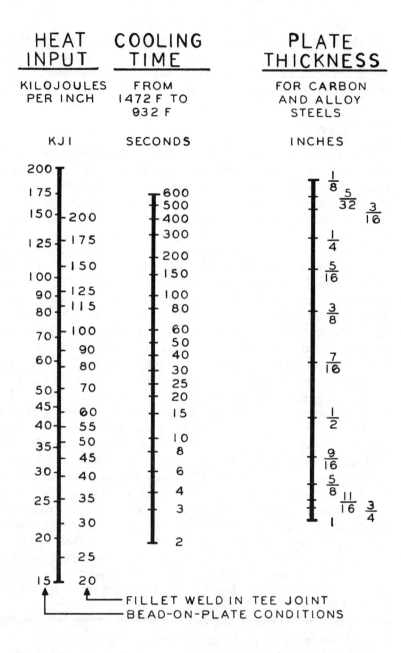

Fig. 211 — Nomograph for calculating cooling time which elapses between 1472 and 932 F when the base metal heat-affected zone cools from an arc-welding operation. (After Inagaki and Sekiguchi)

they approach the cooling end-point. Note also that increased heat input during welding results in longer cooling times, and that the investigators found small differences in the cooling rates of welds made by the gas metal-arc process as compared with welds made by the shielded metal-arc process for given heat inputs.

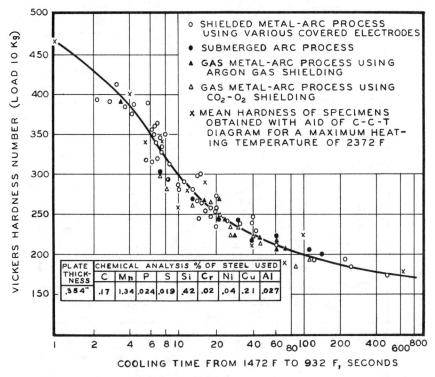

Fig. 212 — Relationship between cooling time (for 1472–932 F temperature range) and maximum hardness in base metal heat-affected zone as determined for various welding processes. (After Inagaki and Sekiguchi)

Now let us see how the investigators predicted the approximate micro-structure and hardness of a heat-affected zone using their CCT diagram in Fig. 213. If the heat input during welding is very low and cooling takes place at a rate more rapid than the "Z"-cooling curve, then the heat-affected zone structure will be entirely martensitic and its hardness will exceed 415 DPH. If cooling should occur at a rate that falls between the "Z"-cooling curve and the "F"-cooling curve, some transformation to an intermediate structure (Widmanstätten structure), which the investigators have identified by the symbol "Z_w", will develop, and the final heat-affected zone structure will be a blending of martensite and intermediate structures. The hardness of this zone will be lower than 415 DPH. Slower cooling along a curve passing to the right of the "F"-cooling curve will see the formation of some proeutectoid ferrite, and the final structure will consist of ferrite, intermediate structure, and martensite. If cooling is carried out a slower rate than marked by the "P"-cooling curve, some pearlitic structure also develops and the final structure consists of pearlite, ferrite, intermediate structure, and martensite. A further decrease in cooling rate beyond the "E"-cooling curve usually enables transformation in the heat-affected zone to proceed entirely to ferrite and pearlite. The investigators found that heat-affected zones which cooled at a rate sufficiently slow to produce at least some transformation to proeutectoid

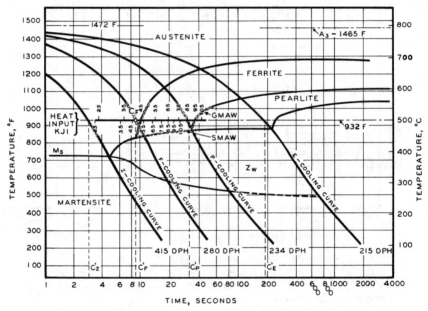

Fig. 213 — CCT diagram for continuous-cooling transformation showing critical points, critical cooling curves and critical cooling times. (After Inagaki and Sekiguchi)

The diagram depicts the transformation behavior of the 0.17% carbon steel described in Fig. 212. The scale correlating heat input and cooling rate placed along the 932 F temperature level applies to the heat-affected zones produced in a ⅝-inch thick plate welded under bead-on-plate conditions. The maximum hardness values shown usually were found in the coarse-grain region immediately adjacent to the fusion line.

ferrite ordinarily did not crack spontaneously and exhibited a reasonable degree of ductility and toughness. They concluded, therefore, that the cooling rate which marked the appearance of proeutectoid ferrite could be identified by the symbol "C_F", and that this rate represented a limiting weldability index. Accordingly, a given steel always should be welded by a procedure (heat input, or possibly through preheat) which produces a heat-affected zone cooling rate slower than C_F; or when the welding procedure is fixed, the steel employed should have the smallest practicable value of C_F and yet provide the desired strength. In any event, the welding should be carried out in a manner that heat-affected zones cool over a longer period that C_F (or C'_F as shown on Fig. 213). The value of the CCT diagram will be discussed further in Chapter 15.

Bainite

So far, we have covered only the structures that may be created in the heat-affected zone of a weld under continuous cooling conditions. Suppose that before the temperature of the metal immediately adjacent to the weld entered the range of martensite formation, we had arrested the cooling by depositing a second bead over the first. If the cooling had been arrested completely in Fig. 210 (b) at point A, the austenite retained in the base metal near the first bead would have transformed to the product known as bainite, for we have intersected the transformation curve well below the nose and yet above the martensite formation range. On the other hand, the temperature of the austenite might be raised by the deposition of the second bead and ferrite and pearlite may have formed. Still another possibility is that the austenite had changed partly to martensite and had then been reheated by the second bead into the bainite region. The resulting structure would then consist of some bainite and some martensite that had been tempered by reheating, Fig. 214.

We cannot expect to predict quantitatively the nature of the changes that will occur in the heat-affected zone of a multipass weld, because the variations in welding conditions are too great for precise calculations. The discussion of possible conditions serves, nevertheless, to show whence arise the variety of structures that are found in the heat-affected zones of welds. As a general rule, the addition of alloying elements, and particularly an increase in carbon content, will shift both the I–T and the CCT curves to the right. The shift of the curves to the right signifies a decrease in the critical cooling rate, which we defined earlier as the slowest rate at which a steel can be cooled and still develop a martensitic structure. However, as we shall point out in Chapter 15, the addition of alloying elements can promote the formation of the bainitic type of structure rather than martensite. The bainitic structure can offer desirable strength and toughness providing the carbon content of the steel is relatively low, for example, about 0.20% or less.

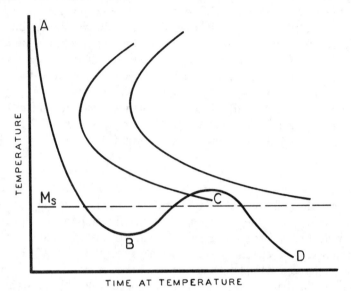

TIME AT TEMPERATURE

Fig. 214 — Curve ABCD is the time-temperature record of the zone close to the weld in a thick plate.

From A to B the zone is cooling rapidly enough to pass the nose of the transformation curve. As it passes below the point of martensite formation (M_s) temperature, some of the austenite transforms to martensite, the transformation continuing until the temperature falls to B. At B the zone feels the heating effect of the next bead and the fall in temperature is arrested. Likewise the further decomposition of austenite to martensite is stopped. The temperature of the zone then commences to rise and upon crossing the left transformation curve, the remaining austenite commences to transform to bainite. Meanwhile the martensite is changing to a mixture of ferrite and cementite, that is, the temperature has risen sufficiently high for the martensite to be tempered. Beyond C the second bead has passed by and the zone cools to room temperature along the curve CD. Caution: Interpretation of time-temperature curves in terms of transformation curves requires consideration of Fig. 210 (a) and (b)

In the heat-affected zone, a wide variety of structures are to be expected corresponding to the wide range of cooling rates in the zone while it is cooling below 1300 F. The finer pearlite and martensite tend to appear to an increased extent in the heat-affected zones of the higher-carbon steels compared with the lower carbon. In plain-carbon steels with less than 0.20% C the critical cooling rate is so high that, except under most unusual welding conditions, the heat-affected zone will consist of ferrite and pearlite, the individual grains of each being finer the higher the cooling rate. In the higher carbon (0.35% C) and alloy steels (for example, 0.25% C, 1.5% Mn) the critical cooling rate will be sufficiently slow that martensite forms close to the welds with high cooling rates, such as the first or root layer of a butt or fillet weld in thick plates. The heat-affected zone will consist of a layer of martensite sandwiched between weld metal and the softer parts of the zone, Fig. 215. Of course, if a

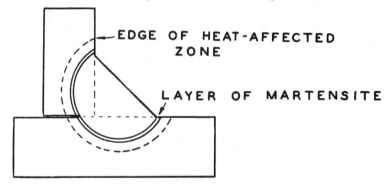

Fig. 215 — If Martensite forms in the welding of high-tensile steels, it is found at the fusion line.

steel having a very slightly higher critical cooling rate (due to lower carbon and manganese contents) were welded under these same conditions, the heat-affected zone may display a structure adjacent to the weld which is only partly martensitic. The remainder of the structure, like that shown in Fig. 209 (c), would consist of the products that form by nucleation and growth, namely, ferrite and pearlite. This is commonly referred to as a *mixed* structure, rather than a hardened (wholly martensitic) structure. Mixed structures form because the cooling curve for the heat-affected zone has followed a *continuous* course through only the *nose* of the upper transformation range on the CCT diagram (the ferrite and pearlite region). If cooling were somewhat slower, transformation would tend to proceed more to ferrite and pearlite, and the final structure would contain less martensite.

STRUCTURE OF WELD METAL

The microstructure of carbon steel weld metal will be noticeably different than that of the base metal, or even the base metal heat-affected zone. The reasons for this difference were touched upon in Chapter 9, and were given considerable attention in Chapter 10. As described for simple welds in steel, the weld structure forms from the liquid state, which involves a solidification mechanism of nucleation and columnar growth. In many cases, dendritic segregation occurs during solidification. Furthermore, the metal cools from a very high temperature and at a rather rapid rate. The actual structure of the weld metal will depend heavily, of course, upon its composition. However, these conditions favor four features commonly observed in carbon steel weld metal structures: (1) the macrostructure displays columnar growth which follows the direction of thermal flow from the weld area, (2) the grain size of the microstructure is extremely fine, (3) the substructure contains a very large number of dislocations, and (4) a Widmanstätten pattern develops as the weld metal undergoes the austenite-to-ferrite transformation. Although Widmanstätten pattern (Fig. 216) ordinarily develops only in a limited range of carbon content, usually 0.20 to 0.40%, the high initial temperature of weld metal favors its formation even in somewhat lower-carbon

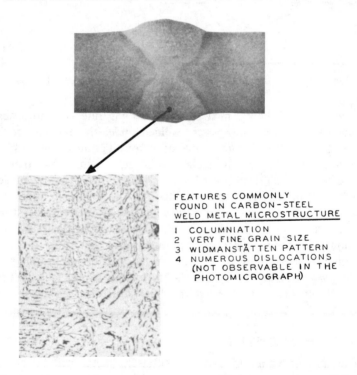

FEATURES COMMONLY
FOUND IN CARBON-STEEL
WELD METAL MICROSTRUCTURE

1 COLUMNIATION
2 VERY FINE GRAIN SIZE
3 WIDMANSTÄTTEN PATTERN
4 NUMEROUS DISLOCATIONS
   (NOT OBSERVABLE IN THE
   PHOTOMICROGRAPH)

Fig. 216 — Microstructure of typical low-carbon steel weld metal.

weld metal. The presence of this peculiar pattern of acicular ferrite with its preferred orientation acts to lower the ductility and toughness of weld metal. This is one of the reasons for favoring very low-carbon contents in weld metal. Close examination of the Widmanstätten structure will show that the ferrite, which would normally develop in the austenite grain boundaries, and therefore be located around the pearlite grains upon complete transformation of the austenite, is present to a large extent as needle-like particles traversing the pearlite grains.

MECHANICAL PROPERTIES OF WELDED JOINTS

Knowing that there are a number of different structures in the vicinity of any weld, we inquire about their properties, which can be determined on tiny microspecimens cut from the joint or on large specimens that have been heat treated so as to have the same structure as different parts of the weld. Neither procedure is quite satisfactory. Results from tiny specimens 1/16 inch in diameter are never so accurate as those determined on large specimens ½ inch in diameter, nor is it certain that there is only one type of structure present even in the tiny specimen. On the other hand, it is not easy to duplicate the structures in a weld joint. If specimens are heat treated in a furnace, they must be held a long time to attain uniform temperature. They never cool at the same rate in the center as on the surface when quenched in any medium. Furthermore, the time–temperature record of a piece of hot steel cooling in a quenching bath, such as oil, has a number of retardations and accelerations, due to flaking of scale, and formation of vapor pockets, that are not found in the time–temperature record of a single-pass weld during cooling. A superior technique for reproducing the microstructures found in base metal heat-affected zones is to make use of a programed, thermocouple-controlled resistance heating device. These are rather costly pieces of equipment, but they very accurately simulate the heat-effect of welding and thus synthetically produce weld-like structures in a specimen of reasonable size.

With these reservations in mind, we study Fig. 217. The curves labeled *annealed* apply to specimens that have been cooled slowly in a furnace, while the curves labeled *quenched* apply to specimens that have been cooled by water quenching. As the carbon content of the slowly cooled steel rises, the strength and hardness increase, the ductility slowly decreases. The hardness of the quenched specimen rises as the carbon content increases, but quenching has lowered the ductility. The ductility of steels with up to 0.20% C is not greatly lowered by quenching, but with 0.30% C or more, quenching lowers the ductility to values, which would justify the adjective *brittle* for many applications. Cooling rates in welds fall between the two extremes of *annealed* and *quenched*. The faster the cooling, the more nearly the properties approach the quenched curve.

The effect of alloying elements on the curves in Fig. 217 can be

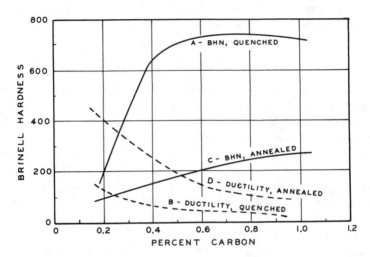

Fig. 217 — Hardness (tensile strength) and ductility of steels as a function of carbon content.

The curves for ductility are schematic only; their positions will depend upon the stress system prevailing in the test from which the ductility is determined.

Curve A — Brinell hardness of water-quenched samples
Curve B — Ductility of water-quenched samples
Curve C — Brinell hardness of annealed samples
Curve D — Ductility of annealed samples

estimated only in a general way. For a given hardness, the alloy steel will be more ductile than the plain-carbon steel. Counter-balancing the advantage of greater ductility in the hardened state is the characteristic that the alloy steels of a given carbon content harden at slower cooling rates than the plain-carbon steels of the same carbon content.

The benefit of adding alloying elements to steels for welding depends upon utilizing both the greater ductility and the lower critical cooling rate conferred by the alloying element. Quench as drastically as we please, we cannot drive the quenched curve in Fig 217 more than a very few units higher than for plain-carbon by adding alloying elements. This is true because the maximum attainable hardness with any plain-carbon or alloy steel is governed by the carbon content. When handling plain-carbon steels of lower carbon content (up to 0.20% C), to secure the maximum hardness and strength shown by Fig. 217 nothing less than a drastic quench in water will suffice. Cooling in air will leave the properties closer to the annealed condition. With an alloy steel of the same carbon content, however, the critical cooling rate is lower than in the plain-carbon steel. Moderate rates of cooling will suffice to create a fine-grained structure with which the high strength is associated. Furthermore, some of the alloying elements may lend a little strength to the steel by dissolving in the iron. The net effect is that regardless of the cooling rate in welding, the hardest structure in the weld will have acceptable ductility, yet the as-rolled or normalized alloy steel will have high strength.

THE PROPERTIES OF MARTENSITE

Some of the fundamental facts embodied in Fig. 217 are elaborated in Fig. 218. As the rate of cooling is increased the tensile strength of mild steel slowly increases; the maximum attainable strength requires rapid quenching, corresponding with the critical cooling rate of the steel.

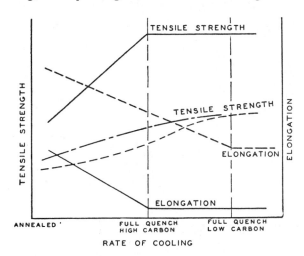

Fig. 218 — Schematic diagram showing that increase in cooling rate from above the critical range generally lowers the ductility but raises the strength of a given steel.

—·—·— Low-alloy steel with low-carbon content
– – – – Low-carbon unalloyed steels
———— High-carbon steels

Addition of suitable alloying elements to the steel lowers the critical cooling rate (and incidentally introduces complexities into the transformation curves), and maximum strength is attainable at lower cooling rates than in the unalloyed steel of the same low-carbon content. The tensile strength of a higher-carbon steel, Fig. 218, rises rapidly with increase in cooling rate until the critical cooling rate is reached. Higher rates have no further effect because the martensite produced at any cooling rate higher than the critical cooling rate is found to be identical in properties with the martensite produced at the critical rate. The ductility of the rapidly cooled higher carbon steel is very low.

Three remarks may be made upon the preceding paragraph. First, the hardness of martensite depends upon its carbon content; that is, on the carbon content of the steel from which the martensite is formed. Figure 219 illustrates the relationship between carbon content and maximum

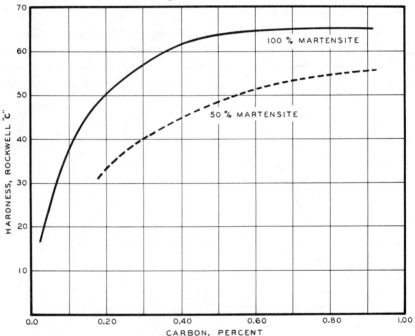

Fig. 219 — Relationship between carbon content and maximum hardness obtainable in any plain-carbon or alloy steel. Upper solid line indicates maximum hardness when the critical cooling rate is exceeded and no austenite is retained (100% martensite). Lower broken line depicts hardness when microstructure contains 50% martensite. This is sometimes used as the criterion in determining whether the steel has a "hardened" structure.

attainable hardness for any plain-carbon or alloy steel; a relationship which has been substantiated by a number of investigators. For a steel of any given carbon content, the maximum attainable hardness is given by the curve in Fig. 219 whenever the steel is heated above its critical range and cooled continuously to room temperature at a rate exceeding the critical cooling rate and providing no austenite is retained. Another property of martensite in which we are interested is ductility. Low-carbon martensite is relatively soft and ductile, whereas high-carbon martensite is relatively hard and brittle. Indeed, so large is the difference in properties and behavior of martensite in steels with over 0.60% C compared with martensite in lower-carbon steels, that the two types are believed by some to differ in certain fundamental respects. The important thing to remember is that the product of rapidly cooled low-carbon steel with or without small quantities of alloying elements is relatively ductile.

The second remark is a reminder that the alloy high-yield strength steels to which reference is made have yield strengths of at least 50,000 psi (compared with 30,000 psi for plain-carbon steel of the same carbon content) and are made in a wide variety of compositions by the different steel manufacturers.

Third, although Figs. 217 and 218 imply that a steel of given strength and hardness will also possess a corresponding ductility, there is no reliable relationship among strength or hardness (these two are very closely related) and ductility and toughness. To assume, for instance, from the fact that an annealed tool steel of 100,000 psi tensile strength has 20 percent reduction of area, that a normalized alloy steel at the same tensile strength will have the same reduction of area is entirely false. The alloy steel will have about 60 percent reduction of area. Likewise, it is incorrect to draw settled conclusions about the toughness of a welded joint from measurements of hardness in the heat-affected zone. Experiments have shown that even though the hardness of the decomposition products of austenite increases as the temperature at which the products were formed is lowered, the ductility in the static tensile test rises and falls in an irregular and as yet unpredictable manner as the temperature of transformation is lowered. Also, fracture toughness, as might be measured by the notched-bar impact test or the precracked tension test, varies in an equally unpredictable way.

Before following further the subject of the cooling of the weld, let us bear in mind the function of metallurgy as we have seen it thus far. The weld is polished and etched for microscopic examination. When we examine the structure, such as pearlite and martensite, we detect structures that we recognize through experience with samples of known heat treatment, and that we know to possess characteristic properties. Whether the properties characteristic of a given structure are retained when the region occupied by the structure is thin, as in the heat-affected zone of a weld, is not known with certainty, but it is a safe guess that any undesirable properties will be retained, although only locally in the narrow zone occupied by the undesirable structure. Fine distinctions among the relative ductilities of different structures observed in the microscope are out of the question. Yet the metallographic detection of martensite in one weld and not in another made by a different process may be a strong argument against the first weld. We may not be able on sight to pick the bandit from a group of suspects, but if we find one of them carrying a gun . . . .

EXPANSION AND CONTRACTION IN WELDS

In addition to changes in temperature and structure during the making of a weld, there are changes in the volume of the steel, Fig. 220.

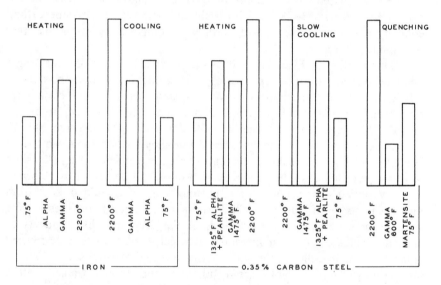

Fig. 220 — Changes in volume (length) of iron and steel.

Iron, upon heating, expands until at 1670 F it commences to change from the alpha form to the gamma form. The gamma form is denser than the alpha at 1670 F, and during the transformation to gamma the steel contracts. Once completely transformed to gamma, the iron expands upon being heated to still higher temperatures, and expands at a greater rate than in the alpha form because the coefficient of expansion of gamma iron is

10×10^{-6} per degree F whereas the coefficient for alpha is only 6.7×10^{-6} per degree F. In other words, gamma iron expands 0.00001 inch in a length of 1 inch for each degree Fahrenheit rise in temperature, whereas alpha iron expands 0.0000067 inch. If, instead of carbon-free iron, 0.35% C steel is heated, the alpha iron in the pearlite changes to the gamma form and dissolves the carbide at the lower critical, 1335 F, accompanied by a contraction. The remaining alpha gradually transforms to gamma while the temperature rises to the upper critical for the 0.35% C steel, 1475 F. Above 1475 F the gamma (austenite) expands as in a carbon-free iron.

During slow cooling the contractions and expansions are exactly the reverse of those observed on heating. If, however, the cooling is rapid, faster than the critical cooling rate for the steel, the austenite transforms only below about 600 F. While it has been cooling below the critical temperature it has been contracting more rapidly than ferrite. Accordingly, the sample may be denser (shorter) at 600 F than was the steel initially. At 600 F, however, the austenite transforms to martensite, which is the most voluminous (least dense) form in which the steel exists at room temperature. On this account the steel expands abnormally during further rapid cooling from 600 F to room temperature, Fig. 221. When the austenite transforms to martensite, the linear expansion may be in the order of 0.004 inches per inch. As the carbon content increases, the volumetric expansion which occurs upon transformation increases. With these facts in mind, it is an interesting exercise to visualize the straining and squeezing undergone by the steel near a weld during welding. As the weld puddle approaches, all the steel in the vicinity expands. The steel heated above the critical contracts in passing through the critical range before expanding further. After the puddle has passed by, contraction sets in, with expansion occuring during the passage through the critical range for those regions that have been heated above it.

There may be a region close to the weld that cools so rapidly as to harden (become martensitic). The rapidly cooling zone contracts abnormally until at about 600 F, when all the steel surrounding it on the base metal side has cooled below 600 F, and the weld metal itself is not far above 600 F (and also contracting for it is low-carbon steel with a very high critical cooling rate) — under these rigid conditions, then, the rapidly cooling zone expands. We do not yet fully comprehend the consequences. The circumstances become further complicated with alloy steels, the austenite of which may transform in a different manner and at different temperatures from plain-carbon steels. Since long, cylindrical bars of steel heated slowly above the critical range and slowly cooled

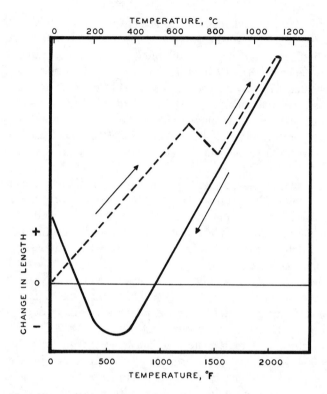

Fig. 221 — Changes in length of a medium-carbon steel during
heating and quenching.

------ Heating
_____ Quenching

The densities and specific volumes of 0.9 percent C steel in
three different conditions at room temperature are:

Condition	Specific Volume, Cubic Centimeters per Gram	Density, Grams per Cubic Centimeter
Pearlite – 0.9 percent C steel	0.1286	7.778
Austenite – 0.9 percent C steel	0.1275	7.843
Martensite – 0.9 percent C steel	0.1310	7.633
Iron	0.1271	7.864
Cementite	0.1304	7.67

The difference in specific volume between martensite and pearlite is less in the lower-carbon steels than in 0.9 percent C steel.
On heating when alpha iron changes to gamma iron at 1670 F there
is a contraction in volume of 0.846 percent; when gamma iron
changes to delta iron there is an expansion in volume of 0.255
percent; when iron melts there is an expansion in volume of 2.8
percent. The reverse changes occur on slow cooling.

undergo a permanent change in length, usually a decrease in length tending to change the bar to a cube or sphere, it is not surprising that a little distortion is not uncommon in welding. Curves showing the expansion of two plain-carbon steels containing 0.06% and 0.23% C, respectively, during slow cooling through their critical ranges can be found in Fig. 222.

The zone that is heated above the lower critical temperature but not above the upper critical during welding is of interest, because it is known that mild steel (up to 0.20% C or so) quenched from slightly above Ac_1 loses a great deal of its ductility. To cite an example, the Izod notch impact value of a mild steel (0.10% C) quenched in water from 1345 F

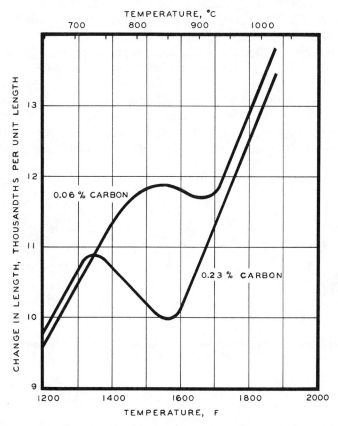

Fig. 222 — The dilation curves show the contraction of two plain-carbon steels during slow cooling through their critical ranges. (after Griffiths)

Metals without critical ranges, such as Type 304 austenitic 18% Cr–8% Ni stainless steel, contract uniformly during cooling.

(slightly above the lower critical) was only 10 ft-lb, whereas after quenching from 1525 F the Izod value was 80 ft-lb. Heating to slightly above the lower critical converts pearlite to austenite, containing about 0.8% C, which tends to form in the grain boundaries and envelop the remaining grains of nearly gamma-free ferrite. Quenching, by converting austenite to martensite, surrounds the ductile ferrite grains with brittle, high-carbon martensite. This structural condition is illustrated in Fig. 223. Under stress, the brittle martensite envelopes govern ductility, which is low. If the steel is cooled slowly from 1345 F, the austenite regions transform to patches of fine grains of ferrite and pearlite, and the steel has high ductility. Ductility is retained, too, if the steel is quenched from 1525 F, for at this temperature the austenite dissolves nearly all the ferrite and has, therefore, a low-carbon content, as the iron-carbon diagram shows. Low-carbon martensite has comparatively high ductility and unusually high notch impact value. These results hold little significance for the welding of mild steel, for it is rare that the zone heated only just above the Ac_1 during welding cools at such a rate as to transform the austenite to martensite. The relatively slow cooling rate in this zone is attributable, of course, to the intermediate location between the higher-temperature zone adjacent to the weld metal and the unaffected base metal.

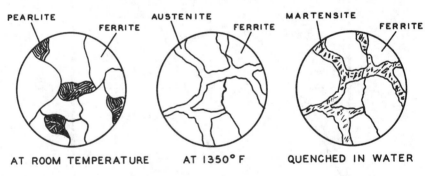

Fig. 223 — Intergranular martensite in low-carbon steel quenched from within the critical range.

METALLURGICAL CONTROL IN WELDING CARBON STEELS

So far, we have discussed in a general way the microstructural changes which occur in the heat-affected zones of the base metal and the structure formed in the weld metal. Usually, a medium-carbon steel was used as an example in describing the microstructural changes. However, the carbon steels to which we hope to apply this knowledge range in carbon content from virtually nil to more than 1%. Obviously, the actual carbon content will be a major factor in determining the exact nature and importance of the microstructural changes. Let us examine the broad class of *carbon steels* to learn the manner in which weldability varies with chemical composition and other aspects. Although we could make use of the AISI-SAE chemical composition specifications for standard types of carbon steels (Table 68) to guide our review, it will be more expedient to group the carbon steels by particular ranges of carbon content. As each group is discussed, we shall note the metallurgical features of specific types of steels that require consideration in welding. For proper coverage of steels in everyday use, it will be necessary to refer also to materials standards of ASTM, API, and several other organizations.

LOW-CARBON STEEL (0.04 TO 0.15% CARBON)

A large amount of the steel used today is of the low-carbon variety. The carbon range of 0.04 to 0.15% mentioned above is not a standard or a specification for low-carbon steel, but is intended as a guide for a group of steels which give practically no difficulty with hardening during welding. Low-carbon steel is found in auto bodies, sheet and strip used for stamped and formed articles, drums, cans, electric motor shells and frames, and thousands of other applications. Many of these mass-produced articles call for steel within a narrower carbon range than 0.04 to 0.15%, and with various restrictions on manganese and silicon contents. For example, if steel were needed for a welded motor frame which would be subjected to severe forming and bending after welding, the material might be ordered as AISI 1006. The carbon maximum of 0.08% would assure low hardness. If steel were needed for an easily-bent and welded tank support on a tractor where somewhat greater strength would be desirable, AISI 1010 might be specified. Composition requirements are needed to tailor the steel for both fabricating operations and end use. However, the examples of steel designations given thus far do not tell the entire story. To obtain the best fabricability, the steel may be made by any one of a number of steelmaking practices. For example, to obtain steel of lowest cost and with excellent surface for forming, the heat of steel may be finished as rimmed steel. Where best drawing quality is needed, a special killed steel may be preferred. Deoxidation is accomplished with aluminum rather than silicon in order to obtain the cleanest steel for this particular practice. Also, the aluminum in excess of that required for deoxidation ties up the nitrogen in the steel and makes the material non-aging; that is, the flat-rolled steel does not undergo an increase in strength and a decrease in ductility with lapse of time after the final cold rolling or flatten-

Table 68 — *CHEMICAL COMPOSITION REQUIREMENTS FOR CARBON STEELS*[a]

Standard Types Promulgated by AISI[b] *and SAE*

Carbon Steel Compositions[c]

AISI–SAE Type No.	C	Mn	P (range or max)	S, max
			Ladle chemical composition limits, %	
1006	0.08 max	0.25-0.40	0.040	0.050
1008	0.10 max	0.25-0.50	0.040	0.050
1009	0.15 max	0.60 max	0.040	0.050
1010	0.08-0.13	0.30-0.60	0.040	0.050
1012	0.10-0.15	0.30-0.60	0.040	0.050
1015	0.13-0.18	0.30-0.60	0.040	0.050
1016	0.13-0.18	0.60-0.90	0.040	0.050
1017	0.15-0.20	0.30-0.60	0.040	0.050
1018	0.15-0.20	0.60-0.90	0.040	0.050
1019	0.15-0.20	0.70-1.00	0.040	0.050
1020	0.18-0.23	0.30-0.60	0.040	0.050
1021	0.18-0.23	0.60-0.90	0.040	0.050
1022	0.18-0.23	0.70-1.00	0.040	0.050
1023	0.20-0.25	0.30-0.60	0.040	0.050
1024	0.19-0.25	1.35-1.65	0.040	0.050
1025	0.22-0.28	0.30-0.60	0.040	0.050
1026	0.22-0.28	0.60-0.90	0.040	0.050
1027	0.22-0.29	1.20-1.50	0.040	0.050
1030	0.28-0.34	0.60-0.90	0.040	0.050
1033	0.30-0.36	0.70-1.00	0.040	0.050
1035	0.32-0.38	0.60-0.90	0.040	0.050
1036	0.30-0.37	1.20-1.50	0.040	0.050
1037	0.32-0.38	0.70-1.00	0.040	0.050
1038	0.35-0.42	0.60-0.90	0.040	0.050
1039	0.37-0.44	0.70-1.00	0.040	0.050
1040	0.37-0.44	0.60-0.90	0.040	0.050
1041	0.36-0.44	1.35-1.65	0.040	0.050
1042	0.40-0.47	0.60-0.90	0.040	0.050
1043	0.40-0.47	0.70-1.00	0.040	0.050
1045	0.43-0.50	0.60-0.90	0.040	0.050
1046	0.43-0.50	0.70-1.00	0.040	0.050
1048	0.44-0.52	1.10-1.40	0.040	0.050
1049	0.46-0.53	0.60-0.90	0.040	0.050
1050	0.48-0.55	0.60-0.90	0.040	0.050
1052	0.47-0.55	1.20-1.50	0.040	0.050
1055	0.50-0.60	0.60-0.90	0.040	0.050
1060	0.55-0.65	0.60-0.90	0.040	0.050
1064	0.60-0.70	0.50-0.80	0.040	0.050
1065	0.60-0.70	0.60-0.90	0.040	0.050
1070	0.65-0.75	0.60-0.90	0.040	0.050

Table 68—(*Continued*)

AISI-SAE Type No.	Ladle chemical composition limits, %			
	C	Mn	P (range or max)	S, max
1074	0.70-0.80	0.50-0.80	0.040	0.050
1078	0.72-0.85	0.30-0.60	0.040	0.050
1080	0.75-0.88	0.60-0.90	0.040	0.050
1084	0.80-0.93	0.60-0.90	0.040	0.050
1085	0.80-0.93	0.70-1.00	0.040	0.050
1086	0.80-0.93	0.30-0.50	0.040	0.050
1090	0.85-0.98	0.60-0.90	0.040	0.050
1095	0.90-1.03	0.30-0.50	0.040	0.050
Free-Cutting Carbon Steel Compositions [d]				
1111	0.13 max	0.60-0.90	0.07-0.12	0.08-0.15
1112	0.13 max	0.70-1.00	0.07-0.12	0.16-0.23
1113	0.13 max	0.70-1.00	0.07-0.12	0.24-0.33
12L14 [e]	0.15 max	0.80-1.20	0.04-0.09	0.25-0.35
Open-Hearth				
1108	0.08-0.13	0.50-0.80	0.040	0.08-0.13
1109	0.08-0.13	0.60-0.90	0.040	0.08-0.13
1115	0.13-0.18	0.60-0.90	0.040	0.08-0.13
1117	0.14-0.20	1.00-1.30	0.040	0.08-0.13
1118	0.14-0.20	1.30-1.60	0.040	0.08-0.13
1119	0.14-0.20	1.00-1.30	0.040	0.24-0.33
1120	0.18-0.23	0.70-1.00	0.040	0.08-0.13
1126	0.23-0.29	0.70-1.00	0.040	0.08-0.13
1132	0.27-0.34	1.35-1.65	0.040	0.08-0.13
1137	0.32-0.39	1.35-1.65	0.040	0.08-0.13
1138	0.34-0.40	0.70-1.00	0.040	0.08-0.13
1139	0.35-0.43	1.35-1.65	0.040	0.12-0.20
1140	0.37-0.44	0.70-1.00	0.040	0.08-0.13
1141	0.37-0.45	1.35-1.65	0.040	0.08-0.13
1144	0.40-0.48	1.35-1.65	0.040	0.24-0.33
1145	0.42-0.49	0.70-1.00	0.040	0.04-0.07
1146	0.42-0.49	0.70-1.00	0.040	0.08-0.13
1151	0.48-0.55	0.70-1.00	0.040	0.08-0.13

a These ranges for alloying elements are applicable to semifinished products for forging, hot rolled and cold finished bars, wire rods, and seamless tubing. Structural shapes, plates, strip, sheet and welded tubing may have slightly different limits. See current AISI-SAE specifications.

b For prefix and suffix letters used by AISI to designate steelmelting process and special requirements see Table 8 in Chapter 2.

c Where silicon is required, the following limits and ranges are commonly used for basic open-hearth steel types: for steel types up to but excluding 1015, 0.10% maximum; for 1015 to 1025, 0.10% maximum or ranges of 0.10/0.20%, or 0.15/0.30%; for over 1025, ranges of 0.10/0.20% or 0.15/0.30%.

d When silicon is required, the following limits and ranges are commonly used for basic open-hearth or basic electric steel types; for steel types 1108 and 1109, 0.10% maximum; for 1115 and over, 0.10% maximum, 0.10/0.20%, or 0.15/0.30%. Silicon is not usually specified for types up to and excluding 1115.

e Lead content 0.15/0.35%.

ing operation. Also, this steel does not display a return of pronounced yield-point elongation which results in localized stretching and breakage during drawing operations. However, from a welding standpoint, these steelmaking practices introduce certain metallurgical conditions in the steel that require forethought when applying many of the welding processes.

Rimmed low-carbon steel, it will be recalled, is not deoxidized, and tends to have a concentration of carbon and certain other elements in the central core area. It is important to recognize that during any fusion joining operation, a rimmed steel will attempt to continue with the chemical reaction between the contained carbon and oxygen just as occurred during the freezing of the ingot. In the case of fusion joining, the carbon monoxide gas formed by the reaction bubbles out of the weld pool. When oxyacetylene welding is performed, the rate of solidification usually is sufficiently slow to allow the gas to escape and a reasonably sound weld can be expected. However, if the rimmed steel is fused and solidified rather quickly, as occurs during mechanized gas tungsten-arc welding, then the solid weld metal will contain many gas pockets.

A practical means of avoiding weld metal porosity in joining a rimmed steel by arc welding is simply to deoxidize the fused metal. This can be accomplished by a number of techniques. In gas tungsten-arc welding, a welding rod containing ample deoxidizers like manganese, silicon or aluminum can be added to the pool, or a thin coating of powdered aluminum can be applied to the edges of the steel to be fused. In metal-arc welding with covered electrodes, the covering usually contains ample amounts of silicon and possibly other deoxidizing agents to tie up the oxygen in the rimmed steel core wire and rimmed steel base metal as well. Submerged-arc welding may, or may not, be capable of accommodating a rimmed steel base metal depending upon the kind of electrode employed and the nature of the flux composition. It is a simple matter to select an electrode or a flux with sufficient deoxidizer, usually silicon, to produce a sound weld. Gas metal-arc welding requires a little more attention when welding a rimmed steel because all of the deoxidizer required must be in the consumable electrode. If the shielding gas contains an appreciable percentage of carbon dioxide, a gas which permits some oxidation of manganese and silicon, then the electrode must be quite high in deoxidation ability. An electrode for gas metal-arc welding a rimmed steel often contains about 0.60% silicon, which is about twice the amount ordinarily found in a low-carbon steel weld deposit. During deposition, approximately half of the silicon in the electrode is lost through oxidation.

When fusion joining a low-carbon killed steel, no particular problem arises in obtaining a sound deposit, unless perhaps the operation is conducted in some manner that permits unnecessary exposure of the molten metal to the air and an excessive quantity of oxygen is absorbed. A problem which sometimes arises with killed steel is the accumulation of slag on the surface of the weld which hampers the proper flow of molten metal. This slag is formed when the deoxidizers employed in the steel tend to form a refractory oxide with a relatively high melting point. Aluminum, titanium and zirconium are examples of excellent deoxidizers, but which tend to produce refractory oxides. When welding a steel containing these elements, the weld slag is formed by the oxide inclusions originally trapped in the steel ingot, and by any additional oxide which may form during the welding operation if the oxidation shielding is less than perfect. These refractory slags are apt to be most troublesome in oxyacetylene welding where the lower temperature heat source does not make the slag fluid by virtue of temperature. In arc welding operations, the weld slag is made quite fluid by the high temperature of the arc or is assimilated by a flux employed in the process. In any fusion joining operation, including the oxyacetylene process, a refractory slag, formed by deoxidizers or deoxidation products in the base metal, can be altered by introducing a filler metal containing generous amounts of manganese and silicon. The oxides of these elements mix with the refractory oxides and lower the melting point of the slag — which in turn tends to increase fluidity. For example, an aluminum-killed low-carbon steel being oxyacetylene welded might produce an objectionable amount of viscous slag consisting mostly of aluminum oxide. The use of a low-carbon steel welding rod containing about 1% manganese and 0.5% silicon would facilitate the operation. In most applications, there should be no objection to adding filler metal of this kind to the weld, except that its cost will be a little higher than steel with lower manganese and silicon.

From the foregoing it would seem that problems with weld soundness and other conditions in melting the metal are likely to be more troublesome than microstructural changes and hardening. This is more or less the case because the structure of low carbon steel at room temperature consists mostly of grains of soft ferrite. The small amount of carbon in the steel is distributed as scattered, tiny particles of carbide when in the annealed condition, or in small islands of pearlite when in the hot rolled or normalized condition. Even though the heat-affected zone at a weld will undergo the customary transformation of ferrite-to-austenite, and then back to ferrite, the hardness produced by carbon contents up to 0.15% seldom is of any significance. According to the curve in Fig. 219, a steel containing 0.15% carbon is capable of being hardened to Rockwell C 38. However, this hardness level is not ordinarily found in the base metal heat-affected zones because of the very low hardenability of this steel. The hardness of the heat-affected zones commonly ranges from about Rockwell C 10 and lower.

One instance where the hardness of weld metal or the base metal heat-affected zone in low-carbon steel may be of concern is the weldment which is subjected to severe cold forming in the weld area. The rapidly cooled weld-affected structure may not have adequate ductility to accommodate the cold forming operation, particularly if the carbon is at the high side of the range, that is, 0.10–0.15%. Weld joints in sheet subjected to sharp bends or lock seaming operations have been observed to crack when the carbon content was high. Lower carbon content, perhaps 0.06% or less, greatly improves the ability of the weld joint to undergo cold forming operations.

VERY LOW-CARBON STEEL (0.03% MAX CARBON)

A number of unique properties are found in steel containing 0.03% carbon or less. The steel has a very high, narrow transformation range. The lower the carbon, the closer the range approaches the transformation point of iron at 1670 F. If the steel also is very low in manganese and silicon contents, the magnetic properties will be comparable to those of pure iron, and therefore the metal will be very useful for electromagnetic equipment. Also, the corrosion resistance of this very low-carbon, low-alloy content steel will be unusually good. This does not imply a degree of corrosion resistance like that of stainless steel, but the metal will rust at a slower rate than ordinary steel and will have substantially longer life in painted and coated products.

Armco Ingot Iron was the original very low-carbon steel, and has been produced for many years as an open-hearth furnace product with a carbon content of about 0.015%. The manganese and silicon contents also are very low. The ingots are cast as a rimmed steel. Ingot Iron is used in a wide variety of articles including porcelain enameled ware. Here, the high transformation range allows firing of the vitreous coatings at temperatures in the range of about 1450 to 1600 F, which is adequate for good fusion of the vitreous coating, and yet the metal does not undergo the phase transformations (ferrite-to-austenite and back to ferrite) which results in warpage and sagging of the enameled article. It must be appreciated that metals and alloys have a very, very low yield strength as they undergo an allotropic transformation. Also, the volume change which occurs during these transformations plays a part in the distortion or warpage that occurs. Many of the articles made of very low-carbon steel or Ingot Iron are welded, and while no difficulty could possibly arise with hardening in heat-affected zones, any high-speed welds made by fusion joining in steel of the rimmed type may require deoxidation of the weld metal to avoid porosity. The techniques for handling the deoxidation of the weld can be about the same as described for the low-carbon steel containing about 0.04 to 0.15% carbon.

DECARBURIZED STEEL (LESS THAN 0.005% CARBON)

As low as the 0.015% carbon content of Ingot Iron may seem, this quantity still is sufficient to cause a defect called "boiling" on the initial coat of a vitreous enameled steel. The boiling is produced by the oxidation of the scattered carbides which are located in the microstructure at the surface of the steel. The carbon monoxide and carbon dioxide gases (generated by the action of oxygen in the firing furnace atmosphere on the carbide particles) attempt to rise through the fused porcelain and may leave bubbles and pockmarks in the initial coating. For many years the enameler was resigned to applying two coats: an initial high-temperature ground coat (1550–1600 F) sufficiently fluid to heal over the escape of boiling, and a second finish coat to obtain a defect-free porcelain enameled surface. However, much research was devoted to making a steel to which a single coat of porcelain could be applied without boiling from the carbon-oxygen reaction, and without flaking of the coating as caused by hydrogen evolution from the steel. Some use has been made of a titanium-containing steel in which the titanium is expected to form a more oxidation-resistant carbide, and possibly tie up much of the troublesome hydrogen in the steel. More recent research, however, has culminated in special decarburized steels containing as little as 0.001% carbon. These steels give absolutely no difficulty with weld hardening, but as might be expected, the tailoring of the steel for best single-coat enameling capability does not result in best weldability under all welding processes.

A brief description was given in Chapter 2 of heat treating techniques which are applied to coils of strip steel to decarburize the material to extremely low levels of carbon. *Open coil annealing* can be applied to steel of any reasonably low-carbon content and virtually eliminate this alloying element. In fact, there appears to be an advantage in starting the decarburizing treatment with a steel that is not too low in carbon. If a steel containing up to approximately 0.15% carbon can be processed to form massive carbides in the microstructure, these large particles will serve a very useful purpose. When the steel is cold reduced by rolling, the massive carbide particles develop microscopic cracks or voids. During the decarburization treatment, the carbide particles are removed, but many microscopic voids remain. These voids serve as cavities into which hydrogen may diffuse during cooling and thus relieve the pressure for the gas to escape from the surface of the sheet by spalling off small flakes of porcelain coating.

With the foregoing background, we now can point out a few pertinent facts about the welding characteristics of decarburized single-coat enameling steel. The microstructure of the steel is composed entirely of ferrite grains, there being no carbon beyond the alpha iron solubility limit to form

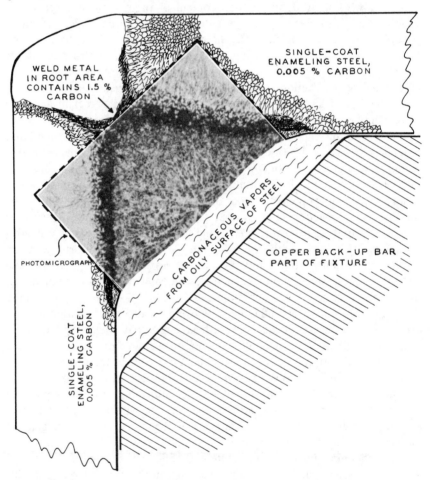

Fig. 224 — Oxyacetylene corner weld between two sheets of decarburized single-coat enameling steel (less than 0.005% Carbon). Oil vapors trapped beneath root of weld by welding fixture have carburized root surface of weld metal to approximately 1.5% carbon.

carbides. The steel for this almost carbon-free product may have been originally produced as a rimmed steel or as a killed steel — usually using aluminum as the deoxidizing element in the killed type. Either type can be decarburized to the 0.001% carbon level by the open coil annealing operation. However, in welding decarburized steel of the rimmed type, a remarkable change in behavior will be noted. Because the carbon has been almost completely removed, no boiling or rimming action can be created by the contained oxygen and a sound weld metal is produced — providing, of course, that no filler metal of higher carbon content has been introduced and that no carbon pickup has occurred from other sources during the welding operation. Precautions against carbon pickup require no little thought. Fig. 224 illustrates carbon pickup which a fabricator of decarburized steel encountered during oxyacetylene welding. Adequate care was taken in adjusting the welding torch to produce a neutral flame for fusing a corner weld between two sheets from the outside. However, a small amount of oil on the surface of the sheet volatilized and formed a carbonaceous atmosphere in the space beneath the joint. This atmosphere, trapped between the inside corner and the welding fixture, was sufficient to carburize the root surface of the weld metal to approximately 1.5% carbon. Cleaning the surface of the sheet prior to welding permitted the corner joint to be oxyacetylene fused without significant carbon pickup.

Although an academic point, one might inquire whether a steel containing only about 0.001% carbon is likely to transform to martensite under *any* conditions of cooling from above the critical range. Surprisingly, research has shown that decarburized steel, and even the purest available iron, can be made to undergo transformation by the martensite or shear mechanism. However, extremely rapid cooling of the austenite or gamma iron is required. This has been accomplished experimentally by quenching a tiny austenitized specimen with a supersonic blast of helium gas. Studies show that iron containing less than 0.002% carbon has a critical cooling rate of at least 60,000 degrees F per second. The M_s point of this material was determined to be approximately 1380 F. Both the M_s point and the critical cooling rate markedly decrease as the carbon content increases slightly. With sufficient carbon to lower the M_s to about 1000 F, the critical cooling rate to cause martensite transformation is about 9000 degrees F per second. As a practical observation, even if the cooling of an austenitized portion of a weld joint in decarburized steel should exceed its very high critical cooling rate, the martensitic structure developed would not be hardened significantly because of the lack of carbon atoms to strain the crystallographic lattice.

MILD STEEL (0.15 TO .30% CARBON)

Mild steel is an overworked term that is as flexible as saying, "We are having *mild* weather." Unless we know whether the remark applies to Florida or Maine, we may be completely misled. Mild steel, to a civil engineer, may be significantly different from what a tool designer usually has in mind. According to some metal or engineering handbooks, *mild steel* is a steel containing a carbon content in the range of 0.10 to 0.25%. We shall take the liberty of considering mild steel as containing approximately 0.15 to 0.30% carbon because this is the range within which a large amount of the steel fabricated by welding falls. Many weldment designers and welding engineers consider carbon steel in this range to be readily weldable, and use the term "mild steel" in everyday discussion of this material. Mild steels are used in products and weldments in many fields: buildings, bridges, piping, castings, pressure vessels, and machine bases being typical examples. The fabricators and users of these products in many cases have generated specifications to cover the steel employed in their particular commodity. While these specifications are necessary for reasons of surface finish, dimensional tolerances, and quality standards required by each particular industry, it is unfortunate that they also present a very large number of seemingly different steel compositions. Close study will show, however, that the analysis requirements differ mostly in the numbers used to define the limits. A good portion of the permissible ranges overlap so frequently that the composition of a single type of steel will meet the requirements of many specifications. Sometimes, the designation of the steel is the only difference between specifications. The whole lot could be reduced to a reasonable number of standardized steels by some coordinated effort. Rather than attempt a complete list of all the carbon steels in the 0.15 to 0.30% carbon range, it should suffice to discuss steels which are representative of the various types within this category.

A survey of the hot rolled carbon steels containing 0.15 to 0.30% carbon (see Table 69) will show that a modest change occurs in properties as the three major elements, carbon, manganese and silicon, are varied from low levels to the maximum permissible limits for these elements in a *carbon* steel. Yet, these changes apparently are sufficient to make the types of steels better suited for particular kinds of weldments. At the low side of the ranges for C, Mn and Si, steel exhibits a tensile strength of about 45 to 65 ksi and a yield strength of about 25 to 30 ksi. These strength properties serve very well for a great number of articles, but in many cases a higher strength could be used to advantage to reduce the weight of the article. By increasing the carbon, manganese and silicon to the top of our "mild steel" ranges (see ASTM A440-59T, Table 69), a tensile strength approaching 90 ksi and a minimum yield strength of 50 ksi can be secured. To gain higher strength in a hot rolled *carbon* steel, it would be necessary to increase the carbon content. The adverse influence of this kind of alloying on weldability will be explained in the next section on "medium-carbon" steels. To gain higher strength by alloying and also retain good weldability, the kind of alloying required elevates the steel into a "high-strength, low-alloy" category to be described in Chapter 15. Even the modest increases in carbon, manganese and silicon employed in the mild steels will increase the cost of the steel. However, if the desired higher strength can be achieved with a minimal alloy increase, it is possible to lower the total material cost for the article. This simple relationship between the alloy content of steel, its strength, and its cost often is a foremost consideration in selecting carbon and alloy steels. Another important consideration at the moment, however, is whether a variation in alloy content from the low side to the high side of the mild steel range affects in anyway the reputed good weldability of this class of steel.

A critical examination of the behavior of mild steels during welding, and the performance of the weldment in service shows that this class of steels varies in weldability over its strength range. Not only is there a gradual increase in the need for welding precautions as the tensile strength is shifted from a low of 45 ksi to a high of 90 ksi, but certain mild steels, depending upon the steelmaking practice, have other characteristics which exert a profound influence on weldability. In evaluating each of these mild steels, it is necessary to consider much more than just the chemical composition. The thickness of the sections, the form, the steelmaking practice, and the condition of heat treatment will be important factors. The weldability probably will vary with the different welding processes that are applicable. The final estimation of weldability must take into account the service for which the weldment is intended, particularly the temperature range over which the weldment must exhibit satisfactory performance.

Welding Hot Rolled Structural Steel

Probably the most widely-used of the mild steels is "A7", more properly shown at the moment as ASTM A7-61T (see Table 69). Steel manufactured to this specification has been used for years in buildings, bridges, machinery, tanks, and many other applications. However, it is becoming increasingly important for users of "A7" steel to recognize that the requirements of this specification exert a bare minimum of control over the chemical and mechanical properties of the steel furnished. Phosphorus and sulfur are the only elements limited by the composition requirements. The amounts of carbon, manganese and silicon likely to be found in the steel are controlled indirectly by the strength requirements (which demand a small, but definite, amount of alloying and strengthening effect from carbon and manganese), and by the tensile ductility and bend requirements (which limit the alloying effect that can be tolerated). These strength and ductility limitations, in actual practice, allow a fairly broad range of compositions to qualify. Depending upon the form of the steel and the mill practice, carbon content may range from 0.15 to 0.35%. It is important from a welding standpoint to keep in mind that heavy sections generally require higher carbon content to maintain strength; yet, these are the sections that produce the more rapid cooling rates during metal-arc fusion joining. Consequently, there is no real assurance in welding A7 steel that a dangerous degree of hardening cannot occur in a weld heat-affected zone. Of course, the likelihood of encountering A7 steel of this character is small. However, the chemical requirements of A7 allow the steel to be produced by killed, semikilled, or rimming steel practices. Therefore, the toughness of the steel, as measured by notched-bar impact strength, drop-weight test, or any other test for brittle fracture susceptibility, is not subjected to any particular control.

The lack of adequate composition control in A7 steel for weldability assurance has been recognized for many years, and ASTM A373 was written to provide steel with modest, but realistic, controls on carbon, manganese and silicon to provide more consistent weldability. A373 steel is specified rather than A7 in certain specifications and codes where consistent mechanical properties and weldability are deemed advisable. However, this steel has not gained as widespread popularity as A7 — one reason being the slightly lower minimum tensile and yield strengths which are counter to the demands of design engineers seeking ways to reduce the dead-weight of structures.

The more practical *carbon* steel commercially available for welded structures is ASTM A36, which is a steel with optimum composition for providing strength and weldability. The minimum yield strength of 36 ksi provides a small, but useful, strength advantage over A7 or A373. The higher strength of A36 is gained by increasing the manganese content to approximately 1% while carbon is restricted to 0.28%. This appears to be the practical limit for unqualified weldability in a hot rolled C–Mn steel. ASTM A440 steel might seem to be a more desirable structural material since the somewhat higher manganese content (1.10–1.60%)

provides a minimum yield strength of 50 ksi. However, this steel is intended for riveted or bolted construction, and although welding is permissible for repair of defects in the material the special precautions demanded by a hardenable steel should be observed in welding operations.

In summary, carbon steel containing no more than about 0.28% carbon and 1% manganese, which provides a minimum yield strength of 36 ksi, represents the practical limit for unqualified weldability. If the carbon or the manganese contents are increased beyond these levels, special precautions will be required in welding. This may amount to no more than maintaining low-hydrogen conditions in fusion joining, a mild preheating, or controlling the weld cooling rate; however, it is necessary to weigh a number of factors related to the welding operation and the weldment to decide upon a satisfactory procedure. While it may seem expedient to simply apply an overwhelming number of precautions, these safeguards in the procedure add to the cost of the welding operation. Consequently, a steel with excellent weldability like that of A36 usually is preferred.

Because structural sections like I-beams and angles usually do not deteriorate (rust) in buildings, many times these sections are salvaged and stocked for reuse. The welding of this material may require some analytical work to ascertain the procedure required. This remark also applies to the structural welding performed in remodeling buildings, bridges, etc. Many old structures are constructed of steels which were not intended to be welded. In fact, they often were erected long before welding was looked upon as a practical process for structural assembly. These old sections sometimes represent compositions higher in carbon content than the 0.30% discussed herein, and may contain amounts of manganese and silicon which make the base metal heat-affected zones prone to martensite formation. Obviously, material of this kind must be chemically analyzed to assess its weldability according to the procedures in use today.

Welding Carbon Steel Pressure Vessels and Other Important Structures

Mild steels are extensively used in pressure vessels, but here again a new array of specifications are employed which introduce additional type or grade designations. Because the well-being of the public often is dependent upon the structural integrity of pressure vessels, many of these weldments must be fabricated in accordance with codes of the municipality in which the unit is to be operated, or codes stipulated by the insurer of the equipment. Often the codes are those of ASME or ASA, in which

Table 69 — REPRESENTATIVE CARBON STEELS

STEELS CONTAINING APPROXIMATELY 0.15/0.30% CARBON

Common Usage or Designation	Applicable Specifications	Typical Limits for Composition					Range of Approx. Strength, ksi[a]	
		C	Mn	P	S	Si	Tensile	Yield
Hot-rolled structural steels								
For buildings and bridges	ASTM A7	...	...	0.04 max	0.05 max	...	60–75	33 min
For welded bridges and buildings	ASTM A373 (Discontinued 1965)	0.28 max	0.50–0.90	0.04 max	0.05 max	0.15–0.30	58–75	32 min
For welded bridges and buildings	ASTM A36	0.29 max	0.80–1.20	0.04 max	0.05 max	0.15–0.30	58–80	36 min
For riveted and bolted high-strength structures	ASTM A440	0.28 max	1.10–1.60	0.04 max	0.05 max	0.30 max	70 min	50 min
Flat-rolled sheets for structural use	ASTM A245 Grade D	0.30 max	...	0.04 max	0.05 max	...	55 min	40 min
Steels for Pressure Vessels								
Mild steel	ASTM A285 Grade C	0.30 max	0.80 max	0.04 max	0.05 max	...	55–65	30 min
Carbon-silicon	ASTM A201 Grade B	0.35 max	0.80 max	0.04 max	0.05 max	0.15–0.30	60–72	32 min

Material	Specification	C	Mn	P	S	Si		
Carbon-silicon	ASTM A212 Grade B	0.35 max	0.90 max	0.04 max	0.05 max	0.15–0.30	70–85	38 min
Carbon-manganese-silicon	ASTM A442 Grade 60	0.27 max	0.60–0.90	0.04 max	0.05 max	0.15–0.30	60–72	32 min
Carbon-manganese-silicon	ASTM A299	0.31 max	0.90–1.40	0.04 max	0.05 max	0.15–0.30	75–90	40 min
Carbon steel for intermediate and higher temperature service	ASTM A515 (Requirements for plates 1 inch and under)							
	Grade 55	0.20 max	0.90 max	0.04 max	0.05 max	0.15–0.30	55–65	30 min
	Grade 60	0.24 max	0.90 max	0.04 max	0.05 max	0.15–0.30	60–72	32 min
	Grade 65	0.28 max	0.90 max	0.04 max	0.05 max	0.15–0.30	65–77	35 min
	Grade 70	0.31 max	0.90 max	0.04 max	0.05 max	0.15–0.30	70–85	38 min
Carbon steel for atmospheric and lower temperature service	ASTM A516 (Requirements for plates ½ inch and under)							
	Grade 55	0.18 max	0.60–0.90	0.04 max	0.05 max	0.15–0.30	55–65	30 min
	Grade 60	0.21 max	0.60–0.90	0.04 max	0.05 max	0.15–0.30	60–72	32 min
	Grade 65	0.24 max	0.85–1.20	0.04 max	0.05 max	0.15–0.30	65–77	35 min
	Grade 70	0.27 max	0.85–1.20	0.04 max	0.05 max	0.15–0.30	70–85	38 min
Steels for Piping								
Welded and seamless steel pipe	ASTM A53	See Specification					45 min	25 min
Seamless pipe for high-temperature service	ASTM A106 Grade B	0.30 max	0.29–1.06	0.048 max	0.058 max	0.10 min	60 min	30 min

TABLE 69 — (Continued)

Common Usage or Designation	Applicable Specifications	C	Mn	P	S	Si	Range of Approx. Strength, ksi [a] Tensile	Yield
Line pipe	API Std. 5L Seamless Grade B	0.27 max	1.15 max	0.04 max	0.05 max	...	60 min	35 min
High-test line pipe	API Std. 5LX Seamless, Grade X52	0.31 max	1.35 max	0.04 max	0.05 max	...	66 min	52 min
	API Std. 5LX Welded, Grade X60[b]	0.26 max	1.35 max	0.04 max	0.05 max	...	75 min	60 min
Cast Steels								
For general use	ASTM A27 Grade 60-30	0.30 max	0.60 max	0.05 max	0.06 max	0.80 max	60 min	30 min
For high-temperature service	ASTM A216 Grade WCA	0.25 max	0.70 max	0.05 max	0.06 max	0.60 max	60 min	30 min
Heat treated for high-strength structural purposes	ASTM A148 Grade 90-60	...	...	0.05 max	0.06 max	...	90 min	60 min
Normalized Carbon Steels								
Manganese-silicon; normalized	ASTM A537 Grade A[c]	0.20 max	0.70-1.40	0.040 max	0.050 max	0.15-0.50	70-85	50 min
Armco-Lo-Temp	ASTM A537 Grade A	0.20 max	0.70-1.40	0.04 max	0.05 max	0.15-0.50	70-85	50 min
Lukens LT-75N	ASTM A537 Grade A	0.20 max	0.70-1.35	0.04 max	0.05 max	0.15-0.30	70-90	50 min

USS Char-Pac N	ASTM A537 Grade A	0.20 max	0.70–1.35	0.04 max	0.05 max	0.15–0.30	70–90	50 min
Armco LTM		0.14 max	0.70–1.35	0.04 max	0.05 max	0.15–0.35	62–82	42 min

Quenched and Tempered Carbon Steels

Manganese-silicon; quenched and tempered	ASTM A537 Grade B[c]	0.20 max	0.70–1.40	0.04 max	0.05 max	0.15–0.50	80–100	60 min
Armco-Super-Lo-Temp	ASTM A537 Grade B	0.20 max	0.70–1.40	0.04 max	0.05 max	0.15–0.50	80–100	60 min
Lukens LT-75 QT	ASTM A537 Grade B	0.20 max	0.70–1.35	0.04 max	0.05 max	0.15–0.30	80–100	60 min
USS Char-Pac QT	ASTM A537 Grade B	0.20 max	0.70–1.35	0.04 max	0.05 max	0.15–0.30	80–100	60 min
Armco QTC	...	0.20 max	1.15–1.50	0.04 max	0.05 max	0.20–0.50	100–120	80 min
Lukens 80[d]	...	0.20 max	1.10–1.60	0.04 max	0.05 max	0.20–0.60	100–120	80 min
USS Con-Pac	...	0.20 max	1.00–1.50	0.04 max	0.05 max	0.30–0.60	100 min	80 min

a Strength and toughness requirements of the various steels will change with plate thickness. In general, thicker plates offer somewhat lower strength. See specification or product bulletin for exact mechanical property assurances, and current limits for chemical composition.

b Cb 0.01 min and/or V 0.02 min.

c Small amounts of certain alloying elements will be present but shall not exceed the following amounts; copper 0.35%, nickel 0.25%, chromium 0.25%, and molybdenum 0.08%.

d This steel also contains 0.20 to 0.40% copper. Plate thickness over 3/4 to 1 1/2 inches incl. are permitted to contain 0.22% C max., while 1 1/2 to 2 inches incl. in thickness are permitted 0.25% C max. Plates over 1 1/4 to 2 inches incl. are required to have 95–115 ksi UTS and 75 ksi YS min.

case the composition requirements for the materials of construction are those promulgated by ASTM. Table 69 provides examples of steels containing about 0.15/0.30% carbon intended for pressure vessel usage. Of course, if the construction is not code-governed, the fabricator is at liberty to use any steel he may desire. It is well to keep in mind, however, that code-governed weldments have a much better record for trouble-free performance than non-code weldments, and many fabricators follow the code practices simply to profit from the experience embodied therein.

If a study is made of the hot rolled steels employed in pressure vessels as compared with structural steels, a strong similarity will be found in the progressive increases in strength of the steels as their carbon and manganese contents are raised. The carbon and manganese are limited to approximately 0.30% and 1.40%, respectively, for safeguarding weldability. While there may appear to be some superfluous overlapping of strength capability among the steels qualified for pressure vessel usage, the various types are separated by maximum permissible thickness and certain qualities described in the detailed specification requirements. These requirements are important for a number of reasons, one being their direct effect upon the cost of the steel. Of greater importance to the welding engineer is their effect upon weldability.

GUIDELINES FOR THE WELDABILITY OF A HOT ROLLED CARBON STEEL (FIG. 225)

EXAMPLE OF MATERIAL

¾-Inch Carbon Steel Plate
ASTM A 285, Grade C, Firebox Quality
Hot Rolled Condition

CHEMICAL COMPOSITION

	C	Mn	P	S	Si
ASTM Specified Limits	0.25 max	0.80 max	0.035 max	0.04 max	...
Representative Ladle Analysis	0.20	0.45	0.015	0.025	0.03

MECHANICAL PROPERTIES

	UTS ksi	YP ksi	Elong. % in 2 In	Bend Test	Hardness Rockwell	Brinell
ASTM Specified Limits	55–65	30 min	29 min	180° min	...	...
Representative Values for ¾-Inch Thick Plate	60	36	35	OK	68-B	121 Bhn

REPRESENTATIVE VALUES FOR TESTS INDICATIVE OF TOUGHNESS

Nil-Ductility Transition Temperature (NDT)	Drop-Weight Tear-Test; 50%-Shear Temperature	Charpy V-Notch Impact Test (Longitudinal) Energy Absorption Values, Ft-Lbs Test Temperature, F					
		RT	0	−20	−40	−60	−80
20F	80F	50	15	8	6	4	4

MICROSTRUCTURE AND HARDENABILITY INDEXES

Critical Temperatures for Transformation Upon Heating; F		McQuaid-Ehn Grain Size	Martensite Formation Temperature; Calculated, F
Ac₁	Ac₃		
Ac_1	Ac_3	Coarse	838
1335	1555		

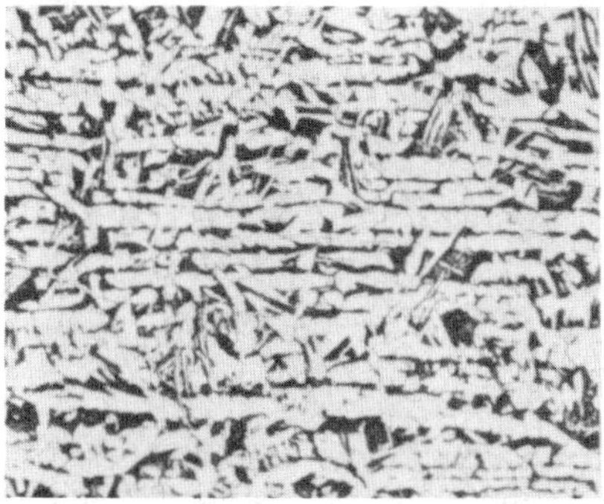

Nital   100X    Nital   500X

Hot rolled plate has a microstructure of grains of pearlite and ferrite. The occurrence of banding in the microstructure is not unusual. The grain size and the coarseness of the carbide lamellae in the pearlite will be dependent upon the temperature at which hot rolling is completed on the mill (finishing temperature).

Grossmann Ideal Critical Size, D₁	Jominy Bar Position for 50% Martensite	Maximum Hardness If Quenched to 100% Martensite	Critical Cooling Rate to Produce Martensitic Microstructure
0.4 Inch	J-1 (1/16 Inch)	48 Rc	Greater than 400 degree F per second at 1300F

Fig. 225 — Useful information for assessing the weldability of a hot rolled "mild" steel. Typical data for ASTM A 285, Grade C, steel plate ¾-in. thick.

The most widely used mild steel for pressure vessel construction is ASTM A285, Grade C, firebox quality (see Table 69, and Figs. 225 and 225A). This steel offers adequate strength for many ordinary vessels. The absence of a silicon requirement allows this steel to be manufactured by rimming or semikilled practices. Usually, the semikilled practice is used, which provides adequate quality and yet maintains low cost. When

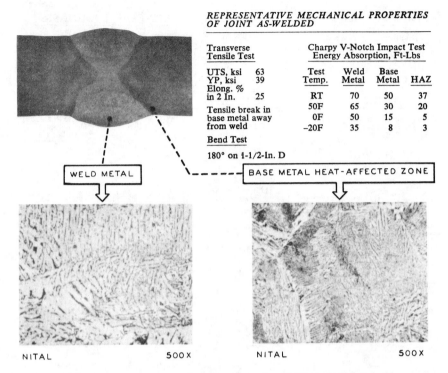

REPRESENTATIVE MECHANICAL PROPERTIES
OF JOINT AS-WELDED

Transverse Tensile Test		Charpy V-Notch Impact Test Energy Absorption, Ft-Lbs			
UTS, ksi	63	Test Temp.	Weld Metal	Base Metal	HAZ
YP, ksi	39				
Elong. % in 2 In.	25	RT	70	50	37
Tensile break in base metal away from weld		50F	65	30	20
		0F	50	15	5
		–20F	35	8	3
Bend Test					
180° on 1-1/2-In. D					

WELD METAL   BASE METAL HEAT-AFFECTED ZONE

NITAL   500X   NITAL   500X

Fig. 225A — Typical data on welded joint in ASTM A 285, Grade C,
hot rolled steel plate, ¾-inch thick, made by shielded metal-arc welding
process with E6010 electrodes.

steel with best homogeneity and uniformity of mechanical properties is
believed to be needed, a killed steel, as indicated by a silicon requirement
(usually 0.15/0.30%) is specified. ASTM A201 steel is the first step
above A285 steel. In addition to being a killed steel, A201 is available
in thick sections and provisions are made to insure a fine grain structure
in sections over 2 inches in thickness. To obtain higher strength in a
killed steel, the fabricator would select A212 steel, which is available in
two grades of different strength capability. Notice the higher maxima permissible for carbon and manganese to gain additional tensile and yield
strengths. ASTM A442 and A299 are pressure vessel steels which make
use of higher manganese contents to gain strength. A442 is intended
to provide maximum weldability by limiting the carbon to a very safe
level, namely, 0.27%. The higher permissible carbon and manganese of
A299, of course, provide higher strength. A515 and A516 are recently-
issued standards, and are intended to supplant A201 and A212 by pro-

viding specifications for steels which are specifically tailored for either high-temperature, or low-temperature services. More will be said about important features of these steels which are not discernible from their chemical requirements.

There will be little to distinguish between the aforementioned pressure vessel steels during the actual welding operation. Of course, if the sections being joined are massive and restraint on the joints is very great, the higher-strength steels (containing 0.30/0.35% carbon and/or 1.0–1.6% manganese) could give difficulty with underbead cracking unless precautions were taken in the welding procedure. ASA Code B31.3 mentioned in Chapter 12 indicates that preheating ordinarily is not required for P-1 steels (the class into which these "mild steels" fall); however, it is not possible to state that preheating is never required, or to give the safe procedural requirements for every possible weldment that might be made from a given type of steel. Therefore, the welding engineer regularly plans the welding procedure using the requirements of the code as key points, but supplements with such features as preheating, low-hydrogen electrodes, controlled heat input, etc., as he deems advisable.

Often the service conditions are an important denominator in the weldability of the 0.15 to 0.30% carbon mild steels; particularly if the operating temperature to which the weldment will be exposed is substantially below room temperature. We have seen repeatedly that low temperature challenges the steel to resist brittle fracture. The steel often is put to a disadvantage by weld flaws or other conditions which demand the accommodation of localized over-stress when the steel is at a low temperature. When A201 and A212 steels are ordered for low temperature service applications, the requirements of ASTM A300 are added to the purchasing conditions for these carbon steels. By compliance with both the material standard and the supplementary low-temperature property requirements, the steel is made with fine-grain melting practice. The plates must be heat treated by a normalizing operation. As a measurement to determine if the steel has adequate fracture toughness, a 15 ft-lb minimum Charpy-keyhole, or U-notch impact requirement is specified at stipulated temperatures as low as −50 F. Consequently, steels ordered to A300 have at least three attributes that improve toughness, namely, thorough deoxidation, fine-grain steelmaking practice, and a normalized microstructure. The toughness promoted by these features is a property that may be needed at many stages when fabricating a weldment, when testing the weldment non-destructively upon completion, and when the weldment performs its service function. ASTM A516 covers carbon-manganese-silicon steels of four different strength ranges (having minimum UTS of

55, 60, 65 and 70 ksi, respectively) intended for service where fracture toughness is important. In addition to being silicon-killed steels, they must be made with fine grain practice. The requirements of A300 also can be imposed upon A516. Because fine grain can be detrimental to the strength of steel at elevated temperatures, A515 covers steels which are almost identical to those of A516 except that coarse grain steelmaking practice must be employed.

The welding engineer must realize that fusion joining operations will impose a new heat treatment upon the heat-affected zones of these carefully pretreated base metals, and unless he exercises some control over the welding operation the beneficial effects of pretreatment may be virtually lost in the heat-affected zones. Consequently, the procedures for fabricating these heat treated steels into a weldment for high-temperature service or low-temperature service will include a number of precautions intended to minimize degradation of the heat-affected zone during welding or postweld heat treatment. Applicable welding procedures will be discussed shortly. A more detailed review of steels especially designed for low-temperature application will be found as we next discuss carbon steels which are heat treated by quenching and tempering. Chapter 15 includes further information under "Steels for Cryogenic Service," and "Steels for Elevated Temperature Service."

To this point, we have been measuring steels in units of chemical composition and mechanical properties, and relating these to weldability. Now, with the mention of *normalized* steel plate, as per ASTM A300, we have introduced a new factor which also controls the toughness and strength of the steel. The heat treatment of plate *prior* to welding is very important to the welding engineer because it provides a very effective means of increasing strength and toughness, and, at the same time, provides improved weldability. To gain a well-rounded concept of the ways in which heat treatment is employed to produce stronger, tougher, more-weldable steels, it is necessary to study both the carbon steels described in the present chapter and the quenched and tempered alloy steels described in Chapter 15. It will be observed that chemical composition no longer has hard-and-fast index points at which carbon steels are differentiated from alloy steels. Heat treated steel plates are being marketed which range in composition from bona fide *carbon* steel to highly alloyed steel. A step above the carbon steels, such as A201 and A212, a number of proprietary "carbon" steels have appeared which typically contain small amounts of chromium, copper, nickel and molybdenum. The levels of these elements are somewhat higher than the usual residual amounts, and might represent about 0.25% Cr, 0.20% Cu, 0.15% Ni, and 0.06% Mo. The steelmaker does not stipulate the ranges with which these elements will comply because the heat treated plate is furnished to specified mechanical properties, usually tensile, bend and impact values. Although the product is being marketed as a "carbon" steel, the Madison Avenue metallurgists already are referring to these materials as the "micro-alloyed steels." Certainly there is justification in calling attention to the small amounts of alloying elements which play a vital role during heat treatment to help gain the required properties, but need the welding engineer be concerned about the presence of these alloying elements? The answer is found in the carbon content of the steels, which, in most instances, is limited to 0.20% and in no case exceeds 0.25%. By holding carbon in the range of approximately 0.15 to 0.20%, and by having judicious amounts of other alloying elements present, either a normalize, or a quench and temper heat treatment can be applied to produce substantially higher strength than would be found in a hot rolled steel of equivalent carbon content. Also, toughness is greatly improved in the heat treated steels. Whereas the normalized A201 and A212 steels may be required to display a minimum Charpy V-notch value of 15 ft-lb at a temperature of –50 F, certain of the special heat treated carbon steels may offer this desirable degree of toughness to a temperature of –60 F when normalized, and –75 F when quenched and tempered (see Figs. 226 and 226A for a normalized steel). This assurance of good toughness makes these steels well suited for vessels and other structures which will be exposed to subzero temperatures in service. It also should be recognized that these steels fill a gap in strength which has long existed among the weldable constructional steels which do not require post-weld heat treatment. They effectively cover the yield strength range of about 50 to 80 ksi, below which the high strength, low-alloy (hot rolled) steels reigr, and above which the quenched and tempered alloy steels prevail (see Chapter 15). The ASTM recently issued a standard specification (A537) for manganese–silicon steel plate for pressure vessels for low-temperature service which covers steels having minimum yield points ranging from 46 to 60 ksi. As indicated in Table 69, Grade A steels of A537 are required to be treated by normalizing, while Grade B steels may be the same composition in the quenched and tempered condition.

Much can be said about the manner in which these heat treated carbon steels achieve higher levels of strength and better toughness. This information helps explain their excellent weldability. The final microstructure and mechanical properties of each steel are dependent, of course, upon (a) hardenability (which is commensurate with the amount and number of alloying elements present and the austenite grain size prior to accelerated cooling), (b) rate of cooling from the austenitizing temperature through the transformation range, and (c) resistance of the steel to softening during tempering. None of the normalized carbon steels shown in Table 69 have sufficient hardenability to develop a martensitic structure during their heat treatment. Instead, the microstructure ordinarily consists of very fine pearlite grains distributed in a matrix of small ferrite grains. Even when spray-quenched, the steels containing no alloy (other than carbon, manganese and silicon) do not fully harden, but display a very fine grain structure with a dispersion of extremely fine pearlite and carbide particles. Tempering this microstructure does not produce any marked change in appearance, but softening occurs prin-

GUIDELINES FOR THE WELDABILITY OF A NORMALIZED CARBON STEEL (FIG. 226)

EXAMPLE OF MATERIAL

¾-Inch Thick Manganese-Silicon Steel Plate
ASTM A 537, Grade A, Firebox Quality
(Armco Lo-Temp Steel)
Heat Treated by Normalizing (1650F — AC)

CHEMICAL COMPOSITION

	C	Mn	P	S	Si	Cr	Ni	Mo	Cu
Producer's Limits	0.20 max	0.70– 1.40	0.035 max	0.04 max	.15– .50	0.25 max	0.25 max	0.08 max	0.35 max
Representative Ladle Analysis	0.18	1.25	0.010	0.020	0.35	0.18	0.23	0.07	0.23

MECHANICAL PROPERTIES

	UTS ksi	YP ksi	Elong. % in 2 In	Bend Test	Hardness Rockwell	Brinell
ASTM and Producer's Limits	70– 85	50 min	24 min	180° D=1-½T min	...	...
Representative for ¾-Inch Thick Plate	79	58	35	OK	85-B	165 Bhn

REPRESENTATIVE VALUES FOR TESTS INDICATIVE OF TOUGHNESS

Nil-Ductility Transition Temperature (NDT)	Drop-Weight Tear-Test; 50%-Shear Temperature	Charpy V-Notch Impact Test (Longitudinal) Energy Absorption Values, Ft-Lbs Test Temperature, F								
		RT	0	–20	–40	–60	–80	–100	–125	–150
–80F	–20F	69	50	40	32	26	20	12	10	6

(ASTM A 537 requires 15 ft-lb minimum Charpy test at –75F)

MICROSTRUCTURE AND HARDENABILITY INDEXES

Critical Temperatures for Transformation Upon Heating; F		McQuaid-Ehn Grain Size	Martensite Formation Temperature; Calculated, F
Ac_1	Ac_3		
1335	1550	Fine	770

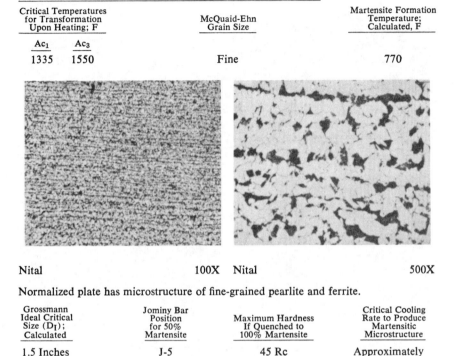

Nital   100X   Nital   500X

Normalized plate has microstructure of fine-grained pearlite and ferrite.

Grossmann Ideal Critical Size (D_I); Calculated	Jominy Bar Position for 50% Martensite	Maximum Hardness If Quenched to 100% Martensite	Critical Cooling Rate to Produce Martensitic Microstructure
1.5 Inches	J-5 (5/16 Inch)	45 Rc	Approximately 100 degree F per second at 1300F

Fig. 226 — Typical data for a ¾-inch thick normalized carbon steel plate made to ASTM A 537, Grade A (Armco-Lo-Temp Steel). Used where higher strength and/or greater toughness at low temperatures are required.

cipally through the recovery and relaxation mechanisms described in Chapter 12. Steels of this character, that is, which do not fully harden upon quenching, are not likely to develop martensite in their heat-affected zones upon being welded. Therefore, they do not pose any real threat of underbead cracking during welding under ordinary conditions. To fully utilize the benefits of the quenching and tempering heat treatment, it is desirable to have the spray-quenched plates form a martensitic or bainitic structure. It also is desirable that this structure be capable of withstanding a tempering temperature in the vicinity of 1100 to 1250 F to produce suitable ductility and toughness. This capability also gives assurance that the steel will not suffer a serious loss of strength in the heat-affected zone of a weld, and that stress-relief heat treatment can be applied after welding

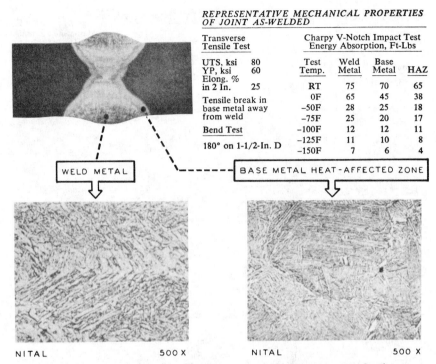

REPRESENTATIVE MECHANICAL PROPERTIES
OF JOINT AS-WELDED

Transverse Tensile Test		Charpy V-Notch Impact Test Energy Absorption, Ft-Lbs			
UTS, ksi	80	Test Temp.	Weld Metal	Base Metal	HAZ
YP, ksi	60	RT	75	70	65
Elong. % in 2 In.	25	0F	65	45	38
Tensile break in		−50F	28	25	18
base metal away		−75F	25	20	17
from weld		−100F	12	12	11
Bend Test		−125F	11	10	8
180° on 1-1/2-In. D		−150F	7	6	4

WELD METAL · · · · · BASE METAL HEAT-AFFECTED ZONE

NITAL · · · · 500 X · · · · NITAL · · · · 500 X

Fig. 226A — Typical data on welded joint in normalized A 537, Grade A, manganese-silicon steel plate (Armco-Lo-Temp) made by shielded metal-arc welding process with E8018-C2 electrodes.

without adverse effect upon strength. The steelmaker gains these properties by making certain that the hardenability of the steel is adequate for the maximum thickness of plate under the cooling rate produced by the spray-quenching press. Jominy tests are employed to measure hardenability and predict the maximum thickness that can be treated and still produce a hardened structure throughout the section. The softening which occurs upon tempering at various temperatures is dependent upon many aspects of the composition of the steel. The quenched and tempered steels contained in Table 69 represent a variety of practices with respect to regulation of hardenability and tempering resistance through alloying. Some of these steels are made with coarse-grain steelmaking practice to gain increased hardenability; some use boron as a highly-effective hardenability agent; while in others small amounts of hardenability-producing alloys are expected to be present. Even so, the composition is carefully adjusted to favor weldability. Typical analyses of steels supplied to these proprietary designations suggest that underbead cracking propensity is slight even when welding under hydrogen-producing conditions. Yet, the welding engineer will note that low-hydrogen welding conditions are regularly suggested for these steels. The explanation for this precaution lies in the area of mechanical properties rather than cracking difficulties.

The welding procedures for heat treated carbon steels are guided to a large extent by the need to have the toughness of the weld metal and the base metal heat-affected zones approximately equal to that of the unaffected base metal. Low-hydrogen welding conditions are prescribed, therefore, mainly to avoid the embrittling effect of hydrogen, albeit rather mild in steels of this composition, microstructure and strength level. Shielded metal-arc welding is performed with electrodes bearing the EXX15, −16, and −18 flux coverings. Adequate precautions should be taken to insure that other welding processes are applied with low-hydrogen or hydrogen-free conditions. For example, the flux for submerged-arc welding should be thoroughly dry; if not, it should be baked at approximately 250 F prior to using.

Normal techniques are applied with the commonly-used shielded metal-arc, submerged-arc, and gas metal-arc processes since the cooling rates in the heat-affected zones are sufficiently rapid to reproduce a microstructure similar to that which developed upon normalizing, or upon quenching. With carbon content limited to about 0.20%, no difficulty ordinarily is encountered with either underbead cracking or lack of toughness in the heat-affected zones of the base metal. This is true even with low heat input which results in rapid cooling. In fact, objectionable welding conditions are those where abnormally high heat input (or abnormally high preheat and interpass temperature) causes a rather slow rate of cooling which acts to increase the base metal grain size and produce coarser pearlite grains. These microstructural conditions, as would be expected, detract from strength and toughness. Consequently, any procedure or process which subjects the base metal heat-affected zones to prolonged heating, higher temperature, and slow cooling (electroslag welding, for example) probably will require that the weldment be given a post-weld heat treatment to restore strength and toughness in these zones. Since retreatment often is uneconomical and impractical, the welding engineer must make certain that the rate of cooling in the weld affected zones will be sufficiently rapid to produce a microstructure of adequate strength and toughess. This task can be guided by any of the systems which relate preheat temperature and heat input to cooling rate in a given joint, and by plotting the anticipated cooling curves on a continuous-cooling transformation diagram (CCT diagram, see Fig. 213) if available for the particular steel under consideration. In general, the commonly-used arc welding processes are applied to the heat treated carbon steels shown in Table 69 without preheat, but never when the base metal temperature is below about 50 F. In fact, it is prudent to raise this minimum starting temperature to a preheat of about 100 F if the plate is quite thick, perhaps greater than 1-inch thick, or even higher if the joint is highly restrained.

The alloy composition of the weld metal employed for the heat treated carbon steels is important both for its influence upon strength and upon toughness at low temperatures. The customary steps in selecting a filler metal for a given process are: first, decide upon the strength required at the weld joint; second, be certain the final weld area will meet toughness requirements. For butt-joints, the weld metal usually must meet the same strength requirements stipulated for the base metal. However, fillet welds often can be made with somewhat lower strength weld metal as permitted by fillet size and applied loads. It is considered good practice to employ weld metal of lower strength in fillets, if permissible, because of the greater capability generally found for accommodating the restraint, notch-effect, and other unfavorable conditions regularly associated with fillet welds that promote cracking. Yet, the welding engineer cannot assume that *all* weld metals of lower strength will provide greater assurance against cracking difficulties. Another aspect of weld metal strength which must be gaged carefully is the influence of dilution in the weld metal by the base metal. As mentioned in Chapter 10 (and discussed in detail in Chapter 15), the welding engineer frequently applies electrodes of a prescribed strength classification to high-strength steels, but finds the weld deposit substantially higher in strength because of alloying elements which have been picked up from the base metal by dilution. At least, this has been the experience in welding high-strength *alloy* steels. However, in the case of the high-strength *carbon* steels presently under discussion, which gain their strength principally through heat treatment, the process of dilution is likely to result in weld deposits of lower alloy composition. Therefore, we must consider first the composition and strength offered by undiluted weld metal from the filler metal, and second the change in composition which is likely to occur by dilution during deposition of the filler metal in the joint. At this point, we often are hard-pressed to predict the strength and toughness of the new diluted weld composition. Nevertheless, only by exploring these details can we guard against overestimating the properties that will be realized in the actual weld joint.

When the welding engineer takes up the task of selecting a filler metal for joining a heat treated carbon steel, it is not uncommon to find that the filler metal and/or flux must not only provide alloyed weld metal in the joint that meets property requirements, but must be the most economical choice as well. Fortunately, covered low-alloy steel electrodes, bare electrodes, and fluxes are available which offer both progressive increases in weld metal strength, and various degrees of low-temperature toughness, all at due cost, of course. As an exercise in selecting a covered electrode to metal-arc weld a quenched and tempered carbon steel of 60 ksi minimum YS and 80 ksi minimum UTS, let us imagine that the weldment will be expected to perform at service temperatures which may be as low as –60 F. Let us picture that the user has demanded qualification of the welding procedure and has included a Charpy-V impact test requirement of 15 ft-lbs minimum at –60 F. The nickel-containing electrodes of the E80 series would be logical to consider here, since the relatively low dilution which occurs in the manual, shielded metal-arc process is not likely to reduce the strength of the deposited weld metal below the minimum strength requirements of the base metal. The matter of notched-bar impact toughness, however, requires more detailed study. Three classes of nickel-containing electrodes are offered in the E80 series. These contain nickel contents of approximately 1, 2, and 3%, and are identified as E80XX-C3, E80XX-C1, and E80XX-C2, respectively. At this point, the welding engineer might be tempted to use the Charpy-V impact data shown earlier in Table 47, and the requirements for the electrodes as listed in Table 49, in a simple, straight-forward manner in making his electrode selection. The E80XX-C3 (1% Ni) electrode probably would be passed over as having inadequate toughness. The E80XX-C1 (2% Ni) electrode might seem to offer adequate toughness, but here the engineer must appreciate that the data in Table 47 and the electrode requirements are for *undiluted* weld metal. Although weld metals from various classes and lots of electrodes display impact test values which vary over a fairly broad range, the low-temperature capability tends to improve with increasing nickel content in the E80 series. In the final analysis, the engineer must judge the amount of dilution which will occur in the joints of the weldment, and, depending upon the base metal composition, the change which will occur in weld metal composition. While economics favor selection of the E80XX-C1 electrode, the welding conditions may be such that the higher-nickel E80XX-C2 electrode is needed to assure meeting the impact toughness requirements.

For the higher-strength steels, as found in the quenched and tempered group in Table 69, electrodes of the E90, E100 and E110 series might be required (see Figs. 227 and 227A). Fortunately, electrode classes are available in these series which offer good low-temperature toughness in addition to high strength. However, it must be remembered that certain classes were designed for other applications, such as elevated temperature service, and the low-temperature toughness of their deposits may not be particularly good. The information contained in Chapter 10 will be helpful in guiding electrode selection for lower-temperature service. Electrodes of the EXXX18-M classifications, originally developed for the needs of military applications, provide weld deposit compositions which have very attractive combinations of strength and toughness. Electrodes for gas metal-arc welding, and electrode and flux combinations for submerged-arc welding the heat treated carbon steels have not been. standardized. Consequently, most suppliers of these steels will suggest suitable filler metal for joining their particular product.

GUIDELINES FOR THE WELDABILITY OF A QUENCHED AND TEMPERED CARBON STEEL (FIG. 227)

EXAMPLE OF MATERIAL

¾-Inch Thick Carbon Steel Plate
Armco QTC Steel, Firebox Quality
Heat Treated by Quenching and Tempering

CHEMICAL COMPOSITION

	C	Mn	P	S	Si	Cr	Ni	Mo	Cu	B
Producer's Limits	0.20 max	1.15– 1.50	0.035 max	0.04 max	.20– .50	0.20 max	0.15 max	0.08 max	0.20 min*	0.0015 min
									*when specified	
Representative Ladle Analysis	0.18	1.35	0.012	0.017	.30	0.18	0.12	0.06	0.23	0.0019

MECHANICAL PROPERTIES

	UTS ksi	YS .2% ksi	Elong. % in 2 In	Bend Test	Hardness Rockwell	Brinell
Producer's Limits	100– 120	80 min	18 min	180° D=2T min	. . .	. . .
Representative for ¾-Inch Thick Plate	108	90	30	OK	21-C	235

REPRESENTATIVE VALUES FOR TESTS INDICATIVE OF TOUGHNESS

Nil-Ductility Transition Temperature (NDT)	Drop-Weight Tear-Test; 50%-Shear Temperature	Charpy V-Notch Impact Test (Longitudinal) Energy Absorption Values, Ft-Lbs Test Temperature, F							
		RT	0	–20	–40	–60	–80	–100	–125
–80F	–55F	55	41	38	30	26	21	15	8

(Producer will furnish to 20 ft-lb minimum Charpy-V limit at –25F)

MICROSTRUCTURE AND HARDENABILITY INDEXES

Critical Temperatures for Transformation Upon Heating; F		McQuaid-Ehn Grain Size	Martensite Formation Temperature; Calculated, F
Ac_1	Ac_3		
1335	1550	Fine	768

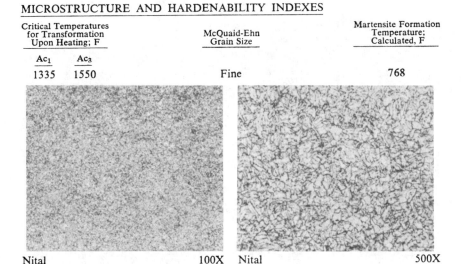

| Nital | 100X | Nital | 500X |

Microstructure of quenched and tempered plate (Austenitized 1650F, WQ + Tempered 1050F Minimum) consists of ferrite and tempered martensite and/or tempered bainite.

Grossmann Ideal Critical Size, D_1	Jominy Bar Position for 50% Martensite	Maximum Hardness If Quenched to 100% Martensite	Critical Cooling Rate to Produce Martensitic Microstructure
2.3 Inches	J-7 (7/16 Inch)	45 Rc	Approximately 40 degrees F per second at 1300F

Fig. 227 — Typical data for a quenched and tempered carbon steel plate (Armco QTC). Used for applications requiring higher strength and improved low-temperature toughness.

As a final word of caution regarding filler metal selection, the welding engineer must be careful not to use weld metal which over-matches substantially the strength of the base metal. Weld metal which is too strong will be likely to present problems in mechanical testing specimens from the weld joints, and may cause difficulties during fabrication and in service. When making bend tests with regular transverse specimens, weld metal that is substantially stronger will force a much greater amount of bending to occur in the adjacent base metal. The specimen may fracture prematurely because of this excessive localized elongation. Weld metal of excessive strength may increase reaction stresses to the point where cracking will occur during assembly. If the welded joints are to be subjected to some kind of cold work during fabrication, such as straightening or forming, a fracture may be generated at the weld joint. These are but

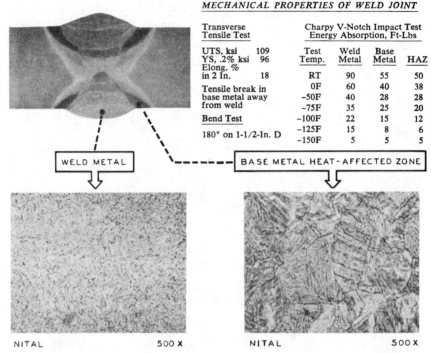

MECHANICAL PROPERTIES OF WELD JOINT

Transverse Tensile Test		Charpy V-Notch Impact Test Energy Absorption, Ft-Lbs		
UTS, ksi 109		Test Temp.	Weld Metal	Base Metal	HAZ
YS, .2% ksi 96					
Elong. % in 2 In. 18		RT	90	55	50
		0F	60	40	38
Tensile break in base metal away from weld		−50F	40	28	28
		−75F	35	25	20
Bend Test		−100F	22	15	12
180° on 1-1/2-In. D		−125F	15	8	6
		−150F	5	5	5

WELD METAL

BASE METAL HEAT-AFFECTED ZONE

NITAL   500 X   NITAL   500 X

Fig. 227A — Typical data on welded joint in quenched and tempered carbon steel plate (Armco QTC) made by shielded metal-arc welding process with E9018-M electrodes.

a few of the reasons for striving to obtain a reasonable match in mechanical properties between weld metal and base metal.

Welding Carbon Steel Piping and Tubing

Tremendous amounts of steel piping and tubing which typically contain about 0.15 to 0.30% carbon are used in welding transport pipelines for gas and oil, systems for power, heating and refrigeration, and tubular structures of many kinds. Steel piping and tubing usually are ordered to standards written by ASTM or API for tubular products. Specification writers prescribe chemical composition limits for the various forms of piping and tubing: namely, seamless, electric-welded, submerged-arc welded, butt-welded, cast, cold expanded, nonexpanded, etc. Therefore, a review must be made of the particular standard being specified and the "grade" in question whenever discussing an item of piping or tubing. The standards of the ASTM cover a variety of tubular products.

Two of the most widely used are A53 for welded and seamless steel pipe and A106 for seamless pipe for high temperature service as shown in Table 69. As might be judged from their composition requirements, these standards do not cover high-strength steels and the tubular products should offer no particular difficulty with hardening or underbead cracking during welding. Most pipe for gas and oil pipeline usage is purchased to API Standard 5L or Standard 5LX. Standard 5L covers line pipe of modest strength requirements while 5LX deals with "High Test Line Pipe." The high-strength steels under 5LX are deserving of discussion here because of two specific points. First, the composition requirements of certain grades under 5LX (see Grade X52 in Table 69) permit carbon and manganese maximums which could place the steel just at the edge of the range of "foolproof" weldability. Second, because of many factors involved in pipeline construction, much use ordinarily is made of the cellulosic-covered (EXX10) type of electrode. Consequently, the weldability of these steels must be measured by performance during a "hydrogen-introducing" arc-welding operation.

API 5LX includes four grades identified as X42, X46, X52 and X60. The numerical portion of these designations indicate the minimum yield strength of the pipe in ksi. While a large tonnage of pipe is made to X52 requirements, it is important to know that a substantial amount is made to an "X56" designation which *is not* officially recognized under the 5LX Standard. The chemical composition and tensile property requirements of the X56 pipe are set by agreement between the purchaser and manufacturer using all other applicable specifications of the 5LX Standard. Study of the composition of the X56 steel will show that this higher-strength steel requires great consideration in welding. This comes as no surprise, of course, but again the most efficient way of determining satisfactory welding procedures is to know the actual composition and to understand the metallurgical behavior of these steels. The X60 grade is a recent addition to the 5LX Standard and although chemical composition limits are provided (as indicated in Table 69) other compositions may be agreed upon between purchaser and producer.

Examination of the X42 grade will reveal that the pipe producer is able to satisfy the 42 ksi YS requirement by employing steel with about 0.20 to 0.26% carbon and 0.40 to 0.90% manganese. Silicon is very low because the steel ordinarily is made with a semi-killed melting practice. To obtain the strength required in the X46 and X52 grades, relatively small increases are made in carbon and manganese contents. The increased yield strength required is also influenced by the amount of cold work imparted to the steel during manufacturing and testing operations.

Steel for X52 pipe usually is found to contain approximately 0.20 to 0.28% carbon and 0.80 to 1.20% manganese. In view of our earlier appraisal of the weldability of hot rolled structural steel, the X52 grade has a composition which is weldable. It is difficult to extend our study of composition to the X56 grade because the limits for non-standard steels are negotiated between producer and purchaser. Therefore, the variations in composition are likely to be more numerous than found among the standard steels. However, some of the X56 steel is made by incorporating higher carbon and manganese contents than in X52, but still below limits of about 0.32% carbon and 1.35% manganese. Some welding difficulty with underbead cracking has been experienced when the X56 contains carbon and manganese near the uppermost limits. This cracking occurs with the use of cellulosic covered electrodes, and its likelihood of occurrence is increased by a delay in completing all of the passes required in the joint, particularly if the interpass temperature drops to a very low level. The underbead cracking would be avoided if an interpass temperature above about 200 F were maintained, if electrodes with a low-hydrogen covering were used, or if the welding were performed by gas metal-arc, submerged-arc, or any arc-welding process which employs low-hydrogen conditions. However, there are many reasons why E6010 and E7010 electrodes see continued use in welding pipelines and we shall not debate this electrode application here.

Because X56 steel presses the limit of weldability (under hydrogen-introducing conditions) for a carbon–manganese steel, an effort is being made by some steel producers to make use of small additions of columbium and/or vanadium to gain the required strength rather than employ a carbon increase. The columbium–vanadium containing steels are being successfully exploited as readily-welded, high-strength low-alloy steels in many applications, and are described in detail in Chapter 15. It should suffice to say here that a certain amount of X56 pipe steel, and all of the X60 pipe steel is being made by alloying techniques other than simply increasing the carbon and manganese within the limits prescribed for a carbon steel. In most instances, columbium and/or vanadium are added to a steel containing about 0.20 to 0.26% carbon and 1.00 to 1.35% manganese. This composition, along with a relatively low, controlled finishing temperature in hot rolling, produces a finer-grained, stronger steel to meet X56 or X60 pipe requirements. Furthermore, by virtue of lower carbon content, the welding of these higher strength, low-alloy steels can be carried out as safely as the lower strength carbon-manganese steels.

Much information appears in the literature about the composition of steels for pipelines, not only regarding the influence of composition upon weldability, but also regarding its influence upon fracture toughness. The latter property is quite important in a line pipe steel because the initiation of a running crack can lead to the destruction of many *miles* of the pipeline system. Because the speed of propagation of a running or cleavage crack exceeds the rate at which loss of pressurization occurs through fracture, the crack is supplied with ample energy to keep it running. Only when a very effective "crack stopper" is encountered in the system does the running crack come to a halt. This problem has attracted considerable attention because of the spectacular aspects of such failures and the appreciable losses incurred. The problem possibly could increase in severity because the preference for higher-strength steels naturally encourages the introduction of higher-carbon steels in pipelines. Since carbon impairs the fracture toughness of steel, many pipeline engineers have inquired why the manganese content should not be increased rather than carbon to gain the desired strength level. This seemingly simple question has spawned reams of literature by investigators attempting to find optimum steel compositions for satisfying fracture toughness, weldability, and cost. Perusal of activity in this field shows much work being conducted to determine factors which influence the initiation and propagation of running cracks. A study sponsored by the American Gas Association is notable for its experiments with sections of full-scale pipeline to establish the speed of propagation and other characteristics of a running crack in pressurized pipelines of various kinds of steel. The welding engineer concerned with pipelines must maintain close watch on the progress of this experimentation, not only for the information provided concerning weld joint properties and weld defects, but because the conclusions reached regarding fracture toughness are likely to define the compositions of steels which will be employed in welded pipelines of the future.

Let us examine some of the metallurgical concepts which have evolved from studies of the mechanical properties and the welding behavior of hot rolled steels in pipelines. Turning first to strength, ductility and fracture toughness, we find that carbon is a desirable element for strengthening pipeline steels because it raises the yield strength about five times and the tensile strength about eight times as does manganese on an equal weight basis. Both elements tend to lower the ductility (tensile elongation) of the steel; however, carbon has a more deleterious effect than manganese. Surprisingly, additions of manganese raise the yield strength more rapidly than the tensile strength. Therefore, steels strengthened principally by alloying with manganese will have a higher YS-UTS ratio. The fracture toughness of the hot rolled steels appears to be related to the pearlite volume in the microstructure. Carbon has a more detrimental effect upon fracture toughness than does manganese because carbon increases the pearlite volume more rapidly. This also accounts for the lesser strengthening effect of manganese, which seems to impart strength more by its solution-strengthening of the ferrite in the microstructure. Manganese acts to lower the toughness transition temperature. Steels with higher Mn–C ratio therefore tend to display improved fracture toughness when comparison is made on an equal strength basis. The indication that manganese lowers the transition temperature by strengthening the ferrite is supported by the effect of silicon. Ferrite is solution-strengthened by silicon more effectively than by manganese. However, silicon is not taken into consideration on strength because it is present only in very small amounts in these semikilled pipeline steels. The effects of carbon and manganese depend to a considerable extent upon the rate of cooling from the austenite temperature. Faster cooling produces pearlite grains which have lower carbon content. Consequently, the microstructure has a larger pearlite volume upon faster cooling, which increases strength. Grain size varies with the finishing temperature and the amount of reduction during the final rolling pass. Heavier reductions and lower finishing temperatures produce finer grain size. Although it is well known that higher Mn–C ratios lowers the toughness transition temperature, there is no particular ratio above which complete assurance against brittle fracture is secured. The problem is a complex one because other matters not directly associated with Mn–C ratio also have an appreciable effect upon fracture toughness.

If we next examine the weldability of pipeline steels, much of the welding research thereon will be found to deal with the relationship between composition and underbead cracking susceptibility; apparently because the commonly used cellulosic covered electrode easily produces this defect whenever the hardenability of the steel exceeds a certain value. We use the term "hardenability" here as a matter of convenience. Perhaps we should say "hardening propensity" because the heat-affected zones do not necessarily develop a completely martensitic structure. We are dealing, therefore, with the tendency of the steel to develop higher levels of hardness with increasing cooling rate, but at cooling velocities just below the familiar *critical cooling rate*. Although the heat-affected zones do not develop an entirely martensitic structure, which would exhibit the highest susceptibility to hydrogen-embrittlement cracking, this zone nevertheless can develop a mixed structure of ferrite, pearlite, and martensite having sufficient hardness so as to display underbead cracking. Mention was made earlier in this Chapter that a mixed structure forms because the cooling curve for the heat-affected zone has followed a continuous cooling course through only the nose of the upper transformation region. It would be interesting to know what percentage of the heat-affected zone structure must be martensite in order to have the short-range stresses and other attendant features of this transformation culminate in cracking. Investigators have found that appreciable susceptibility to underbead cracking appears when the hardness of the heat-affected zone adjacent to a weld bead from a cellulosic covered electrode exceeds about 300 Vickers hardness (Diamond Pyramid) number, which is about Rockwell C 30, or 285 BHN. Because the composition of the steel is known to be the major factor controlling this hardness, the investigators have attempted to develop a method of appraising each steel for the likelihood of underbead cracking occurrence. Actually, this effort on pipeline steels has been paralleled by studies on other steels conducted in many laboratories to develop a weldability formula or equations that would predict for a given steel: (a) the maximum hardness of its heat-affected zone, (b) the ductility or toughness of its heat-affected zone, and (c) the susceptibility of the heat-affected zone to underbead cracking. This concerted effort has produced a number of equations all based upon "carbon equivalency." Briefly, the alloying elements which influence hardness, ductility, or cracking in the heat-affected zone are assigned factors which relate them to the influence of carbon. Solving the equation for a given steel provides a "carbon equivalent," usually identified as *C. E.*, which is correlated with the properties and cracking propensity of heat-affected zones in the steel when welded in a carefully prescribed manner. In view of the wide interest in a weldability guide of this kind, the concluding portion of this chapter is devoted to the development and application of these formulas or equations.

Welding Procedures Used on Pipeline Steel Joints

The principal guide for welding pipelines is API Standard 1104, a document written by representatives of API, AGA, PLCA, AWS and SNT. This standard provides the requirements for obtaining welded joints of adequate quality for gas and oil transmission pipeline or other high-pressure services using skilled welders, and commercially available materials and equipment. A standard also is available for welding pipelines in limited-pressure distribution systems. API 1104 outlines the methods of testing and the test requirements for qualifying welders, procedures, and materials for a specific kind and size of welded pipe joint. Wide use is made of API 1104 as a code for governing the quality of welded pipelines much in the same manner as the ASME Code for Boilers and Unfired Pressure Vessels.

Although API 1104 does not include welding procedures, as such, for joining steel pipelines, the API 1104 Committee has collected and cataloged successfully-used procedures, and the Committee Secretary provides them upon request as guides for those seeking to avoid a trial and error approach to qualification. These API Procedure Specifications are identified by the position of the pipe (horizontal or vertical) whether rolled during welding, or in a fixed position, and the ranges of diameter and wall thickness for which the procedure is considered suitable. These are not *pre-qualified* procedures, but are *suggested* procedures by which the skilled welder with proper materials and equipment is assured of gaining qualification. When API 1104 is applied to any pipeline project, it is mandatory that the method employed in making, testing, and inspecting welded joints be in complete conformance with the requirements of the Standard. The fabricator is expected to provide details of the procedure which he plans to use on each particular pipe size, including the following essential information:

1. *Process.* The specific arc or gas welding process using manual, semi-automatic or automatic operations, or a combination of processes.

2. *Pipe and Fitting Material.* API Std. 5L pipe, and API Std. 5LX pipe, and materials conforming to applicable ASTM standards may be grouped. Separate procedures are required for materials not conforming to these standards.

3. *Diameter-Group-Wall Thickness Group Combination.* The outside diameter groups, in inches, are:
Under 2⅜
2⅜ to 12¾ inclusive
Over 12¾
The wall thickness groups, in inches, are:
Less than 3/16
3/16 to ¾ inclusive
Over ¾

4. *Joint Design.* Shape of groove or angle of bevel, size of root face, and root opening or spacing between abutting members. Shape and size of fillet welds. Type of backing if used. The most-commonly used joint design is a single-vee groove weld with a 60° groove angle and about a 1/16-inch root face with a root opening of about 1/16-inch.

5. *Filler Metal and Number of Beads.* Size and classification numbers of filler metal, minimum number and sequence of beads.

6. *Electrical Characteristics.* Current and polarity, voltage and amperage for each size electrode. Or, if gas welding is employed, the welding flame characteristics, size of orifice in torch tip for each size welding rod.

7. *Position.* Rolled or fixed-position welding.

8. *Direction of Welding.* Vertical-up, or downhill. Downhill welding is faster, but requires more skill to avoid defects. Downhill welding is confined to non-weaving deposition and is not practicable in wide grooves. When the joint is wide, a vertical-up weaving technique is employed.

9. *Number of Welders.* Minimum number of root bead welders, and minimum number of second bead welders must be stipulated.

10. *Time Lapse Between Passes.* Maximum time between completion of root bead and the start of second bead; also maximum time between completion of second bead and start of other beads.

11. *Type of Line-Up Clamp If Used.* Internal, external, or none required. Internal line-up clamp is preferred because the root bead can be deposited without stopping, except to change electrodes. External line-up clamps present cross-bars around the periphery of the pipe which requires stopping and starting at these obstacles. Defects occur with greater frequency at these areas.

12. *Removal of Line-Up Clamp.* After root bead welding is 50% completed, or after root bead is 100% completed. If possible, the line-up clamp should be left in place until the root bead is completed. This is usually practicable with internal clamps, but is not always possible with external clamps. Smaller-diameter, lower-strength pipe generally will allow the line-up clamp to be removed safely after the root bead is 50% complete.

13. *Cleaning.* Procedures and tools used for cleaning surfaces of prepared pipe ends and the weld beads.

14. *Preheat, Stress-Relief.* Methods, temperature, temperature control methods, and ambient temperature range expected. If pipe temperature is below 32 F prior to welding, preheating to 150 to 200 F is advisable.

15. *Shielding Gas and Flow Rate.* Composition of gas and flow rate for gas metal-arc or gas tungsten-arc processes.

16. *Shielding Flux.* Manufacturer, designation, and particle size; as might be employed in submerged-arc welding.

17. *Speed of Travel.* Welding speed in inches per minute.

18. *Sketches and Tabulations.* Sketches are required on separate sheets showing the joint design and weld bead sequence, together with tabulations of data regarding pipe diameter, wall thickness, and all details of the welding process or processes incorporated in the procedure.

Many of the joints in a pipeline welded in the field must be made from the outside only, and with the pipe in a fixed position. Sometimes the pipe sections must be pre-placed in a trench, and a bellhole must be dug around the joint area to provide clearance within which the welder may work. Consequently, the welder is faced with the task of depositing weld metal in the joint from all positions, that is, 360° around the periphery. The root pass, commonly called the "stringer bead," is the most critical portion of the weld because it must not contain an unfused root notch by reason of inadequate penetration, nor can the root pass have gaps (often called "windows") because of excessive penetration. Deposition of the root bead under the trying conditions of field welding calls for such great skill that only the most highly trained welders are entrusted with this part of the welding operation. "Stringer bead welders" are very demanding about the electrodes and power sources which they use in their work. For shielded metal-arc welding, they usually use E6010 or "E6010-Iron Powder" electrodes because of their penetration ability and all-position operating characteristics. Covered electrodes of the low-hydrogen variety have not been accepted for fixed-position pipe welding because of (a) their low penetration ability, (b) the large volume of rather viscous slag which hampers the downhill welding technique, and (c) the greater difficulty encountered in overhead deposition. However, it is widely recognized that a low-hydrogen covered welding electrode would be an asset in welding the higher strength grades of pipe, and electrode manufacturers are striving to develop a suitable electrode for this purpose.

When the stringer bead is deposited in the downhill direction by a certified pipe welder, his technique must be seen to be appreciated. Of metallurgical importance is the fact that the root bead is a relatively small, thin pass and any movement of the pipe is liable to crack this bead. Furthermore, the operation (because of the cellulosic covering on the electrode) has supplied hydrogen to the heat-affected zone of the base metal; therefore, depending upon the C. E. (carbon equivalent) of the base metal, and the temperature to which the joint cools after deposition of the root bead, a distinct risk of underbead cracking can arise. For these reasons, modern pipeline welding practice calls for a "filler bead welder" to start deposition of subsequent layers *within 5 minutes* of the completion of the root pass. The filler bead welders customarily deposit all of the remaining required layers of weld metal except the last. The last layer is called the "capping pass," and the deposition of it is also entrusted to a welder of better than average skill in order to comply with requirements for reinforcement height, undercutting, and so forth. A pipeline welding crew is a highly-trained, fast-moving team that skillfully walks a tightrope of metallurgical qualities when handling high-strength pipe steels.

Electrode selection for pipe welding calls for careful consideration of a number of operating and metallurgical conditions. Mention has been made of the need for the operating characteristics of electrodes with the

EXX10 or EXX10-Iron Powder covering. Although the strength of weld metal from the E60 series is adequate for joints in pipe up to the X52 grade, a point will be reached where stronger weld metal is judged necessary. For welding "X56" pipe, E7010-A1 electrodes are commonly used. Incidently, E7010-A1 electrodes are preferred by some welders for the root bead in the lower strength grades of pipe in order to provide greater resistance to cracking prior to application of filler beads. A problem with electrode selection arises when dealing with the X60 grade pipe inasmuch as the minimum yield strength of this base metal appears to be slightly above the minimum yield strength of weld metal from E7010-A1 electrodes. Experience shows that E7010-A1 electrodes can be used to join the lighter wall thickness pipe of X60 grade and the weld will be slightly stronger than the base metal. Dilution results in a small elevation of the weld metal strength as compared to all-weld-metal tensile properties. However, the heavier sections of X60 pipe present a problem because electrodes of the E80 series are not regularly manufactured with the cellulosic E8010 covering desired for pipe welding. Also, the only E80 series electrodes currently manufactured are either of the chromium-molybdenum steel composition for elevated temperature service, or of the nickel steel composition for low-temperature service. At least one electrode manufacturer has recognized this problem and is marketing a modified E7010-A1 electrode in which an increased molybdenum content is employed to provide the higher strength required for the heavy-wall X60 pipe. To emphasize the importance of electrode selection, it can be mentioned that some experimental "X100" steel pipe has been produced and used as gas transport lines. Shielded metal-arc welding could not be applied to manually weld this pipe in the field because electrodes which deposit weld metal of 100 ksi minimum yield strength are not regularly made with the cellulosic covering desired for fixed-position pipe welded by the downhill direction technique. Furthermore, the use of a hydrogen-bearing electrode possibly would lead to underbead cracking difficulty with a steel of the X100 grade. In the case of the X100 pipe, the welding engineer turned to the gas metal-arc process to make field welded joints.

Gas metal-arc welding suddenly acquired a great potential for fixed-position welding of joints in pipe with the introduction of the shorting-arc form of weld metal deposition (see Chapter 3). This form of the GMAW process has proved very satisfactory for depositing weld metal in all positions, and the close control of heat input inherent with the shorting-arc is a valuable asset in depositing root beads. The newer pulsed-arc type of metal transfer is also expected to be of value in pipe welding. Some difficulty has been encountered, however, with the shorting-arc GMAW process because novice welders become so charmed with the ease of depositing the weld beads in any position that they fail to apply the bead with adequate heat input. This neglect leads to incomplete fusion, or localized "cold laps" along the groove faces of the joint. The condition is particularly prone to occur in the root area. These defects are quickly detected in tensile and bend tests, but are very difficult to detect by nondestructive test methods. It is very important, therefore, to employ sufficient current in gas metal-arc welding to accomplish some penetration into the sidewalls or groove faces of the joint and thus establish good fusion.

Welding Machinery Steel

The mild steel used in the construction of machinery usually does not exceed 0.30% carbon. Frequent use is made of castings, but even these usually contain about 0.30% carbon or less. Many castings for machinery use are made to ASTM A27-60, Grade 60-30, which has typical composition limits for a readily weldable mild steel, except for the silicon requirement which is 0.80% maximum. Greater amounts of silicon are permitted in castings in order to promote good flowing properties. If the foundryman anticipates difficulty in properly filling a complex mold, he may call for molten metal with the silicon in the range of about 0.65 to 0.80%. Ordinarily, a base metal containing this amount of silicon will not adversely affect a welding operation. However, if a weld is made with filler metal containing a high silicon content, and the joint is under considerable restraint, then some difficulty with weld metal hot cracking may be experienced because of an abnormally high silicon content in the final diluted weld deposit.

Machinery weldments may contain a variety of carbon steels — all being loosely referred to as "mild steels." Because the materials employed in machinery are seldom stipulated by codes or specifications, the manufacturer has a free hand in selecting materials that appear attractive from the standpoints of cost, fabricability, and service performance. It is not unusual to find more attention being paid to other properties, like machinability, rather than weldability. For example, if a component requires a great deal of machining, a free-cutting carbon steel, containing high sulfur, or high phosphorus and sulfur contents, or even an addition of lead as contained in Type 12L14, may be employed under the guise of "mild steel." As explained in Chapters 10 and 13, phosphorus and sulfur in large amounts can result in cracking and porosity unless suitable remedial measures are taken. Circumstances may arise where the ma-

chinery builder may desire a little greater strength or hardness in a particular component. He may, in fact, consider a localized heat treatment
(flame hardening) of the part to increase wear resistance. Knowing that
steel containing 0.30% carbon or less does not respond particularly well
to a hardening treatment, he may call for steel with a higher carbon
content. If his selection does not exceed 0.35% carbon, he probably will
not encounter any particular difficulty. Of course, a mild preheat or the use
of a low-hydrogen arc-welding process would be prudent under these circumstances. He can easily secure this kind of steel by ordering AISI C1030
type. If his needs for strength or hardness require a higher carbon content
than 0.35%, then the product moves out of the mild steel category and,
as will be discussed next, he must deal with more critical weldability.

Welding Cast Steel

Steel castings often are used as valve bodies, pump cylinders and
machinery parts. Castings to be welded usually are limited to 0.30%
carbon, as illustrated by ASTM A27-60, Grade 60-30 in Table 69. This
carbon limit is observed more closely in carbon steel castings than in
wrought steel because of the opinion generally held that higher susceptibility to underbead cracking prevails in the cast form. Yet a number
of investigators have observed a *lower* sensitivity to underbead cracking
of the selfsame composition in cast form. No clear-cut reasons have been
established to explain the phenomenon.

MEDIUM-CARBON STEELS (0.30 TO 0.60% CARBON)

Carbon steels containing about 0.30% carbon already have been
described as having generally good weldability, with some need for
caution if the carbon and the manganese simultaneously border at the
maxima arbitrarily set for mild steel. However, in the medium-carbon
steels, over a small spread of 30 points of carbon, i.e., from 0.30 to
0.60%, a pronounced change occurs in weldability. The steel containing
0.60% carbon when welded by ordinary procedures easily may be fully
hardened (martensitic) in the heat-affected zones. This level of carbon
not only provides the *hardenability* to achieve a fully martensitic structure,
but the *hardness* of the martensitic zone will be about Rockwell 63-C,
which is almost the maximum hardness that can be attained in a carbon
or an alloy steel. These heat-affected zones will be low in toughness and
ductility. They have a strong propensity to develop cracks upon cooling
to room temperature and they may fracture in service, particularly if subjected to impact loading. If the weld metal is substantially increased in
carbon content by virtue of dilution with the 0.60% carbon base metal,

the weld also will be likely to display high hardness, cracking susceptibility, and a tendency toward brittle failure. The procedure for welding a steel containing 0.60% carbon might well include (1) preheating to about 500 F, (2) welding with a low-hydrogen process, (3) avoiding carbon pickup in the weld deposit by minimizing dilution with melted base metal, (4) maintaining a 500 F minimum interpass temperature, and (5) transferring the weldment without dropping below the interpass temperature to a postweld heat treating furnace for annealing or an equally suitable heat treatment. Whether all of these precautions are mandatory in the procedure will depend upon the actual article to be welded, its size, joint design, joining process, kind of filler metal, and so forth. Of course, if the steel being welded contained less than 0.60% carbon, less need would exist for the precautionary measures outlined. It is quite difficult to predict the minimum precautionary measures required in the welding procedure for a medium carbon steel. Attempts have been made by a large number of investigators to provide empirical formulas for calculating the required preheat temperature, etc. from the known base metal composition, thickness, and process to be applied. More will be said at the conclusion of this chapter about these systems for predetermining optimum welding procedure. In lieu of any guidance from a weldability prediction system, or experience with a comparable weldment, every available precaution would have to be taken to insure against an unsound or unreliable weldment. Despite the unfavorable response of these steels to the thermal cycle of fusion joining, many machinery parts of medium-carbon steel are assembled without difficulty by welding through the use of a properly planned procedure.

Steels containing 0.30 to 0.60% carbon are extensively used in machinery. Tractors, earthmoving vehicles, mining equipment, power shovels, derricks, and pumps are examples of the many kinds of machinery which have components made of medium-carbon steels. This kind of steel often is selected for wear resistance rather than its greater strength. The parts frequently are used in the heat treated condition to insure strength or hardness in the required range. Assembly by welding may be performed before or following final heat treatment depending upon the nature of the weldment. Medium-carbon steels usually are produced as fully-killed steels using hot-topped ingots to avoid pipe in the product. Defects of this nature are highly undesirable in the higher carbon steels because they often produce splitting during hot rolling or forging, and cracking during welding and during heat treatment. These steels often are produced with a controlled austenitic grain size. Fine grain steels usually help gain better notched bar impact strengths. Coarse grain steels generally display greater hardenability and sometimes are preferred for heavier sections to be heat treated. While carbon steels have a relatively low hardenability as compared to alloy steels, this feature often is evaluated and considered very carefully before proceeding with the production of heat treated parts. The actual hardenability of a particular steel may determine whether production parts are to be quenched in water or in oil for hardening, and this in turn may call for some adjustment of welding procedure if the weld metal also must meet specified mechanical property limits. Carbon steels cannot be purchased to standardized hardenability limits (H-Bands) as can the alloy steels. Little has been published about the comparative weldability of fine and of coarse (McQuaid-Ehn) grain size steels. Both appear equally susceptible to grain coarsening in the higher temperature portion of a heat-affected zone immediately adjacent to a weld made by fusion joining. The addition of aluminum to steel for purposes of deoxidation and grain refinement has been reported by some investigators to reduce susceptibility to underbead cracking while others have claimed the reverse. Considerably more work has been conducted on alloy steels containing 0.30 to 0.60% carbon (see Chapter 15).

HIGH-CARBON STEELS (ABOVE 0.60% CARBON)

Steel containing carbon in the range of about 0.60 to 1.00% usually is pictured in springs, cutting tools, gripper jaws, mill rolls, crane and railroad car wheels, and other articles which seldom call for assembly by welding. More often, welding is applied as a maintenance or repair operation. This alone would justify attention being given to the metallurgy of welding high carbon steels. However, a much greater amount of welding is being performed on high-carbon steels than might be imagined, and this arises because of an interesting case of economical salvage. Each year, hundreds of tons of worn railroad rails are removed from service and are sent to mills which specialize in hot slitting and rerolling. Each length of rail is heated to about 2000 F and passed through a slitter which separates the head and flange from the web. These three components are passed through hot rolling mills which shape the pieces into rounds, squares, flats, angles, and special shapes. Rail steel often contains as high as 0.80% carbon. Bars of this steel will display a tensile strength ranging from 100 to 150 ksi depending upon how well the cooling is retarded after rolling, or whether an annealing treatment is applied. Rerolled rail steel is used to some extent in manufacturing farm implements, fence posts, auto jacks, concrete reinforcing bars, and other miscellaneous hardware that does not require extensive drilling or machining, and where limited toughness and ductility are not likely to be a shortcoming.

A difference of opinion exists among welding engineers on the required procedures for joining high-carbon steel, particularly the 0.80% carbon rerolled rail steel. The procedure obtained by extrapolation from the medium carbon steels would entail, of course, preheat, low-hydrogen conditions during fusion, maintaining of high interpass temperature, and postweld heat treatment. Some claim, however, that rail steel and similar high-carbon steels can be successfully welded for many applications without preheat and postweld heat treatment. Instead, high heat input is advocated, along with good protection of the molten metal, and a low-hydrogen type welding electrode. This practice may produce joints free of underbead cracking because avoiding hydrogen pickup in the base metal heat-affected zone eliminates the strongest promoter of this defect. However, the final microstructure of the heat-affected zone still is a matter deserving of careful consideration. Many weldments can be devised to make maximum use of (a) retarded cooling rates from high heat input, (b) multi-layer welds to secure the tempering effect from each pass, and (c) tempering beads deposited atop the weld reinforcement for the restricted heat effect. Yet, our knowledge of the limited toughness in a weld-affected zone of 0.80% carbon steel suggests that as-welded joints in steel of this kind be employed with the greatest of caution. A safer approach is to use a postweld heat treatment to reduce the hardness of the heat-affected areas and increase their toughness and ductility. For example, when making butt joints between railroad rails by the flash or the submerged-arc processes, a postweld heat treatment can be applied locally to restore a desirable microstructure throughout the weld area. If the softening from a tempering or sub-critical annealing operation is undesirable, a treatment consisting of heating to 1550 F, spray quenching with water, and tempering at 900 F can be applied locally. Of course, some softening occurs at the extremities of the area locally heated to 1550 F, but this ordinarily can be controlled in width and hardness by employing a rapid heating method.

CAST IRON (ABOVE 1.7% CARBON)

The general term *cast iron* covers iron in cast form and containing a very high carbon content, perhaps 1.7 to 4.5%. However, this carbon may be varied in the mode of distribution in the microstructure, and this gives rise to a number of different forms of cast iron which differ to a surprising extent in mechanical properties — and in weldability.

Grey Cast Iron

This is the most widely used form, so named because of the dull grey surfaces on fractured pieces. By adding approximately 1 to 3%

silicon, the cast alloy, upon slowly cooling in the sand mold, will precipitate its carbon as flakes of free graphite in the microstructure. Consequently, grey cast iron has the unique properties of a ferrite matrix with
numerous soft flake-like inclusions (of graphite) dispersed throughout.
Grey cast iron has a tensile strength of 25 to 50 ksi and displays no yield
strength. It has a very high compressive yield strength, very good damp-
ing capacity, and excellent machinability. The toughness and ductility of
grey cast iron can vary considerably depending upon the exact size and
shape of the graphite flakes, and whether any combined carbon remained
in the alloy to form some pearlitic microstructure during cooling. However, at best, grey cast iron has modest toughness.

White Cast Iron

White cast iron is not widely used because of extreme brittleness.
By control of chemical composition (principally holding a relatively low
silicon content) and use of accelerated cooling (usually chilling against
a metal or a graphite mold or a chill-plate inserted in the mold), the
structure of white cast iron is kept free of graphitic carbon. Therefore,
a fractured surface will appear white, as contrasted with the grey-colored
fracture of grey cast iron. The microstructure of white cast iron consists
of primary carbides in a fine dendritic formation. The matrix may be
either martensite or a fine pearlite depending upon the composition and
the cooling rate. While the hardness of martensitic white cast irons may
be as high as 600 BHN, the material may exihibit only 20 ksi in a tensile
test because of its very low ductility. Sometimes, through use of the chill-
plate in the mold, only a skin of white cast iron is produced on a casting
to gain this high hardness for abrasion resistance.

Malleable Iron

Malleable iron is made in two types, (1) ferritic malleable iron,
or (2) pearlitic malleable iron. Both types are made from essentially
the same iron–carbon alloy composition, but different heat treatments are
employed to obtain the particular microstructures that distinguish the
two types. Ferritic malleable iron consists of a matrix of ferrite grains in
which is dispersed all of the carbon as tiny patches of *temper carbon*
(graphite). Pearlitic malleable iron contains patches of temper carbon,
but some of the carbon is dispersed in the matrix as cementite. Depending
upon the heat treatment, this combined carbon may appear in pearlite,
tempered martensite or spherodized carbide.

Malleable iron, especially the ferritic type, exhibits a higher tensile strength and better ductility than grey cast iron simply because of the mechanical effect of *patches* of graphite as compared with *flakes* of graphite. Malleable iron castings are used, therefore, in a wider variety of articles. Good machinability still is one of the chief advantages of the material.

Nodular Cast Iron

Nodular iron is cast iron in which free carbon or graphite is dispersed as tiny balls or spherulites instead of flakes as found in grey iron, or patches as found in malleable iron. The composition of nodular iron is similar to that of grey iron except for a small addition of a nodularizing agent, which may be cerium, calcium, lithium, magnesium, sodium, or a number of other elements. Magnesium is commonly used for this purpose. The nodularizing treatment is so effective in causing the carbon contained in the molten iron alloy to form spheroids of graphite that some castings are used in the as-cast condition. More often, the castings are heat treated much in the same manner as malleable iron castings to produce a matrix that is ferritic, pearlitic, or tempered martensite.

Weldability of Cast Iron

All cast irons, whether grey, white, malleable or nodular, suffer from essentially the same handicap in fusion joining — *too much carbon*. While the manufacturing process, that is, casting and possibly heat treating, may be capable of producing a microstructure that possesses useful mechanical properties, the thermal cycle of fusion joining ordinarily does not produce a desirable microstructural condition. The temperature immediately adjacent to the weld becomes too high and the cooling rate of the entire heat-affected zone is too rapid. Massive carbides tend to form in the zone immediately adjacent to the weld, while the remainder of the heat-affected zone tends to form a high-carbon martensite. Both of these microstructural conditions are very brittle and are subject to cracking, either spontaneously, or from service applied loads. The degree of brittleness and propensity to cracking will depend to some extent upon the kind of cast iron, its condition of heat treatment, and the welding procedure.

Fusion joining, because of its localized nature, produces stress in the weld area. The base metal must be capable of some plastic deformation on a localized scale to accommodate these stresses or else cracking will result. Nodular iron and malleable iron treated to a ferritic matrix are better suited to absorb the stresses from welding than are grey or white cast iron. Arc welding exaggerates weld stress and is more likely to cause cracking than gas welding.

The composition and structure of the cast iron plays a part in determining the brittleness and cracking susceptibility of a weld joint by affecting the amount of carbon that goes into solution during the austenization of the heat-affected zone. To minimize the formation of massive carbides and high-carbon martensite, it is most helpful to have all carbon present as free carbon (graphite) and in the form of not-too-small spheroids. The smaller the surface area of graphite in contact with the hot austenitic matrix, the less carbon that will be dissolved to appear later as combined carbon in the structure at room temperature. Flakes of graphite, as are present in grey iron, display the greatest tendency to enter solution because of their greater surface area; however, the graphite is rather slow to dissolve and free graphite often remains in the weld melt. In general, the process of fusion joining is a reversal of the solidification process. Those areas last to solidify are the first areas to melt. The composition of a typical cast iron might be: 3.5% carbon, 0.5% manganese, 0.04% phosphorus, 0.06% sulfur, and 2.5% silicon. The addition of 0.07% magnesium to this composition would promote the formation of nodular graphite. Increasing the manganese content would act to decrease graphitization. Higher phosphorus encourages embrittlement. Higher sulfur also acts to decrease graphitization. Silicon, it will be remembered, promotes graphitization of the carbon.

Avoidance of hydrogen pickup during any arc-welding on cast iron reduces the likelihood of cracking upon cooling. However, this factor is of lesser importance than in the welding of hardenable steels, and it must not be assumed that the use of a low-hydrogen flux covering on a mild steel arc-welding electrode spells success in welding cast iron.

The mechanical properties of weld metal employed on cast iron can play a major part in the success of the operation. If the yield strength is held quite low, the weld metal imposes stresses of lower intensity during cooling, which reduces the likelihood of cracking. During service, the weld metal deforms easily to minimize stress concentrations on the brittle base metal. This sacrificial action by weld metal can be seen to a degree when using austenitic stainless steel weld deposits. However, weld metals of nickel, or an alloy of approximately 50% nickel and 50% iron, are so effective in providing this kind of relief that considerable use is made of nickel and nickel-iron alloy filler metals in arc-welding cast iron (see AWS A5.15, Specification for Welding Rods and Covered Electrodes for Welding Cast Iron). Ordinary low-carbon steel electrodes are not satisfactory for welding cast iron because the carbon picked up by the weld deposit quickly increases the yield strength — to say nothing of the low ductility that is also likely to be found. Another advantage of the austenitic-like weld deposits of stainless steel, or nickel alloy is the ease with which they can be machined in the as-welded condition.

Preheating cast iron to modest temperatures (up to 600 F) does not insure success in an arc-welding operation with mild steel filler metal as often is the case with hardenable steel. Positive benefit from preheating is secured in gas welding cast iron with a cast iron filler rod; in which case the entire joint area of the cast iron article is preheated to almost a red heat (900 F or higher), and is slowly cooled after fusion joining has been completed. This procedure produces a weld with a microstructure of graphitic carbon in a matrix of ferrite and pearlite. A preheat of 300 to 400 F often is applied when arc-welding cast iron with nickel or nickel-iron alloy electrodes; although a temperature in the range of about 400 to 600 F is to be strongly recommended.

Postweld heat treatment of cast iron weldments can be performed to relieve residual stresses and to improve the microstructure in the area of the weld joint. One practice is to heat slowly to about 1150 F immediately upon completion of welding, and to slowly cool after soaking at temperature for about one hour. A more thorough postweld anneal, often called a "graphitizing-ferritizing" treatment, requires heating to soak at 1650 F for four hours, furnace cooling at 60 degrees F per hour to 1000 F or lower, and cooling in air to room temperature.

A novel procedure recommended for welding nodular iron which does not require a postweld heat treatment to obtain optimum weld joint ductility is based upon a surfacing or "buttering" technique. The procedure requires advance knowledge of the surfaces of the casting to be joined. A thick layer (about 5/16-in. thick) of weld metal is deposited on these surfaces prior to assembly into a weldment and at a time when the cast components can be conveniently annealed immediately after the surfacing or buttering operation. The weld metal employed for surfacing does not necessarily have to be the same as subsequently used for joining the cast pieces together; however, it must be a weld metal which is suitable to serve as part of the base metal. This surfacing-annealing-welding procedure has been successfully demonstrated with shielded metal-arc welding (employing a preheat of 600 F) and covered electrodes of ENiFe, E307-15 and E6016. These electrodes represent nickel base alloy, austenitic Cr–Ni stainless steel, and a mild steel (low-hydrogen covering), respectively. The object of the surfacing weld is, of course, to arrange for the heat-affected zone of the final assembly weld to fall within the surfacing weld, rather than the cast iron base metal.

ESTIMATING THE WELDABILITY OF CARBON STEELS

Our discussion of carbon steels has been carried from "steel" containing less than 0.005% carbon to cast iron which may contain as much as 5% of this alloying element. Although we probed unusual aspects of steel, like degree of deoxidation, in assessing weldability, the property which obviously exerted the greatest influence was the propensity to harden when heated to a high temperature and quickly cooled. The manner in which the *hardness* of the heat-affected structure was controlled by the carbon content, and the *ability* to harden on cooling was controlled by the carbon, manganese and silicon contents was explained by describing the formation of martensite and its properties. The carbon range over which the greatest change occurred in the weldability of steel appeared to be about 0.30 to 0.50%. Below this range, there appeared to be little cause for concern that the hardenability of the steel might produce underbead cracking or brittle heat-affected zones. Above this range, there was little doubt that precautions had to be taken in planning the welding procedure to avoid underbead cracking or brittle heat-affected zones. Within the 0.30 to 0.50% range, steels responded according to the amounts of carbon, manganese, and silicon present. Because of the demand for strength, which is most readily (and economically) induced in the steel by alloying with carbon, welding engineers are continually seeking ways of welding steel in the 0.30 to 0.50% carbon range without risk of cracking, without serious impairment of toughness or ductility, and without costly or inconvenient innovations in the procedure. It does not appear possible to develop a simple system for precisely predicting the entire behavior of a given steel during a welding operation (with respect to cracking), and the performance of welded joints in the steel in service (particularly the fracture toughness). The features embodied in an actual weldment and the conditions of service are much too diverse to be represented in a reasonable number of practicable weldability test specimens. Progress has been made, however, on simple evaluations of a number of the major individual features involved in a welding procedure which affect weldability. These pieces of information can be used as guideposts by the welding engineer in developing a satisfactory procedure. Further discussion on this subject will be found in Chapter 16.

Evaluation of Base Metal Chemical Composition

Early work to assess the role of base metal composition in controlling weldability dealt with the level of hardness produced in weld heat-affected zones. Experience suggested that a maximum hardness of about 35-C Rockwell could be tolerated and still insure against underbead cracking, and a maximum of about 25-C Rockwell could be tolerated and still assure satisfactory performance of as-welded heat-affected zones during loading in service. It was found rather quickly that the correlation between *hardness,* per se, and cracking, and service performance was not so regular that the permissible limits for welded joints could be spelled out in terms of hardness alone. Further work led to the use of underbead cracking tests, and notched-bead slow-bend tests. In the course of these studies, the concept of carbon equivalency developed which appeared to simplify studies of relationships between chemical composition and the factors involved in weldability. Figure 228 shows in a general way the

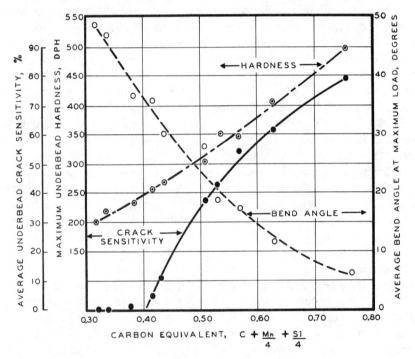

Fig. 228 — Relationship between steel composition expressed as *carbon equivalent* and underbead hardness, cracking sensitivity, and notched-bead slow-bend capability (after Voldrich and Harder).

relationships between composition and (1) hardness, (2) underbead cracking sensitivity, and (3) notched-bead slow-bend capability. Note that manganese and silicon were found to be one-fourth as potent as carbon in influencing these three weldability criteria. The curve depicting cracking sensitivity in this illustration shows that under the conditions of the test, underbead cracking susceptibility first appears with a carbon equivalent of 0.40 and increases quite rapidly as the alloy content (carbon, manganese, *OR* silicon) rises to a carbon equivalent of 0.75. These results were obtained with 1-in. thick test plates arc-welded with E6010 electrodes. While the influence of base metal composition is shown clearly, and simply, the problem still remains of ascertaining whether the conditions which promote underbead cracking in an actual weldment will be of greater or lesser severity than the test conditions. For example, when welding a pipeline of X52 or X56 steel, experience has shown that underbead cracking is not a real threat until the carbon equivalent (C.E.)

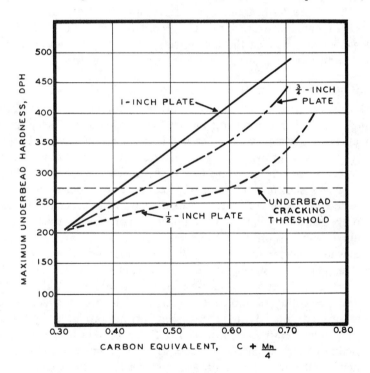

Fig. 229 — Influence of plate thickness upon relationship between steel composition (expressed as carbon equivalent) and maximum heat-affected zone hardness. Horizontal dotted line at approximately 275 DPH represents hardness threshold above which underbead cracking is likely to be encountered when welding under hydrogen-producing conditions. (after Martin)

exceeds approximately 0.55. This better performance of steel in a pipe joint might be attributable to thinner wall thickness or the greater heat input and slower cooling rate associated with qualified or standardized multipass welding procedures. Conversely, another application may involve welding conditions that make the heat-affected zone of the steel more prone to underbead cracking. If the effect of the base metal thickness were evaluated in the bead-on-plate test, the trend of results with respect to underbead cracking would be as shown in Fig. 229. The heavier plates produce cracking at lower levels of C. E. because their greater mass increases the hardness of the heat-affected zone and the intensity of residual stresses. If a similar evaluation was made of the influence of heat input during welding, the results would show that for any given plate thickness, greater heat input would permit higher levels of C.E. before the onset of underbead cracking. This trend is explained, of course, by the slower cooling rate in the heat-affected zone and the lower levels of hardness which develop as the welding heat input is increased.

Preheating Carbon Steels for Welding

One of the first remedies proposed for the prevention of underbead cracking with higher carbon-equivalency was preheating. This proved to be an effective measure because it put into operation several beneficial mechanisms — one of which is now recognized as the prime factor in the underbead cracking problem; that is, hydrogen diffusion and effusion. Preheating was shown in Chapter 12 to reduce the cooling rate of the heat-affected zone. Consequently, the likelihood of the austenitized portion undergoing transformation to a completely martensitic structure (with maximum cracking sensitivity) was reduced. Also, the arrest of cooling at an elevated temperature could allow any martensite that formed to become tempered (allow minute carbide particles to precipitate). Thus the short-range stresses in the heat-affected zone would be reduced. More important, preheating promoted the escape of hydrogen which entered the heat-affected zone during the heating period produced by welding. Preheating to temperatures as low as 150 F can prevent underbead cracking only in borderline cases. In fact, some experimental evidence was mentioned in Chapter 13 that suggests preheating in the vicinity of 150 to 200 F might promote the delayed cracking from hydrogen rather than prevent it from occurring. A preheat, interpass, and postweld temperature of 250 F is more effective, and is frequently employed for weldments of carbon steels having a C. E. in the range of approximately 0.40 to 0.55. Of course, the preheat, interpass and postweld temperature should be raised as the carbon equivalent increases. With a carbon equivalent above 0.55, preheat and interpass temperatures from 250 to 400 F may be necessary.

Control of Hydrogen in Welding Carbon Steels

The use of a low-hydrogen arc-welding process often will obviate the need for preheating, or maintaining a high interpass temperature. This is particularly true in welding steels having a carbon equivalent below about 0.55 where the effect of hydrogen overshadows residual stresses, hardening, and other factors that favor underbead cracking. Much welding of carbon steels is performed with E6010 electrodes, and as explained in Chapter 13, the cellulosic covering on this electrode saturates the weld pool with hydrogen during deposition, and a portion of this hydrogen diffuses into the base metal heat-affected area. The increase in hydrogen in the heat-affected zone starts the chain of events which can result in cracking if the hardenability of the base metal provides a hardened, or partly-hardened structure. If the steel has a carbon equivalent below about 0.40, we have no cause for concern, but when above this level some precautions ordinarily should be taken. Either preheating, or a change to a low-hydrogen class of electrode covering would be the first step. Preheating is not always convenient in modern, high-production operations, so the low-hydrogen alternative has received a good deal of attention. Equally good (low-hydrogen) results can be secured with other fusion joining processes that do not ordinarily liberate hydrogen in an arc in contact with the molten metal. Submerged-arc, gas metal-arc, and the gas tungsten-arc welding processes all are capable of welding joints which remain free of underbead cracking when hydrogen pickup is the factor that spells the difference between success and failure.

Weldability Formulas

Susceptibility to underbead cracking has been hypothesized by some investigators to be influenced to a large degree by the temperature range over which transformation from austenite to martensite, or to a mixed microstructure containing martensite, takes place; particularly the temperature level at which transformation is completed, or possibly has reached 90% of completion. Naturally, the lower the temperature of completion the greater the likelihood that cracking will occur in the transformed structure. The following formula has been proposed for predicting the 90% transformation temperature:

$$M_{90} \text{ (degree F)} = 850 - \%C(630 + 195\% \text{ Mn})$$
$$- 40 \text{ (\% Ni)} - 80 \text{ (\% Cr)} + 14 \text{ (\% Mo)}$$
$$+ 85 \text{ (\% V)} - 20 \text{ (\% Cu)}$$

Only limited data appear in the literature which correlate underbead cracking susceptibility with the 90% transformation completion temperature. If this temperature is above 500 F, the majority of steels display no susceptibility to underbead cracking. However, certain compositions appear to require a 90% completion temperature above 700 F to ward off underbead cracking. There is no doubt that the performance of the various steels is affected by transformation end-point. If the martensite in the heat-affected zone of the base metal is formed at a high enough temperature, underbead cracking will not occur.

Enthusiasm for a weldability formula to guide the welding engineer on predicting underbead cracking susceptibility has led several investigators to pursue the subject into the alloy steels. This activity is mentioned here inasmuch as the carbon steels may contain significant amounts of other alloying elements, either as residual alloys or as a result of "micro-alloying." Regardless of the explanation for their presence, these small amounts of alloys should be considered in any appraisal of the composition from the standpoint of hardenability. In fact, these alloys may impart more hardenability than their relatively small total sum may suggest because hardenability appears to be governed by a *multiplicative* function of the alloys present. The most comprehensive formula for evaluating composition, again based upon carbon equivalency, is:

$$C.E. = \%C + \frac{\%Mn}{6} + \frac{\%Ni}{20} + \frac{\%Cr}{10} + \frac{\%Cu}{40} - \frac{\%Mo}{50} - \frac{\%V}{10}$$

Note that negative values are assigned to molybdenum and vanadium. The effects of these elements actually depend upon whether they are present in solid solution, in which case they assist hardenability and should be treated as a positive factor, or whether they are present in complex carbides which do not go into solution during the period when the heat-affected zone is austenitized. In the latter case, not only is the molybdenum and vanadium ineffective as a hardenability promoter, but the carbon contained in the complex carbide particles also is prevented from performing its familiar roles as a promoter of hardenability and as the principal element for establishing hardness in transformed structures. A formula of this kind cannot be more than a rough guide, not only because of differences in welding conditions between the test specimen and the actual weldment, but also because the formula does not take into account variations in grain size, deoxidation practice, microstructure of the base metal prior to welding, and the hydrogen content of the heat-affected area of the base metal; all of which are known to play a part in controlling underbead cracking susceptibility.

Suggested Reading

Welding Handbook, Fifth Edition, Section 4, (Metals and Their Weldability), American Welding Society, New York, N. Y.

"Continuous Cooling Transformation Diagrams of Steels For Welding and Their Applications," by M. Inagaki and H. Sekiguchi, Transactions of the National Research Institute for Metals (Japan), v 2, no. 2, pp 102-125, 1960.

"Gas and Oil Pipeline Welding Practices," by A. G. Barkow, Welding Research Council Bulletin Series, No. 76, April 1962.

Metals and How to Weld Them, by T. B. Jefferson and Gorham Woods, Published by the James F. Lincoln Arc Welding Foundation, Cleveland, Ohio, 1954.

"Weldability Prediction from Steel Composition to Avoid Heat-Affected Zone Cracking," by K. Winterton, The Welding Journal, v 40, no. 6, Research Suppl. pp 253s-258s, June 1961.

"The Welding of Ductile Iron," by G. R. Pease, Ibid, v 39, no. 1, pp 1s to 9s, January 1960.

"Welding Nodular Iron Without Postweld Annealing," by R. C. Bates and F. J. Morely, Ibid, v 40, no. 9, pp 417s-422s, September 1961.

Chapter 15

WELDING ALLOY STEELS

Alloy steels present a provocative challenge to the metallurgical proficiency of the welding engineer. The addition of alloying elements to iron and steel can produce such a diversity of outstanding results that more than a dozen general categories of alloy steels have developed. Steels are alloyed most often to (1) increase strength, (2) improve toughness, and (3) impart corrosion resistance. Other useful effects induced by alloying include increased magnetic saturation, increased coercive force, lower magnetic permeability, changes in thermal expansivity, elimination of allotropy in crystal structure, and improved machinability. These effects may be induced singly or in combinations, and controlled in degree by judicious alloying. For example, a steel can be alloyed to increase its strength and at the same time make it corrosion resisting. Also, through a different combination of alloying elements, it is possible to gain the same strength and corrosion resistance, and, furthermore, make the steel non-magnetic. More useful combinations of physical and mechanical properties can be secured with iron through alloying than with any other metal as the base.

Chapter 7 covered the mechanics of alloying and the effects of other elements in iron. This earlier discussion dealt mainly with the effects of individual alloying additions. The development of commercially useful alloy steels is far more complex than Chapter 7 indicates. Part of this complexity arises from synergism, which is the greater-than-expected total effect obtained when two or more added elements act cooperatively rather than the effect commensurate with independent action by each element. In the past, the development of alloy steels had been accomplished largely by laborious cut-and-try procedures. However, knowledge of the fundamental mechanisms by which alloying controls properties and characteristics is nearing the state where practical use can be made of computers to calculate the probable effects of interactions between a number of alloying elements. Soon it may be possible to stipulate the properties required and then compute the least amount and kind of alloying needed to gain these properties. Incidentally, one of the first practical uses of this idealized computer technique should be to eliminate some of the repetition among the currently used steels; that is, discard steels that simply duplicate the properties of another, and trim off the excess fat (alloy) to conserve metals and reduce cost.

DEFINITION AND CLASSIFICATION OF ALLOY STEELS

Steel is considered to be an *alloy steel,* according to the AISI, when either (1) the maximum of the range given for the content of alloying elements exceeds one or more of the following limits: manganese 1.65%, silicon 0.60%, copper 0.60%, or (2) in which a definite range or a definite minimum quantity of any of the following elements is specified or required within the limits of the recognized field of alloy steels: aluminum, boron, chromium (up to 3.99%), cobalt, columbium, molybdenum, nickel, titanium, tungsten, vanadium, zirconium or any other alloying element is added to obtain a desired alloying effect. This definition has been developed to distinguish carbon steels from alloy steels mainly to promote standardization of tolerances, methods of inspection, and chemical check analysis required for each type of product. While this definition is helpful in pointing out which steels should be classified as alloy steel, we still have need for some form of grouping that will enable us to make a systematic study of their welding metallurgy. Alloy steels have been cataloged in many ways: by cost, chemical composition, microstructure, mechanical properties, and so forth. However, the method of grouping that appears best to serve here is to place them in categories according to principal attributes or the kind of use for which the steel was developed. The categories that best fit our needs are:

High-Strength, Low-Alloy Steels
Quenched and Tempered Alloy Steels
Abrasion-Resisting Alloy Steels
Heat-Treatable Alloy Steels
Corrosion Resisting Irons
Stainless Steels
Heat-Resisting High-Alloy Steels
High-Temperature Service Alloy Steels

Cryogenic Service Alloy Steels
Nuclear Service Alloy Steels
Electrical Steels
Tool Steels
Permanent Magnet Steels
Nitriding Steels
Carburizing Steels

A discussion of all of these categories will not be possible in this book, so where welding information is not needed little or no space will be devoted to the steel. Some of the categories are extensive and complex. As examples, the stainless steels, which are more properly classified as "high-alloy steels," consist of roughly one hundred standard and proprietary types. The high-alloy steels (containing 4% or more of chromium, and including the stainless and heat resisting steels) are not covered in this book but will be treated in a separate volume scheduled for future publication. The electrical steels, which will be discussed in some detail later, embrace at least twenty-five different kinds. Specialists often devote their entire careers to the technology of producing and fabricating the steels in a single category. In the case of the welding engineer, however, it is commonly his lot to be expected to prescribe a welding procedure for any one of the approximately five hundred different steels found in the various categories. The best background for synthesizing a welding procedure for an alloy steel is a knowledge of its metallurgical behavior, not blind adherence to condensed instructions in a materials catalog.

ALLOYING STEELS FOR STRENGTH

Increased strength has been pointed out as the most prevalent reason for making alloy additions to steel. Higher-strength steels, though more costly, are justified by circumstances that vary from one application to another. Sometimes the use of an alloy steel is imperative because the thickness of the required members precludes gaining the required mechanical properties in a carbon steel. Sometimes a keen analysis is required to determine whether any real benefit will be gained with an alloy steel. Higher-strength alloy steels, in the main, offer two advantages: (1) greater unit loads can be carried by members of the structure, or (2) the size of members required to carry a specified load can be decreased. These two general benefits lead to a variety of selling points for the use of alloy steels.

Higher-strength steel can be used to carry higher unit loads (psi) provided the higher strength capability is recognized by the designer or any ruling code and higher working stresses are allowed. With higher allowable stresses, larger loads can be placed upon the equipment for increased operating efficiency, or the section size of load-carrying members can be reduced to decrease the dead weight of the equipment. Of course, this will not be true if the equipment must be designed on the basis of elastic properties, or if certain formulas dealing with buckling or crippling of sections under compressive loads must be followed. A reduction in the weight of the structure often can be translated to an increase in useful payload. Also a reduction in material costs may be found providing the higher strength was achieved by comparatively little alloying. Many high-strength alloy steels cost approximately 0.5 to 3.0 cents per pound more than carbon steel. If a weight-saving of about 17% or more can be accomplished with an alloy steel, then a saving in material cost usually will be realized. When very large loads are to be carried by members, the section size required in a steel of relatively low strength actually may exceed mill limits for casting, rolling or forging. Further obstacles could be encountered when the extremely large or thick sections were to be machined, manipulated in a jig or fixture, or welded. It is not unusual to find that a higher-strength alloy steel has been selected because the reduction in cross section will allow the members to be fabricated by existing facilities.

A fact of great importance to the welding engineer is that alloy steels containing judicious proportions of alloying elements often can be welded with less difficulty than can carbon steels producing the same yield strength in the weldment. From another viewpoint, steels with higher yield strengths can be welded if the strength is secured by the effect of alloying elements rather than mainly by high carbon content. To further illustrate this fact, a high-strength *alloy* steel with a carbon content of about 0.10% can have strength equivalent to a *carbon* steel containing about 0.30% carbon. Yet, during welding, the alloy steel will have less tendency to produce a brittle structure in its heat-affected zone or to develop underbead cold cracking. It is not unusual, however, to read or hear that alloy steels are more difficult to weld "because of their propensity to harden and tendency to crack." This is generally true only because the alloy steels, as a whole, offer high strength, and any carbon steel designed to produce equivalent strength would prove even more difficult to weld because of cracking susceptibility.

At least seven different metallurgical effects may be employed to gain high strength in currently used low-alloy and medium-alloy steels, and can be captioned:

1. Solid Solution Hardening
2. Changes in Mass and Distribution of Carbide Phase

3. Grain Size Refinement
4. Precipitation Hardening
5. Transformation Hardening
6. Cold Work Hardening
7. Mar-Strain Response

The fundamental mechanics of these effects, and several additional effects which occur in the high-alloy steels and other alloys, were explained in Chapters 5 and 7. Generally speaking, it is possible to design a steel to make use primarily of only one or two of these effects. However, because most alloying elements exert more than one specific effect simultaneously in steel, it is not unusual to find evidence of several strengthening mechanisms operating simultaneously in a given alloy steel. Nevertheless, it can be most helpful to the welding engineer to know which mechanisms are being employed as the *principal* sources of increased strength. Often, the welding procedure must be controlled in a particular manner to either avoid trouble from hardening, or to avoid loss of strength in heat-affected zones from maltreatment by the amount of heat employed in welding. Depending upon the principal strengthening mechanisms employed, some high-strength alloy steels are best welded with high heat input, whereas other steels may require low or restricted heat input. The manner in which we can identify these different steels will be discussed shortly. First, let us re-examine the strengthening mechanisms mentioned above for facts pertinent to the subject of welding alloy steels.

SOLID SOLUTION HARDENING

Any element dissolved in iron will increase its strength and hardness. If the alloying element enters into a substitutional arrangement, the strengthening effect comes from the distortion of the crystallographic planes as the matrix crystals accommodate the slightly smaller or larger foreign atoms. The presence of these off-size atoms also tends to increase the number of dislocations in the crystalline structure. If the alloying element is very small in atom size, it may enter into interstitial solid solution, in which case the presence of these small foreign atoms acts to pin the movement of dislocations and prevent slip on crystallographic planes. In either case, the strengthening effect is small as compared to other effects to be discussed. Little quantitative data are available concerning the solid solution hardening effect of alloying elements in steel; yet, deliberate use is made of elements for this purpose. As examples, phosphorus and nitrogen have a very noticeable strengthening effect.

However, these elements can be used only as limited additions inasmuch as unfavorable phosphorus compounds, or porosity caused by nitrogen, result from substantial additions. Other elements which exert a solid solution hardening effect, listed in order of apparent increasing effectiveness, are chromium, vanadium, molybdenum, nickel, manganese and silicon. While these elements may be added with the intention of utilizing their solid solution hardening effect upon the ferritic matrix of the steel, they may be free to exert other influences that also result in hardening. In studies of the influence of dissolved elements upon fracture toughness, the results have suggested that the interstitial elements, particularly carbon and oxygen, are more harmful in raising the ductile–brittle transition temperature than are the substitutional elements. For example, in a basic study, the addition of only 0.01% oxygen to iron increased the transition temperature by almost 350 degrees F. It has been suggested that one important role of alloying elements in steel is to tie up interstitial elements and thus improve the fracture toughness of the ferrite.

MASS AND DISTRIBUTION OF CARBIDE PHASE

The properties of steel have been shown to be profoundly affected by the mass and distribution of carbide particles in the microstructure. In working with a carbon steel of a particular carbon content, the distribution of the carbide phase could be varied considerably through heat treatment. The further addition of alloying elements, however, can have a marked effect upon the composition of the carbide phase, which in turn can increase its mass and also influence its distribution. Nickel, silicon and aluminum make no significant changes in the composition of carbides, *per se*. However, manganese, chromium, molybdenum, tungsten, vanadium, columbium and titanium are carbide-forming alloying elements, and are listed in order of increasing propensity to enter into the carbide phase which may be present in the microstructure. These metals may replace iron atoms in the carbide crystal lattice, or varying amounts of the metals may be dissolved in the lattice structure of the carbide. As a result of this composition change, the complex alloy-type carbides often are more massive for a given carbon content. The alloy carbides usually dissolve at a slower rate in austenite upon heating, and coalesce much less rapidly in ferrite at elevated temperatures. Their precipitation from martensite during tempering often is delayed, so much that a *secondary hardening* sometimes is observed as progressively higher tempering temperatures are applied. Vanadium, for example, causes a marked secondary hardening effect.

GRAIN SIZE REFINEMENT

Fine grain size in steel generally acts to increase strength by a modest amount and to improve toughness. A fine grain size can be effected in steel by limiting the size of the austenite grains, and by other means of increasing the nucleation of ferrite grains as the austenite undergoes transformation on cooling. Control of austenite grain size can be accomplished (a) by inducing an inherent characteristic in the steel, (b) by limiting the temperature over the Ac_3 point to which the steel is heated, and (c) by hot working the austenitized material to break up and recrystallize the austenite grains. A steel which inherently forms fine austenite grains can be made by adding small amounts of grain refining elements, like aluminum, vanadium, columbium, or nitrogen, to the molten steel during steelmaking. These elements, particularly aluminum, encourage the formation of many small grains whenever the steel is austenitized. A comparatively fine grain size can be maintained to temperatures as high as about 2000 F. These inherently "fine grained" steels are checked by the McQuaid-Ehn test (ASTM Standard E-112) at a temperature of 1700 F to establish a numerical grain size rating. Usually fine grain steels have an austenite grain size of 5 to 8 at 1700 F. This does not necessarily mean that the ferrite or pearlite grain size in the steel at room temperature will be in the order of 5 to 8. The actual austenite grain size attained by the steel still is a deciding factor. Even a steel rated "fine grained" by the McQuaid-Ehn test can grow coarse austenite grains if held at a high temperature; for example, in excess of 2000 F; hence, the need for limiting any heating above the Ac_3 point to the lowest possible temperature. When the steel is to be normalized or otherwise heat treated, the austenizing temperature should be certainly no higher than the 1700 F McQuaid-Ehn test temperature to insure a fine grain size. If the steel is not a fine-grain type, then the matter of limiting the austenitizing temperature becomes even more important to control grain size. Of course, when steel is hot worked the temperatures involved regularly are in excess of 2000 F; that is, the soaking temperature of ingot, bloom or billet, and the temperature of the piece during hot reduction. However, the austenite grain size is constantly refined as the steel section is reduced. The important aspect of this operation with respect to grain size is the *finishing temperature*. This is the temperature of the finally-shaped piece of steel. This temperature determines the size of the austenite grains. The lower the finishing temperature, the smaller the austenite grains, and, consequently, the smaller the ferrite and pearlite grains which nucleate and grow during transformation upon cooling to room temperature.

To encourage many small grains to nucleate in the austenite grains during transformation on cooling, help may come from alloying elements within the steel and from extraneous conditions. Alloying elements, like aluminum, vanadium and columbium, in addition to exerting a restricting influence upon the growth of austenite grains, also encourage the nucleation of many ferrite grains in the austenite during transformation upon cooling. Columbium and vanadium are particularly effective in producing a fine grain structure even in a hot rolled steel. Of course, a low finishing temperature also can aid in accomplishing this desirable condition. Another condition which aids in gaining fine grain size is supercooling of the austenite, which is accomplished by faster cooling. It will be remembered from our examination of the I–T diagrams in Chapter 14 that as the cooling of the austenitized steel is accelerated, the transformation temperature is depressed and the transformation products become finer (both the ferrite grains and the interlamelar spacing of the pearlite). Certain high-strength, low-alloy steels capitalize on the benefits of a very fine grain size and secure this type of structure in the hot rolled condition through the combined effects of (a) the addition of columbium, vanadium, or vanadium and nitrogen, (b) a low finishing temperature off the rolling mill, and (c) accelerated cooling through the transformation range.

PRECIPITATION HARDENING

A fine distinction was drawn between *precipitation hardening* and *transformation hardening* when microstructural changes were discussed in Chapter 5. Precipitation hardening occurs when a phase or compound can be induced to form as discrete particles in the matrix crystalline structure. A condition of supersaturation of the element or elements which form the precipitate is the usual driving force for forming the new compound or phase. The maximum strengthening or hardening effect from the formation of the precipitate occurs when the particles are still submicroscopic, are coherent with the lattice of the matrix structure, and are highly dispersed.

Precipitation hardening is employed only to a limited extent in the low-alloy steels. This is not due to any oversight of this hardening phenomenon, but transformation hardening has proved far more effective in these steels. Furthermore, a heat treatment often is required to properly produce the precipitation hardened condition. Nevertheless, a few of the high-strength, low-alloy steels employ an addition of about 1% copper and a heat treatment at approximately 1100 F to obtain strength by precipitation hardening. Incidentally, this copper addition generally is accompanied by an equal addition of nickel to avoid unfavorable surface effects during heating and hot working operations. Other alloying elements which exert a precipitation hardening effect in the ferritic structure of alloy steel are columbium, titanium, and vanadium. Nitrogen is often added with vanadium. One aspect which is lacking in the matrix structure of the alloy steels to produce highly dispersed (and therefore highly effective) precipitated particles is a state of stress or strain. If this condition can be introduced by cold rolling or some other technique, the effectiveness of the precipitation hardening can be markedly increased.

A recent innovation in the use of precipitation hardening will be found in the *maraging steels* which will be discussed later. As briefly mentioned in Chapter 1, these steels do not "age harden," but require a heat treatment which produces precipitation hardening. The novelty of the maraging steels lies in the method of obtaining a highly satisfactory matrix in which to produce a precipitate. As will be explained in some detail, the two essential matrix conditions, supersaturation and residual stress or strain, are achieved by arranging for transformation of the structure to martensite, albeit a relatively soft martensite because of the extremely low carbon content. The hardening of the martensite matrix then is brought about by a precipitate-producing heat treatment.

TRANSFORMATION HARDENING

Transformation hardening is the unique mechanism of hardening which is so readily employed in steel because of iron's favorable crystallographic allotropy. While this hardening mechanism is to be prized for the remarkable properties it produces in steel, it can be the principal troublemaker or point of concern in welding steels — particularly the alloy steels. Transformation hardening, it will be recalled, generally is separated into the *hardness* level attained by the steel when a martensitic structure is formed, and *hardenability* which is a relative measure of the cooling rate at which a steel in the austenitized condition can be converted to the martensitic structure. All alloying elements added to steel except one, namely cobalt, have been determined to help transformation hardening; that is, increase hardenability. This is accomplished by reducing the critical cooling rate. Alloying elements vary in their hardenability potential. Some elements are quite effective in reducing the critical cooling rate and thus encourage martensite to form. Other elements produce only a weak effect. Often, the effectiveness of a given alloying element varies with the amount present, and also may depend upon the presence of other alloying elements. A point to be kept in mind is that alloying elements in steel influence hardenability whether this effect is wanted or not. For example, chromium may be added to increase corrosion resistance. The resulting chromium alloy steel, in addition to being more resistant to corrosion, will be more hardenable as well! In fact, it may harden on cooling from a high temperature in still air. Hence the expression "air hardening steel." Hardenability is a very important part of the behavior of alloy steels and controls to some extent their weldability. To understand this relationship better, and to appreciate the significance of "air hardening," let us make a closer study of the hardenability of alloy steels.

Air Hardening

Cooling in air from above the critical temperature may harden plain-carbon steel if it is in wire form and the air is cool and moving. However, in thicker sections, such as ¼-inch bar, plain-carbon steel fails to harden when cooled in air. If alloying elements, particularly manganese, but with the exception of cobalt, are added to the plain-carbon steel, the thicker sections tend to harden when cooled in air. The "air-hardening" of alloy steels is the tendency of thicker sections of the steel to harden completely during air cooling, whereas the same thickness of plain-carbon steel of the same carbon content will not harden completely.

Air hardening is important in welding, but it is easy to misapply the term. It is a common misconception to imagine that, since welded plates and other parts cool in air after welding, the structure of the heat-affected zone should be the same as the structure of a bar of the same steel having the same thickness as the part being welded after it has cooled in air from above the critical temperature. From what has been shown in Chapters 4 and 9, we know this is far from the truth. The cooling of the heat-affected zone of a weld is entirely different from the air cooling of a uniformly hot bar.

To grasp the difference, suppose a red-hot razor blade is cooled in still air. The blade will be soft. If, instead, the red-hot blade is pressed between two cold blocks of steel (contact quench), the blade is hardened. In welding, molten metal is deposited between cold steel plates. While the groove faces usually are heated somewhat in advance of the weld, so that the thermal shock of molten metal on steel is not so abrupt as in the contact quenching of razor blades, the rate of cooling in the heat-affected zone of a weld cannot be estimated on the basis of air cooling alone.

Judge then, the difficulty of producing ductile welds in a steel which hardens completely in thick sections on cooling from above the critical range. There will be a stronger tendency for the appearance of martensite in the heat-affected zone of the alloy steel weld than the plain-carbon steel weld. As a result, cracking will be more likely to occur in the vicinity of the alloy steel weld than in the plain-carbon steel *if they are of equal carbon content.*

Alloying elements tend to make a steel air harden because they increase the time that elapses before the first cementite or ferrite crystal separates from undercooled austenite, as shown schematically in Fig. 230. The alloying elements seem to get in the way of the iron and carbon atoms that otherwise would unite more quickly to form cementite. Then, too, the alloying elements can move only very slowly in crystal changes represented by the transformation of austenite to pearlite. Furthermore, the critical ranges themselves are lowered by many alloying elements, such as manganese and nickel.

If further argument for the unfortunate effect of most alloying elements on weldability is required, it may be mentioned that alloying elements that form carbides, such as vanadium and molybdenum, do not

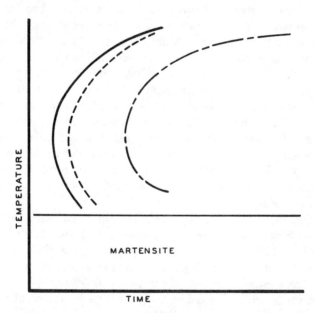

Fig. 230 — Schematic diagram showing that fine grain size tends to prevent the formation of martensite during rapid cooling. Alloying elements generally tend to lower the required cooling rates at which martensite can appear, and hence make it easier for martensite to appear in rapidly cooled steels.

————————————　　Fine-grained, plain-carbon steel
— — — — — — —　　Coarse-grained, plain-carbon steel
——— - ——— - ———　　Alloy steel

dissolve rapidly in austenite except at high temperatures, say above 1800 F. When the carbide is broken down and the alloying element dissolves in the austenite, the element exerts its full effect in producing air hardening. It so happens that until the carbides dissolve, the grains of austenite cannot grow as they normally would. The highly heated zone next to the weld melt therefore has the alloying elements in solution, has coarse grain size, and no longer has small carbide particles that promote inoculation of undercooled austenite. All effects of the alloying element are toward air hardening; that is, to the undercooling of the austenite until a temperature of 200 to 400 F is reached during air cooling. Therefore, martensite and cracks tend to accompany the welding of alloy steel when sufficient carbon is present to produce a hard martensitic structure.

The air-hardening tendency increases with increase in alloy content. For example, a steel containing 0.10% C, 1.5% Mn will be less likely to crack during welding (less air-hardening tendency) than a steel containing 0.30% C, 0.5% Mn, providing the same welding conditions prevail. At the same time, a steel with 0.30% C, 0.5% Mn will be less likely to cause trouble than a steel with 0.30% C, 1.5% Mn. The higher the content of the alloying element at a given carbon content, the greater is the air-hardening tendency.

Hardenability

Hardenability can be defined as the property of a steel that determines the depth and distribution of hardness induced by quenching. Even though we measure *hardness* as part of an evaluation of hardenability, there is no close relationship between the two properties. Hardness was explained in Chapter 6 as resistance to deformation. The maximum obtainable hardness of a given steel was shown (Fig. 219) to occur when a fully martensitic microstructure was formed. Furthermore, the hardness of martensite was governed primarily by the carbon content in both carbon steels and alloy steels. Since martensite forms in steel whenever the critical cooling rate is exceeded, it appears that hardenability is essentially a reflection of the critical cooling rate of the steel and its carbon content.

A simple technique for measuring hardenability is to determine the depth of the martensite (hardened zone) in a round bar of the steel under investigation that has been water quenched under standardized conditions. The cooling rate in a bar of a given diameter during quenching is known to decrease as the center is approached. The cooling rate — a measure of hardenability — corresponding to the boundary of the martensitic zone is expressed by the depth of the martensitic zone, which thus becomes a measure of hardenability. Hence arises the expression *deep-hardening* steel. A steel which hardens deeply forms a thick or deep martensitic zone when quenched in water from above the critical range, whereas a thin zone is secured when a *shallow-hardening* steel of the same diameter is quenched under the same conditions. The deep-hardening steel has a *slower* critical cooling rate than the shallow-hardening steel. Consequently, the austenite of the shallow-hardening steel will transform to ferrite and carbide at cooling rates at which the austenite of the deep-hardening steel will refuse to transform to anything else than martensite.

Another method of measuring hardenability is to heat above the critical range and quench a series of round bars of the same steel, but having progressively larger diameters. Then the bars are sectioned and examined to determine the largest bar which has hardened completely to the center, or perhaps which does not display less than 50% martensite at any point including the center area. Because the cooling rate at the center of the bar decreases as the diameter increases, the larger the bar that will harden completely then the greater is the steel's hardenability. The principal criterion in gauging hardenability is whether a hardened or martensitic structure has been obtained. If the level of hardness is to be taken into consideration, then a hardness traverse customarily is made on an internal cross section in order to plot hardness versus distance from the surface, or, in other words, hardness versus cooling rate.

The most popular kind of hardenability test is that which uses the Jominy specimen. The latter is a 1-inch diameter bar several inches in length which is heated above the steel's critical range and then quenched from one end by directing a stream of water against the end face. The cooling of the cylindrical surface by air is negligible as compared with the cooling accomplished from the end by the impinging water stream. Because the water quench rate is standardized, the cooling rates at specific distances along the length of the bar are always the same and, indeed, have been measured. Obviously, the cooling rate is at a maximum immediately adjacent to the water quenched end and decreases progressively at greater distances from this end. A hardness survey along the length of the bar will give a measure of hardenability of the steel as well as the level of hardness produced by any cooling rate within the limits of the bar. In Chapter 16, a method of correlating weldability and hardenability as determined by the Jominy test bar is discussed.

Hardenability does not mean that the steel can harden to some arbitrary figure, such as 600 Brinell. It signifies rather that the steel can become martensitic, the hardness of which depends almost entirely on the carbon content, Fig. 219. A deep-hardening steel has a greater, higher, or simply deeper hardenability than a shallow-hardening steel, which has the faster critical cooling rate. In welding, the deeper hardening steel will form hard heat-affected zones under less severe conditions than the shallow-hardening steel. For example, the need for preheating increases as the depth of hardening of the steel increases.

The degree of hardenability of a steel depends upon some inhibition of transformation of the austenite of which the steel is composed to the softer ferrite and carbide aggregates. There are two stages in the transformation of steel if it is permitted to proceed in more or less normal fashion to an unhardened microstructure during cooling from the austenitic state, namely, nucleation and growth. During the first stage, no austenite transforms, but the austenite is becoming ready for the appearance of nuclei. Perhaps nuclei form at once but immediately re-dissolve, being too small to live. We know that nuclei form more quickly at any discontinuity in the lattice of the austenite, than in the undistorted lattice itself. Discontinuities occur at grain boundaries and particles of any material that is not austenite, such as slag, oxide, and carbides.

We also know that the addition of elements to austenite generally delays the appearance of nuclei of ferrite or carbide during cooling. Two reasons are offered: (1) The atoms of added elements, which have no prior knowledge about austenite transformation, replace iron atoms to whom austenite transformation is instinct. With unresponsive strangers occupying the place of neighbors, the remaining iron atoms require more time to find other iron atoms with which to undergo mass crystal change to ferrite or carbide. (2) Alloying elements strengthen the austenite and make crystal movement more difficult than in unalloyed iron. Neither reason is completely satisfactory because one alloying element at least, cobalt, hastens the transformation of austenite.

Nucleation then is retarded by: (1) addition of alloying elements, (2) increase in grain size, which decreases the amount of the grain boundaries, and (3) absence of inclusions, particularly tiny ones. If nucleation is effectively suppressed during the cooling of the austenite to a temperature in the vicinity of 800 F, then transformation by nucleation and growth is not likely to occur. Instead, the face-centered cubic structure of austenite attempts to change to the body-centered cubic form by an instantaneous shear-type (martensitic) lattice movement. Again, the propensity for a steel to by-pass the nucleation and growth transformation and resort to the bainite or martensite-producing shear-type transformation is called hardenability. It would simplify matters if we could express quantitatively the influence of such factors as grain size, inclusions, and so forth upon hardenability. Unfortunately, numerical estimates of a foolproof sort cannot be made at present. We can state that from the welding viewpoint the composition of the base metal is more important than the grain size and inclusion factors. The heat-affected zone always is relatively coarse grained in any type of weld, and the presence of inclusions influences the hard zone only if steels of otherwise the same composition are compared.

The main alloying element increasing the hardenability of iron is carbon. Thus, carbon content governs not only the maximum hardness that can be attained by a steel, but the hardenability as well. For example, the critical cooling rate may fall from 2500 degrees F per second for iron containing 0.20% C to 1300 degrees F per second with 0.60% C. Other alloying elements are less influential than carbon. A rough ranking of familiar alloying elements starting with those that exert the strongest effect in lowering the critical cooling rate would be: manganese, molybdenum, chromium, nickel, vanadium, tungsten, and silicon. Many other elements have a measurable effect in increasing the hardenability of steel: phorphorus, copper, nitrogen, boron, columbium, and titanium serving as examples. In the case of columbium and titanium, these elements must be in *solution* in the austenite to promote hardenability. Boron can be added only to a completely deoxidized steel or else the boron will be lost through combination with oxygen. The nitrogen content also must be relatively low; perhaps below about 0.010%, if the boron is not to be tied up as boron nitride and rendered ineffective. Of course, if a greater quantity of nitrogen is present, but is "fixed" in a stable form, such as titanium nitride by virtue of adding a stronger nitride-former, then the boron will be free to impart increased hardenability. Boron is unique in its effect upon hardenability inasmuch as (a) a very small amount, in the order of 0.002%, has a powerful influence, (b) the increased hardenability imparted by boron is not as great in high-carbon steels as found in the low-carbon steels, and (c) high austenitizing temperatures reduce the hardenability effect of boron. Consequently, it is not unusual to find boron used in many of the low-carbon alloy steels used in weldments. Even hydrogen is suspected of increasing hardenability, but this helpful trait is far outweighed by other objectional effects of this element in steel. Cobalt is the only element which will decrease hardenability when present in solution in the austenite. However, cobalt is desirable as an alloying element because of its beneficial influence upon other properties which it exerts through solid-solution effects.

Alloying elements also may reduce hardenability by forming inclusions or carbides difficult to dissolve. Aluminum in steel may form aluminum oxide (alumina), which hastens the transformation of austenite. Molybdenum and vanadium may form complex carbides which, by removing the alloying elements from solid solution in the austenite as well as by acting as inclusions, also hasten austenite transformation. It is possible, for example, that molybdenum carbide is not dissolved during the brief heating period of welding and may hasten austenite transformation during cooling. However, welding experience with molybdenum-containing alloy steels is contrary to this supposition, for they are found to display an increased propensity for hardened heat-affected zones as compared to

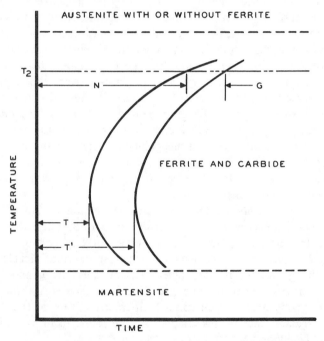

Fig. 231 — The I–T diagram as a basis for estimating hardenability.

T = Least time during which austenite is stable before its transformation sets in (possibly a measure of hardenability)

T' = Least time during which austenite is transformed completely to ferrite and carbide.

N = Nucleation stage. Time during which no nuclei of ferrite or carbide appear in the austenite at temperature T_2. The first nucleus forms at the expiration of the time N. The curve shows that N is different for each temperature at which the specimen is held.

G = Growth stage. Time during which nuclei grow from the austenite. At the expiration of time $N + G$ no austenite remains.

molybdenum-free steels of equivalent carbon content. Presumably, the relatively high temperature reached by the heat-affected zone immediately adjacent to the weld facilitates the solution of even the complex carbides.

The second stage in the process of transformation of austenite remains to be considered, namely, growth. Once the nuclei of ferrite and carbide form in the austenite, they grow in the manner described in Chapters 9 and 14. The time occupied in the growth of the ferrite and carbide, which is the same as the time required, G in Fig. 231, for the austenite to disappear, is important for the formation of hard zones. Austenite may start to transform rapidly, but if it requires a long time to complete its transformation, a large proportion is likely to persist to the temperature at which the remaining austenite changes to martensite. Despite rapid nucleation, the austenite forms hard zones consisting mainly of martensite under gentle cooling conditions. We see that the rate of growth of the nuclei is as important as the time elapsed before the nuclei appear. The rate at which the nucleus grows, expressed as inches of radius per second, is slow at first, because its area of contact with the austenite is small, that is, the grain boundary area. As the nucleus becomes larger, its rate of growth increases; later to decrease as the amount of remaining austenite becomes insignificant. The alloying elements tend to concentrate in the remaining austenite, which, as well as its small surface area, accounts for the decrease in rate of growth of the nuclei in the final stages of transformation.

The same factors tending to retard nucleation of austenite during cooling retard the growth of the ferrite and carbide nuclei to which the austenite transforms. So strong is the effect of large quantities, say 10 percent, of some alloying elements (manganese and nickel) in preventing the growth of ferrite nuclei that the austenite cannot be transformed at any temperature. These are the high-alloy steels which remain partly or wholly austenitic at room temperature. Some of the "Maraging Steels" discussed later in this chapter will be found to display this microstructural behavior.

Using Quantitative Hardenability to Control Welding Procedures

Let us picture a hardened, martensitic heat-affected zone in an alloy steel base metal. We know that the cooling rate here has exceeded the critical cooling rate of this particular steel. We know that the hardness of this zone should correlate closely with the carbon content of the steel, and that in general the toughness of this zone will be poorer as the hardness increases. We also know that the amount of volumetric expansion which took place during transformation of austenite to martensite was strongly affected by carbon content, and that higher carbon contents produce a greater volume increase. This, in turn, increases the severity of residual stresses. All of these facets of hardening must be kept in mind as we use the term hardenability to express the relative rate of cooling that is required to prevent transformation of austenite to anything else than martensite. Assuming that the martensite in our hypothetical case has a level of hardness and toughness which is unsatisfactory, let us see how hardenability can be gauged in order to decide how rapidly the heat-affected zone may be permitted to cool and yet *avoid* the formation of martensite.

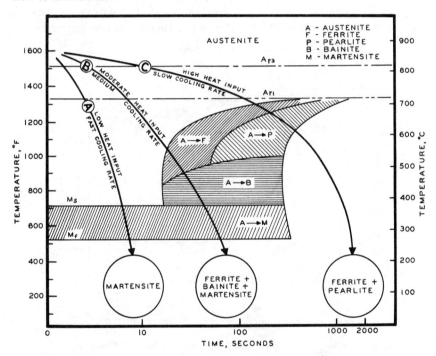

Fig. 232 — Schematic CCT diagram showing how the cooling curves for heat-affected zones for welds made with low, moderate, and high heat input can be plotted to determine the general nature of the microstructure formed with each procedure.

Turning again to the transformation diagram in Fig. 231, the time T might be used to express hardenability quantitatively, except that we know that the time T is not the only decisive factor for preventing the transformation of austenite. Although we may be moved by curiosity to plot a cooling curve for a heat-affected zone on this I–T diagram, it should be recalled from our discussion in Chapter 14 that a CCT diagram (indicating transformation during continuous cooling) is better suited for our purpose. On the schematic CCT diagram in Fig. 232, the continuous cooling curves for three welds made with heat inputs described as low, moderate, and high have been plotted to learn what structure is predicted by the diagram. By noting whether the cooling curves intersect the nose or upper portion of the transformation curve (curves B and C), we can foretell that pearlite will be formed, and can roughly estimate the fineness of the interlamellar spacing. If the cooling curve drops rapidly (see cooling curve A), which naturally is the result of low heat input, it may not intersect the upper transformation curve, but its first intersection will be the M_s line showing that the final structure will be martensite.

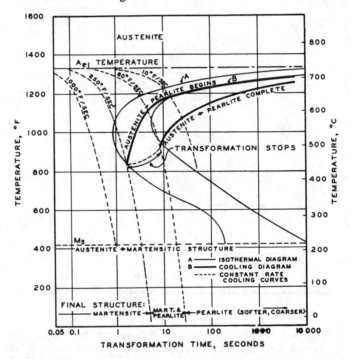

Fig. 233 — Transformation in steel containing 0.85 percent carbon. Curve A for isothermal conditions, previously shown in Fig. 119, has been modified by empirical formula of Grange and Kiefer to produce curve B which illustrates transformation under conditions of continuous cooling at a constant rate.

Although I–T diagrams are available in the literature for a goodly number of types of steels, we are faced with the problem of gauging transformation under constant cooling conditions and only a relatively small number of the CCT diagrams have been prepared. In addition to the direct determination of CCT diagrams, as mentioned in Chapter 14, one team of investigators has proposed a method of modifying the available I–T diagrams by means of an empirical formula to fit constant cooling conditions. Fig. 233 is the familiar I–T diagram for eutectoid steel (0.85% carbon) on which has been superimposed the new curves predicted by the formula to illustrate start and completion of austenite transformation to pearlite under constant cooling conditions. Again, the upper transformation curves are shifted slightly downward and to the right-hand side. As a second example, the diagram for an alloy steel of high hardenability is presented in Fig. 234, and superimposed on this

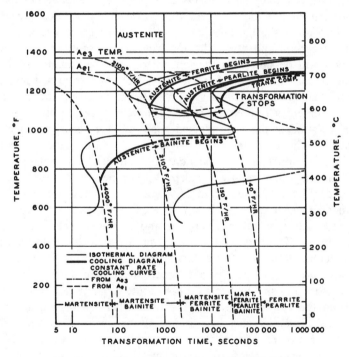

Fig. 234 — Transformation diagrams for SAE 4340 steel.
Curves for continuous cooling at a constant rate (by Grange and Kiefer) is superimposed on curve for isothermal conditions (by Davenport).

diagram is the modified curve showing the transformation as it occurs under conditions of continuous cooling at a constant rate. The original I–T diagram and the new modified form for constant cooling conditions will provide an excellent general picture of the transformation and hardening characteristic of a steel. However, neither of these diagrams can be used for determining, with sufficient accuracy, the critical cooling rate for a steel to be welded so that a particular kind of structure and range of hardness may be secured in the weld heat-affected zone. In the first place, because the data required to plot a C-curve are expensive to prepare, we can find these diagrams only on the more popular steels. The diagrams that can be found are usually based upon the performance of one particular heat of steel which was carefully selected to represent the nominal or typical composition. Variations in austenitic grain size, carbon content, or other alloying elements within the permissible ranges for the type of steel will cause the C-curve to shift. Increasing grain size, carbon content, or other alloying elements that promote hardenability move the upper transformation curves to the right. Conversely, a lower austenitizing temperature or a shorter time can result in finer grain size and a lesser amount of carbon and other alloying elements in solution, and therefore the curves will be shifted to the left. Obviously, we cannot use a typical diagram of this kind which was established by data from a representative piece of steel of the specified type, to predict *precisely* the cooling rate needed to obtain a desired structure in a weld affected zone. The coarse grain size found in the heat-affected zone and the variations in chemical composition which we find from one lot of steel to another have far too much influence on the exact location of the upper transformation curves.

Engineers often inquire whether the hardness and the hardenability of steel can be calculated from its chemical composition, and whether adjustments can be made in an I–T or a CCT diagram according to computations based upon actual grain size and chemical analysis of a specific section of steel. The maximum *hardness* in any area cooled faster than the critical cooling rate has been demonstrated to be predictable, at least to a close approximation, from the carbon content (Fig. 219). It can be added that alloying elements do contribute to some degree to the hardness when the carbon content is low and when quenching is employed for cooling. Some of this hardening can be credited to solid solution hardening. However, the hardness predicted by the curve in Fig. 219 usually is sufficiently close for most metallurgical considerations. However, the *hardenability* of the steel has proved far more difficult to predict because of the many factors in addition to composition which influence this property. These would include the homogeneity of the austenite, the grain size of the austenite, presence of nonmetallic inclusions, and undissolved carbides or other intermetallic compounds or phases. Even where these factors are held in control or are known, the synergistic effect of including small amounts of additional alloying elements so far has thwarted close calculation of hardenability. Nevertheless, the welding engineer must be aware that hardenability is an important property to the metallurgist, who designs high-strength alloy steels, because the best starting point for developing optimum combinations of strength and toughness in a given steel is to first form a martensitic or fine bainitic structure and then, if necessary, temper this structure to decrease the strength to the lowest permissible level in order to gain maximum toughness. From another viewpoint, we have employed the hardenability of the steel to avoid the nucleation-and-growth type of transformation which would have produced relatively coarse grains of ferrite and pearlite. Instead, the austenite is supercooled until a more rapid transformation occurs somewhere beneath the nose of the I–T curve. This could be a transformation to bainite or to martensite. In either case, the grain size is extremely fine and any cementite formed is highly dispersed. With relatively low carbon contents, perhaps below about 0.20%, the toughness of the martensitic and fine bainitic structures is surprisingly good. If reheating to an elevated temperature is possible, that is, in the range of 800 to 1100 F, a still greater measure of toughness can be attained.

The alloy composition of bainite or martensite, aside from carbon content, has little influence upon their strength (as has been repeatedly brought out in terms of hardness). Therefore, we might conclude that the only reason for including alloys in the composition is to insure obtaining bainite or martensite under particular conditions of heat treatment. To a large degree this is true; however, the alloys do contribute other benefits, like increasing resistance to atmospheric corrosion, and improving fracture toughness.

As our review of the high-strength alloy steels proceeds, it will be shown that degrees of hardenability ranging from quite low to very high (air hardening, at least) are incorporated in alloy steels depending upon the condition and section size in which the steel is to develop its expected properties. Some steels are designed with hardenability so low that they do not normally undergo transformation hardening. Instead, they achieve their predicted strength through the other hardening mechanisms; i.e., solid solution, fine grain, and carbide mass and distribution. At the moment, we are concerned with the stronger steels that depend mainly upon transformation hardening for their predicted strength. In these steels, hardenability control is quite important. For example, a particular alloy steel may be designed to have a minimum yield strength of 80 ksi, which it achieves in final form by virtue of having a tempered martensitic structure. If it is anticipated that this steel will be used in sections no thicker than 1 inch, and under heat treatment conditions that involve water quenching or an equivalent cooling rate, then no particular difficulty will be encountered in determining the degree of hardenability required in the steel to insure a martensitic structure throughout the heaviest section in the initially quench-cooled condition. Because of weldability considerations, let us assume that the carbon content of this steel will be limited to approximately 0.20%. For economic reasons, the alloying element additions required to supplement this carbon content should be only large enough to insure martensite formation in a water-quenched section *no thicker than* 1 inch. Should a section of this 80 ksi yield strength steel be desired in 2-inch thickness, then additional alloying element content probably will be required to insure the expected properties; or as a more precise explanation, to insure that martensite will be produced even in the central portion of the 2-inch thick section. Only by starting with a martensitic structure will the tempering operation produce the expected combination of strength and toughness throughout the steel's cross section. Only by having adequate hardenability will the steel form the desired hardened structure throughout its cross section under the stipulated cooling conditions.

One feature of the I–T diagram which has been found relatively easy to calculate is the start of the martensite transformation range. Brief mention was made of this fact in Chapter 9 in connection with carbon steel. The M_s point appears almost entirely dependent upon chemical composition. It is important to know that while the majority of alloying elements lower M_s, a few have no effect, or have an opposite effect. Table 70 contains information on the influence of many of the alloying elements used in steels, and also provides an equation for calculation of the M_s temperature.

The value of I–T and CCT diagrams is unquestioned for gaining an understanding of the approximate temperature ranges over which the important microstructural transformations occur. Even this information is helpful in devising a suitable welding procedure. However, if the degree of hardening which takes place in the heat-affected zone is to be predetermined, it will be necessary to know accurately the structure and level of hardness produced by different rates of cooling, in other words, accurate assessment of quantitative hardenability. It appears that the best way to gather these data is to make a hardenability test using some simple form of test specimen which can be austenitized in a manner similar to a bona fide heat-affected zone, and which permits cooling rates to be precisely correlated with structures and hardnesses. This subject will be discussed further in Chapter 16.

Welding engineers often have expressed a need for a simple system

Table 70 — *INFLUENCE OF ALLOYING ELEMENTS IN STEEL UPON MARTENSITE FORMATION*

I — Qualitative Effects of Alloying Elements on Martensite Formation (M_s) Temperature

Alloying Element	Qualitative Effect
Carbon	Lowers M_s markedly
Manganese	Lowers M_s
Silicon	Virtually no effect
Chromium	Lowers M_s
Nickel	Lowers M_s
Molybdenum	Lowers M_s
Copper	Lowers M_s
Vanadium	Lowers M_s
Tungsten	Lowers M_s
Cobalt	Raises M_s
Aluminum	Raises M_s

II — Calculation of Martensite Formation (M_s) Temperature from Chemical Composition

$$M_s \text{ (deg. F)} = 1000 - 650\,(\%C) - 70\,(\%Mn) - 35\,(\%Ni) - 70\,(\%Cr) - 50\,(\%Mo)$$

This equation is applicable to steels falling within the following composition limits:

Carbon	0.1 — 0.55
Manganese	0.2 — 1.75
Silicon	0.1 — 0.35
Chromium	3.5 max
Nickel	5.0 max
Molybdenum	1.0 max

of classifying the hardenable alloy steels to help indicate the welding precautions required. At least a half-dozen promising systems have been proposed. Some are quite simple, while others are complicated to the point of creating confusion. It can be said that the simpler systems do not take into account all of the factors involved in welding a specific joint, and they tend to apply more precautions than necessary in order to safeguard joints subject to unusual conditions. A favorite starting point for weldability classification systems is to arrange steels into groups as shown in Table 71. Here, the first group contains those steels which are foolproof from a welding standpoint. One might argue that the carbon content of a steel in this group could rise as high as 0.25% and still be trouble free. While this might be true in many instances, we know that if the manganese content is near 1% and the sections being welded are very thick and highly restrained then some care must be exercised. Even the guideline of 0.15% maximum carbon may not be realistic under these joint conditions if all of the alloying elements listed were present in the steel in the maximum quantities shown. In general, steels in Group 1 never develop a hardness in weld heat-affected zones exceeding about

Table 71 — *SUGGESTED SYSTEM FOR CLASSIFICATION OF ALLOY STEELS COMMONLY USED IN WELDMENTS ACCORDING TO WELDABILITY*

(For Purpose of Illustration)

Group	Class	Guide Lines to Importance of Composition	Precautions to be Incorporated in Welding Procedure
1	Trouble-Free	Less Than — C 0.15 Mn 1.00 Cr 0.50 Ni 0.50 Mo 0.50 Cu 0.60	None
2	Weld with Care	Less Than — C 0.30 Mn 1.50 Cr 1.50 Ni 1.50 Mo 1.00	Higher carbon contents and greater base metal thickness will require: 1. Preheat or Low-Hydrogen Arc Atmosphere 2. Postheat Treatment for Best Service Performance
3	Special Welding Procedure	Less Than — C 0.55 Mn 2.00 Cr 6.00 Ni 3.00 Mo 1.50	For all Sections: 1. Preheat 2. Low-Hydrogen Arc Atmosphere 3. Controlled Heat Input 4. Maintain High Interpass Temperature 5. Postheat Treatment

200 BHN because of the carbon limit of 0.15% and the limited hardenability which the carbon and other alloying elements impart. The steels which fall in Group 2 are those which may contain adequate alloy content to cause hardening (martensite) in the heat-affected zones. Here, the carbon content must be considered very carefully. If the carbon content is below 0.20%, the formation of martensite would not be cause for concern since a relatively low-carbon martensite is not brittle. With carbon in the range of 0.20 to 0.25%, however, a martensitic heat-affected zone may be a source of trouble. Cold cracking (underbead) may occur; particularly if hydrogen was introduced during welding and if the section is extremely thick and causes the zone to become highly stressed. With carbon contents over 0.25%, martensitic heat-affected zones are deserving

of care and attention. A low-hydrogen welding arc, or preheating, usually is a necessary precaution to prevent underbead cracking. Of course, if the alloy content of the steel is inadequate to cause martensite to form in the heat-affected zone under the particular weld cooling rate, then carbon contents as high as 0.30% and even beyond, will not be as likely to cause underbead cold cracking. The steels in Group 3 exhibit dangerously low ductility in heat-affected zones. In addition to being prone to underbead cracking, the heat-affected zones (untempered) may not have sufficient toughness for reliable service. Consequently, special welding procedures which may entail five specific precautions as outlined in Table 71 are required. These are preheating, the use of a low-hydrogen arc, controlled heat input to secure slow cooling rate, maintaining a high interpass temperature, and postweld heat treatment.

COLD WORK HARDENING

Occasionally, alloy steel is encountered which has been strengthened or hardened by cold rolling, cold drawing, or some cold working process. The hardening of steel by these processes was described in Chapter 6, and the structure of cold worked iron illustrated in Fig. 76. Cold working to obtain a significant increase in strength is most often carried out on bars, wire, and thin sheet. Seldom is plate of any substantial thickness cold rolled to increase strength, purely for reason of mechanical equipment limitations. The alloy content of steel plays a minor role in the work hardening rate of a "ferritic" microstructure as compared with an austenitic microstructure found in high-alloy steels. It has been pointed out on several occasions that the heat of any fusion welding operation is sufficient to remove the effects of cold working in the zone immediately adjacent to the weld. Consequently, the welding engineer must be prepared to accept a loss of strength in these areas which usually is irreplaceable.

MAR-STRAIN RESPONSE

When a small amount of plastic strain is imparted in certain alloy steels which have been previously quenched-and-tempered, a re-tempering treatment can raise the yield point of the steel significantly. Several metallurgical phenomena appear to be responsible for this strengthening effect. They can be briefly described as (1) substructure formation, (2) dislocation pinning, and (3) further carbide precipitation and dispersion. To appreciate the interaction of these mechanisms, it is necessary to picture the tempering of martensite in greater detail than described in Chapter 12.

When medium-carbon martensite (solid solution of carbon in body-centered tetragonal iron) is subjected to increasing tempering temperatures, the following important decomposition steps are believed to occur:

At Temperatures Up to About 600 F

A first stage of tempering occurs in which metastable carbide (epsilon carbide, $Fe_{2.4}C$) precipitates from the lattice leaving approximately 0.25% carbon in solution.

A second stage then commences, particularly at temperatures approaching 600 F, during which the low-carbon martensite continues to precipitate carbon from solution and the lattice proceeds to the body-centered cubic (ferrite) form. The precipitated particles now decompose to cementite (Fe_3C).

At Temperatures Above About 600 F

Following closely behind, or in conjunction with the formation of cementite particles, complex carbides and other compounds are precipitated in the lattice.

As the tempering temperature is increased, the precipitated particles of cementite and other compounds agglomerate and eventually reach a size that permits observation by microscopy.

When martensite is strained and re-tempered, a noticeable change can be observed in the distribution of carbide particles in certain steels. Additional particles of finer size appear to be highly dispersed in the matrix. This change can be caused by the precipitation of additional carbides during tempering which were not precipitated during the initial tempering operation, or could be the result of re-solution of some of the originally precipitated carbides with subsequent migration to the strained areas in the lattice and re-precipitation at substructure sites. In either event, the newly-precipitated carbides appear to be located at dislocation sites introduced during pre-straining. They effectively discourage further movement of these dislocations under stress until the prestraining stress has been exceeded. The strengthening of steel by mar-straining and re-tempering is dependent, therefore, upon (a) the strain hardening characteristics, which determine the increase in yield strength and dislocation density brought about by pre-straining, and (b) the response of the steel through the mechanisms described above during the re-tempering operation. Steels vary greatly in their mar-strain response. It is an important characteristic in the heat treatable alloy steels to be described later. Both the alloy composition and the microstructure of the hardened and tempered steels have a strong influence upon the strength that can be realized through mar-straining treatment.

TOUGHNESS OF ALLOY STEEL WELDMENTS

Because correct utilization of higher-strength steels almost always involves higher unit working stresses, the amount of elastic energy stored in the weldment is greater than in one constructed of steel of lower strength capability. Consequently, there is a greater need for toughness; that is, resistance to crack propagation in the steels employed for higher-strength weldments. Fortunately, the alloying of steel and attendant alloy steel-making practices often result in better fracture toughness than is exhibited by carbon steel. However, this benefit cannot be assumed adequate for every weldment or every service because alloy steels, in general, are more likely to be adversely affected with respect to fracture toughness when fabricated into a weldment.

Estimating the likelihood of brittle fracture in an alloy steel weldment is considerably more complicated than determining the toughness of base metal as discussed in Chapter 6. Each weld joint presents a variety of microstructures, in the weld metal, heat-affected areas, and unaffected base metal. Depending upon the welding process employed and the final condition, these structures may range from soft annealed forms to the hardened (martensitic) form. Furthermore, residual stresses and reaction stresses may be present in the weldment in addition to the service loads imposed. Hydrogen may have been inadvertently introduced into the weld metal and heat-affected zone with its attendant embrittlement. While postweld inspection or nondestructive testing will seek out most defects, it would be unrealistic to believe that any weld is *completely* free of minute internal flaws or cracks. The manner in which these defects escape detection and enter into the complex mechanism of fracture propagation was discussed in Chapter 13. Here, however, we shall review the factors in alloy steel which play a part in establishing the fracture toughness of weldments. Proper control of these factors will greatly improve toughness capability, even under conditions of high loading rates, multiaxial stresses, and low temperatures.

Influence of Alloying Elements

It is not possible to closely predict the fracture toughness of a steel by appraisal of chemical composition. To date, research has determined only the qualitative effects of the commonly used alloying elements. Little is known about the synergistic effect of multiple alloying additions and the influence of residual elements. In general, the observed effects of alloys appear to depend upon the form and condition of the steel; that is, whether the form is weld metal, cast base metal, or wrought, and whether pearlitic, bainitic, or martensitic. Of all the alloying elements used in steel, *carbon* exerts the greatest influence upon fracture toughness. The explanation for this strong relationship appears to lie in the microstructure where carbon plays a leading role in determining the amount of carbides in the ferritic matrix. Increasing carbon content, in general, acts to decrease toughness. However, the net effect of carbon is highly dependent upon the manner in which the carbide is distributed in the matrix. Finely dispersed carbides, as found in fine bainite or in tempered martensite, will provide optimum toughness at a given carbon level. The addition of alloying elements which affect carbide composition, i.e., carbide-formers, appear to have little influence upon fracture toughness unless they change the carbide size and form. Elements which promote massive carbides tend to decrease fracture toughness.

Alloying elements other than carbon appear to influence fracture toughness principally through their effects upon the ferritic matrix. It is well established that the simple ferrite grain structure undergoes a ductile-to-brittle toughness transition as conditions of temperature, rate of loading, or multiaxiality of stress become more severe. The occurrence of this transition is dependent upon the amount and kind of alloying elements dissolved in the ferrite grains. While it is assumed that these same effects are in force when the alloying elements are present in steels having a pearlitic, bainitic, or martensitic structure, their influence is augmented or counteracted by other factors like carbide distribution and grain size, and therefore the benefit derived from individual alloys as part of a multiple alloy addition is difficult to assess. Much research has been conducted on the influence of alloying additions on the toughness of steel. Many studies in the past have used the 15 ft-lb transition temperature in the Charpy-V impact test as the criterion for fracture toughness. More recent work, however, makes use of the NDT test (see Chapter 16) as an attempt to evaluate the fracture toughness of steel in the *weld heat-affected* condition. The complexity of the subject has spawned reams of literature on the fracture toughness of steel, particularly the transition temperature for fracture mode and for energy absorption. While some disagreement exists between the studies reported, the general conclusions usually reached on the effects of alloying elements are those summarized in Table 72.

Two alloying elements have a powerful adverse influence on the fracture toughness of steel; that is, they have been found to markedly raise the fracture-transition temperature. These elements are carbon and phosphorus. Of the two, phosphorus is the more harmful on a percentage basis. Investigators have attempted to express the influence of these and other alloying elements quantitatively. However, these quantitative expres-

Table 72 — *INFLUENCE OF ALLOYING ELEMENTS UPON FRACTURE TOUGHNESS OF STEEL*

Qualitative Effect as Judged from Individual Additions of Elements Over Indicated Ranges

Alloying Element	Range, %	Expected Influence on Fracture Toughness
Carbon	0 to 0.4	Marked decrease
Manganese	0.2 to 2.0	Mild increase
Phosphorus	0.01 to 0.07	Very marked decrease
Sulfur	0.01 to 0.05	Very small decrease
	0.05 to 0.15	Moderate decrease
Silicon	0.1 to 0.5	Small increase
	0.5 to 1.5	Moderate decrease
Chromium	0 to 0.5	No significant influence
	0.5 to 1.0	Small decrease
Nickel	0 to 3.0	Moderate increase
Molybdenum	0 to 0.5	Small decrease
Copper	0 to 2.0	Small increase
Vanadium	0 to 0.15	Small decrease
Titanium	0 to 0.4	Moderate increase
Aluminum	0 to 0.05	Very small increase
	0.5 to 0.1	No further influence
Boron	0 to 0.004	Small decrease
Nitrogen	0.005 to 0.04	Small decrease
Hydrogen	0 to 0.003	Significant decrease
Oxygen	0 to 0.12	Small decrease

sions apply only to very restricted types of steel and in particular forms and conditions. Any use of the values to compare unlike forms or conditions usually is unsuccessful because of the strong effects of grain size, carbide distribution, and other factors. Therefore, the information in Table 72 for alloy steels is intended to be qualitative.

Other alloying elements which exert an adverse effect upon toughness, but to a lesser degree than carbon or phosphorus, are sulfur, molybdenum, vanadium, boron, and nitrogen. Sulfur is looked upon as a residual element unless the steel has been resulfurized to aid machinability. Below about 0.05%, sulfur has little influence upon the toughness of alloy steels of low and medium strength. However, at high strength levels, perhaps in excess of 200 ksi tensile strength, even residual sulfur has a significant influence upon toughness. In resulfurized steel (above 0.05%), the loss in toughness is especially apparent when wrought steel is stressed normal to the rolling direction. The increased number of sulfide inclusions imparts a pronounced directionality to steel, and in this manner decreases the transverse toughness. The manner in which molybdenum, vanadium, boron and nitrogen adversely affect toughness is not well understood. Silicon in amounts up to about 0.5% appears to improve toughness, possibly because of its ability to tie up oxygen in a stable form. However, silicon above 0.5%, which exceeds the amount required for deoxidation purposes, causes toughness to decrease.

None of the alloying elements regularly used in steel have a particularly strong ability to improve fracture toughness. Nickel is the best element found to date, and steels for low-temperature service may contain as much as 9% of this element. The majority of steels intended to have good toughness are developed by multiple alloy additions. Manganese and titanium provide some improvement in most alloy steels. Aluminum in amounts up to about 0.05% appears to assist toughness, but above this level the element seems to be ineffective. Copper promotes a small increase in toughness providing the steel is not given a subcritical heat treatment where a copper precipitate is formed.

Influence of Grain Size

Fine grain size is an important contributing factor to good fracture toughness; both in weld metal and in base metal. This partly accounts for the good toughness of bainitic and tempered martensitic structures. Fine grain size has a measurable benefit in pearlitic-ferritic structures. In certain low strength steels, the 15 ft-lb Charpy-V transition temperature can be lowered by as much as 30 degrees F for each unit increase in ASTM grain size number. A growing appreciation of this benefit of fine grain in the microstructure has increased the use of (a) fine grain steelmaking practice, (b) the addition of alloying elements (columbium, vanadium, or nitrogen) which act to form fine grained ferritic structures, and (c) low finishing temperatures and accelerated cooling after hot rolling to secure a fine grain size as-rolled. Note that even though vanadium and nitrogen have been cited in Table 72 as elements which tend to promote a small *decrease* in toughness, if these elements are employed effectively to secure a fine grain size their net effect is to *increase* toughness.

Influence of Condition or Heat Treatment

Proper heat treatment of cast or of wrought (hot rolled or forged) alloy steel can be very effective in increasing fracture toughness. The object of heat treatment should be to secure a fine grain size and the finest possible distribution of carbide in the microstructure. In pearlitic steels, a normalizing treatment is commonly used to produce a fine ferrite grain size and fine lamellar pearlite. Of course, if a wrought steel has been finished at a low temperature to obtain a fine grain size, then a subsequent normalizing treatment may not produce any real improvement in toughness. The heat-affected zones of fusion welds may require consideration because here the grain size may be coarsened in a narrow zone by the high temperature reached immediately adjacent to the weld zone.

Quenching and tempering probably is the most effective heat treatment for improving toughness, particularly if the steel can be quenched to fine bainite or martensite. The subsequent tempering operation then can remove the internal stresses associated with these microstructures, lower the hardness if necessary by permitting precipitation and some agglomeration of carbide particles, and obtain the microstructural condition which appears to possess optimum toughness for a given alloy composition.

Other Factors Influencing Toughness

The fracture toughness of alloy steel can be affected by at least a half-dozen additional factors, any one of which can be a major factor in a particular weldment. *Directionality,* or anisotropy, is a condition which may detrimentally affect the steel only when stressed on one or two of the three major axes. Directionality can be caused by (1) numerous stringer-like nonmetallic inclusions, (2) banding of constituents in the microstructure, and (3) segregation of alloying elements into bands or localized zones. Directionality is more likely to be observed in wrought steel, particularly that which has been rolled in one direction. However, cast steel and weld metal which display strong columniation in their grain structure also can be quite directional in mechanical and physical properties. When steel with pronounced directionality is stressed transverse to the rolling axis, the mechanical behavior may be much like a piece of wood or timber which, when stressed across its grain, tends to split or crack because of the relatively easy separation of the grain laminations. Highly directional steel tends to fracture early when bent in the same manner. This early fracture (lower toughness in transverse loading) is apt to be more important in high-strength steels, and particularly in thick material where banding and segregation tend to be more acute. It behooves the designer to avoid high loads on directional steels along the transverse axis. However, the designer sometimes cannot avoid the development of residual or reaction stresses from welding in the transverse direction, and these stresses may find the transverse toughness of the steel inadequate to prevent fracture initiation and propagation.

Cold working of steel tends to lower fracture toughness; particularly if this operation is followed by exposure to elevated temperatures — perhaps in the range of 500 to 800 F. The phenomenon which occurs often is called "strain aging." This term is, of course, erroneous because the embrittlement which occurs will not develop further in the strained steel while *aging* at room temperature. Since an elevated temperature is required, the damage to toughness appears attributable to a strain-induced precipitation-hardening mechanism. This kind of damage to toughness also is more likely to be encountered in the higher strength alloy steels. The "strain-aging" susceptibility of steel must be kept in mind because weldments sometimes are fabricated from cold formed components. The heat of welding alone may be sufficient to lower the toughness in strained areas. Preheating a weldment of this kind would, of course, be a greater threat to toughness. Consequently, consideration possibly should be given to heat treatment of the formed parts to remove the cold work effect, or postweld treatment of the finished weldment at a temperature well above the precipitation-hardening (aging) range.

Most steels, and the alloy steels are no exception, tend to decrease in fracture toughness as the section size or thickness increases. This has been a particularly troublesome tendency because many times preliminary tests are carried out on subsize, prototype weldments. Later, when the actual weldment to be employed in service is scaled up in all dimensions (including thickness), the steel in the weldment probably will not have the same level of toughness as the prototype. Furthermore, the size of internal defects in the heavier weld joints, which go undetected or are deemed tolerable, also may be larger than in the prototype. Consequently, the full-size weldment may be prone to brittle failure because the applied load is concentrated at a defect which exceeds the critical size and a running crack will propagate across the section.

Finally, it should be pointed out that, as a general rule, increasing strength in alloy steels results in decreasing fracture toughness — at least in the types of steels which have been developed in the past. However, with fracture toughness now recognized as a highly important criterion of performance, we have every reason to expect that steels of the future will be improved in this respect and probably will display better toughness at given levels of strength. Some progress in this direction will be noted as the various kinds of alloy steel are discussed.

Temper Brittleness

A brief explanation will be given here of a metallurgical phenomenon which can seriously affect the fracture toughness of alloy steels, and which will be pointed out later to occur in postweld stress-relieved weldments, particularly in certain alloy steel weld metals. Temper brittleness may be found to have occurred in steel after heating in the temperature range of approximately 900 to 1250 F. The strength and hardness of the steel does not increase significantly during the embrittlement, but toughness, as might be measured by notched-bar impact testing, will be markedly decreased at all temperatures of testing. The embrittlement is time dependent and becomes more severe with prolonged exposure at elevated temperature. The temperature at which embrittlement occurs most rapidly varies with different steels. The mechanism by which the steel becomes embrittled upon tempering is not understood, although the presence of certain alloying and residual elements is known to promote temper brittleness.

A steel which has become temper brittle tends to fracture intergranularly. Under metallographic examination, this steel often will etch heavily along the prior austenite grain boundaries of the microstructure. For many years, temper brittleness was suspected to be promoted by alloying elements, such as vanadium, because they encouraged the formation of complex carbides in the structure. However, this hypothesis does not explain all of the characteristics of temper brittleness. The presence of residual elements, such as phosphorus, silicon, antimony, tin, and arsenic, has been shown to promote temper brittleness. Furthermore, small amounts of molybdenum, a strong carbide former, appears to retard temper brittleness. Although temper-embrittled steel can have toughness restored by heating above the embrittlement temperature range and cooling rapidly, this is a treatment which is seldom convenient to apply. Therefore, the welding engineer must be alert to anticipate strong susceptibility to temper brittleness by any of the base metals or weld metals incorporated in a weldment whenever postweld stress-relief heat treatment is to be applied.

CRACKING DURING WELDING

Although cracking was covered as a welding defect in considerable detail in Chapter 13, there is good reason to give this subject further attention here. Cracking during welding has been classified as (1) hot cracking and (2) cold cracking. Both forms were shown to occur in (a) the weld metal, and (b) the base metal heat-affected zone. The occurrence of hot cracking and cold cracking in weld metal as influenced by alloy composition was described in Chapter 10 on filler metals. The behavior of base metal heat-affected zones with respect to cracking deserves further discussion because of unusual recent findings concerning the high-strength alloy steels.

Hot Cracking in Base Metal Heat-Affected Zone

Hot cracking in the base metal heat-affected zone, for many years, was very seldom observed in carbon or low-alloy steels. With the advent of weldable alloy steels having yield strengths of about 80 ksi and higher, hot cracking in this area has proved to be more of a problem. Of greater importance, there is strong evidence that the occurrence of cold cracking in the heat-affected zone of the higher-strength alloy steels may have been actually triggered by the formation of hot cracks. The high-temperature form of cracking may have initiated only to a small extent, but this defect apparently can propagate extensively as cold cracking when the heat-affected zone cools and internal stresses develop as the structure undergoes transformation. Identification of hot cracking at the point of initiation of heat-affected zone cracking can be quite difficult. Yet, its occurrence may provide a very logical explanation for cold cracking that occurs under welding conditions normally considered adequate to avoid the low-temperature form of cracking. More important, ignorance of the true cause of heat-affected zone cracking might allow the application of an improper remedy on subsequent weldments. For example, bona fide cold cracking can be prevented by preheating. However, if hot cracking is the actual initiator, the use of preheating might aggravate the over-all problem rather than eliminate it.

Hot cracking in the heat-affected zone invariably is intergranular, and the majority of investigators of this defect agree the boundary separation is a result of liquation. It appears that certain alloys in the steel foster the segregation of fusible or low melting compounds in the grain boundaries. During the weld thermal cycle, the base metal immediately adjacent to the weld is heated and two key changes are set in motion. First, this zone is forced to upset because its expansion to match the temperature rise is constrained by adjacent metal at a lower temperature. Second, the boundaries which contain the fusible segregate develop a molten film. When the welding heat-source moves away and the heat-affected zone commences to cool, a tensile stress immediately begins to develop in the metal because of the earlier upsetting. At some point in the cooling, the molten film in the grain boundaries will again solidify. The all-important question is — will the boundaries become solid early enough to sustain the slowly developing contraction stresses? Or, will the boundaries still have an appreciable film of liquid or merely a very weak solid that is easily ruptured by the contraction stresses. Obviously, the state of the grain boundaries and their ability to cope with the cooling stresses depend upon the exact nature and amount of the compounds that are segregated here.

Sulfur has been singled out by a number of investigators as the most offensive element in this hot cracking problem. Moreover, the role of other alloying elements which seem to affect susceptibility to hot cracking appears to be mainly one of aiding, or of counteracting, the sulfur. Carbon and phosphorus are particularly malicious in their support of sulfur in causing hot cracking. Sulfur appears to exert its harmful effect through the sulfide inclusions in which it exists in the steel. In some flagrant cases of cracking, the sulfide inclusions could be clearly observed in the grain boundaries where high-temperature rupture had occurred. More often, the sulfur content was quite low and relatively few sulfide inclusions could be seen, yet the cracking susceptibility of the steels could be directly correlated with sulfur content. As shown in Fig. 235, if the sulfur content of a high-strength alloy steel is allowed to approach the permissible maximum of 0.04%, this steel would be likely to display a very high susceptibility to hot cracking in the heat-affected zone when welded under conditions of high restraint. To eliminate virtually all susceptibility to hot cracking, the sulfur content must be reduced below

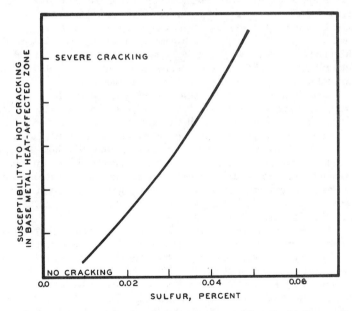

Fig. 235 — Typical effect of sulfur on susceptibility of a high-strength alloy steel (e.g., AISI 4340) to hot cracking in base metal heat-affected zone of highly restrained weld test specimen.

approximately 0.01%. Furthermore, this low sulfur content should be accompanied by an equally low phorphorus content; that is, the combined phorphorus and sulfur contents of AISI 4340 steel should not exceed 0.02% to reduce the cracking sensitivity in a highly restrained test to zero.

The other elements present in an alloy steel affect hot cracking susceptibility in the following manner:

Carbon increases cracking tendency appreciably. Carbon has been shown to promote interdendritic segregation of sulfur which increases the likelihood of concentrating lower-melting compounds in grain boundary areas. Decreasing the carbon content, even by decarburization, reduces the hot cracking tendency. An annealing treatment which produces spheroidized carbide particles also tends to reduce cracking propensity; apparently because the short austenitizing time in welding does not dissolve all the globular particles. Therefore, the actual carbon content in the matrix is lower than the over-all carbon analysis for the steel.

Manganese has been found to counteract the effect of sulfur with respect to hot cracking tendency. This benefit is believed to arise from the strong tendency of manganese to form stable, higher melting point sulfides in steel. Rather than attempt to use large manganese additions as a cure-all, however, most steel makers attempt to reduce hot cracking tendency through reduction of sulfur content.

Phosphorus already has been cited as a strong promoter of hot cracking. It appears to act in this manner by increasing the segregation of sulphur and carbon in the steel — to the point where banding of the sulfide inclusions and carbide particles can be observed in the microstructure of wrought material. This banded condition greatly increases the likelihood of hot cracking, and if the banding of carbon is particularly marked, these localized areas of high carbon may be particularly prone to cold cracking as a continuation of the hot cracks.

Silicon is believed to cause sulfur to segregate, and in this manner is likely to increase hot cracking. Ordinarily, silicon does not have a marked effect on hot cracking susceptibility because less than ½% usually is present in high-strength alloy steels and the content varies over a relatively narrow range. However, some of the very high strength (heat-treatable) alloy steels to be described later make use of silicon contents above 1% because this element inhibits softening during tempering in certain temperature ranges. These steels usually are made with very low sulfur content to avoid undue segregation which might be promoted by the high silicon content.

Chromium, molybdenum, and *vanadium* are believed to have a mild beneficial effect upon hot cracking; particularly if a high carbon content is present to aggravate the problem. These elements possibly tie up some carbon as complex carbides thus reducing cracking susceptibility by lowering the effective carbon. *Nickel* exerts an adverse effect upon hot cracking tendency. Its effect is particularly noticeable when significant sulfur also is present. Presumably, the presence of nickel affects the composition of sulfides formed in the grain boundaries. *Aluminum* is another element that seems to influence the composition and distribution of sulfide inclusions. Residual aluminum in the range of about 0.02/0.06% appears to foster intergranular sulfides which noticeably increases cracking susceptibility.

Although investigators have attempted to weigh the effect of various elements on hot cracking, little quantitative data have been secured. It is not surprising that the degree of restraint upon the joint, the heat input of the welding process, and other welding factors all exert significant effects which complicate the cracking problem. Therefore, most knowledge of the hot cracking susceptibility of specific types of steels is secured from welding tests (described in Chapter 16), and from experience in fabricating weldments.

Cold Cracking in Base Metal Heat-Affected Zone

Cold cracking in the heat-affected zone of base metal has been long recognized as a problem in welding hardenable steels. In describing this defect in Chapter 13, the principal factors which controlled its occurrence were pointed out as (1) the formation of the hardened *martensitic* structure with its limited toughness, (2) the development of multiaxial stresses from reaction to contraction under restraint and volume changes during microstructural transformation, and (3) embrittlement by hydrogen which can be picked up in the weld metal and then can diffuse into the heat-affected zones. Hydrogen appears to be the most powerful factor in promoting cold cracking in the base metal heat-affected zones. The finding discussed earlier that cold cracking also can be initiated by hot cracking in the zone immediately adjacent to the weld probably will help explain some of the puzzling cases of cold cracking which have occurred with seemingly safe welding conditions. However, let us concentrate at this point on bona fide cold cracking and the properties of alloy steel which control its occurrence in welding.

Alloy content obviously must be important in connection with the cold cracking problem because the amount and kind of alloying elements exert major control over the formation of martensite. However, if the role of alloys is examined closely, at least three aspects of martensite formation will be found to exert an important influence on the initiation of cold cracks: First, as the amount of alloying elements (including carbon) increases and causes higher hardness levels in the hardened heat-affected zones, the likelihood of underbead cold cracking becomes greater. The first real danger of cold cracking will arise when a hardness level of approximately 30-C Rockwell develops in the heat-affected zones. The susceptibility to cracking increases steadily as the hardness of the martensitic structure rises, and, at hardness levels of about 45-C Rockwell and above, the danger of cracking is acute with ordinary welding procedures. The second important aspect of alloy content is the temperature at which the transformation of austenite to martensite starts and is completed in the heat-affected zone; these temperatures being identified as the M_s point and M_f point, respectively, on I–T and CCT diagrams. Considering that a sharp decrease in the solubility of hydrogen occurs as the structure transforms to martensite, it is quite understandable that higher martensite formation temperatures reduce susceptibility to cold cracking by providing some opportunity for hydrogen to diffuse out of the heat-affected zone. The transformation at higher temperatures also may allow some tempering of the martensite to occur — which, of course, acts to reduce hardness and lower the residual stresses. The various alloying elements exert different effects upon the temperature of martensite formation. Generally, alloying elements act to lower the M_s and M_f temperatures as pointed out in Table 70. However, little data is available to indicate the extent to which the entire martensite formation range is lowered by alloy additions; particularly when simultaneous additions are made of a number of alloys. Most of the information deals with specific types of steels. Nevertheless, experience in welding these alloy steels indicates that if the transformation of martensite in the heat-affected zones is completed before a temperature of about 500 F is reached upon cooling, the welded joint is not likely to develop cold cracking. However, it is not unusual for certain alloy steels to display an M_f temperature appreciably below 500 F. In fact, some of the richly alloyed steels have an abnormal characteristic which constitutes the third important aspect of transformation from austenite to martensite; namely, the retention of small amounts of austenite to unusually low temperatures before transformation takes place. These small areas of retained austenite can be pictured as reservoirs for hydrogen. Their ability to hold the hydrogen is suddenly decreased by transformation at a low temperature where its effect is most distressing.

These general remarks about the role of alloys with respect to cold cracking in weld heat-affected zones apply equally well to thermal cutting, chamfering, and gouging. Even though these operations ordinarily produce a narrower heat-affected zone than does welding, this zone also may display susceptibility to cold cracking. The most effective assurances against cracking are the same as for welding; namely, preheating, and in extreme situations, preheat plus post-operation heat treatment.

PICKUP AND DILUTION OF ALLOYS DURING WELDING

Pickup and *dilution* are terms frequently used in discussing the welding of alloy steels, but no standard definition is provided for them in the welding literature. They have opposite meanings, and yet engineers frequently make the mistake of using them interchangeably. For reasons soon to be pointed out, their proper use is becoming increasingly important.

Pickup

Pickup can be defined as an addition or increase in any alloying element in a weld deposit by virtue of melting and incorporating some of the base metal. It is true that when we make a weld without the use of a filler rod, the weld melt may pick up gases. However, the more usual sense of the term *pickup* relates to the welding of an alloy steel with a filler metal of a lower-alloy dissimilar steel. For example, suppose we weld 3 percent nickel steel with a nickel-free, plain-carbon steel filler rod. The operator melts the filler rod into the groove faces, but also melts a little of the base metal in order to insure a perfect joint. The mixture of base metal with filler metal which forms the weld melt, therefore, contains some nickel, perhaps 1 percent. In a multi-layer weld, the first beads naturally *pick up* the greatest amount of alloying elements from the base metal.

Since alloying elements may pass from the base metal to weld melt, it might be supposed mistakenly that alloying elements also might pass from the weld to the base metal. The two situations are not identical. The weld melt picks up alloying elements from base metal because the latter is melted into the weld. The alloying element itself is not abstracted from the base metal; the alloying element and all other elements in the melted region are stirred into the agitated puddle. On the other hand, for alloying elements to pass from the weld melt to base metal they must enter and pass through the crystals of the solid base metal. The passage of alloying elements through crystals of steel even at high temperatures is extremely slow, as the slow processes of nitriding and case carburizing bear witness.

Penetration of the fused area into the base metal also controls alloy pickup in the weld metal. The extent of penetration varies somewhat with the different fusion joining processes, and generally can be controlled in each process over a reasonable range. In many cases of welding alloy steels, the pickup of alloy by the weld metal deposit is anticipated, and is expected to help impart certain properties to the weld metal. The pickup of alloy by the weld metal may increase its strength to the prescribed level, or may increase its corrosion resistance. In discussing the welding of specific types of alloy steels later, particularly the high-strength alloy steels, examples will be given where lower-alloy filler metals are employed for welding. Yet, the weld metal is equal to the base metal in strength. While this may be attributable in part to the characteristically higher strength of weld metal (see Chapter 10), some part probably is the result of alloy pickup in the weld metal.

Dilution

Dilution may be defined as the reduction in alloy content of a weld deposit by virtue of melting and incorporating melted base metal of *lower* alloy content. Dilution is commonly discussed as the percent of base metal which has entered into the weld metal. If the chemical composition of the filler metal being deposited is known, and the composition of the base metal or metals is known, then by knowing the percent dilution we can easily calculate the weld metal composition. Dilution, or conversely, alloy pickup, can markedly change the actual composition of weld metal from that reported for an undiluted deposit. From the metallurgical standpoint, the mixing of base metal with metal from the filler rod is most important in governing the composition of the metal constituting the weld. The extent of the mixing is quoted as the percentage of the entire cross section of the weld metal revealed by a macrograph that falls within the outlines of the base metal before welding. To measure the percentage, a cut is made through the weld perpendicular to both the direction of welding and the surface of the plates. The cut section is polished roughly with abrasive paper and is etched with acid, which reveals the boundary of the metal that has been melted during welding; that is, the junction between the weld and base metal.

Sections through several types of welds are shown in Fig. 236. The percentage of the entire cross section of weld metal falling within the initial outlines of base metal, which we call the *dilution percentage,* is:

$$\% \text{ Dilution} = \frac{B + D}{A + B + C + D} \times 100$$

as illustrated in Fig. 236(b). The dilution percentage is high for welds on thin sheet, Fig. 236(a), for which little filler rod is required. Of course, if no filler metal is added, we have made an *autogenous* weld in which the weld metal is self-generated by the base metal. The dilution percentage is 100%; in which case the weld composition can be essentially the same as that of the base metal. With beveled groove faces in thicker plate, Fig. 236(b) and (c), the dilution may be as low as 20%. The dilution percentage is approximately 25% in Fig. 236(d) and 65% in (e).

Depositing the same electrode under identical conditions of current and speed will yield a higher penetration on thin plate, Fig. 236(f), than

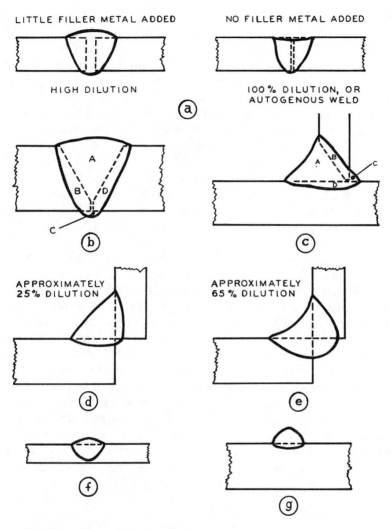

Fig. 236 — Determining the dilution percentage.

(a) Unbeveled butt weld

(b) V-butt weld, penetration percentage $= \dfrac{B + D}{A + B + C + D} \times 100$

(c) Single bevel Tee joint
(d) Low penetration percentage
(e) High penetration percentage
(f) Bead penetrating into sheet
(g) Bead of same size barely penetrating below surface of a thick plate

on thick plate, (g); the reason for which was explained in Chapter 4. Ordinarily, the dilution percentage increases with the melting point of the electrode. Thus the dilution percentage will be nearly zero for a bronze electrode (melting point 1475 F) deposited on low-carbon steel, but will be high for a low-carbon steel electrode. A low-carbon steel electrode will exhibit a higher penetration on cast iron (melting point 2100 to 2200 F) than on steel (melting point 2750 F) under the same conditions of deposition. Dilution percentage is higher for neutral flame technique than for carburizing flame technique in the oxyacetylene welding of steel.

It used to be a general rule in welding that the weld metal should have as nearly as possible the same composition as the base metal. As explained in Chapter 10, no longer does the rule apply, except possibly for unusual applications where galvanic corrosion is a factor of great importance. Bronze and nickel often are used as filler metals for welding cast iron. Where corrosion is a factor, it is wise to have a weld metal of approximately the same composition as the base metal. If it is desired to use an electrode of different composition, the weld metal should have considerably greater corrosion resistance than the base metal, assuming, as is usually the case, that the area of weld metal exposed to the corrosive fluid is small compared with the area of the base metal. Under these circumstances the base metal will not corrode appreciably faster than with weld metal of the same composition. Of course, there are exceptions to every rule, and instances have been found where accelerated attack took place on base metal immediately adjacent to a weld metal of greater corrosion resistance. With weld metal of inferior corrosion resistance, practically all corrosion will be concentrated on the welds, which will be eaten away rapidly. The metal of inferior corrosion resistance, for example, weld metal deposited by a bare electrode, forms an electrolytic cell with base metal. Being the anode of the cell, the bare-electrode weld metal rapidly dissolves through electrolytic action.

RECOVERY OF ALLOYING ELEMENTS

An important difference between the welding of plain-carbon and alloy steels is found in the behavior of the alloying elements in the weld melt. If we melt iron in air, the iron absorbs or picks up a little nitrogen and also reacts with oxygen to form an oxide slag. If we melt a high-carbon steel in air, the carbon in the steel reacts with oxygen to form gaseous carbon monoxide, which bubbles out of the steel. There is a loss in carbon. Similarly, if we melt an alloy steel in air there may be absorption of gases, formation of slag, or loss in alloying elements.

Recovery is the amount of alloying elements found in deposited weld metal as compared to the alloy content of the filler metal and any adjuvant material. Recovery is expressed as the percentage:

$$\% \text{ Recovery} = \frac{\% \text{ of alloying element in deposit}}{\% \text{ of alloying element in filler metal}} \times 100$$

The deposit from a bare electrode containing 0.50% C generally will contain not over 0.05% C. The recovery is 10 percent. If the electrode is flux covered, the carbon recovery may rise to 50 or 100 percent, depending upon the protection afforded by the covering. Copper is recovered completely in depositing a copper-containing steel rod because copper has a high boiling point and less affinity than iron for oxygen, nitrogen and other gases that may be present in the welding atmosphere. Nickel is also recovered completely for the same reasons. Silicon, on the contrary, often is oxidized completely from a bare electrode. Recovery can be improved through the use of some form of shielding. Chromium and tungsten, while lost by oxidation to some degree, are not oxidized nearly as easily as silicon. We can list the alloying elements used in steel according to their tendency to oxidize during transfer across the arc by starting with those whose recovery is low (are oxidized easily) and ending with those that are recovered almost completely: magnesium, aluminum, titanium, silicon, columbium, manganese, vanadium, chromium, tungsten, molybdenum, copper and nickel. The efficiency of transfer of alloying elements in an electrode, flux covering, or other adjuvant material ordinarily is anticipated by the manufacturer and compensating amounts are added to offset loss. However, some loss of alloy may occur from the molten weld pool which includes base metal alloying elements. Low recovery of an alloying element may be due to the low boiling point of the element (volatility), or its tendency to join the slag (affinity for oxygen or nitrogen). The probable changes in weld metal composition during welding can be deduced from the physical and chemical characteristics of the alloying elements involved, and the temperature and atmospheric conditions of the welding process as described in Chapter 3.

HIGH-STRENGTH, LOW-ALLOY STEELS

The first category of alloy steels which we shall review covers steels which *are not* regarded as alloy steel by the trade. This commercial fact is of metallurgical importance because these steels are not subject to chemical check analysis limits and other tolerances regularly imposed upon alloy steels. Instead, the *High Strength, Low Alloy Steels* are marketed on a commodity basis even though the alloy content qualifies many of them as alloy steels in the metallurgical sense. The wide usage of high strength, low alloy steels for reasons of weight-saving and/or atmospheric corrosion resistance has resulted in separate product recognition.

One of the first widely-used standards for high strength, low alloy steels was prepared by the SAE as a recommended practice and now bears the designation SAE J410b. This document provides a series of minimum standards for tensile properties which may be gaged by yield strengths that range from 40 to 70 ksi. Chemical composition requirements are deliberately minimal. Broad limits have been set only for carbon, manganese, phosphorus, sulfur and silicon. Provisions have been made for the purchaser to indicate whether semikilled, or killed steel is wanted. Under SAE J410b, the steel may range from a simple carbon-manganese composition to an alloyed composition designed to provide the special properties desired. A number of alloy steels are described in J410b as general information, but no particular limits are set for alloying elements. Somewhat later, ASTM Specification A242 was issued to cover high strength, low alloy steels in the form of structural shapes, plates and bars in the most frequently called-for strength range, namely, 50 ksi minimum yield strength and 70 ksi minimum tensile strength. This specification soon was followed by ASTM A374 dealing with cold rolled sheet, and ASTM A375 dealing with hot rolled sheet. These ASTM specifications also were written with minimal chemical composition requirements (carbon, manganese and sulfur) and allow the producer a choice and use of alloying elements to provide the mechanical properties specified, and any other special characteristics agreed upon between producer and purchaser.

The preparation of specifications for high strength, low alloy steels encountered more than usual delay because of opposing views on the need for chemical requirements. Furthermore, demands for steels with higher levels of strength, as well as steels with greater capacity for cold forming or drawing at somewhat lower levels of strength encouraged producers to market new steels as quickly as they could be developed. Naturally, these steels must carry the producer's trade name or designation until a standard or specification is issued that serves all concerned.

High strength, low alloy steels are sold on the basis of minimum mechanical properties. Chemical compositions, which often are proprietary, usually are left to the discretion of the steel producer. Analysis of the steel ordinarily is reported for information purposes. Competition is keen in the marketing of high strength, low alloy steels and the reams of literature emblazoned with trade names and glowing with application testimonials have not provided the welding engineer with exactly the kind of information needed to assess weldability under unusual conditions.

The composition limits of the aforementioned ASTM standards are carbon 0.22% max, manganese 1.25% max, and sulfur 0.05% maximum. If the carbon content is limited to 0.15% max, then the manganese content can be as high as 1.40%. Any further alloying is left to the ingenuity of the producer. In general, these steels must produce the required properties with the smallest possible alloy content in order to compete cost-wise. Of course, there are exceptions to this general rule, as, for example, where the steel offers additional improved properties beside strength. The added property may be corrosion resistance, or may be toughness at low temperatures. There are a very large number of high strength, low alloy steels, and as might be expected, each is claimed to justify its alloy content (and cost) by virtue of offering a combination of properties claimed to be optimum for certain constructional usage.

RELATIONSHIP BETWEEN COMPOSITION AND PROPERTIES

The sheer number of high strength, low alloy steels will not allow a tabulation here of all trade names and compositions available. Because the potpourri of compositions makes generalization difficult, it will be necessary to use typical steels for purposes of illustration. A half-dozen or so will be selected at each strength level. Their inclusion does not imply that these are the most popular steels in the class. They merely serve to best illustrate combinations of composition, strength, weldability and other properties. Complete lists of high strength, low alloy steels currently on the market should be secured from a materials publication. A goodly amount of composition duplication will be noted among the supposedly different steels.

AISI has suggested a simplified system of classifying the high strength, low alloy steels. They emphasize that when making a selection, the designer can favor *strength* to reduce weight, choose *ductility* to reduce fabrication costs, obtain a steel that offers *corrosion resistance,* or choose one that provides *higher fatigue resistance* than non-ferrous metals. These attributes may be obtained singly, or in any combination to fit a particular application. AISI divides high strength, low alloy steel sheets into three groups: A, B and C, according to similarities of characteristics. Table 73 summarizes briefly the properties or characteristics offered by each of the three groups, and lists the names of representative steels produced in each group. This information is helpful to the designer or materials engineer in showing the steels available for satisfying the general requirements of a particular structure or article, but it does little for the welding engineer who must decide on a safe welding procedure. This, we know, depends heavily upon such factors as chemical composition, thickness of section, condition, and steelmaking practice.

High strength, low alloy steels ordinarily are sold in the hot rolled condition as part of the effort to minimize cost. While the steelmaker may not be burdened with a treatment that involves reheating the rolled product, the "hot rolled" condition may entail more than the term implies. To effectively utilize the alloy additions in gaining high strength, some of the low alloy steels must be finished at rather low hot rolling temperatures and cooled at an accelerated rate to secure a fine grain size and

Table 73 — *HIGH-STRENGTH LOW-ALLOY SHEET STEELS*

Cross-Reference for Typical Proprietary Steels[a]	GROUP A — high-strength low-alloy steels meet specifications for 50,000 psi minimum yield point and 70,000 psi minimum tensile strength. Their atmospheric corrosion resistance is four to six times that of plain carbon steel. Lower yield and tensile strengths can be specified to get improved ductility.	GROUP B — high-strength low-alloy steels are fully-killed for special soundness. Typical yield point is 45,000 psi, and variations are available at yields above or below this to satisfy special design requirements.	GROUP C — the most widely used high-strength low-alloy steel sheets, are semi-killed with minimum yield points and typical tensile strengths as follows: Minimum Yield Point / Typical Tensile Strength — 60,000 psi / 75,000 psi; 55,000 psi / 70,000 psi; 50,000 psi / 65,000 psi; 45,000 psi / 60,000 psi

Trade Names

Producer	Group A	Group B	Group C
Acme Steel Company	Cor-Ten	---	---
Alan Wood Steel Company	Dynalloy 50	---	Al Ten / AWX
Algoma Steel Corporation, Ltd.	Cor-Ten	---	---
Armco Steel Corporation	High Strength A		High Strength C
Bethlehem Steel Company	Mayari R	---	V-Steels
Dominion Foundries & Steel, Ltd.	Dofascoloy P	Dofascoloy M V	Dofascoloy W
Granite City Steel Company	---		Hi-Yield
Great Lakes Corporation	N-A-X High-Tensile	N-A-X Finegrain	GLX-W
Inland Steel Company	Hi-Steel / Cor-Ten	---	INX
Jones & Laughlin Steel Corporation	Ni-Cu-Ti / Cor-Ten	Jalten #1	JLX
Kaiser Steel Corporation	Kaisaloy 50 CR	Kaisaloy FG, Kaisaloy MV	Kaisaloy CB
McLouth Steel Corporation	ML-50	ML-F	MLX
Pittsburgh Steel Company	PITT-TEN #1 / N-A-X High-Tensile	PITT-TEN #2	PITT-TEN X
Republic Steel Corporation	Republic "50" / N-A-X High-Tensile / Cor-Ten	Republic A-441 Modified	Republic XW
Sharon Steel Corporation	Cor-Ten / N-A-X High-Tensile	---	---
Steel Company of Canada, Ltd.	Stelcoloy "G"	---	Stelco-Columbium
United States Steel Corporation	Cor-Ten	Par-Ten / Tri-Ten	Ex-Ten
Weirton Steel Company	N-A-X High-Tensile	N-A-X Finegrain	GLX-W
Wheeling Steel Corporation	Cor-Ten	---	---
The Youngstown Sheet and Tube Company	Yoloy "E" HS / Yoloy HSX	YB-Ten	YSW
Specifications	Hot rolled sheets ASTM A375 SAE J410a* MIL-S-7809 Cold rolled sheets ASTM A374		50,000-psi minimum yield: MIL-S-13281 Class B Grade 2 ICC 4BA 45,000-psi minimum yield: MIL-S-13281 Class B Grade 1 ICC MC 303

*SAE 950 has been completely revised as of June 1962. All of the steels in Groups A, B and C will meet one or more of the six classifications in the new J410b Recommended Practice.

[a] Abstracted from AISI Publication "Introduction to High-Strength Low-Alloy Steel Sheets."

proper distribution of carbide in the microstructure. Control of mill finishing temperature is not easily accomplished, and the rolling of high strength, low alloy steels often entails reduced production rates. The steel must be maneuvered through the mill in a manner that allows it to emerge from the last stand of rolls at the required lower temperature. Thus the finished temperature establishes the size of the austenite grains in the hot rolled product. Accelerated cooling of the hot rolled product requires special equipment. In addition to water sprays used on many mills to secure moderately accelerated cooling, some mills have multi-nozzle heads which provide rod-like streams of low-velocity water which are carefully designed to break through the film of steam that tends to form adjacent to the surface of the red-hot steel and retard cooling. Rapid cooling of the steel also promotes the various forms of hardening described earlier in this Chapter, but of course, the rate of cooling is not carried to the point where transformation (martensite) hardening occurs. Controlled finishing and accelerated cooling of hot rolled strip and plate almost may be regarded as a special heat treatment executed directly from the hot rolling temperature. This technique in handling the hot rolled products is more easily carried out with the lighter thicknesses of strip, plate and bar. Thin sheet which must be cold rolled to the required gage may be annealed or normalized after cold rolling to restore ductility, for which condition a decrease of 5 ksi often is allowed in the tensile and yield strength minima of specifications.

The steels currently offered by producers have minimum yield strengths ranging from about 42 ksi to 70 ksi. This represents a substantial extension of strength capability from the 36 ksi yield strength of ASTM A36, the weldable carbon steel described in Chapter 14. Referring now to Table 74, it will be noted that minimal use is made of carbon as an alloying element. For a yield strength of 42 ksi minimum, a typical carbon content of 0.10% is needed and only a small amount of additional alloy (usually manganese and a pinch of columbium or vanadium). This steel, of course, would fall in the "Trouble Free" welding class defined earlier in Table 71.

Steels of 45 and 50 ksi yield strength capability present a broader array of compositions. In general, they can be divided into two classes: those which contain a minimum alloy addition to gain the required strength, and those which are more highly alloyed to *also* gain some atmospheric corrosion resistance. The latter types usually contain additions of copper, chromium, and sometimes phosphorus. Generally speaking, the higher alloy content demands a higher price. From a welding standpoint, all of these steels are reported to have good weldability.

Table 74 — TYPICAL HIGH STRENGTH, LOW ALLOY STEELS

Trade name	C max	Mn	P max	Si	Cu	Cr	Ni	Others	UTS, ksi min	Yld. Point ksi, min
				Chemical composition – percent a					Tensile properties b	
Kaisaloy 42-CV	0.20	0.90 max	0.04	0.30 max	...	...	...	Cb or V 0.01 min	65	42
Republic X42W	0.22	1.10 max	0.04	0.10	...	...	...	Cb or V 0.01 min	57	42
USS Ex-Ten 42	0.21	0.90 max	0.04	0.30 max	...	...	...	Cb or V 0.01 min	63	42
Armco High Strength C-45	0.22	1.35 max	0.04	0.30 max	...	...	...	Cb 0.005/0.05 and/or V 0.01/0.10 N 0.015 max	60	45
Bethlehem V 45	0.22	1.25 max	0.04	...	...	...	...	V 0.02 min	65	45
GLX-45W	0.20	1.25 max	0.04	...	...	...	...	Cb 0.01 min	60	45
Kaisaloy 45FG	0.12	0.60 max	0.04	0.50 max	0.30 max	0.25 max	0.60 max	Mo 0.10 max Ti 0.005 min V 0.02 max	60	45
Tri-Ten	0.22	1.25 max	0.04	0.30 max	0.20 min	...	...	V 0.02 min	60	45
Bar & Plate, typical	0.18	1.14	0.02	...	0.28	...	...	0.045	...	...
Sheet & Strip, typical	0.10	0.72	0.02	...	0.26	...	...	0.042	...	...

Steel								Other		
Armco High Strength A (To ¾ in.)	0.12	0.60 max	0.04	0.25–0.70	0.30–0.50	0.50–1.00	0.80 max	Mo 0.10 max, Ti 0.07 max	70	50
Armco High Strength A (Over ¾ in.)	0.20	1.20 max	0.04	0.25–0.70	0.30–0.50	0.50–1.00	0.80 max	Mo 0.10 max, Ti 0.07 max	70	50
Armco High Strength B	0.22	0.85–1.25	0.04	0.30 max	0.20 min	...	...	V 0.02 min	70	50
Armco High Strength C-50	0.23	1.35 max	0.04	0.30 max	...	...	...	Cb 0.005/0.05 and/or V 0.01/0.10 N 0.015 max	65	50
Bethlehem V 50	0.22	1.25 max	0.04	...	...	...	...	V 0.02 min N 0.015 max	70	50
Cor-Ten Over ½ in.	0.10–0.19	0.90–1.25	0.04	0.15–0.30	0.25–0.40	0.40–0.65	...	V 0.02/0.10	70	50
Typical	0.16	1.15	0.02	0.20	0.32	0.50	...	0.05 Al 0.01/0.06, (Fine Grain)	...	...
Cor-Ten ½ in. & under	0.12	0.20–0.50	0.07–0.15	0.25–0.75	0.25–0.55	0.30–1.25	0.65 max	...	70	50
Typical	0.09	0.38	0.09	0.48	0.41	0.84	0.28	...	...	50
Man-Ten	0.25	1.10–1.60	0.045	0.30	0.20 min	...	...	...	70	50
Mayari R	0.12	0.50–1.00	0.12	0.20–0.90	0.50 max	0.40–1.00	1.00 max	Zr 0.10 max	70	50
N-A-X High	0.15	0.50–1.00	0.04	0.60–0.90	0.25 max	0.40–0.70	...	Mo 0.20 max Zr 0.05/0.15	70	50
Republic X-50-W	0.20	1.00 max	0.04	0.10 max	...	...	...	Cb or V - 0.01 min	65	50

TABLE 74 — (Continued)

Trade name	Chemical composition – percent [a]								Tensile properties [b]	
	C max	Mn	P max	Si	Cu	Cr	Ni	Others	UTS, ksi min	Yld. Point ksi, min
USS Ex-Ten 50	0.22	1.35 max	0.04	0.30 max	...	...	...	Cb or V - 0.01 min	70	50
Yoloy HS	0.15	1.00 max	0.04	0.30 max	0.50–1.00	...	0.75–1.25	Mo 0.15/0.25	70	50
Armco High Strength C-55	0.25	1.35 max	0.04	0.30 max	...	...	...	Cb 0.005/0.05 and/or V 0.01/0.10 N 0.015 max	70	55
Bethlehem V 55	0.22	1.25 max	0.04	...	...	...	...	V 0.02 min N 0.015 max	70	55
INX-55	0.24	1.40	0.04	0.30 max	...	...	...	Cb or V - 0.01 min	...	55
Jalloy Grade 1	0.13–0.18	1.00–1.30	...	0.15–0.30	...	...	...	Mo 0.10/0.20 B added	...	55
Armco High Strength C-60	0.26	1.35 max	0.04	0.30 max	...	...	...	Cb 0.005/0.05 and/or V 0.01/0.10 N 0.015 max	75	60
Bethlehem V60	0.22	1.25 max	0.04	...	...	...	...	V 0.02 min N 0.015 max	75	60
USS Ex-Ten 60	0.25	1.35 max	0.04	0.30 max	...	...	...	Cb or V - 0.01 min	80	60

Steel	C	Mn	P	Si			Other	Tensile[b]	Yield[b]
INX-60	0.26	1.60 max	0.04	0.30 max	...	...	Cb or V - 0.01 min	75	60
Armco High Strength C-65	0.26	1.35 max	0.04	0.30 max	...	...	Cb 0.005/0.05 and/or V 0.01/0.10 N 0.015 max	80	65
Bethlehem V65	0.22	1.25 max	0.04	...	...	...	V 0.02 min N 0.015 max	80	65
INX-65	0.26	1.65 max	0.04	0.30 max	...	...	Cb or V - 0.01 min	80	65
Kaiser Mo-B	0.15	0.60 max	...	0.35 max	...	...	Mo 0.40/0.60 B 0.001 min	...	65
Republic 65	0.15	1.00 max	0.04	0.15 max	0.90–1.40	1.00–1.50	Mo 0.20/0.30	85	65
Armco High Strength C-70	0.26	1.35 max	0.04	0.30 max	...	...	Cb 0.005/0.05 and/or V 0.01/0.10 N 0.015 max	85	70
Republic 70	0.20	1.00 max	0.04	0.15 max	0.90–1.40	1.20–1.75	Mo 0.20/0.30	...	70
Republic X-70W	0.26	1.65 max	0.04	0.30 max	...	...	Cb or V - 0.01 min	85	70
INX-70	0.26	1.65 max	0.04	0.30 max	...	...	Cb or V - 0.01 min	85	70
USS Ex-Ten 70	0.26	1.35 max	0.04	0.30 max	...	...	Cb 0.01 min V 0.02 min	90	70

a Composition limits shown may not apply to all thicknesses of material supplied in a particular steel, but they serve satisfactorily for purpose of illustration. Single values are maximums unless indicated to be minimum, or typical values.
b Tensile properties may be different for various ranges of thickness. Values shown are considered to be representative.

However, it is helpful to note the carbon content of each particular steel. To gain the 50 ksi yield strength level, carbon is limited to approximately 0.15%, 0.20%, or 0.25% depending upon the amount of other alloying elements present. The corrosion resisting steels contain the lower carbon contents. Where corrosion resistance is not to be enhanced, the producer is likely to use as much as possible of the least expensive of the strength-gaining elements, namely, carbon. Since we are now well aware of the practical limitations of this element in a steel designed for welding, it should not come as a surprise to see carbon no higher than about 0.26% in any of the high strength, low alloy steels. At this level of carbon, relatively little alloy is required to gain high yield strengths. However, steel containing about 0.26% carbon and sufficient alloy to gain 65 ksi yield strength or higher in the hot rolled condition will be found to possess enough hardenability to form martensite on rapid cooling — as might be occasionally experienced in the heat-affected zone of a very small arc-weld or a resistance spot weld. This is not a favorable structure to allow to remain in the joint area, particularly if the carbon is nearing the 0.26% level. These steels just fall within the scope of the "Weld with Care" classification of Table 71, and the welding engineer would do well to avoid martensite formation through control of the process applied. The need for this arises mostly in welding heavy sections to be used in the as-welded condition and in resistance-spot and projection welding. The guide to weldability described in Chapter 16 under the caption "Jominy Hardness-Bend Ductility System" can be very useful in deciding when martensite is likely to be encountered. If the carbon content of the steel is known and its Jominy curve is available, we can tell quickly whether a specified set of arc-welding conditions will produce a cooling rate in the base metal heat-affected zone that is faster than the critical cooling rate of the steel. It would be prudent to conduct the welding operation under conditions of heat input that would produce heat-affected zones that cooled slower than the martensite formation rate. Perhaps it should be emphasized again that this kind of special control is not often required on the high-strength, low-alloy steels.

Many of the steels of 55, 60, 65 and 70 ksi yield strength capability show an obvious composition similarity; that is, the use of columbium, vanadium and nitrogen as alloying elements in a steel otherwise containing up to approximately 0.25% carbon and 1½% manganese. Reference has been made in earlier chapters to these columbium and vanadium treated steels, and it would be an oversight to not examine more closely the mechanism by which these elements increase strength. We are interested, of course, in the actual amounts of these elements which are incorporated in the composition since the producers usually indicate only a general minima, or maxima. Remember, these steels are sold on the basis of properties rather than chemical composition. Nevertheless, we are interested in metallurgical behavior as affected by composition in order to determine what precautions might be required in welding.

Columbium, when added in amounts from 0.01 to 0.10% to form a high strength, low alloy steel, increases the strength of the hot rolled material by grain refinement and precipitation hardening, but decreases its hardenability somewhat because of stable carbide formation. Usually, the yield strength is increased by about 15 to 30% by the columbium addition while the tensile strength receives a little less benefit. This increased strength is realized both at elevated and at subzero temperatures, and ordinarily is accompanied by good fracture toughness. The percentage increase in strength imparted by columbium is greater over the range of 0.01 to 0.05%, and this lower level of columbium, in addition to being less costly, provides best toughness.

Columbium additions can be made to either semikilled or killed steels to increase strength in the manner just described, but when added to aluminum-killed steel the columbium carbides that form tend to be larger and are more difficult to dissolve on heating than the carbides in a semikilled steel. The introduction of columbium, by virtue of inducing grain refinement acts to improve impact properties, including better fracture toughness at lower temperatures. However, if massive carbides are formed, which robs the matrix of columbium and detracts from the mechanics of grain refinement, then the toughness of the steel may suffer. This sometimes happens with steel of higher carbon content, and with the aluminum-killed steel. Increasing thickness of section, primarily because of slowing cooling and difficulties in securing a fine grain size, also tends to lower toughness in the columbium-containing steel. This effect of thickness is quite strong, and plates heavier than ½ inch require much more attention in production to assure good fracture toughness. Whereas hot rolled carbon steel may show a toughness transition (for example, NDT) somewhere in the temperature range of 40 down to – 20 F, the hot rolled, fine-grained, columbium-containing steels easily may be expected to delay this transition to a temperature in the range of approximately –20 to –80 F. When hot rolled properties are not satisfactory from the standpoint of toughness, normalizing these steels in the temperature range of about 1650 to 1700 F usually is helpful in improving toughness without lowering strength significantly.

The commercial production of high strength, low alloy steels of the columbium-containing variety involves controlling the manganese–carbon ratio, the addition of about 0.02% columbium, a finishing temperature in the vicinity of 1600 F for grain size control, and rapid cooling of the hot rolled product. A high manganese content (about 1 to 1½%) appears instrumental in obtaining good low-temperature toughness. The cold work hardening rate of the columbium-containing steels is reduced to some extent; the vanadium-containing steels are affected to a greater degree. Therefore, these materials will display less increase in strength as a result of such cold working operations like the cold rolling of sheet, or the cold expansion of pipe.

Encouraging results have been reported regarding the welding of columbium-containing steels. No susceptibility to underbead cracking has been encountered in the fabrication of weldments, even with cellulosic electrodes for arc welding. Bead-on-plate tests conducted at temperatures as low as 0 F also revealed no cracking susceptibility. Electrodes for welding the columbium-containing steels are selected from the E60, E70 and E80 series in order to provide strength which equals that of the base metal. The strength of weld metal in the joints of actual weldments will be slightly higher than that of an all-weld-metal (undiluted) deposit because of the pickup of carbon and manganese from the base metal, rather than any dilution-effect of the columbium. Pipelines of columbium-containing steel with a 60 ksi minimum yield strength have been welded as described in Table 75 with no difficulty attributable to the composition or properties of the base metal.

Concurrent with the development of the columbium-containing steels, investigators have found that vanadium can be employed in precisely the same way as columbium. In fact, vanadium appears to be a more satisfactory alloying element for use in the heavier sections of plate or bar. Furthermore, it has been discovered that additions of both vanadium and nitrogen to a steel will increase its strength (particularly the yield strength) by an amount greater than would be obtained by individual additions of these elements. Hence, the commercial introduction of vanadium–nitrogen containing steels in which the synergistic effect of these alloys can be used to raise the yield strength of hot rolled material (having a base composition of about 0.18% carbon and 1.10% manganese) to levels from 45 to 65 ksi. Carbon steels generally are found to contain less than 0.01% vanadium and about 0.005% nitrogen as residual elements. These levels are increased to about 0.05% vanadium and 0.010% nitrogen in the Mn–V–N high strength, low alloy steels. In studies of the strengthening mechanisms operating in these steels, it was found that the addition of only vanadium resulted in the formation of vanadium carbides. A steel containing only a nitrogen addition showed no evidence of

Table 75 — *WELDING PROCEDURE FOR A PIPELINE CONSTRUCTED OF HIGH STRENGTH, LOW ALLOY STEEL CONTAINING COLUMBIUM*[a]

BASE METAL: XC-60, Pipe Produced by Electrical Flash-Butt Welding Longitudinal Seam, Nominal Wall Thickness 0.250 in. Nominal Diameter 24 in. OD

Chemical Composition

	Carbon	Manganese	Columbium
Specification	0.26 max	1.30 max	0.05 max
Typical	0.22	1.10	0.015

Mechanical Properties (Pipe cold expanded 1½%)

	UTS ksi	YS ksi	YS–UTS Ratio	⅔ Size Charpy-V Impact Mean Transition Temp. – Energy	Mean Transition Temp. – 50% Shear
Max	101	83	85%		
Min	82	65	76%		
Avg	92	72	79%	–10 F	20 F

Hydrostatic Rupture Tests of Pipe at 30 to 40 F

Pipe sections failed in 100% shear fracture away from longitudinal flash-butt weld, and away from circumferential girth weld.

WELDING PROCEDURE:

Preheating — None. Ambient temperature varied from –25 to 80 F.

Process   — Shielded Metal-Arc Manual as regularly carried out per API 1104. E6010 electrodes used for root and cover passes; E7010 electrodes for 2nd and 3rd passes.

Fabricator concluded that other than XC-60 steel appearing to increase the fluidity of the weld puddle (a matter of considerable importance to the operator welding in all positions) the material could be handled as safely as a lower strength, carbon steel.

Some welding by the submerged-arc process using electrode and flux designed to deposit weld metal equivalent to that from E7010 electrodes. No difficulty encountered.

[a] Data by Barkow

vanadium carbide, nitride, or carbonitride. Therefore, the strenthening mechanism from nitrogen appeared to result from atmosphere locking of dislocations and dislocation sources in the lattice. Steels containing additions of both vanadium and nitrogen were found to have extremely fine platelets of vanadium nitride precipitated along the (100) planes of the ferrite lattice. These platelets when examined by electron microscopy appeared to be about 100 to 400 A in diameter and 20 to 90 A thick. Some of the platelets appeared to be coherent with the lattice of the ferrite, which of course would make these particles very effective in strengthening the ferrite. Heating the vanadium–nitrogen containing steels to temperatures up to about 1400 F does not decrease their strength; in

fact, temperatures in the vicinity of 1200 to 1300 F cause strength to increase a little. However, heating to temperatures above about 1450 F
produces a marked decrease in strength because the number of precipitated
platelets of vanadium nitride is reduced. The benefit gained from adding
nitrogen has led a number of producers to explore the use of elements
other than vanadium to act as the nitride-former. As a result of this
research, steels sometimes are made with a controlled addition of nitrogen
along with a nitride-former such as aluminum, beryllium, columbium, titanium or zirconium. One producer is reported to use a special stirring
method on the molten steel bath when adding the materials which represent his source of nitrogen and nitride-former. This method is claimed
to provide an improved dispersion of nitride particles in the structure of
the steel.

The use of nitrogen as a strengthening alloying element is indicated
by the patent literature to have been extended to weld metal. One investigator claims that gas metal-arc welding can be performed with nitrogen
present either in the electrode, or in the shielding gas. By having a strong
nitride-forming element present in the weld metal (selected from the
group of Al, Ti, Zr, Be, Cb and V, and alloys thereof), the nitrogen
supplied through the filler metal or the shielding gas is picked up by the
weld metal in a manner that causes the formation of fine, solid nitride particles dispersed throughout the weld structure. A similar technique is
reported to be feasible with submerged arc welding wherein the nitrogen
also can be introduced into the flux as manganese nitride. During welding,
nitrogen is evolved by the manganese nitride and combines with a stronger
nitride-former, such as aluminum, to produce the desired dispersion of
strengthening nitride particles in the weld structure.

The fine-grained, semikilled vanadium-containing steels also are reported to have excellent weldability, and the procedures suggested are
like those ordinarily used for welding the lower-strength carbon steels. One
producer of the vanadium–nitrogen-containing steels, however, advocates
somewhat greater caution in shielded metal-arc welding these high strength,
low alloy steels, and recommends the use of either low-hydrogen electrodes,
or mild preheating with the conventional cellulosic covered electrodes as
the thickness of the base metal increases and as the steel represents
higher levels of yield strength. An outline of these recommendations is
provided in Table 76. The majority of high strength, low alloy steels, however, can be welded with cellulosic covered electrodes without preheat —
at least, in sections approximately ½-inch thick or less. Of course, the
welding procedure should be tailored not only to the composition and
thickness of the base metal, but also to the restraint upon the joints, the

Table 76 — *RECOMMENDATIONS FOR ELECTRODE SELECTION AND PREHEATING FOR WELDING HIGH STRENGTH, LOW-ALLOY STEELS OF THE VANADIUM-NITROGEN CONTAINING VARIETY*[a]

Minimum Preheat Temperatures for Arc Welding

*Thickness to be welded	Welding electrode	\multicolumn{5}{c}{Preheat recommended for steel}
		V45	V50	V55	V60	V65
Up to ⅜ in.	**Conventional	None	None	None	100 F	150 F
	Low hydrogen	None	None	None	None	None
Over ⅜ to ¾ in.	**Conventional	None	100 F	150 F	200 F	250 F
	Low hydrogen	None	None	None	100 F	150 F
Over ¾ to 1½ in.	**Conventional	150 F	150 F	200 F	250 F	
	Low hydrogen	None	None	100 F	150 F	
Over 1½ to 2 in.	**Conventional	200 F	250 F	300 F		
	Low hydrogen	150 F	150 F	200 F		
Over 2 to 3in.	**Conventional	300 F	300 F	350 F		
	Low hydrogen	200 F	250 F	300 F		

*Thicknesses shown cover the entire range of thicknesses encountered in V Steel sheets, plates, bars, shapes, and piling, including both the webs and flanges of shapes.

**Low hydrogen electrodes are recommended for most applications for all grades of V Steels, particularly for thicknesses over ¾ in. and for all thicknesses in V55, V60, and V65. Low hydrogen electrodes should be properly stored and dried according to the manufacturer's recommendation.

If the temperature of the shop or the steel to be welded falls below 50 F, for those conditions where no preheat is shown, preheat the steel to 100 F before welding.

Welding of massive or highly restrained parts may require additional preheat, weld sequence control, or both.

Where V Steels are to be welded to lower strength grades (e.g., A36) select electrodes to match the strength of the lower strength steel, but employ welding practice for the higher strength steel.

Covered Electrodes for Shielded Metal-Arc Welding

Grade	\multicolumn{3}{c}{Tensile properties of steel}	\multicolumn{2}{c}{Tensile properties of weld metal}
	Yield point, min, psi	Tensile strength min, psi	†Recommended electrode	Yield point, min, psi	Tensile strength min, psi
V45	45,000	65,000	E60XX	50,000 or 55,000	62,000 or 67,000
			E70XX	60,000	72,000
V50	50,000	70,000	††E60XX	50,000 or 55,000	62,000 or 67,000
			E70XX	60,000	72,000
V55	55,000	70,000	E70XX	60,000	72,000
V60	60,000	75,000	††E70XX	60,000	72,000
			E80XX	67,000	80,000
V65	65,000	80,000	††E70XX	60,000	72,000
			E80XX	67,000	80,000

†Electrode classification numbers and all weld metal tensile properties are contained in AWS-ASTM Specifications A-233 and A-316. Low hydrogen electrodes are recommended for most applications, see note above (**) . Low hydrogen electrodes are covered by class EXX15, EXX16, EXX18, and EXX28.

††It is generally desirable that all welds (particularly buttwelds) be made with electrodes whose properties match those of the base metal. How-ever, under some conditions (e.g., single pass fillet welds) the designer may elect to use a weld metal of lower strength than the base metal.

FOR SUBMERGED ARC WELDING
For submerged arc welding, combinations of electrodes and flux should be used that will produce weld metal having the tensile properties of the steel being welded, except as referred to in the note (††) at the left.

[a] Recommended for Bethlehem V Steels.

likelihood of notches at the joint, the ambient temperature, and the many other conditions that the welding engineer should consider.

Toughness of Weldments

Because of their low cost per unit of load carried, the high strength, low alloy steels containing columbium, vanadium and nitrogen are becoming increasingly popular for weldments. Applications include pipe lines, buildings, bridges, road building machinery, earth moving equipment, and many kinds of transportation equipment. The weldments employed in many of these applications must have good toughness. As mentioned earlier, these steels contain the lowest possible carbon content that will allow the combination of (1) manganese content, (2) additions of columbium, vanadium and nitrogen, and (3) mill hot rolling and cooling practice to achieve the required strength. These steels, when processed under the newly-developed mill practices, will display greater toughness than carbon steels. Lower impact transition temperatures and NDT temperatures cannot be solely credited to the alloying effects of columbium, vanadium or nitrogen because the lower carbon and higher manganese contents as well as the finer grain size resulting from the controlled hot rolling play a role in promoting toughness. This improved toughness permits welding at lower ambient temperatures without preheating and less likelihood of cracking during welding from stress concentration at notches. Also, the service performance of the weldment is less likely to be marred by a catastrophic cracking failure.

Corrosion Resistance of Weldments

The alloying elements contained in the high strength, low alloy steels impart different degrees of corrosion resistance. Some of these steels are not any more rust-resisting than ordinary carbon steel, while others display a surprising resistance to atmospheric corrosion. When improved corrosion resistance is wanted, the simplest composition adjustment is to increase the copper content above about 0.20%. The atmospheric corrosion resistance of this copper-bearing steel will be approximately twice that of plain carbon (low copper) steel, but of course, even the copper-bearing steel ordinarily requires some kind of rust protection in most outdoor applications. However, the addition of comparatively small amounts of other alloying elements can increase the corrosion resistance of high strength, low alloy steels to the point where it is resistant to deterioration during exposure to rural and mild industrial atmosphere. Certain of these steels will form a dense superficial film of adherent mahogany-brown oxide in the atmosphere that effectively stops further rusting and eliminates the need for painting under ordinary conditions of exposure. Large structures (buildings, bridges, transmission towers) are being erected in rural areas with these low-alloy steels and are allowed to develop their own protective rust coating. This remarkable performance by a *low-alloy* steel can be gained through a number of alloying techniques. Increasing the copper content beyond 0.20%, up to about 1% increases corrosion resistance. Phosphorus additions to the copper-bearing steels appear to inhibit corrosion markedly. Manganese inhibits corrosion in some low alloy steels in marine environments, but does not appear effective in industrial atmosphere exposure. Nickel has been reported to be an effective element in promoting corrosion resistance in the low alloy steels, particularly in the copper-bearing variety. The degree of improvement generally is proportional to the nickel content. Nickel in steels also decreases corrosion rates as a function of time. Chromium, especially in high-phosphorus steels, very effectively inhibits corrosion, the effect being particularly pronounced with long exposures. To secure a steel which is capable of developing a self-protecting oxide film in outdoor exposure, multiple additions of small amounts of alloying elements usually are made as can be seen from the steels listed under Group A in Table 73, and their respective compositions as shown in Table 74. From the standpoint of welding, it is important to mention that weld joints need not be made with filler metal having the same alloy composition as the base metal. Apparently, when ordinary carbon steel filler metal is deposited by electrodes, the pickup of alloy in the weld metal plus the inherently greater corrosion resistance of the weld metal provides a weld joint that is equal to the base metal in developing a protective rust film in the atmosphere.

ALLOY STEELS

Despite effort to classify logical groups of alloy steels and describe their weldability in some orderly fashion, it must be admitted here that a very large number of compositions have developed through the years which defy simple classification by usage, properties, or condition of treatment. A large group of these steels are the standard types of the AISI and SAE as shown in Table 77. Here they are presented in their usual order of numerical designation and composition as described in Chapter 2. These steels cover broad ranges of compositions; consequently, they are capable of developing wide ranges of mechanical properties. From what has been said about the relationships between composition and welding behavior to this point, these steels obviously must cover the gamut

Table 77 — CHEMICAL REQUIREMENTS FOR ALLOY STEELS

Standard Types Promulgated by AISI and SAE

SAE or AISI Number	C	Mn	P Max	S Max	Si	Ni	Cr	Others
1330	0.28–0.33	1.60–1.90	0.040	0.040	0.20–0.35	...	...	...
1335	0.33–0.38	1.60–1.90	0.040	0.040	0.20–0.35	...	...	...
1340	0.38–0.43	1.60–1.90	0.040	0.040	0.20–0.35	...	...	...
1345	0.43–0.48	1.60–1.90	0.040	0.040	0.20–0.35	...	...	...
TS 14B35*	0.33–0.38	0.75–1.00	...	...	0.20–0.35	...	...	...
3140	0.38–0.43	0.70–0.90	0.040	0.040	0.20–0.35	1.10–1.40	0.55–0.75	...
E3310**	0.08–0.13	0.45–0.60	0.025	0.025	0.20–0.35	3.25–3.75	1.40–1.75	Mo
4012	0.09–0.14	0.75–1.00	0.040	0.040	0.20–0.35	...	...	0.15–0.25
4023	0.20–0.25	0.70–0.90	0.040	0.040	0.20–0.35	...	...	0.20–0.30
4024	0.20–0.25	0.70–0.90	0.040	0.035–0.050	0.20–0.25	...	...	0.20–0.30
4027	0.25–0.30	0.70–0.90	0.040	0.040	0.20–0.35	...	...	0.20–0.30
4028	0.25–0.30	0.70–0.90	0.040	0.035–0.050	0.20–0.35	...	...	0.20–0.30
4037	0.35–0.40	0.70–0.90	0.040	0.040	0.20–0.35	...	...	0.20–0.30
4042	0.40–0.45	0.70–0.90	0.040	0.040	0.20–0.35	...	...	0.20–0.30
4047	0.45–0.50	0.70–0.90	0.040	0.040	0.20–0.35	...	...	0.20–0.30
4063	0.60–0.67	0.75–1.00	0.040	0.040	0.20–0.35	...	...	0.20–0.30
4118	0.18–0.23	0.70–0.90	0.040	0.040	0.20–0.35	...	0.40–0.60	0.08–0.15
4130	0.28–0.33	0.40–0.60	0.040	0.040	0.20–0.35	...	0.80–1.10	0.15–0.25
4135	0.33–0.38	0.70–0.90	0.040	0.040	0.20–0.35	...	0.80–1.10	0.15–0.25
4137	0.35–0.40	0.70–0.90	0.040	0.040	0.20–0.35	...	0.80–1.10	0.15–0.25
4140	0.38–0.43	0.75–1.00	0.040	0.040	0.20–0.35	...	0.80–1.10	0.15–0.25
TS 4140*	0.38–0.43	0.80–1.05	...	...	0.20–0.35	...	0.90–1.20	0.08–0.15
4142	0.40–0.45	0.75–1.00	0.040	0.040	0.20–0.35	...	0.80–1.10	0.15–0.25
4145	0.43–0.48	0.75–1.00	0.040	0.040	0.20–0.35	...	0.80–1.10	0.15–0.25
4147	0.45–0.50	0.75–1.00	0.040	0.040	0.20–0.35	...	0.80–1.10	0.15–0.25

Grade								
4150	0.48–0.53	0.75–1.00	0.040	0.040	0.20–0.35	...	0.80–1.10	0.15–0.25
TS 4150*	0.48–0.53	0.80–1.05	...	...	0.20–0.35	...	0.90–1.20	0.08–0.15
4320	0.17–0.22	0.45–0.65	0.040	0.040	0.20–0.35	1.65–2.00	0.40–0.60	0.20–0.30
4337	0.35–0.40	0.60–0.80	0.040	0.040	0.20–0.35	1.65–2.00	0.70–0.90	0.20–0.30
E4337*	0.35–0.40	0.65–0.85	0.025	0.025	0.20–0.35	1.65–2.00	0.70–0.90	0.20–0.30
4340	0.38–0.43	0.60–0.80	0.040	0.040	0.20–0.35	1.65–2.00	0.70–0.90	0.20–0.30
E4340	0.38–0.43	0.65–0.85	0.025	0.025	0.20–0.35	1.65–2.00	0.70–0.90	0.20–0.30
4422	0.20–0.25	0.70–0.90	0.040	0.040	0.20–0.35	...	...	0.35–0.45
4427	0.24–0.29	0.70–0.90	0.040	0.040	0.20–0.35	...	...	0.35–0.45
4520	0.18–0.23	0.45–0.65	0.040	0.040	0.20–0.35	...	...	0.45–0.60
4615	0.13–0.18	0.45–0.65	0.040	0.040	0.20–0.35	1.65–2.00	...	0.20–0.30
4617	0.15–0.20	0.45–0.65	0.040	0.040	0.20–0.35	1.65–2.00	...	0.20–0.30
4620	0.17–0.22	0.45–0.65	0.040	0.040	0.20–0.35	1.65–2.00	...	0.20–0.30
4621	0.18–0.23	0.70–0.90	0.040	0.040	0.20–0.35	1.65–2.00	...	0.20–0.30
4718	0.16–0.21	0.70–0.90	0.040	0.040	0.20–0.35	0.90–1.20	0.35–0.55	0.30–0.40
4720	0.17–0.22	0.50–0.90	0.040	0.040	0.20–0.35	0.90–1.20	0.35–0.55	0.15–0.25
4815	0.13–0.18	0.40–0.60	0.040	0.040	0.20–0.35	3.25–3.75	...	0.20–0.30
4817	0.15–0.20	0.40–0.60	0.040	0.040	0.20–0.35	3.25–3.75	...	0.20–0.30
4820	0.18–0.23	0.50–0.70	0.040	0.040	0.20–0.35	3.25–3.75	...	0.20–0.30
5015	0.12–0.17	0.30–0.50	0.040	0.040	0.20–0.35	...	0.30–0.50	...
50B40	0.38–0.43	0.75–1.00	0.040	0.040	0.20–0.35	...	0.40–0.60	...
50B44	0.43–0.48	0.75–1.00	0.040	0.040	0.20–0.35	...	0.40–0.60	...
5046	0.43–0.50	0.75–1.00	0.040	0.040	0.20–0.35	...	0.20–0.35	...
50B46	0.43–0.50	0.75–1.00	0.040	0.040	0.20–0.35	...	0.20–0.35	...
50B50	0.48–0.53	0.75–1.00	0.040	0.040	0.20–0.35	...	0.40–0.60	...
50B60	0.55–0.65	0.75–1.00	0.040	0.040	0.20–0.35	...	0.40–0.60	...
5115	0.13–0.18	0.70–0.90	0.040	0.040	0.20–0.35	...	0.70–0.90	...
5120	0.17–0.22	0.70–0.90	0.040	0.040	0.20–0.35	...	0.70–0.90	...
5130	0.28–0.33	0.70–0.90	0.040	0.040	0.20–0.35	...	0.80–1.10	...
5132	0.30–0.35	0.60–0.80	0.040	0.040	0.20–0.35	...	0.75–1.00	...
5135	0.33–0.38	0.60–0.80	0.040	0.040	0.20–0.35	...	0.80–1.05	...
5140	0.38–0.43	0.70–0.90	0.040	0.040	0.20–0.35	...	0.70–0.90	...

TABLE 77 — (Continued)

SAE or AISI Number	C	Mn	P Max	S Max	Si	Ni	Cr	Others
5145	0.43–0.48	0.70–0.90	0.040	0.040	0.20–0.35	...	0.70–0.90	...
5147	0.45–0.52	0.70–0.95	0.040	0.040	0.20–0.35	...	0.85–1.15	...
5150	0.48–0.53	0.70–0.90	0.040	0.040	0.20–0.35	...	0.70–0.90	...
5155	0.50–0.60	0.70–0.90	0.040	0.040	0.20–0.35	...	0.70–0.90	...
5160	0.55–0.65	0.75–1.00	0.040	0.040	0.20–0.35	...	0.70–0.90	...
51B60	0.55–0.65	0.75–1.00	0.040	0.040	0.20–0.35	...	0.70–0.90	...
E50100**	0.95–1.10	0.25–0.45	0.025	0.025	0.20–0.35	...	0.40–0.60	...
E51100**	0.95–1.10	0.25–0.45	0.025	0.025	0.20–0.35	...	0.90–1.15	...
E52100**	0.95–1.10	0.25–0.45	0.025	0.025	0.20–0.35	...	1.30–1.60	...
								V
6118	0.16–0.21	0.50–0.70	0.040	0.040	0.20–0.35	...	0.50–0.70	0.10–0.15
6120	0.17–0.22	0.70–0.90	0.040	0.040	0.20–0.35	...	0.70–0.90	0.10 min
6150	0.48–0.53	0.70–0.90	0.040	0.040	0.20–0.35	...	0.80–1.10	0.15 min
								Mo
8115	0.13–0.18	0.70–0.90	0.040	0.040	0.20–0.35	0.20–0.40	0.30–0.50	0.08–0.15
81B45	0.43–0.48	0.75–1.00	0.040	0.040	0.20–0.35	0.20–0.40	0.35–0.55	0.08–0.15
8615	0.13–0.18	0.70–0.90	0.040	0.040	0.20–0.35	0.40–0.70	0.40–0.60	0.15–0.25
8617	0.15–0.20	0.70–0.90	0.040	0.040	0.20–0.35	0.40–0.70	0.40–0.60	0.15–0.25
8620	0.18–0.23	0.70–0.90	0.040	0.040	0.20–0.35	0.40–0.70	0.40–0.60	0.15–0.25
8622	0.20–0.25	0.70–0.90	0.040	0.040	0.20–0.35	0.40–0.70	0.40–0.60	0.15–0.25
8625	0.23–0.28	0.70–0.90	0.040	0.040	0.20–0.35	0.40–0.70	0.40–0.60	0.15–0.25
8627	0.25–0.30	0.70–0.90	0.040	0.040	0.20–0.35	0.40–0.70	0.40–0.60	0.15–0.25
8630	0.28–0.33	0.70–0.90	0.040	0.040	0.20–0.35	0.40–0.70	0.40–0.60	0.15–0.25
8637	0.35–0.40	0.75–1.00	0.040	0.040	0.20–0.35	0.40–0.70	0.40–0.60	0.15–0.25
8640	0.38–0.43	0.75–1.00	0.040	0.040	0.20–0.35	0.40–0.70	0.40–0.60	0.15–0.25
8642	0.40–0.45	0.75–1.00	0.040	0.040	0.20–0.35	0.40–0.70	0.40–0.60	0.15–0.25
8645	0.43–0.48	0.75–1.00	0.040	0.040	0.20–0.35	0.40–0.70	0.40–0.60	0.15–0.25
86B45	0.43–0.48	0.75–1.00	0.040	0.040	0.20–0.35	0.40–0.70	0.40–0.60	0.15–0.25

Grade	C	Mn	P	S	Si	Ni	Cr	Mo
8650	0.48–0.53	0.75–1.00	0.040	0.040	0.20–0.35	0.40–0.70	0.40–0.60	0.15–0.25
8655	0.50–0.60	0.75–1.00	0.040	0.040	0.20–0.35	0.40–0.70	0.40–0.60	0.15–0.25
8660	0.55–0.65	0.75–1.00	0.040	0.040	0.20–0.35	0.40–0.70	0.40–0.60	0.15–0.25
8720	0.18–0.23	0.70–0.90	0.040	0.040	0.20–0.35	0.40–0.70	0.40–0.60	0.20–0.30
8735*	0.33–0.38	0.75–1.00	0.040	0.040	0.20–0.35	0.40–0.70	0.40–0.60	0.20–0.30
8740	0.38–0.43	0.75–1.00	0.040	0.040	0.20–0.35	0.40–0.70	0.40–0.60	0.20–0.30
8742	0.40–0.45	0.75–1.00	0.040	0.040	0.20–0.35	0.40–0.70	0.40–0.60	0.20–0.30
8822	0.20–0.25	0.75–1.00	0.040	0.040	0.20–0.35	0.40–0.70	0.40–0.60	0.30–0.40
9255	0.50–0.60	0.70–0.95	0.040	0.040	1.80–2.20	…	…	…
9260	0.55–0.65	0.70–1.00	0.040	0.040	1.80–2.20	…	0.25–0.40	…
9262	0.55–0.65	0.75–1.00	0.040	0.040	1.80–2.20	…	1.00–1.40	…
E9310**	0.08–0.13	0.45–0.65	0.025	0.040	0.20–0.35	3.00–3.50	1.00–1.40	0.08–0.15
94B15	0.13–0.18	0.75–1.00	0.040	0.040	0.20–0.35	0.30–0.60	0.30–0.50	0.08–0.15
94B17	0.15–0.20	0.75–1.00	0.040	0.040	0.20–0.35	0.30–0.60	0.30–0.50	0.08–0.15
94B30	0.28–0.33	0.75–1.00	0.040	0.040	0.20–0.35	0.30–0.60	0.30–0.50	0.08–0.15
94B40	0.38–0.43	0.75–1.00	0.040	0.040	0.20–0.35	0.30–0.60	0.30–0.50	0.08–0.15
9840	0.38–0.43	0.70–0.90	0.040	0.040	0.20–0.35	0.85–1.15	0.70–0.90	0.20–0.30
9850	0.48–0.53	0.70–0.90	0.040	0.040	0.20–0.35	0.85–1.15	0.70–0.90	0.20–0.30
Standard Nitriding Steel	0.38–0.43	0.50–0.70	0.040	0.040	0.20–0.40	Al 0.95–1.30	1.40–1.80	0.30–0.40

Source—American Iron & Steel Institute, 1963

*No corresponding SAE number.
**SAE numbers do not have prefix E.

General Notes
1. TS denotes tentative standard steels.
2. Boron steels indicated by B can be expected to have 0.0005 percent minimum boron content.
3. Grades with prefix E are manufactured by basic electric furnace process. All others are normally produced by basic open hearth process but may be made by basic electric furnace process with adjustments in phosphorus and sulfur.
4. Ranges and limits apply to steel not exceeding 200 sq. in. cross-sectional area.
5. All chemical ranges and limits are subject to standard variations for check analysis over or under specification.
6. For explanation of prefix letters to indicate steelmaking process, and suffix letters to indicate special requirements see Chapter 2, *Specifications for Steels*.

7. Phosporus and sulfur limitations for each process:
   Basic electric furnace ....0.025% max
   Basic open hearth ....0.040% max
   Acid electric furnace ....0.050% max
   Acid open hearth ....0.050% max
8. Minimum silicon limit for acid open hearth or acid electric furnace alloy steel is 0.15 percent.
9. Small quantities of certain elements in alloy steel are not specified or required. They are considered as incidental and may be present in these maximum amounts: Copper, 0.35%; nickel, 0.25%; chromium, 0.20%; molybdenum, 0.06%.
10. Where sulfur content range is shown, it is indicative of resulfurized steel.
11. "H" Steels (Guaranteed Hardenability) when indicated by a letter H suffix are permitted slightly broader chemical ranges than those shown above. See separate standards published by AISI and SAE.

of weldability from "trouble-free performance" to "weld-with-greatest-of-care," and beyond (see Table 71). These AISI–SAE types are widely used steels and frequently are found in weldments. A number of the most popular types or modifications thereof are incorporated in the specifications of many other agencies.

AISI 4130, a Cr–Mo alloy steel containing about 0.30% carbon, has been a very popular steel for many years, particularly in the construction of aircraft. It falls just short of being an air-hardening steel, and the carbon limitation of 0.33% avoids the formation of very hard martensite when the critical cooling rate is exceeded. The maximum obtainable hardness is approximately 57-C Rockwell. The steel can be heat treated to gain a maximum useful tensile strength in the order of 180 ksi, but if a higher tempering temperature is used to reduce the tensile strength to about 150 ksi then a much higher level of toughness is obtained. AISI 4130 has been welded in the annealed condition, and in the heat treated condition. Aircraft engine mounts of AISI 4130 heat treated tubing have been used in the as-welded condition, but of course the heat-affected zones do not have optimum strength or toughness. More often, the weldments of AISI 4130 are given a heat treatment which consists of austenitizing at 1575–1600 F, quenching in oil or water spraying, depending upon the nature of the article, and tempering somewhere in the temperature range of 800 to 1100 F to gain the final desired properties. The ideal procedure for arc-welding AISI 4130 steel is to employ a filler metal of the selfsame composition, preheat to about 500 F, weld while maintaining a 500 F minimum interpass temperature using low-hydrogen arc conditions, stress-relief heat treat at about 1200 F immediately upon completion of welding, and finally apply a postweld heat treatment to develop the strength and toughness which this steel is capable of attaining. In actual usage, however, AISI 4130 is frequently welded with lower preheat or at room temperature. The low-hydrogen arc usually is employed, but considerable liberty often is taken with the filler metal composition. This may range from an austenitic Cr–Ni stainless steel deposit to any one of the standard classes of AWS–ASTM alloy steel electrodes or rods. The details of the procedure will depend upon the nature of the article, the section thickness, the welding process employed, and the performance required of the weld joint in service. From the standpoint of the welding metallurgy of AISI 4130, this is a steel of modest hardenability and limited hardness capability. Therefore, some variation can be safely permitted in the welding procedure.

AISI 4140 is a cut above AISI 4130 both in hardenability and hardness capability. The higher carbon content and slightly higher manganese content of AISI 4140 brings this steel to the brink of being an air-hardening type. In fact, thin sections cooled in rapidly moving cold air will become martensitic. This indicates that sections welded with a limited heat input (and consequently a rapid cooling rate) will produce martensitic heat-affected zones. Here, the hardness values are likely to measure a little above 60-C Rockwell. The optimum welding procedure mentioned above for AISI 4130 might also apply to AISI 4140. But, we must hasten to add, considerably less liberty can be taken with the welding procedure. In actual practice, AISI 4140 is seldom welded without pre-heat. Any temperature less than 300 F is almost an invitation for under-bead cracking trouble unless the weld joint is made with favorable con-trolled high heat input. A low-hydrogen arc is a necessity. The need for postweld heat treatment deserves close attention because the base metal heat-affected zones will be lacking in toughness if any substantial amount of untempered martensite is present.

AISI 4340 is a Cr–Ni–Mo alloy steel which often is used where greater hardenability is needed to achieve thorough heat treatment (mar-tensite formation plus tempering) in either thick sections, or where sec-tions cannot be quickly cooled. AISI 4340 generally is regarded as an air-hardening steel, although oil quenching is preferred to insure good final properties. From a welding standpoint, it is sufficiently air-hardening to produce martensite whenever the heat-affected zones cool faster than about 15 degrees F per second at a temperature of 1300 F. This is a relatively slow rate of cooling, and would require a hot, slow welding operation to avoid exceeding the rate. The more practical approach is to employ preheat, which not only reduces the rate of cooling in the heat-affected zone, but also tempers any martensite that may form. The recom-mended preheat temperature for welding AISI 4340 is about 600 F mini-mum, but with favorable joint conditions and a low-hydrogen welding process preheat temperatures as low as 350 F have been successfully used. It is important to maintain an elevated interpass temperature and to hold this temperature until the application of a postweld heat treatment. Briefly, all aspects of welding a highly hardenable steel are quite important in the handling of AISI 4340, especially if the sections to be joined are massive, or highly restrained, and if the welded joints are expected to exhibit high strength and toughness in service. Because steels like AISI 4340 display best properties when employed in the heat treated condition, more will be said shortly about welding *Heat Treatable Alloy Steels;* that is, steels which ordinarily are given a heat treatment following any welding operation.

Mention also must be made here of the alloy steels standardized

Table 78 — REPRESENTATIVE ASTM ALLOY STEELS

Applicable specification	Common designation	Chemical requirements (illustrative)						Approximate strength ranges, ksi		Principal area of usage
		C	Mn	Si	Cr	Ni	Others	Tensile	Yield	
A204	Carbon–molybdenum Grade C	0.28 max	0.90 max	0.15–0.30	...	...	Mo 0.45–0.60	65–100	37–53	Elevated temp. service
A302	Manganese–molybdenum	0.25 max	0.95–1.50	0.15–0.30	...	...	0.45–0.60	75–100	45–60	High strength
A357	Chromium–molybdenum	0.15 max	0.30–0.60	0.50 max	4.00–6.00	...	0.45–0.65	60–85	30–50	Elevated temp. service and improved corrosion resistance
A387	Chromium–molybdenum Grade A	0.21 max	0.40–0.80	0.15–0.30	0.50–0.80	...	0.45–0.65	60–85	30–50	Elevated temp. service
	Grade E	0.15 max	0.30–0.60	0.50 max	2.75–3.25	...	0.90–1.10	60–85	30–50	Elevated temp. service
A336	Chromium–molybdenum Class F2	0.10–0.20	0.30–0.80	0.10–0.60	0.80–1.10	...	0.45–0.65	60–85	30–50	Elevated temp. service

	C	Mn	Si	Cr	Ni	Other			
Class F22	0.15 max	0.30–0.60	0.50 max	2.00–2.50	...	0.90–1.10	60–85	30–50	Elevated temp. service
A202 Chromium–manganese–silicon Grade B	0.25 max	1.05–1.40	0.60–0.90	0.35–0.60	...	...	75–100	45–55	High strength
A225 Manganese–vanadium Grade B	0.20 max	1.45 max	0.15–0.30	...	...	V 0.09–0.14	70–90	40–55	High strength
A410 Chromium–copper–nickel–aluminum	0.12 max	0.55–1.00	0.10–0.35	0.50–0.95	0.50–0.95	Cu 0.40–0.75, Al 0.04–0.30	60–75	30–50	Low temp.
A203 & A300 2¼% Nickel Grade B	0.25 max	0.80 max	0.15–0.30	...	2.10–2.50	...	65–85	37–50	Cryogenic use to –75 F
3½% Nickel Grade E	0.23 max	0.80 max	0.15–0.30	...	3.25–3.75	...	65–85	37–50	Cryogenic use to –150 F
A353 9% Nickel Grade B	0.13 max	0.90 max	0.15–0.30	...	8.50–9.50	...	90–115	60–90	Cryogenic use to –320 F
A553 9% Nickel (Q & T)	0.13 max	0.90 max	0.15–0.30	...	8.50–9.50	...	100–120	85 min	Cryogenic use to –320 F

by the ASTM. These steels do not vary greatly from those of AISI–SAE in chemical composition, but the type designations and the limits set for alloying elements are quite different. Table 78 lists a number of representative alloy steels selected from ASTM Standards which are widely used in weldments. Their compositions present a number of points of metallurgical interest. Incidentally, the composition requirements listed are for illustration purposes only. The limits for elements vary with the form of steel being employed; that is, whether forged, cast, rolled, pierced, welded, and so forth. In fact, the limits will differ a little depending upon the particular material specification being followed. A review of the original ASTM Standards which contain these alloy steel types will show several important points not apparent from Table 78.

In many ASTM specifications covering steel plates, the maximum permissible carbon content is raised in increments for the thicker sections. The higher carbon contents are needed to obtain the desired strength in these heavier sections which cool at a slower rate after hot rolling or during heat treatment. Yet, the carbon content must not be permitted to rise too high, or else difficulty will be experienced with low ductility and toughness and cracking in welding. This is one reason why heavier plates require more care in fabricating operations. Some specifications require plates which are heavier than a specified thickness, for example, about 2 in., to be normalized before being supplied to the fabricator. The purpose of this heat treatment is to make proper use of the carbon in the composition by providing an accelerated cooling treatment from above the critical range. Sometimes the uniformity of properties desired in very heavy plates can be obtained only by a quenching and tempering heat treatment.

The ASTM alloy steels listed in Table 78 are readily welded and require only modest precautions in the welding procedure as dictated by conditions. It will be noted that the steels which permit higher carbon contents (A202, A204 and A302) are relatively low in alloy content, whereas the higher alloy steels are much lower in carbon content. This conservative control of hardness and hardenability explains the suitability of the steels for welding. On the other hand, the strengths offered by these steels, while substantially higher than the readily-weldable carbon steels, certainly are not spectacular. Yet, any bold increase in carbon content to gain strength surely would lead to impaired weldability, while a wholesale increase in other alloying elements to gain strength would raise the cost of the steel excessively. This is the strength plateau upon which weldable alloy steels stood in the year 1945. The next alloy steels to be discussed are based upon a unique metallurgical concept which gains higher levels of strength in the base metal, requires only modest precautions in welding, and does not require postweld heat treatment.

QUENCHED AND TEMPERED ALLOY STEELS

A distinct category of high-strength alloy steels has developed which does not yet have a commonly accepted name. This new family of steels is referred to by various terms, including "heat treated constructional alloy steels," and "quenched and tempered low-carbon alloy steels." The latter designation seems to fit the category best because all of these steels receive a heat treatment that involves quenching (usually a high-pressure water spray quench) and subsequent tempering. However, to say that these are *low-carbon* alloy steels would be certain to bring on debate. Steels of the quenched and tempered alloy category should be of special interest to the welding engineer; not just because they possess high strength and remarkable toughness, but they are steels which have been *designed* to have good weldability with currently used commercial processes and procedures. Most important, as will be explained shortly, they are designed to be welded with little or no preheat, and used in most applications in the as-welded condition.

The quenched and tempered alloy steels seem to have had their beginning with homogeneous alloy armor plate which was used so extensively in the Navy's ships and the Army's tanks during World War II. Much of this armor plate was called "special treatment steel" (STS) and contained about 0.30% carbon with sufficient chromium, nickel, and other alloying elements to allow the plate sections to be quenched to martensite throughout their cross section regardless of their thickness. This required considerable juggling of alloy content and careful selection of quenching medium — which usually amounted to water, but might be an immersion quench or a spray quench. Naturally, the hardened plate next was heated to the vicinity of 1000 F or more to produce a tempered structure having the required hardness. Pertinent to our interests is the fact that this quenched and tempered alloy plate could be welded, and without any postweld retreatment would give very creditable performance from the standpoint of strength and toughness in resisting catastrophic fracture under shellfire. It must be added that the welding of this steel was not trouble-free, particularly at the start of the war when the importance of avoiding hydrogen pickup was not known. Much of this armor plate was arc-welded with austenite stainless steel electrodes to avoid underbead cracking. When the role of hydrogen was uncovered, investigators were able to successfully develop a satisfactory low-alloy or "ferritic" welding electrode, which amounted to a low-alloy steel electrode covered with the low-hydrogen type flux regularly found on stainless steel electrodes at that time. This ferritic armor-welding electrode was the forerunner of our present EXX15 (low-hydrogen) classification.

Following World War II, steelmakers set out to develop improved constructional steels by capitalizing on the premise that a quenched and tempered steel would be stronger and tougher, and, if properly alloyed, would endure the thermal cycle of a low-hydrogen welding procedure without cracking and would be suitable for many services in the as-welded condition. At the start, some use was made of a Cr–Ni–Mo armor plate composition with the carbon content reduced to a much lower level. With a carbon content of about 0.15%, this quenched and tempered alloy steel produced a yield strength of at least 80 ksi, and, furthermore, retained good weldability. A commercial steel of this variety became known as HY-80, and has been widely used in large weldments which could not be postweld heat treated, particularly submarine hulls. However, the cost of HY-80 (because of its relatively high nickel content) and its level of strength did not offer sufficient inducement to designers of commercial structures, so metallurgists set their sights upon developing a steel with at least a 100 ksi yield strength capability. Furthermore, they were pressured to gain this objective with the least amount of costly alloying elements since the selling price of the steel would be a very important factor in commercial marketing. Success in this area is evidenced by the availability today of many quenched and tempered alloy steels which offer yield strengths of 100 ksi and higher. Table 79 lists representative quenched and tempered alloy steels offering yield strengths ranging from 70 to 220 ksi. Many of the compositions are quite novel, but despite this diversity in composition much information concerning the welding of these steels can be generalized. After a review of similarities in properties and welding behavior, we shall examine some of the details which are important in the welding of specific steels.

CHEMICAL COMPOSITION

The composition of a quenched and tempered alloy steel can be examined for at least four principal aspects: (1) hardness capability, (2) hardenability, (3) tempering resistance, and (4) toughness potentiality. Usually, the lowest carbon content that will provide the desired strength after quenching and tempering is employed in the steel. Low carbon content is desired for a number of reasons: (1) to raise the M_s temperature and encourage automatic tempering of any martensite that forms, (2) to minimize the hardness of the martensite and improve its toughness and thus reduce cracking susceptibility, and (3) to reduce the degree of volumetric expansion which occurs when martensite forms. A low carbon content also favors a low toughness–transition temperature. Carbon will raise the temperature range of brittle fracture almost 5 degrees F for each 0.01% increment of carbon present. Yet, carbon is of primary importance in gaining high strength and cannot be reduced to a very low level. To gain a yield strength of about 80 ksi minimum, approximately 0.12 to 0.18% carbon is needed. To gain 100 ksi minimum yield, the carbon content may have to run as high as approximately 0.23%. Of course, the amount of carbon needed will depend upon the amount and nature of other alloying elements present. For example, if large additions of nickel, chromium, or molybdenum are employed, it is possible to achieve a yield strength of 150 ksi with as little as 0.15% carbon. In brief, carbon is the cheap, efficient route to gain strength, but, in most cases, not without increasing the susceptibility to heat-affected zone cracking and decreasing the toughness. Some attention is being given to the use of small additions of nitrogen to supplement the effect of carbon and increase the strength of the steel. The nitrogen must be added during steelmaking and requires a special technique to control the amount retained in the steel consistently within a prescribed range. Because many of the alloying elements employed in these steels have a strong affinity for nitrogen (e.g., chromium, aluminum, titanium) the nitrogen probably is present in the form of nitrides. Only a very small amount of nitrogen can be added, perhaps in the order of 0.02%, because an excess will result in various difficulties. Porosity in the ingot is the most obvious result of excess nitrogen. There appears to be some question about the influence of nitrogen on the toughness of the steel. At lower strength levels, nitrogen appears to be useful as a strengthener without adversely affecting toughness. However, at very high strength levels, nitrogen, like carbon, seems to detract from toughness. Some use is made of boron in the quenched and tempered steels to increase hardenability. Most of the steels are produced with killed, fine-grained steelmaking practice.

The hardenability of quenched and tempered alloy steels is shrewdly gauged to not only produce a hardened microstructure when the plate is water spray-quenched during heat treatment, but also to produce this microstructure when a heat-affected area adjacent to a weld is cooled to room temperature. This is a more complex matter than it might appear because the cooling conditions during heat treatment do not correspond with those during welding. That is, with increasing plate thickness a higher hardenability is required to secure a hardened structure throughout the plate section. Yet, thicker plates generally produce faster cooling rates in their heat-affected zones during welding. Therefore, thicker plates require

Table 79 — REPRESENTATIVE QUENCHED AND TEMPERED HIGH-STRENGTH ALLOY STEELS

(Steels which are intended to be welded in the heat-treated condition)

Common designation	Applicable specifications	Chemical requirements (illustrative)[a]							Approximate strength ranges, ksi	
		C	Mn	Si	Cr	Ni	Mo	Others	Tensile	Yield
N-A-XTRA 75		0.14–0.18	0.70–0.85	0.70–0.90	0.50–0.70	...	0.14–0.18	Zr 0.08–015	90–100	70–80
Ni–Cr–Mo Steel	ASTM A543 Class 1	0.23 max	0.40 max	0.20–0.35	1.50–2.00	2.60–4.00	0.45–0.60	V 0.03 max	105–125	85 min
Ni–Cr–Mo Steel	ASTM A543 Class 2	0.23 max	0.40 max	0.20–0.35	1.50–2.00	2.60–4.00	0.45–0.60	V 0.03 max	115–135	100 min
HY-80	MIL-S-16216G (SHIPS)	0.18 max	0.10–0.40	0.15–0.35	1.00–1.80	2.00–3.25	0.20–0.60	V 0.03 max Ti 0.02 max Cu 0.25 max	...	80–100
Jalloy-S-90		0.10–0.20	1.10–1.50	0.15–0.30	...	...	0.20–0.30	B 0.005 min	105 min	90 min
SSS-100	ASTM A514 & A517 Grade E	0.12–0.20	0.40–0.70	0.20–0.35	1.40–2.00	...	0.40–0.60	Ti and/or V 0.04–0.10, Cu 0.20–0.40, B 0.0015–0.0050	115–135	100–115
SSS-100A	ASTM A514 & A517 Grade D	0.13–0.20	0.40–0.70	0.20–0.35	0.85–1.20	...	0.15–0.25	Ti and/or V 0.04–0.10, Cu 0.20–0.40, B 0.0015–0.0050	115–135	100–115
SSS-100B		0.13–0.20	0.40–0.70	0.20–0.35	1.15–1.65	...	0.25–0.40	Ti and/or V 0.04–0.10, Cu 0.20–0.40, B 0.0015–0.0050	115–135	100 min

Steel	Specification	C	Mn	Si	Cr	Ni	Mo	Other		
T-1	ASTM A514 & A517 Grade F	0.10–0.20	0.60–1.00	0.15–0.35	0.40–0.65	0.70–1.00	0.40–0.60	V 0.03–0.08, Cu 0.15–0.50, B 0.002–0.006	105–135	90–115
T-1 Type A	ASTM A514 & A517 Grade B	0.12–0.21	0.70–1.00	0.20–0.35	0.40–0.65	...	0.15–0.25	V 0.03–0.08, Ti 0.01–0.03, B 0.0005–0.005	115–135	100–115
T-1 Type B		0.12–0.21	0.95–1.30	0.20–0.35	0.40–0.65	0.30–0.70	0.20–0.30	V 0.03–0.08, B 0.0005 min	115–135	100 min
N-A-XTRA 100	ASTM A514 & A517 Grade A	0.15–0.21	0.80–1.10	0.40–0.80	0.50–0.80	...	0.18–0.28	Zr 0.05–0.15, B 0.0025 max	115–135	100–115
Jalloy-S-100	ASTM A514 & A517 Grade C	0.10–0.20	1.10–1.50	0.15–0.30	...	...	0.20–0.30	B 0.001–0.005	115–135	100–115
HY-100	MIL-S-16216	0.20 max	0.10–0.40	0.15–0.35	1.00–1.80	2.25–3.50	0.20–0.60	V 0.03 max, Ti 0.02 max, Cu 0.25 max	...	100–120
N-A-XTRA 110		0.18	0.80	0.70	0.60	...	0.20	Zr 0.07	125 min	110 min
Jalloy-S-110		0.10–0.20	1.10–1.50	0.15–0.30	...	...	0.20–0.30	B 0.0005 min	125 min	110 min
N-A-XTRA 125		0.18–0.22	0.70–0.85	0.70–0.90	0.50–0.70	...	0.14–0.18	Zr 0.08–0.15	135–145	120–130
5 Ni-Cr-Mo-V		0.10	0.75	...	0.50	5.0	0.50	V 0.07	...	140 min
HY-150		0.16–0.20	0.40–0.60	...	1.25–1.75	3.50–4.00	0.30–0.50	V 0.07–0.12	145–165	135–155
N-A-XTRA 150		0.26–0.30	0.70–0.85	0.70–0.90	0.50–0.70	...	0.14–0.18	Zr 0.08–0.15	160–170	150–160
HP 150		0.25	0.20 max	0.10 max	1.50	3.10	0.90	Cb 0.05	140–165	125–155
HP 9-4-25		0.28	0.35	0.10	0.50	8.00	0.50	Co 4.00, V 0.10	200–250	190–220

a Composition may differ slightly from the limits shown depending upon the specification applied. Single values are for typical composition where specification has not been developed.

a composition of higher hardenability principally for reason of heat treatment *prior* to welding. Because alloying is costly, it is equally important that a steel not contain unnecessary alloy content. Consequently, thinner plates can be permitted to have a leaner composition with respect to the alloying combination employed. It will be noted in Table 79 that at least two of the 100 ksi minimum yield strength steels (SSS-100 and T-1) have modifications which contain lesser amounts of alloying elements (carbon excepted) than the original alloy. The more highly-alloyed parent steel is designed to have sufficient hardenability to secure the necessary hardened structure during heat treatment of any plate thickness up to the maximum size produced in the particular steel. This may include plates as heavy as 6 inches in thickness in certain steels. Since thinner plates do not have need for the generous hardenability, the producer may offer to make plates up to a certain modest size from a less-expensive, leaner-alloy version of the same alloy steel. These modifications customarily are designated as supplementary types; for example, SSS-100 alloy steel is supplemented by SSS-100A, and by SSS-100B, which are more-economically alloyed versions for use in lighter gage plates. While this matter of alloy adjustment for plate thickness is important for reasons of cost and properties in the quenched and tempered plate, the original steel and its lower-alloy modifications have essentially the same mechanical properties and weldability. All three versions of the same steel are expected to quench to martensite during heat treatment and to temper to the same strength level. Also, they are expected to form hardened structures in heat-affected zones during welding, but with the carbon content favorably low and the remainder of the alloy content properly selected, these zones are tough as well as strong. Incidentally, the alloying elements are selected to produce transformation characteristics that favor tempered martensite and lower bainite structures.

Fig. 237 provides an I–T diagram for an alloy steel of the quenched and tempered variety which shows how transformation characteristics favor the formation of lower bainite or martensite during the cooling of austenite. The shape of the transformation curve indicates that decomposition of an austenitized heat-affected zone to ferrite and pearlite, or upper bainite is effectively suppressed by the alloying elements present in the steel, and that the cooling cycles ordinarily experienced during welding will carry the austenite to some point below 900 F whereupon transformation to lower bainite or to martensite will take place. Studies of the kinetic features of the bainite transformation have indicated that upper and lower bainite can be differentiated metallographically. Lower bainite is characterized by precipitation of carbides at about a 60 degree angle to the major axis of the bainitic-ferrite plate, whereas upper bainite may be identified by carbide precipitation parallel to this plate axis. The difference in the orientation of precipitated carbides in upper and lower bainite apparently is the cause of strength–toughness variations between the two forms of microstructure; that is, the lower bainitic structures generally display a lower toughness-transition temperature than do the upper bainitic structures.

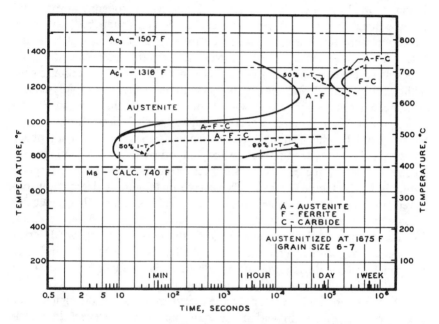

Fig. 237 — Isothermal transformation diagram for a quenched and tempered alloy steel (USS "T-1").

Diagram shows long delay time before transformation to pearlite or upper bainite, strong likelihood of transformation to lower bainite, and relatively high temperature for start of martensite transformation. (Illustrative material from United States Steel Corp.)

Much investigative work is being conducted to evaluate the fracture toughness of base metal heat-affected zones in welded quenched and tempered steels. Although the bainitic and martensitic structures in these relatively low-carbon alloy steels frequently have been referred to as being "tough"; just how tough are they? Current studies are employing both steel specimens which have been subjected to a simulated weld thermal cycle, and actual welded specimens. The synthetic specimens have been treated to represent the as-welded condition, and welded and tempered at various temperatures. These specimens have allowed regular mechanical tests to be conducted, such as notched-bar impact and crack-notch tensile tests. The welded specimens have proved more difficult to evaluate for fracture toughness. Even though this work is in its infancy, it is of more than casual interest to note that although these steels exhibit a very high degree of fracture toughness when in the quenched and tempered condition; heat-affected zones, when (1) rapidly cooled, or (2) slowly cooled during a welding operation, usually display lower toughness than did the base metal originally. When either rapidly cooled (quenched) or slowly cooled, fracture toughness, as measured by impact or crack-notch tensile tests, may be reduced by one-half. Nevertheless, this reduction is by no means as severe as that which takes place in welding higher-carbon steels. With most quenched and tempered, low-carbon steels, the rapidly-cooled heat-affected zones display somewhat better toughness than do the slowly-cooled zones. Furthermore, when the rapidly-cooled heat-affected zones are tempered by the heat of a subsequently-deposited weld bead, or by a postweld heat treatment, fracture toughness usually is substantially improved. However, the *slowly-cooled* heat-affected zones do not respond favorably to the tempering heat. The degree of toughness degradation observed in heat-affected zones depends, therefore, upon the particular thermal cycles to which it may have been subjected. Also, different steels, depending upon their composition and strength level, show different degrees of toughness degradation. We shall point out shortly the steps that can be taken during welding to alleviate the unfavorable aspects of the welding thermal cycle upon fracture toughness.

A thorough study of the heat-affected zone must distinguish the various regions that form within the zone, and the differences in metallurgical behavior between these regions. There is a grain coarsened region immediately adjacent to the weld metal. Investigators often simulate the thermal cycle of this region by heating specimens rapidly to 2400F for a short period and cooling at a rate intended to duplicate that of the same region in a particular welded joint. Moving away from the weld metal, and across the grain-coarsened region, we next find a region which was austenitized by temperatures in the range of about 1600 to 2000F, and where the structure does not display unusual grain coarsening. This region is followed by another in which the steel was heated to temperatures between the Ac_1 and Ac_3 points. Therefore, this region is called the *intercritical* region of the heat-affected zone. The final region, moving still further away from the weld, is the tempered region; wherein the original base metal microstructure is subjected to temperatures that are sufficiently high to accomplish over-tempering to temperatures which have little effect. The first three general regions of the heat-affected zone which exceed the Ac_3 temperature do not undergo an equal decrease in toughness under a particular weld thermal cycle. Studies of certain quenched and tempered low-carbon alloy steels have shown that the grain-coarsened region usually suffers the greatest damage to toughness. Complete agreement does not exist among investigators on the explanation for the greater loss of toughness at this location. Although the loss of toughness ordinarily is not as severe in the intercritical region, the microstructural changes which occur here are complex. Only limited work has been carried out to define these changes and relate the structures which are present in the intercritical region to the properties displayed in mechanical tests. Even the tempered region is deserving of close attention. This region, of course, normally is made tougher by the heat effect of welding, but at the cost of lowered strength and hardness. However, the various quenched and tempered steels vary in their resistance to softening in the tempered region, and in the degree of improvement which takes place in toughness.

A feature to be observed in the steel compositions of Table 79 is the frequent use of strong carbide-forming alloying elements, such as titanium, vanadium and zirconium. These elements retard softening during tempering. Therefore, the spray-quenched plates may be tempered at high temperatures (up to 1250 F) for maximum ductility and toughness. Furthermore, the weld heat-affected zones resist excessive softening during repeated exposure to sub-critical temperatures in multi-pass welding.

An important recent finding about the composition of quenched and tempered alloy steels concerns their residual element content. The higher-strength base metals, like the highest-strength weld metals discussed in Chapter 10, display markedly better toughness when residual or impurity elements like phosphorus, sulfur, silicon, nitrogen, oxygen and hydrogen are kept as low as possible. The benefit derived from reducing these elements to very low levels (0.005% maximum each, for example) becomes very noticeable in steels having yield strengths above 125 ksi. Consequently, it is not unusual to find that steels having 150 ksi yield strength and higher are produced using special steelmaking practices, possibly involving electric-furnace melting, vacuum degassing, or vacuum remelting.

In summary, the composition of a quenched and tempered alloy steel is designed to provide sufficient hardenability to secure a hardened structure of martensite or lower bainite, sufficient resistance to tempering to maintain high strength even with limited carbon content, and a combination of alloys that fosters a low toughness-transition temperature. These steels have admirable toughness considering their high strength. It is not unusual for a steel with 100 ksi minimum yield strength when properly welded to display a 15 ft-lb minimum V-Charpy transition temperature as low as –90 F. Ordinarily, the NDT temperature is equally as low.

WELDING CHARACTERISTICS

Considering their high strength, the quenched and tempered steels are relatively simple to weld. Most of the welding processes regularly used on low-alloy steels can be applied, and, with little or no restriction, can produce as-welded joints with strength and toughness comparable to the quenched and tempered base metal. This remarkable performance must be credited largely to the good toughness which accompanies the low-carbon martensitic or bainitic structure. However, two cardinal rules must be observed during any fusion welding operation:

1. The cooling rate of any austenitized heat-affected area must be sufficiently rapid to reform a martensitic or a lower bainitic structure.
2. Low-hydrogen conditions must be strictly maintained to avoid underbead cracking.

If the cooling rate of the heat-affected zone is too slow, transformation will proceed to ferrite with high-carbon martensite regions or to coarse bainite. Consequently, the strength and toughness of this zone will be adversely affected. The minimum rate of cooling required to produce the desired hardened structure will vary, of course, with the particular steel being welded. Some steels are more critical than others with respect to the minimum cooling rate required in weld heat-affected zones; or stated in another way, with respect to the maximum heat input that can be tolerated in making a weld. It will be recalled from discussion in Chapter 4 that the cooling rate in the heat-affected zone is reduced as the heat input per linear inch is increased. Although we have described the care taken in welding many of the hardenable alloy steels to insure a sufficiently high heat input to avoid martensite formation, *proper welding of the quenched and tempered alloy steels calls for just the opposite technique.* Table 80 contains information on the maximum heat input recommended for arc-welding one of the steels (T-1) listed earlier in Table 79. This guidance for commercial operations follows the principles set forth in Chapter 4. As the plate thickness increases, a higher heat input can be tolerated without encountering too slow a cooling rate because the larger mass of base metal is a more effective heat sink. Note that as the preheat or interpass temperature increases, the heat input must be reduced. This

Table 80 — *MAXIMUM HEAT INPUT RECOMMENDED FOR ARC WELDING T-1 QUENCHED AND TEMPERED ALLOY STEEL*

Preheat and interpass temp. deg. F	Maximum heat input in joules per inch plate thickness, inches							
	3/16	1/4	1/2	3/4	1	1¼	1½	2
70	27,000	36,000	70,000	121,000	NL	NL	NL	NL
200	21,000	29,000	56,000	99,000	173,000	NL	NL	NL
300	17,000	24,000	47,000	82,000	126,000	175,000	NL	NL
350	15,000	21,500	43,500	73,500	109,500	151,000	NL	NL
400	13,000	19,000	40,000	65,000	93,000	127,000	165,000	NL

NL indicates no limit.

Heat input values are joules per inch of weld, which are calculated by the formula

$$H = \frac{60 \, A \, V}{S}$$

Where
H = Joules per inch
A = Welding current in amperes
V = Welding arc voltage
S = Travel speed in inches per minute

(From United States Steel Corp. Design and Engineering Seminar — 1964)

action is dictated by the smaller temperature difference between heat-affected zone and unaffected base metal, which slows down the thermal flow. The limiting values set forth in Table 80 do not apply to all quenched and tempered alloy steels. Steels of lesser hardenability, or having different transformation characteristics, will require that lower maximum heat inputs be observed in welding to insure cooling in the heat-affected zones faster than the critical rate. Using HY-80 alloy steel as another example, an I–T diagram for steel of this composition (Fig. 238) shows that a faster rate of cooling is needed to avoid the appearance of proeutectoid ferrite in the transformed structure than in the case of T-1 steel. Again, it must be kept in mind that these are I–T (isothermal transformation) diagrams, and some adjustment must be made for transformation of heat-affected zones under constant cooling conditions. Nevertheless, the HY-80 steel in Fig. 238 is indicated to require a faster cooling rate than the T-1 steel in Fig. 237 to produce a properly hardened microstructure. This explains the more restrictive limitations on heat input regularly recommended for the arc-welding of HY-80 steel as outlined in Table 81. Note that a ½-inch thick plate of HY-80 steel at room temperature should be arc-welded with a heat input less than 45,000 joules, whereas a similar plate of T-1 steel could be welded under conditions of heat input as high as 70,000 joules. Quenched and tempered steels of higher

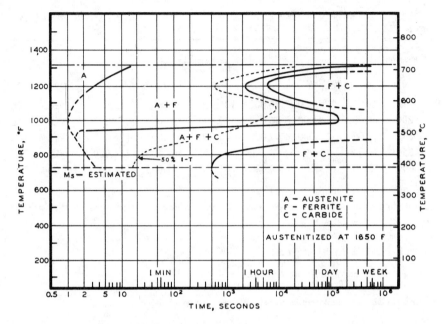

Fig. 238 — Isothermal transformation diagram for a quenched and tempered alloy steel of Cr–Ni–Mo composition (HY-80).

Diagram shows that faster rate of cooling must be maintained to suppress appearance of proeutectoid ferrite in microstructure than is necessary with the T-1 steel shown earlier in Fig. 237.

hardenability, which naturally have a slower critical cooling rate for transformation to a hardened structure, can be welded with somewhat higher heat input. Therefore, it is important when preparing to weld a quenched and tempered steel to consult the latest literature concerning its hardenability and weldability to determine the limitations on heat input. When such information is not available, it would be well to avoid abnormally high heat input during thermal cutting and welding. In the face of this well intended advice, some fabricators have insisted on welding quenched and tempered steels with high heat inputs in order to deposit larger beads and thus more quickly accomplish the welding of a given joint. They reason that such practice is permissible where optimum fracture toughness of the base metal heat-affected zones is not required. Data have been published on the tensile properties of weld joints made under so-called "hot" production welding conditions, but little information is given on the fatigue and impact properties of these joints.

Heat input, while subject to specific limitations for certain steels,

Table 81 — *PREHEATING TEMPERATURES AND HEAT INPUT CONTROL EMPLOYED IN GOUGING AND WELDING HY–80 STEEL*

Preheating Temperatures for Air Carbon-Arc Gouging

Plate Thickness, Inches	Minimum Temperature, F
1⅛ or less	75
Over 1⅛	150

Preheating for Arc Welding

Plate Thickness, Inches	Minimum Preheat and Interpass Temperature, F *
½ or less	75
Over ½ but under 1⅛	125
Over 1⅛	200

*Under no circumstances shall 300 F be exceeded.

Heat Input During Arc Welding

Plate Thickness, Inches	Joules/Inch, Maximum
½ or less	45,000
Over ½ but under 1⅜	60,000
Over 1⅜	80,000

always should be guided by the following general points when cutting and welding quenched and tempered alloy steels.

Oxyacetylene torch cutting may be used to cut plate and bevel edges, but care should be taken to maintain at least normal cutting speeds and avoid overheating, particularly in localized areas at starting points. If postcut heating is employed to reduce the hardness of the torch cut surfaces for machining, the plate surfaces should not be heated above about 1150 F. Oxyacetylene torch gouging for the preparation of joints ordinarily is not satisfactory because the slow travel speed and the occasional stops and re-starts easily result in excessive heat input. Gouging by the air carbon-arc process is a more satisfactory operation providing the precautions against carburization as described in Chapter 3 are closely followed.

Preheating is not a favored precaution in the welding of quenched and tempered alloy steels because of its strong effect in reducing cooling rate. However, if a satisfactory fast rate of cooling can be obtained in the heat-affected zone with a given amount of preheat, there normally is no further objection to preheat. In fact, preheat can provide insurance against cracking which might occur from a variety of causes. The customary practice in welding these steels is to start with the base metal at room temperature (65 to 100 F). Lower temperatures are avoided because they promote cracking. If the joints are heavy and highly restrained, or if any other factor which favors cracking is present (see later remarks on hydrogen), then a modest preheat is advisable. Again, it may be necessary to calculate the expected heat input to insure sufficiently fast cooling; of course, heavy base metal sections help in this regard. The question of interpass temperature is handled in much the same manner as preheat. High interpass temperatures are favored as insurance against cold cracking, slag entrapment and a variety of other difficulties, and yet the high interpass temperature can seriously reduce the heat-affected zone cooling rate. Common practice is to hold to a maximum interpass temperature of about 300 F. Sometimes, 250 F maximum interpass temperature is advised, but seldom any lower because of the time delay in waiting for the joint to cool. Even where a preheat of 200 F has been stipulated as a precaution against cracking, the 300 F maximum interpass temperature likely would be in order to insure a sufficiently rapid cooling rate.

Hydrogen is a potent promoter of underbead cracking in the quenched and tempered steels despite the favorable maximum hardness and high toughness which these steels normally produce in their heat-affected zones. The importance of maintaining low-hydrogen conditions during welding operations must not be underestimated. While the literature is replete with warnings against the use of electrodes with cellulosic coverings, this is not the only source of the treacherous hydrogen. The first area to scrutinize for hydrogen, or hydrogen-containing compounds, is the surfaces of the base metal upon which the welding will be performed. The edge preparation should be clean and dry. Any moisture formed as a condensate, or even scattered raindrops, is a strong threat to the soundness of the weld joint. Traces of oil are considered more objectionable because of the hydrogen contained rather than the carbon also involved. Quantitative data are not yet available on the amount of hydrogen that will cause underbead cracking in quenched and tempered alloy steels, but the damaging level can be quite low. Fillet welds made in a single pass between heavy plates without preheat are particularly susceptible to underbead cracking if hydrogen somehow enters the operation. The control of hydrogen when using the commonly used welding processes will be discussed shortly.

In addition to paying close attention to the two aforementioned rules, namely: (1) control the cooling rate of heat-affected zones, and (2) maintain low-hydrogen conditions, a third feature of good practice in welding the quenched and tempered steels is to employ multipass welding whenever possible to benefit from the tempering effect of subsequent passes.

The practicability of multipass welding will depend upon many factors in each individual application. Multipass welding obviously must be done with smaller electrodes deposited at lower heat inputs than would be employed in a single pass, and therefore the procedure coordinates nicely with (a) the need for rapid cooling in the heat-affected zones, and (b) the improved weld toughness which usually develops in a multipass weld deposit. On the other hand, multipass welding usually increases joining costs, and sometimes leads to distortion problems. The desirability of multipass welding and the finesse with which it must be applied is judged from the weldability of the steel and the toughness estimated to be required in the weld joint area. When a particular steel is found to develop unfavorable levels of hardness and toughness in the heat-affected zones adjacent to an *as-deposited* weld bead, and the tempering effect of multipass welding is therefore deemed advisable, the technique employed is like that illustrated earlier in Fig. 157(c). To emphasize the care that must be taken in depositing the final layer on the face of a butt-joint, note that in Fig. 239 the operator carelessly has not centered the tempering

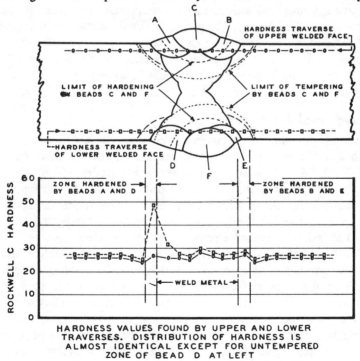

HARDNESS VALUES FOUND BY UPPER AND LOWER TRAVERSES. DISTRIBUTION OF HARDNESS IS ALMOST IDENTICAL EXCEPT FOR UNTEMPERED ZONE OF BEAD D AT LEFT

Fig. 239 — Tempering bead technique for multipass welding of a butt-joint in a quenched and tempered alloy steel.

bead on the lower face. Consequently, the heat-effect of the final pass "F" was not properly distributed to exert significant tempering on the heat-affected zone of a previously deposited bead "D" located at the left-hand side of the joint. Only at the right-hand side of the lower face do we find the heat-affected zone of previously-deposited bead "E" adequately tempered by the heat from bead "F." In fact, if the tempering bead "F" approached the right-hand side of the joint more closely, there would be a distinct possibility of forming a small, newly-hardened zone in the base metal immediately adjacent to bead "E." The upper face of the butt joint, which has an accurately-centered final pass, is shown to have properly tempered heat-affected zones on each side. Effective utilization of the benefits of tempering from multipass welding calls for strict adherence to bead sequence, proper bead size, and accurate placement. Many opportunities will be found to gain tempering-effect with little or no extra welding. Often, logical bead sequence provides the effect desired. For example, many weldments are composite structures employing both ordinary carbon steel and high-strength alloy steel. When welding a Tee joint between mild steel and a quenched and tempered alloy steel, if the fillet is to be made with two or more passes it would be efficacious to split the last layer and deposit the last pass in contact with the mild steel only. Obviously, this practice avoids the formation of an untempered heat-affected zone in the higher-strength quenched and tempered alloy steel. The same basic sequence can be applied to dissimilar-metal butt joints.

Shielded Metal-Arc Welding

Manual welding with covered electrodes is widely used on the quenched and tempered alloy steels because of the standardized classes of AWS-ASTM Low-Alloy Steel Covered Electrodes which are readily available for joining, and which deposit weld metal having suitable properties in either the as-welded or the stress-relieved conditions. For any of the quenched and tempered alloy steels having a tensile strength up to about 125 ksi, a standard electrode can be selected from those listed in AWS A5.5 that will deposit metal in the joint having matching strength, or almost any variation in properties that may be needed. Usually, the strength of the weld metal in the joint is slightly higher than that of undiluted weld metal specimens because of additional alloy picked up from the base metal. Among the alloying elements picked up by the weld metal, a small, but important, increase in carbon content invariably can be seen. This upward shift in weld metal carbon content results from having less than 0.15% carbon present in all welding electrodes designed for as-welded usage while the quenched and tempered alloy steel plate ordinarily contains more than 0.15% carbon. While the carbon increase may seem small, it is, of course, the most potent element for raising the strength of the weld metal. For making butt joints in quenched and tempered alloy steels, the general practice is to select an electrode which produces weld metal in the joint having strength equal to the base metal. This is seldom the practice in making fillet welds because experience shows that the weld metal in a fillet joint rarely is expected to have strength equal to that of the base metal. More important, the fillet joint often calls for the weld metal to exhibit good ductility and toughness to accommodate strain during distortion and notch effect at the root and toe of the weld bead. For example, a quenched and tempered alloy steel designed to have a 100 ksi minimum yield strength often is welded with E110XX electrodes when making butt joints, but E90XX electrodes usually are employed for fillet welds. Note that although the E110XX electrode is expected to display a minimum yield strength of only 97 ksi in undiluted all-weld-metal test specimens, weld metal deposited in actual joints of alloy steel regularly displays a yield strength in the approximate range of 100 to 110 ksi. While E90XX desposits produce a joint yield strength of about 85 to 95 ksi, this lower strength ordinarily is adequate for fillet welds in a 100 ksi yield strength base metal.

Rarely is an exception made to the practice of using electrodes with low-hydrogen type flux coverings for welding the high-strength, quenched and tempered alloy steels. The need for avoiding hydrogen pickup grows more acute as the strength of the base metal increases. While the use of preheat can alleviate the cracking danger from hydrogen, it is common practice to continue with every precaution even though preheat has been applied. In metal-arc welding practice, the precautions usually amount to the selection of EXX15, EXX16 or EXX18 electrodes. Procurement would include the use of hermetically sealed shipping containers or some form of special packaging to avoid a significant pickup of moisture during transit or storage. The moisture content of the electrode covering when issued for use should be very low. A maximum moisture content of 0.20% appears to be a very satisfactory level. Some studies suggest that a maximum moisture content of 0.10% is to be preferred. The moisture content can be determined by the high temperature method described in AWS A5.5. If there is any indication that the covering has picked up moisture, for example, as indicated by a determination which exceeds 0.20%, the electrodes should be given a high temperature baking treatment. Most electrodes will safely withstand treatment at 800 F to regain the low moisture level. It is now common practice to preheat *all* low-hydrogen covered electrodes to approximately 200 to 300 F in an oven or heated electrode cabinet until needed for welding. The well equipped fabricator provides his operators with portable heated containers for about 10 pounds of electrodes which can be placed conveniently at their side. A more common practice is to allow the operator to withdraw any required amount of electrodes from the baking oven and to stipulate the maximum period of time within which these electrodes must be used. Time limits ranging from one to three hours have been put in force. However, the welding engineer must recognize that while a time limit of 3 hours might be perfectly safe for welding in a heated, dry shop, a similar operation being conducted outside in humid weather might be endangered by moisture picked up by the covering on the electrodes during the later stages of the 3 hour period.

A specialized technique has developed for depositing covered electrodes in the joints of quenched and tempered alloy steels. Multiple passes of relatively small beads are preferred because of the beneficial tempering effects associated with the repeated heating. Most weld beads are deposited as stringer beads or with a minimum weave, perhaps no more than 2½ times the electrode diameter. The purpose of minimizing weaving motion is to maintain a reasonably fast travel speed and thus avoid an excessively high heat input. The object of fast travel speed is, of course, to secure the rapid cooling in the heat-affected zone. One characteristic of the higher-strength alloy electrodes, which goes counter to the aim for fast travel speed and rapid cooling, is their tendency to deposit weld metal at the starting point which contains some porosity. This condition frequently arises because most of the electrodes have a conservative addition of silicon. The deposited weld metal often contains 0.40% silicon at the most. This element is held to this level in order to gain the good impact strength regularly expected of the weld metal. However, this amount of silicon may not be sufficient to completely deoxidize the weld metal at the start of deposition where the protection to be afforded by the electrode covering has not yet fully developed. As a result of having experienced porosity at the start of weld beads, operators sometimes employ the technique of striking the arc with a new electrode a little ahead of the real starting point, welding backwards until the real starting point is reached, and finally traveling forward in the usual manner. This manipulation generally removes the porosity from the initially deposited metal, but the heat input over the starting area is somewhat higher than would be indicated by the prescribed current, voltage and travel speed. Indeed, the latter is only one-half the prescribed speed. Whether this increase in heat input at the start will leave an area having an undesirable microstructure will depend, of course, upon the criticality of the steel's transformation behavior.

Submerged-Arc Welding

Close examination of the technology involved in submerged-arc welding will show certain conditions favorable for the quenched and tempered alloy steels while others border on being unfavorable. Submerged-arc weld beads can be deposited at high rates of travel speed which is desirable for minimizing heat input. However, common practice is to complete the joint with as few beads as possible. This practice is likely to be unfavorable, not only from the standpoint of heat input, but because of poor weld metal toughness. Heavy beads often display low impact test values. Results comparable to those obtained with covered electrode welded joints can be secured with multi-pass submerged-arc welded joints using relatively small beads. Much of the submerged-arc welding of quenched and tempered steels is carried out with an electrode of ⅛ in. size and smaller, even on heavy plate.

No specification is yet in existence which standardizes the composition of the electrode or the granular flux used in submerged-arc welding alloy steels. Therefore, selection of electrode and flux must be made from proprietary products which are available. Considerable care must be exercised in selecting an electrode and flux combination to be certain the alloy composition of the deposit will produce the desired mechanical properties. One of the principal objectives is, of course, to provide the required weld metal strength. Butt joints ordinarily require weld metal with strength above the minimum specified for the base metal, but not substantially higher than the actual base metal strength. Excessive strength in the weld metal can cause difficulty in meeting bend test requirements, and may lead to difficulty in fabrication or in service. Predetermination of weld strength is not a simple matter in submerged-arc welded joints because of the important role played by dilution. Weld strength is established to a large degree by weld composition. The latter is determined by the total amount and nature of alloys contributed by the electrode, flux, and base metal. Because base metal composition varies considerably among the quenched and tempered alloy steels, dilution is a highly influential factor. Successful performance by a specific electrode–flux combination in a particular welded joint does not necessarily signal equal success when the combination is applied to another joint which incorporates a change in base metal, joint preparation, or arc welding conditions.

The distribution of alloy in the various electrode–flux combinations offered for submerged-arc welding the high-strength alloy steels varies widely with the different products. It is important to use only combinations of wire and flux for which the deposit composition is known, or which have been specifically designated to weld a given type of base metal. In some cases, all of the required alloying elements are contained in the composition of an alloy steel electrode and practically no alloy is included in the flux. On the other hand, it is feasible to have virtually all of the required alloying elements present in the flux and make use of a carbon steel electrode. Where a substantial amount of alloy is added to the weld deposit from the flux, close control of the welding operation is very important in order to secure weld metal of uniform composition. Little variation can be tolerated in travel speed, current, voltage and other conditions which affect the amount of flux melted without making a noticeable change in weld metal composition.

Welding engineers often pre-calculate the composition of submerged-arc weld deposits as a check on the properties likely to be exhibited by the joint. As a first step in calculating the probable composition, an accurate drawing of the cross section of the joint prior to welding is prepared. Then the size, shape and position of the individual weld beads is sketched to estimate the portion of the bead's cross section which is derived by penetration into the base metal (percent dilution). Square groove butt joints, as ordinarily made in light plate with little or no gap, usually involve about 50% weld dilution. Therefore, electrode–flux combinations which contribute relatively little alloy to the weld still are capable of making full-strength butt joints. Heavier plate, which has been beveled for submerged-arc welding, involves less dilution of the weld deposit. Consequently, more alloy must be present in the filler materials. Beveled joints, and grooves prepared by arc gouging, may involve only 15 to 30% dilution. It is important that joint preparation and weld penetration be held in good control to secure uniform alloy composition and properties in the weld metal. Also, when using an alloyed flux, it is very important that welding conditions be held as constant as possible. Individual changes in current, voltage, travel speed, base metal temperature, flux burden, electrode stick-out, etc., without a compensating change in another factor, will alter the relative amounts of base metal, electrode and flux melted. Consequently, a uniform flux-to-metal ratio must be maintained during deposition to ensure consistent alloy composition. On the average, the weight of flux melted is equal to the weight of the electrode deposited. However, a larger *proportion* of flux will be melted as (1) the voltage is raised, (2) the current is lowered, (3) the travel speed is decreased, and (4) the preheat or interpass temperature is increased.

Submerged-arc welding operations also must be closely guarded against hydrogen pickup. Particular attention must be given to the granulated flux. Although this material may be very low in moisture content as received, the common practice of reusing the unmelted flux may lead to difficulty. The excess flux from the overburden should be carefully screened of all fused pieces and then stored in sealed containers. The presence of excessive moisture in certain fluxes sometimes can be detected by the presence of tiny pinholes in the undersurface of the fused flux which contacts the weld metal. Hydrogen, in submerged-arc welding of high-strength quenched and tempered steels, in addition to causing underbead cracking, may produce cold cracking in the weld metal. Holding the flux in a container heated to about 300 F is a practical way of avoiding difficulty with hydrogen.

Advancements have been made recently in the formulation of granulated fluxes for submerged-arc welding the quenched and tempered steels. These have come about through a determined effort by investigators to ascertain why submerged-arc deposited weld metal, in general, has displayed inferior toughness when compared with weld metal from the shielded metal-arc and gas metal-arc processes; even when the deposits are of equivalent size. A review of the work in this area reveals the following helpful features with regard to flux formulation when aiming for highest fracture toughness in a high-strength, alloy steel weld metal:

1. Use ingredients of highest purity.

2. The ratio of CaO to SiO_2 should be fairly high; i.e., in the vicinity of 1.0 to 1.1.

3. Substantial amounts of fluorspar and titania should be present.

4. The alloying elements contributed by the flux should be coordinated with the alloys present in the electrode. For example, avoid a high level of silicon in the weld metal, but do not risk inadequate deoxidation.

In addition to meeting all of the usual operating requirements of a submerged-arc welding flux, two special objectives were to produce weld metal with (1) a very low non-metallic inclusion content, and (2) the lowest possible oxygen content. The importance of controlling oxygen was indicated by a study which compared the properties of weld metal deposited by the submerged-arc and gas metal-arc processes using the same electrode. The gas metal-arc deposited weld metal displayed better toughness than that from submerged-arc welding. Despite a higher silicon content in the submerged-arc weld metal, its oxygen content was about 6 times that of argon-shielded weld metal.

Gas Metal-Arc Welding

The gas metal-arc welding process would seem to be admirably suited for welding any of the hardenable alloy steels because of the ease with which a hydrogen-free arc atmosphere can be obtained. Welding of the quenched and tempered alloy steels has been performed with shielding of (a) argon, (b) argon plus very small amounts of oxygen, (c) mixtures of argon, helium and carbon dioxide, and (d) pure carbon dioxide. All of these shielding gases are extremely low in hydrogen; hence, the hydrogen content of the weld pool is controlled by the nature of the electrode and the base metal. The particular shielding gas used determines not only the operating characteristics of the arc and mode of metal transfer, but also the composition of the weld metal to some degree. It is important to consider the silicon content of the weld metal. Many of the electrodes manufactured for gas metal-arc welding purposes have an elevated silicon content to insure adequate deoxidation of the deposit. Often the silicon level has been established upon the basis of deposition under carbon dioxide shielding. However, if a shielding gas composed principally of argon and/or helium is employed, the silicon content of the weld metal may be too high for best fracture toughness. Work conducted with both an argon-oxygen (2%) mixture, and a mixture of 80% argon–20% carbon dioxide as shielding gases showed that the properties of gas metal-arc welded joints are very similar to those of joints made by the shielded metal-arc process using covered electrodes. Some evidence was found, however, that shielding gases composed of a 50–50, argon–carbon dioxide mixture, or entirely of carbon dioxide, produce weld metal which has somewhat lower impact strength.

A practical problem which hampers the use of gas metal-arc welding on alloy steels is that of securing welding electrodes of the required alloy composition. Inasmuch as the process does not make use of an electrode covering, or a granulated flux, all of the needed alloying elements must be contained in the electrode (or the base metal if a particular amount of dilution can be anticipated). Since many of the quenched and tempered steels require weld metal of different compositions to achieve matching properties, obviously a number of electrode compositions are required. To date, the limited demand for bare alloy steel electrode wires of suitable compositions to accommodate the various quenched and tempered alloy steels has encouraged only moderate development activity in this area. Undoubtedly, more gas metal-arc welding will be performed on the quenched and tempered alloy steels as electrodes of proper, proved compositions become available.

Postweld Stress-Relief Heat Treatment

To select the proper temperature at which to stress relieve a weld-ment made of quenched and tempered alloy steel, the welding engineer should be quite familiar with the heat treatment originally applied to the base metal. These steels are treated by austenitizing at a prescribed temper-ature above the Ac_3 point and quenching with a water spray. The hardened plate then is tempered by reheating to a prescribed temperature somewhere in the range of about 950 to 1300 F. The tempering temperature will depend upon the composition of the steel and the mechanical properties wanted. Steels in this category having a yield strength of 100 ksi and below usually can be tempered about 1150 to 1250 F. Higher strength steels may require tempering in the range of 950 to 1150 F. Many metallurgists like to see the composition sufficiently alloyed to require a tempering temperature of about 1200 F. This is a good indication that the tempering effect of multipass welding is not likely to soften the heat-affected zones too much. When the quench-hardened steel is tempered below about 1100 F to gain the required strength, there is a strong possibility that regular multipass welding will leave the heat-affected zones at a strength level below that of the original quenched and tempered plate. In this case, the weld joints may be acknowledged to have a strength somewhat lower than the unaffected base metal. The only recourse to regain full strength would be to retreat the weldment by quenching and tempering, which defeats one of the principal objectives of this steel.

Stress-relief heat treatment, when required, should not be performed at a temperature which exceeds that used for tempering the plate. In fact, a stress relieving temperature about 50 to 100 degrees F lower than the earlier tempering treatment is desirable to avoid any danger of lowering the strength of the plate. A temperature in the vicinity of 1100 to 1150 F is preferred because this is sufficiently high to insure a substantial reduction in residual stress in the weldment. Of course, if the steel is of very high strength — some of which is attributable to a relatively low tempering temperature — then any stress relieving heat treatment will be handi-capped. For example, the HY-100 steel listed in Table 79 may be tempered at 1000 F to secure the minimum yield strength of 100 ksi. A weldment of HY-100 if required to be stress relieved ordinarily should be heated no higher than about 950 F during this operation to maintain the original properties in the unaffected base metal. It will be debatable whether this temperature will accomplish sufficient stress relief to assure dimensional stability, prevent stress-corrosion cracking, or whatever the reason for the treatment.

Particular consideration must be given to the weld metal in planning a stress-relief heat treatment for a weldment of quenched and tempered alloy steel. It must be kept in mind that the weld deposit invariably is of a different composition because of the many reasons explained in Chapter 10. While the weld composition may be capable of producing strength and toughness equal to that of the base metal in the as-welded composition, these satisfactory weld metal properties may not necessarily remain unchanged after a stress-relief heat treatment. Because the weld metal usually is of lower carbon content, the stress relieving treatment may lower the strength of the weld metal more than the base metal. Of course, the standard classes of electrodes in AWS A5.5 are required to meet certain minimum strength requirements in the stress-relieved condition in undiluted (all-weld-metal) form. However, the weld metal in an actual joint, particularly in the higher-strength steels, requires close examination to be certain that not only will the required strength be maintained, but adequate toughness as well.

High-strength weld metals containing an appreciable amount of vanadium (perhaps greater than 0.05%) have shown a pronounced tendency to become embrittled by stress-relief heat treatment. This embrittlement apparently is caused by the microstructural change associated with secondary hardening which occurs when vanadium is present in weld metal exposed for some time at temperatures in the vicinity of 1000 F. The embrittlement is sufficiently acute in high-strength weld metals having yield strengths above 90 ksi to shift their toughness–transition temperature from a subzero level to well above room temperature! Consequently, any weldment of quenched and tempered alloy steel which is to be stress-relief heat treated should not be joined with a vanadium-alloyed weld metal if good toughness is a requisite. This shortcoming of vanadium-containing weld metal holds for deposits made by any of the fusion joining processes. Because vanadium is a very effective strengthening element in weld metal, it frequently is used in the composition of high-strength alloy steel weld metals.

Welding HY-80 Steel

Much attention has been directed to the welding of HY-80 steel (80–100 ksi YS), described earlier as the harbinger of the weldable quenched and tempered alloy steels. Despite limited usage in commercial weldments because of offering only modest strength for its cost, HY-80 has been employed extensively in military equipment, particularly as submarine hull plate. HY-80 is highly regarded by the military for displaying a high degree of fracture toughness, not only to low temperatures, but also under ballistic shock loading. Furthermore, the weldability of HY-80, although demanding professional-like handling, has proved to be consistent and adequate for the fabrication of many kinds of large, complex structures.

Specification MIL-S-16216 (SHIPS) provides chemical composition requirements as shown in Table 79, but it is necessary for the steelmaker to tailor the analysis to the particular plate or bar section to be produced. The specification permits the carbon maximum of 0.18% to be raised by 0.02% for plates 6-inches thick and over. Other adjustments within the required ranges often are made in alloy composition according to base metal thickness. These practices have led metallurgists to call the "lean" HY-80 analyses, which are regularly used in thinner sections, as HY-80 (L). The "rich" analyses, used in heavier plates, are referred to as HY-80 (H). In both cases, the steel is made with fine-grain practice and no boron is added to "needle" the hardenability. The percent of phosphorus and sulfur *together* are required to be no greater than 0.045%. Typical analyses for heats of HY-80 steel are as follows:

	C	Mn	P	S	Si	Cr	Ni	Mo	V	Ti
HY-80 (L)	0.15	0.20	0.012	0.025	0.22	1.16	2.25	0.29	0.001	0.003
HY-80 (H)	0.18	0.30	0.011	0.022	0.23	1.52	2.94	0.39	0.002	0.005

	Al	B	N	O
(Continued)	0.06	0.0005	0.0078	0.0034
	0.002	0.0006	0.0075	0.0065

Plates of HY-80 are required to be hardened by quenching with sufficient cooling velocity to attain a microstructure of at least 80% martensite. The final tempering temperature must not be less than 1100 F, and of course, prescribed tensile, and Charpy V-notch impact requirements at −120 F must be met. Brinell hardness is expected to fall within the range of 205–240.

Repair welding is permitted, within certain limitations of MIL-S-16216, on plates of HY-80, but always *prior* to heat treatment. Such repair welding has been performed by the manual shielded metal-arc process using a special low-hydrogen electrode developed for the purpose. This electrode is described in MIL-E-22200/5 (SHIPS) where it is classified as Type MIL-8218 YQT. The deposit composition falls within the following limits:

C	Mn	P	S	Si	Cr	Ni	Mo	V
0.10– 0.15	0.80– 1.15	0.030 max	0.030 max	0.30– 0.60	0.90– 1.20	1.50– 2.00	0.45– 0.75	0.02 max

Note that this weld metal (except for its manganese content) is more or less a "lean" HY-80 composition, and that a firm restriction has been placed upon residual vanadium content to be certain that the weld-repaired areas do not suffer temper brittleness after heat treatment. Weld metal specimens deposited by these electrodes are expected to meet tensile and impact property requirements befitting HY-80 steel.

When fabricating critical weldments of HY-80 steel, preheating and interpass temperatures, and heat input during welding are held to the limitations outlined earlier in Table 81. Common practice is to preheat to 200–300 F whenever possible. Sometimes 150 F will be accepted as a starting temperature if the weld is only a build-up, or the joint is under little restraint. Wide use is made of multipass welding and a final tempering bead. Because of the excellent toughness displayed by weld joints in HY-80, stress-relief heat treatment is applied only for reasons of achieving dimensional stability in weldments, or as assurance against stress-corrosion cracking in certain service environments. When stress-relief heat treatment is applied, the temperature is limited to 1025 F. Postweld stress-relief heat treatment precludes the use of weld metal containing vanadium as an alloying element because of the embrittlement which would be caused by its presence.

Shielded metal-arc welding of HY-80 is performed with electrodes conforming to MIL-E-22200/1; described therein as mineral covered, iron powder, low-hydrogen electrodes suitable for as-welded, or stress-relieved weld application. These electrodes are identical with the classification listed as EXXX18-M currently contained in AWS 5.5 (ASTM A 316). Butt joints usually are made with electrodes of the E11018-M class because the weld metal strength moreoften closely matches the *actual* strength of the HY-80 base metal. However, E10018-M electrodes could be used and should meet the *minimum* strength requirements for joints. Toughness (impact) requirements of joints demand more attention than strength, and close control must be exercised over heat input as outlined in Table 81 to secure satisfactory results. Fillet welds often are made with E9018–M electrodes.

Gas metal-arc welding was the first *automatic* process to qualify for making joints in HY-80 under the Navy's submarine building program. Qualification hinged upon the development of an alloy steel electrode capable of depositing weld metal which would meet the mechanical property requirements. Only one alloy steel electrode presently is approved for use. This is an electrode of Mn–Ni–Mo–V composition, identified as MIL-B88 under specification MIL-E-19822 (SHIPS). The composition limits for this wire are as follows:

C	Mn	P	S	Si	Ni	Mo	V
0.08 max	1.15–1.55	0.025 max	0.025 max	0.35–0.65	1.15–1.55	0.30–0.60	0.10–0.20

Note that this electrode contains vanadium as an alloying addition. So for this reason, joints which are gas metal-arc welded with MIL-B88 electrode are not ordinarily permitted to be stress-relief heat treated. In the as-welded condition, deposits must display a 0.2% YS of 88 ksi minimum, a hardness of 260–300 VPN, and a Charpy V-notch impact value of 20 ft-lbs minimum at −60 F.

Submerged-arc welding was avoided in HY-80 steel fabrication until only recently because of poor toughness in weld deposits by this process. Investigators assigned the task of making joints by submerged-arc welding in submarine construction now have developed two electrode–flux combinations that can produce acceptable welds. MIL-E-22749 (SHIPS) covers electrode–flux combinations that produce *weld metal* compositions within the following limits:

	First Combination	Second Combination
Electrode	MIL–EB82	MIL–MI88
Flux	MIL–EB	MIL–MI
Weld Metal Composition		
Carbon	0.12 max	0.06 max
Manganese	0.80–1.25	1.00–1.50
Phosphorus	0.020 max	0.010 max
Sulfur	0.020 max	0.010 max
Silicon	0.80 max	0.50 max
Nickel	0.80–1.25	1.40–1.90
Chromium	0.30 max	0.10–0.30
Molybdenum	0.15–0.60	0.20–0.40
Copper	0.40–1.10	0.10–0.30
Vanadium	0.05 max	0.05 max
Titanium	....	0.10 max
Zirconium	....	0.10 max
Aluminum	....	0.10 max

These electrode–flux combinations can deposit weld metals that have a yield strength well over 90 ksi and an NDT temperature in the vicinity of −150 F, both in the as-welded, and the stress-relief heat treated conditions. Charpy V-notch impact values for weld metal usually are greater than 40 ft-lbs at −80 F. As would be expected, the fluxes in MIL-E-22749 are based upon the new concepts described earlier — namely, to strive for weld metal which has a low oxygen content, and which contains a minimum number of nonmetallic inclusions.

Some difficulty has been experienced with cracking in the heat-affected zone of HY-80 weldments. One laboratory sampled seventeen welded specimens made with different welding procedures and found most of them to contain microcracks. A few of them contained macrocracks. These defects were located in the heat-affected zone adjacent to the fusion line, and appeared to have initiated in the same manner as the intergranular cracking described in Chapter 13 under "Hot Cracking in Reheated Metal." Welding procedure appears to have little influence upon the severity of microcracking in the HY-80 weldments. Cracking has been found in joints welded by the shielded metal-arc, gas metal-arc, and submerged-arc processes. Many of the microcracks change their mode of propagation from intergranular to transgranular as they grow in size; suggesting that some embrittlement phenomena (quite likely hydrogen embrittlement) also is involved in this problem. The cause of this defect in welded HY-80 has not been conclusively established. Some evidence has been obtained in studies on HY-80 steel that liquation along grain boundaries is responsible for crack initiation. Propensity to boundary liquation seems to be related to sulfur and its tendency to diffuse into the grain boundary area at high temperatures. However, the cracking susceptibility of various heats of HY-80 steel did not correlate closely with sulfur content. One group of investigators speculated that perhaps other elements in the composition control the tendency for sulfur to diffuse into the grain boundary, and so the problem is not necessarily overcome by using a steel with low sulfur content, *per se*.

Welding Steels of 100 ksi Minimum Yield Strength

Welding engineers concerned with weldments for non-military applications will find greatest activity with quenched and tempered alloy steels centered upon those which offer 100 ksi minimum yield strength. At the present time, these steels appear to offer most favorable strength-cost ratio, along with good weldability. Consequently, competition has spawned the largest number of new steels at this strength level. Much of the advertising, articles in trade journals, and technical reports and papers deal with 100 ksi minimum yield strength steels, which, for the sake of brevity, we will refer to as the "YS-100" steels.

Among the YS-100 steels listed in Table 79, is a familiar Cr–Ni–Mo composition bearing the new designation *HY-100*. This steel is a very rich-analysis version of HY-80, and it is tempered at a lower temperature (1050 F minimum) to provide a yield strength in the range of 100–120 ksi. Compared to HY-80, the usage of HY-100 by the military is quite small. This can be attributed to its more recent introduction (1962), and somewhat more critical weldability. HY-100 is not likely to see widespread use because the military now has set their sights on developing a weldable steel of about 150 ksi minimum yield strength, which shall be discussed shortly. Little commercial use is made of HY-100 because of unfavorable cost as compared with other proprietary steels offering similar properties.

Much information can be found in the literature on the welding of "T-1" steel, one of the first designed to fullfill the needs of the commercial market. T-1 steel was mentioned (see Table 80) during initial discussion of the general precautions to be taken in welding alloy steels of the quenched and tempered variety. Welding engineers often ask the question, "Can all of the YS-100 steel be welded with the same procedures?" The answer to this question is that almost exasperating cliche, "Yes and no!" The procedures employed are the same in all general respects, but small details must be altered to properly accommodate each steel representing a different composition. Most certainly, all of the precautionary measures described to this point concerning hydrogen, excessive heat input, and untempered heat-affected zones should be part of the procedure for any of the YS-100 steels. However, let us see what specific conditions or welding materials must be tailored for individual steels.

In the case of T-1 steel, the minimum preheat and interpass temperatures, suggested for welding by any of the three commonly-used arc-welding processes, are shown in Table 82. Although heat input limitations for T-1 steel were shown earlier in Table 80, it is logical that the lower-alloy T-1 type A steel, with its lesser hardenability, would be subject to more-restrictive heat input limitations during welding. Accordingly, the producer suggests the maximum welding heat input for T-1A shown in Table 83.

Selection of covered electrodes for joining the T-1 steels can be guided by the remarks made earlier under *Shielded Metal-Arc Welding,* and by footnote c in Table 82. No particular problems should be encountered in gaining the required joint strength with the standard classes of electrodes available in AWS A5.5 (ASTM A 316). The electrode for gas metal-arc welding given as an example in footnote d of Table 82 is one which conforms to MIL-E-19822(SHIPS), Type MIL-B88. It will be recalled that this is a *vanadium*-alloyed filler metal. Consequently, joints welded with this electrode should not be postweld stress-relief heat treated. Fortunately, other electrodes without vanadium as an alloying addition are available for those weldments which require stress-relief. Some of these are tubular electrodes that contain flux and/or powdered alloys to produce a weld deposit of the required composition. For submerged-arc welding of T-1 steels, the electrode–flux combination may be either (a) alloy electrode–neutral flux, or (b) carbon steel electrode–alloyed flux (see footnotes e and f, Table 82). Note that for plates above ½-inch

Table 82 — *SUGGESTED PREHEAT AND INTERPASS TEMPERATURES FOR ARC-WELDING T-1 STEELS*

Plate Thickness, Inches	MINIMUM PREHEAT OR INTERPASS TEMPERATURE, DEG. F[a]			
	Manual Metal-Arc Process[c]	Gas Metal-Arc Process[d]	Submerged-Arc Process Alloy Electrode – Neutral Flux[e]	Carbon Steel Electrode-Alloyed Flux[f]
Up to ½, incl.	50[b]	50	50	50
Over ½ to 1, incl.	50	50	50	200
Over 1 to 2, incl.	150	150	200	300
Over 2	200	200	300	400

[a] Preheat temperature above the minimum may be required for highly restrained weld joints.
[b] Welding at any initial plate temperature below 100 F will require extreme care to minimize moisture on the steel being welded.
[c] Example: AWS E11018 covered electrode depositing Mn–Ni–Cr–Mo weld metal; a higher-strength electrode such as E12015, E12016, or E12018 may be necessary for thin plates of T1 type A steel; lower-strength low-hydrogen electrodes of E100XX, E90XX, E80XX, or E70XX class — depending upon design — may also be suitable and if dried to moisture level of E110XX and E120XX electrodes.
[d] Example: Electrode type Mil–B–88 (Mil–E–19822 Ships) and argon with 1% oxygen.
[e] A Mn–Cr–Ni–Mo–Cu electrode (see item 10, table 50) and a suitable companion neutral flux as recommended by materiel supplier.
[f] Example: EM12K electrode (AWS A5.17) and suitable companion alloyed flux as recommended by materiel supplier.

(From United States Steel Corporation Design and Engineering Seminar — 1964)

thickness the suggested preheating and interpass temperatures for submerged-arc welding are somewhat higher than for the shielded metal-arc and gas metal-arc processes. Also, slightly higher temperatures are suggested for submerged-arc welding with an alloyed flux than when using an alloy electrode–neutral flux combination. The latter suggestion has been made as added insurance against the occurrence of weld metal cracking, the susceptibility for which is reported to be a little higher when using alloyed fluxes on actual weldments. Reasons for a slightly higher weld metal cracking tendency have not been established, but may possibly arise from improper control of welding conditions that affect the amount of flux melted and change the deposit composition.

In selecting an electrode-flux combination for the submerged-arc welding of T-1 steels, it must be kept in mind that while T-1, type B is essentially a lower alloy modification of the original T-1 steel; the T-1, type A steel is notably different because of the elimination of nickel and copper as alloying elements. In the general remarks made earlier under *Submerged-Arc Welding,* the alloy contributed to the weld deposit by the base metal (pickup) was pointed out as an important factor in establishing weld composition and properties. Therefore, electrode–flux combinations which perform satisfactorily on the original T-1 steel possibly may require some additional alloy in the electrode or flux if the same results are to be obtained in welding T-1, type A steel. This problem is handled very simply in shielded metal-arc welding by selecting an electrode from the next

Table 83 — *MAXIMUM HEAT INPUT RECOMMENDED FOR ARC WELDING
T–1, TYPE A QUENCHED AND TEMPERED ALLOY STEEL*

Preheat and interpass temp. deg. F	MAXIMUM WELDING HEAT INPUT IN JOULES/INCH PLATE THICKNESS, INCHES							
	3/16	1/4	3/8	1/2	5/8	3/4	1	1¼
70	17,500	23,700	35,000	47,400	64,500	88,600	NL	NL
150	15,300	20,900	30,700	41,900	57,400	77,400	120,000	NL
200	14,000	19,200	28,000	35,500	53,000	69,900	110,300	154,000
300	11,500	15,800	23,500	31,900	42,500	55,700	86,000	120,000
400	9,000	12,300	18,500	25,900	33,500	41,900	65,600	94,000

NL indicates no limit

$$\text{Joules per inch of weld} = \frac{\text{amperes} \times \text{volts} \times 60}{\text{speed in inches per minute}}$$

NOTE: Heat-input limits for temperatures and thicknesses included, but not shown, in this table may be obtained by interpolation.

(From United States Steel Corp. Design and Engineering Seminar — 1964)

higher strength series. However, with the gas metal-arc and submerged-arc processes, the procurement of an electrode wire of richer alloy composition may not prove as simple. Of course, if the alloyed-flux technique is being used with the submerged-arc welding process, the additional required alloy is easily incorporated in the flux.

The SSS-100 series of steels, listed in Table 79 as SSS-100, SSS-100A, and SSS-100B, represents the same arrangement of alloy composition throughout the three types, with a gradation in alloy content to tailor the steels for specific ranges of plate thickness. This uniform progression in base metal composition simplifies consideration of alloy pickup through penetration in welding. The SSS-100 steels are reported to have an alloy composition including carbide-formers that maintains strength at sub-critical temperatures in welding and during stress-relief heat treatment. Other alloying elements in the composition which provide hardenability increase the tolerance for a wide latitude of cooling conditions during welding. Sufficiently rapid cooling is obtained when any of the arc welding processes are employed with normal welding procedures. However, when welding thicknesses of base metal less than about ½ inch, the heat input for each pass should be reduced proportionately to ensure rapid cooling. Preheating is normally unnecessary with the SSS-100 steels to prevent cracking providing low-hydrogen conditions are maintained. Moderate preheat of 100–200 F may be applied to dry plates before welding to prevent hydrogen pickup. In cases where high joint restraint is involved, preheat may be desirable, and if applied, should not exceed 500 F for SSS-100, and 400 F for SSS-100A and SSS-100B. Of course, when preheat is employed, consideration should be given the heat input for each pass, since preheating produces slower cooling in the heat-affected zones. Interpass temperature for multilayer welding ordinarily should be held to approximately 300 F maximum. However, when preheat has been applied for reason of joint restraint, a commensurately higher interpass temperature range may be set. Again, the heat input per layer may require a downward adjustment to secure sufficiently rapid cooling through the upper temperatures where transformation to less-tough microstructures can occur. Like any of the YS-100 steels, SSS-100 series steels are readily welded with the standard classes of mineral-covered, low-hydrogen electrodes contained in AWS A 5.5 (ASTM A 316). The selection of covered electrodes can be made in accordance with the earlier general remarks regarding butt joint and fillet welds under *Shielded Metal-Arc Welding*. Gas metal-arc welding may be performed with a solid electrode, or a tubular electrode containing flux and/or powdered metal. Several proprietary electrodes are now available for gas metal-arc welding which deposit weld metals suitable for joints in the YS-100 steels. Any of the shielding gases, or mixtures of gases, such as argon, oxygenated argon, argon–carbon dioxide mixtures, and carbon dioxide may be used. With solid electrodes, the process may be operated with the high current density "spray type" metal transfer, the "shorting arc" which makes use of slope control and dynamic reactance as described in Chapter 3, or the "pulse-arc" which requires a special power source that supplies a pulsing direct current superimposed upon a relatively low direct welding current.

Electrode–flux combinations for submerged-arc welding the SSS-100 steels provide a good example of the manner in which base metal composition is weighed in selecting welding materials. From the information provided in Chapter 10 regarding alloy steel weld deposits, it would appear that a weld composition consisting essentially of about 1% Mn, 1½% Ni, ½% Cr and ½% Mo should be suitable for a joint in SSS-100 to secure good toughness in addition to the required strength. Inasmuch as SSS-100 steels have relatively high chromium content, but no nickel, the electrode–flux combination probably should represent a Mn–Ni–Mo composition for the most part. During deposition, the modest chromium level desired in the weld metal probably would be picked up from the base metal by penetration if no chromium was present in the filler material. The nickel content desired in the weld metal *must* be supplied by the electrode or the flux. Table 84 lists a number of electrode–flux combinations which, according to the producer of SSS-100 steels, have been successfully used in submerged-arc welding operations.

Table 84 — *ELECTRODE AND GRANULATED FLUX COMBINATIONS FOR SUBMERGED-ARC WELDING A YS–100 KSI QUENCHED AND TEMPERED ALLOY STEEL*

(This illustration for SSS–100 Series Alloy Steels)

Electrode Designation	Granulated Flux Designation	Type of Joint	Typical Tensile Properties (As-Welded)	
			UTS, ksi	YS, ksi
Alloy Steel Electrode and Neutral Flux				
110S–1 (Mil –E–23765/2 Ships)	*	Butt and Fillet	115–125	100–115
Mn–Ni–Cr–Mo–V [a]	*	Butt and Fillet	110–130	95–110
AISI 8620	*	Fillet Only	90–110	85–100
Carbon Steel Electrode and Alloy-Containing Flux				
EM12K (AWS A5.17) [b]	**	Butt and Fillet	115–125	95–115
EM12K (AWS A5.17) [b]	***	Butt and Fillet	100–115	95–105

[a] An electrode nominal composition of 0.15%C, 1%Mn, 1%Ni, ½%Cr, ½%Mo and 0.06%V.
[b] Carbon steel electrode of low-carbon, high-manganese, silicon-killed steel.
* A suitable neutral flux as recommended by materiel supplier.
** A suitable flux containing additions of Mn, Cr, Ni and Mo as recommended by materiel supplier.
*** A suitable alloy flux as recommended by materiel supplier.

Welding Steels of Greater Than 100 ksi Yield Strength

More than a half-dozen quenched and tempered alloy steels having yield strengths higher than 100 ksi are listed in Table 79. Although these steels have seen relatively little use in weldments (some steels being barely out of the laboratory development stage), there are serious needs for weldable steels of greater strength capability. Much intensive work is underway to determine their suitability for such weldments as thick hull, deep diving submarines, large diameter casings for solid propellant rocket motors, and heavy wall pressure vessels for nuclear reactors and chemical process retorts. These weldments are of such large size that conventional hardening (austenitizing and quenching) treatment after assembly by welding is not possible in most cases with presently available heat treating equipment; hence the interest in using quenched and tempered alloy steels. In general, these weldments benefit greatly from any improvement which reduces weight without loss in strength. Therefore, it is unlikely that this campaign for stronger, weldable steels will stop until the ultimate is reached; that is, a *tough* steel which displays the *theoretical* strength of iron even at *as-welded* joints.

Some of the steels which offer greater than 100 ksi yield strength are principally extensions of the alloy compositions found in successful steels of lower strength. The higher yield strength may have been secured by raising the carbon content, or by adding nitrogen, or by across the board alloy increases. The procedures for welding these steels will be very much like their lower-strength counterparts, but such details as preheating, interpass temperature, etc., may require some readjustment, which in the main will be commensurate with the carbon and nitrogen contents of the new compositions. Several of the higher strength steels shown in Table 79, however, are of distinctly new alloy composition. These deserve somewhat closer scrutiny to determine whether any real metallurgical innovation has been employed to gain strength without sacrifice in weldability.

Perusal of information available to date on steels identified as HY-150, 5 Ni–Cr–Mo–V, HP-150, and HP 9-4-25 reveals some interesting facts which appear common to all. The general nature of these steels may portend the next generation of high-strength, quenched and tempered alloy steels which we will use in weldments. With regard to strength, we find that no significant breakthrough has occurred here inasmuch as the strength in each instance is that which would be expected of a martensitic structure. From the standpoint of alloy content, all of the steels are highly alloyed to ensure the formation of martensite at almost any cooling rate that is likely to be encountered in a heat-affected zone during welding. It is noteworthy that all four steels have a substantial nickel content because of the ability of this alloying element to increase toughness and to contribute to solid solution strengthening. However, here the composition similarity ends. Carbon contents present an interesting comparison since the steels range from a relatively low level (0.10% maximum in 5 Ni–Cr–Mo–V) to a comparatively high level (0.25% nominally in HP 9-4-25). The 5 Ni–Cr–Mo–V steel obviously capitalizes on the toughness of a low-carbon martensite, and on the "Q-tempering" or self-tempering softening that occurs automatically upon cooling through a martensite range which is characterized by a relatively high M_s temperature. The HP 9-4-25 steel is unique in that cobalt is employed to offset the expected influence of its relatively high carbon content on the M_s temperature, and to avoid the retention of austenite which might ordinarily be promoted by the high nickel content. The presence of 4% cobalt in the HP 9-4-25 steel raises the M_s point from about 475 F to 550 F. This relatively high M_s temperature of the HP 9-4-25 alloy composition encourages self tempering, and is believed to play a significant role in producing microstructures in the as-welded heat-affected zones that possess remarkable toughness for their strength level.

An interesting aspect of these new, so-called *Ultra high-strength* steels is the steelmaking technology applied to control impurity element content, and the amount of residual elements which would remain from deoxidation and other treatments. Remarkable agreement appears to exist among the developers of these new steels that impurity elements, particularly phosphorus, sulfur, oxygen and nitrogen should be as low as possible in order to secure good fracture toughness. Furthermore, silicon, which has been widely used both for deoxidation and as a strengthening alloying element, now is shown to exert an unfavorable influence upon the fracture toughness of many of these steels. A high silicon content in the HP 9-4-25 steel has been shown to introduce the so called "500 F embrittlement" upon tempering within the temperature range of approximately 500 to 900 F. For these reasons, producers of ultra high-strength alloy steels prefer to melt their product under vacuum, or to deoxidize by the vacuum degassing-carbon deoxidation technique (described in Chapter 2).

The welding engineer in industry must appreciate that weldability studies on these higher-strength, quenched and tempered steels are still underway, and it is not possible to comment in any detail on the welding procedures that will be required when these steels are employed in real weldments. The results of highly restrained weld tests, and fracture-toughness tests on welded specimens suggest that these steels can be welded with procedures very much like those applied to the YS-100 steels. The heat-affected zones will vary in fracture toughness from one steel to another, but in general, all of them appear to retain an adequate degree of toughness. As might be expected, providing a filler metal for full strength butt joints in these ultra high strength steels is not a simple matter. Even with E120 series electrodes, shielded metal-arc weld deposits will be lower in strength than the base metal. The filler metal problem is being given attention, and some progress already has been made in developing a covered electrode that provides weld metal of 130–140 ksi yield strength, along with a shelf-energy of 50–60 ft-lbs Charpy-V, and 25–40 ft-lbs at –60 F. To date, the optimum weld metal composition deposited by the SMAW process appears to consist of 0.05% C, 2% Mn, 1% Cr, 2½% Ni and ½% Mo. More recently, work with the GMAW process appeared to offer better results, at least on the 5 Ni–Cr–Mo–V alloy steel, and an electrode containing 0.1% C, 1.7% Mn, 0.4% Si, 2% Ni, 1% Cr and 0.5% Mo was singled out as most suitable for supplying filler metal. Here again we find that the optimum weld metal composition is quite different from that of the base metal. Reasons for this difference were given in Chapter 10. The filler metal composition is established, of course, by coordinating the weld metal composition aims and the base metal analysis. An illustration of this coordination was given in Fig. 124. There is much work to be done in developing filler metals for use as electrodes and welding rods in the arc welding processes to join these ultra high-strength steels. At the moment, great effort is being expended on filler metals for quenched and tempered steels offering a yield strength of at least 180 ksi, even though steels of this character are hardly out of the laboratory stage. A weldable steel of this type and suitable welding materials to make joints of 100% efficiency are urgently needed for several important applications, one example being the hull of deep-diving submarines.

One weldability finding on the ultra high-strength alloy steels which must be singled out of the preliminary weld test results for comment is the occurrence of heat-affected zone cracking. This defect has appeared to a limited extent in highly restrained weld tests, such as performed with the cruciform specimen (to be described in Chapter 16). Two of these higher-strength steels (HY-150 and 5 Ni–Cr–Mo–V) have displayed a small susceptibility to this kind of cracking at the root of fillet welds in the base metal heat-affected zone. The cracking originates at the notch formed at the juncture of weld metal and base metal, and extends into the grain-coarsened microstructure adjacent to the fusion line. Cracking at this location was mentioned in discussing the weldability of HY-80 steel, and while this earlier discussion postulated that the cracking could have originated through grain boundary liquation, studies of this heat-affected zone defect in these higher-strength steels suggest other possible causes. In fact, a study of the 5 Ni–Cr–Mo–V steel has suggested that the alloying elements carbon, manganese, chromium and molybdenum strongly influence susceptibility to this form of cracking through their effect upon the temperature range of martensite formation and the stresses which develop during this transformation. Transformation at relatively high temperatures where self tempering of the martensite can occur is believed to result in lower short-range stresses and thus reduces the cracking tendency. Carbon exerted the strongest effect in promoting the heat-affected zone cracking; apparently because this element directly increases the martensite lattice strain and thereby increases transformation stresses. Statistical analyses were performed on data from cruciform specimens which were welded without preheat, and on M_s temperature determinations to help arrive at the optimum composition for 5 Ni–Cr–Mo–V steel. Even so, the presently used composition displays about 3% cracking in the cruciform weld test. While this is a low incidence of cracking, the defect nevertheless may pose a threat to the soundness of a weldment. Surprisingly, a study of heat-affected zone cracking of identical appearance in HY-150 steel disclosed that preheating to temperatures as high as 300 F did not eliminate this type of defect. Also, the use of weld metal of undermatching yield strength did not appear to reduce the severity of cracking. Although these steels appear to have surmounted the problem of maintaining a tough, strong structure in the heat-affected zones of welds, the problem of heat-affected zone cracking appears deserving of persistent attention until a complete remedy is found.

ABRASION-RESISTING ALLOY STEELS

A wide variety of alloy steels are marketed for applications in which severe wear is encountered because of the nature of the materials being handled. In general, steel plates for these abrasion resisting services are made as hard as practicable because resistance to abrasion increases directly with higher hardness. The addition of alloying elements which form more voluminous, and harder carbide particles in the microstructure also helps to increase abrasion or wear resistance. Over the years, many of the abrasion resisting steels presented a common, familiar problem insofar as welding was concerned — *too much carbon in the composition!* Most of these abrasion resisting plate sections are welded, either when fabricated into a welded article, or when tacked into place to serve as a protective buffer plate. Now, the importance of weldability has received greater recognition, and most of the suppliers of quenched and tempered alloy steel plate for structural or vessel applications also offer to furnish similar plate for use as abrasion resisting material. To secure added abrasion resistance, the plate is tempered at somewhat lower temperatures to secure higher levels of hardness than are customarily found when the same type of steel is employed as a structural or vessel material. Most producers offer abrasion-resisting quenched and tempered alloy steel plate heat treated to hardness levels of 321, 360 and 400 BHN minimum. Perhaps the welding engineer would not have to concern himself specifically with this form of steel were it not for the slightly higher carbon contents which the producers sometimes must employ to meet the higher required hardness levels in the thicker plates. Here again, we find a steel-making problem and weldability on opposite ends of a seesaw. As the plate thickness increases, the cooling rate in spray quenching is reduced in the interior of the plate, and so the carbon content or some hardenability element must be increased to gain the martensitic structure as-quenched which then can be tempered to the desired hardness level. Yet, thicker plates generally present more severe conditions in welding that lead to cracking difficulties. Therefore, when higher carbon content is employed to insure proper hardening of the plate section, the welding engineer must be prepared to cope with the higher hardness and lower toughness in heat-affected zones.

Some of the quenched and tempered alloy steels when manufactured

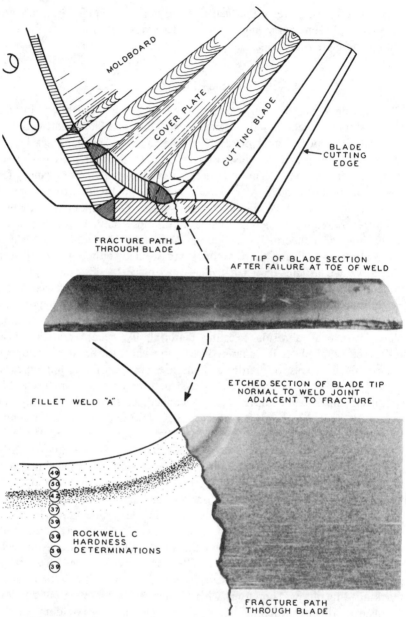

Fig. 240 — Brittle fracture of a landclearing blade of abrasion-resisting quenched and tempered alloy steel promoted by an untempered heat-affected zone beneath a point of stress concentration (toe of fillet weld).

for use in thicker plates of the higher hardness levels contain carbon in the range of 0.20 to 0.25%. Consequently, the hardness of martensitic heat-affected zones may be as high as 55-C Rockwell. With low-hydrogen welding conditions, this zone is not likely to display a serious propensity to underbead cracking, but the low fracture toughness that is likely to be found in steel of this carbon content at this hardness level certainly is cause for concern. The welding engineer must decide whether the service conditions call for the use of a multipass weld which terminates with a "tempering bead," or whether the weldment should be postweld stress-relief heat treated at a temperature that will reduce the hardness of the heat-affected zone and raise its fracture toughness to an acceptable level. Fig. 240 is an illustration of a failure in a typical application of an abrasion resisting quenched and tempered alloy steel. The ¾-inch thick blade of abrasion-resisting steel is attached to the moldboard of a bulldozer and is used for shearing off small trees during land clearing operations. The fabricator ignored the heat-affected zone of 50-C Rockwell hardness which developed beneath the fillet weld "A." In service, a running fracture initiated at the toe of the fillet weld and propagated through the entire plate section. This failure would have been avoided by somehow tempering the heat-affected zone. Also, the toe of the fillet weld should be faired into the surface of the blade without undercutting to avoid unnecessary stress concentration at this point.

HEAT-TREATABLE ALLOY STEELS

The alloy steels proposed for review here as a group are those which when welded *will not retain* the desirable properties imparted to the base metal by a previous heat treatment, but which *must be given* a postweld heat treatment to secure the best combination of properties offered by the steel. A few examples were given earlier in discussing the standard 4130, 4140 and 4340 steels of the AISI–SAE. However, a number of new high-strength alloy steels have appeared on the scene which offer better properties for weldments providing the fabricator is willing to carry out a carefully prescribed welding procedure and a postweld heat treatment. These heat treatable alloy steels are not restricted by the composition limitations imposed on the quenched and tempered alloy steels and therefore they are capable of attaining much higher strength levels. For this reason, our "heat treatable alloy steels" sometimes are called the *superstrength* alloy steels. They are being used in the airframes of supersonic planes and in the cases for solid-propellant rocket motors. Because these structures must meet rigid strength–weight requirements, they must be assembled by welding and the joints usually are expected to have a very high strength efficiency.

Table 85 — *REPRESENTATIVE HEAT-TREATABLE HIGH STRENGTH ALLOY STEELS*

(Steels which ordinarily are postweld heat treated)

Common designation	CHEMICAL REQUIREMENTS (ILLUSTRATIVE)[a]							Approximate max strength, ksi	
	C	Mn	Si	Cr	Ni	Mo	Others	Tensile	Yield
SAE 4335V or AMS 6434	0.31–0.38	0.60–0.80	0.20–0.35	0.65–0.90	1.65–2.00	0.30–0.40	V 0.17–0.23	265	215
300 M	0.41–0.46	0.65–0.90	1.45–1.80	0.70–0.95	1.65–2.00	0.30–0.45	V 0.05 min, Al 0.04–0.10	300	250
Rocoloy 270	0.39–0.45	0.40–0.80	0.90–1.30	1.15–1.60	0.75–1.10	0.40–0.60	V 0.10–0.20	310	270
D–6a*	0.42–0.48	0.60–0.90	0.15–0.30	0.90–1.20	0.40–0.70	0.90–1.10	V 0.05–0.10	300	260
Air Steel X200	0.41–0.46	0.75–1.00	1.40–1.75	1.90–2.25	...	0.45–0.60	V 0.03–0.08	280	250
H–11	0.30–0.40	0.20–0.40	0.80–1.20	4.75–5.50	...	1.25–1.75	V 0.30–0.50	300	260
H–13	0.30–0.40	0.20–0.40	0.80–1.20	4.75–5.50	...	1.25–1.75	V 0.80–1.20	310	265
HP 9–4–45	0.45	0.25	0.10	0.30	8.00	0.30	CO 4.00 V 0.10	290	250

a Single values represent typical levels of alloy content.
* D–6a alloy steel also is available as D–6ac which is produced by consumable electrode vacuum melting, and as D–6av which is air-arc melted, but is vacuum degassed prior to pouring.

Representative heat treatable high strength alloy steels are listed in Table 85. Examination of the chemical requirements will show at a glance the principal reason for their greater strength capability — *increased carbon content.* Whereas the readily weldable quenched and tempered steels contain carbon in the order of 0.10 to 0.25% as an alloying element, this higher strength group regularly makes use of carbon in the 0.30 to 0.50% range. Again, the highest strength which each steel is capable of attaining will be dependent primarily upon its carbon content. However, any steel which contains 0.40% carbon or more will be capable of attaining a tensile strength of 300 ksi, but not much higher. Once again, we encounter the fact that regardless of the amount of carbon added to a martensitic steel, this microstructure cannot be made any harder than about 65-C Rockwell nor any stronger than roughly 300 ksi tensile strength; unless unusual steps are taken in connection with the composition or the heat treatment. For the moment, let us concentrate on the remainder of the alloy composition of the steels in Table 85 to establish why the various compositions are employed even though no particular differences seem to occur in strength and hardness. First, the steels contain sufficient alloy so that any section, after austenitizing, can be easily transformed to martensite. Very highly alloyed steel, like H-11, will form martensite when given a fast air cool. This practice avoids the distortion which accompanies quenching. The other steels ordinarily are oil quenched. The second purpose of alloying is to incorporate a sufficient amount of elements which retard softening during tempering, and to produce some secondary hardening if possible. This accounts for the frequent use of chromium, silicon, molybdenum and vanadium in these steels. In general, the more highly alloyed steels can be tempered at higher temperatures which acts to produce a tougher, lower-stressed microstructure. However, none of these steels can be tempered above 1150 F without significant loss of hardness and strength. Finally, the alloying must be planned to secure good fracture toughness. This is the area where our knowledge of these steels is very weak. Briefly, the high strength exhibited by these steels in the hardened and tempered condition is not necessarily experienced in service, particularly when the steel is in the form of a weldment. Certainly the fundamental factors described in Chapter 6 will influence the behavior of the steel. Transverse properties, notch toughness, and microstructural condition all play a very important part in determining whether these steels will be able to sustain the expected loads under the varied forms of stress concentration regularly found in weldments. Experience in making cylindrical casings for rocket motors has shown that the highest strengths offered by these steels are actually demonstrated only when the vessel is formed, welded and heat treated with near perfection. This is especially true when the steel has been heat treated to its highest obtainable level of strength. In this condition, the structure will have a very low tolerance for even small flaws; that is, the low degree of fracture toughness will make even a small crack of *critical* length. The application of a higher tempering temperature will increase fracture toughness, but not without a decrease in strength. Yet, the technology for fabricating a weldment which possesses the highest strength along with adequate assurance against brittle fracture is not obtained by this simple expedient of trading strength for fracture toughness by tempering. Virtually all of the fabricating operations, including welding, and including some seemingly innocuous operations, must be performed with meticulous care to obtain the performance of which a heat treatable steel is capable in the form of a weldment.

In examining the compositions of the steels in Table 85, it will be noted that AMS 6434 steel is a modification of AISI 4337 and contains vanadium. This alloy addition acts to raise the grain coarsening temperature of austenite during heating so that the microstructure of the heat treated steel tends to have a finer grain size. AMS 6434 has been widely used in the manufacture of welded and heat treated cases for solid propellant rocket motors. The steel identified as D-6a has been used for many years in die blocks for forging and forming operations. However, the original die steel often contained a slightly higher carbon content. The carbon level was reduced in tailoring the D-6a steel for use in high-strength, heat treated weldments. AMS 6434 and D-6a steels frequently are heat treated to provide a yield strength in the range of approximately 185 to 215 ksi. Fracture toughness drops markedly at higher levels of strength and the slightest point of stress concentration in a weldment can cause premature failure under high service loads. The steel identified as 300 M was formerly known as "Tricent" and is a high-silicon modification of AISI 4340 plus a small addition of vanadium. One of the purposes of the high silicon content is to shift the so called 500 F *embrittlement,* or tempered martensite brittleness, to higher tempering temperatures. This allows the hardened steel to be tempered in the 400–600 F temperature range where a desirable level of strength is obtained without the steel suffering from 500 F embrittlement. However, the inherent fracture toughness of this steel at a high level of strength still suffers from the influence of the high silicon content.

Welding Procedures

Because of their relatively high carbon and alloy contents, the majority of heat-treatable alloy steels under ordinary conditions of welding most certainly form martensitic heat-affected zones having maximum obtainable hardness. Therefore, arc welding operations are deserving of every possible precaution, and little difference will be found in the optimum procedures prescribed for various steels. The ideal procedure for AMS 6434 steel, for example, is very much like that recommended for H-11 or X200 steels. However, in planning fusion joining operations on the heat treatable alloy steels, the welding engineer will find himself frequently pressed to find a safe compromise between the ideal treatment and the practicable technique. If welded without preheat, the martensitic heat-affected zones will be quite susceptible to underbead cracking, particularly if any additional factors like hydrogen, high restraint, notch

effect, and so forth are involved. In planning the assembly of a weldment
and its postweld heat treatment, the engineer should set his sights for
the perfect procedure and compromise only where circumstances make
the perfect technique almost utterly impossible and where experience
indicates that something less than perfect can be allowed. For example,
take the matter of preheating for welding. The ideal preheat temperature
for these steels would be about 50 degrees F above the M_s temperature,
because this would foster the formation of bainite on an isothermal basis
completely, and would have the volumetric expansion that occurs upon
transformation take place at an elevated temperature. These conditions
would not lead to the rapid generation of localized peak stresses that
produce cracking. However, as shown in Fig. 241, the M_s point for these
steels is generally in the order of 575 F, and a preheat temperature above

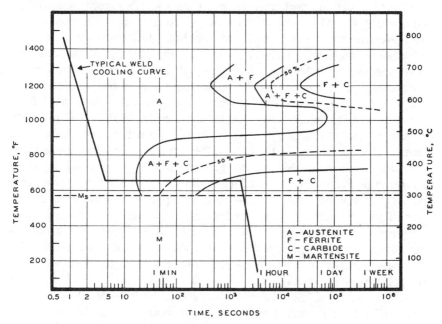

Fig. 241 — Isothermal transformation diagram (I–T curve) for a
heat-treatable alloy steel.

Shows typical weld cooling curve for joint preheated to 650 F.
Predicted microstructure of heat-affected zone is lower bainite.

600 F has certain practical drawbacks. Temperatures above approximately
550 F require apparatus to heat and maintain the joint at temperature.
Preheating the entire weldment is to be preferred over local preheating

of the joint. These high preheat temperatures add greatly to operator discomfort and this human element cannot be disregarded. From a metallurgical standpoint, the temperature is sufficiently high to start the formation of temper coloration or light oxide on the prepared surfaces of the joint. This condition has been suspected to promote small porous voids in the weld metal, and occasionally a lack of fusion at the edge of the joint. Consequently, somewhat lower preheat temperature is to be preferred in welding the heat-treatable alloy steels. A preheat of 450 F appears quite safe for the majority of weldments. Where other factors like section thickness, restraint, and joint design are favorable, a preheat as low as 300 F may be adequate. If preheat is to be applied, little would be gained by using a temperature below 300 F. It is highly unusual to be able to safely weld any of these steels, particularly one containing more than 0.35% carbon, without preheat. When using a preheat temperature lower than the M_s point, it must be appreciated that the austenitized heat-affected zones are subject to athermal transformation. That is, while some martensite forms immediately, the balance of the austenite is retained until the temperature is lowered. For this reason, the preheat temperature is maintained as the minimum interpass temperature during the entire welding operation. A temperature between 400 and 450F is not difficult to maintain, and oxide build-up in the weld joint is tolerable. Although a large percentage of the austenite formed during welding will transform to martensite at the 400–450 F interpass temperature, we know that when the remaining austenite transforms upon cooling to room temperature the danger of cracking again arises. Therefore, upon completion of welding with a 400–450 F interpass temperature, a crucial part of the procedure must be carried out as the weldment is made ready for stress-relief heat treatment. Our objective is to transform the remaining austenite under some condition *other than* at room temperature. This can be accomplished by allowing the temperature to dip just below the M_f point, which probably would be in the vicinity of 150 F. With transformation complete, the weldment then should be immediately heated for stress-relief heat treatment before any possibility of inadvertent cooling to room temperature. Treatment at approximately 1100 F will temper the martensite which formed in the heat-affected zones, and in this condition the weldment can be allowed to cool to room temperature without danger of cracking.

When immediate stress-relief heat treatment is not possible for the weldment being made with a 400–450 F interpass temperature, an alternative can be suggested for disposing of the austenite retained in the heat-affected zones. By raising the temperature of the completed weldment from the 400-450 F interpass level to approximately 750 F, which, for most of these steels, will be the vicinity of the bainite "knee," (see typical I–T curve in Fig. 241) the remaining austenite should transform to a reasonably ductile structure after holding at this higher temperature for about one hour. No cracking should be encountered when the weldment is next cooled to room temperature. Of course, further heat treatment is required to restore a desirable microstructure in the heat-affected zones. As a final comment about using an interpass temperature below the M_s point, it would not be safe practice upon completion of welding to quickly raise the temperature to the level of approximately 1100 F required for stress relief. Under these circumstances, the remaining austenite would be positioned in the "bay" of the I–T curve and would require an unduly long time to undergo transformation. Hence, austenite might still be present when the weldment was cooled from the stress-relieving temperature. The influence and behavior of this remaining austenite would be quite unpredictable.

A stress-relief heat treatment at about 1100 F often is made part of the fabrication procedure to permit a variety of operations to be performed on the weld joints prior to the important final hardening and tempering treatments for gaining high strength. In this intermediate condition, the weld would be inspected for defects. Thus a repair could be made using the same procedure before final painstaking heat treatment. If a weld repair became necessary when the weldment was in the final heat treated condition, the new heat-affected zone, albeit small, would not possess properties equal to those in the unaffected base metal. Therefore, a complete retreatment may be required. A more disturbing situation can arise when considering the weld repair of a weldment that has been heat treated to the highest possible level of strength. If the steel is somewhat limited in toughness, the localized repair weld may trigger a catastrophic fracture in the weldment. A preventative step would be to overtemper the weldment before attempting repair. This step presupposes that the repaired weldment will be retreated (quenched and tempered) to again obtain the high level of strength required. Retreatment of a weldment is not always possible, however, because of problems with accumulated distortion from heating, cooling, quenching, and transformation.

Each of the remaining aspects of planning a welding procedure deserve close attention. Usually, the base metal is in a soft condition, either annealed or overtempered. The lower strength in this condition may help reduce reaction stresses. Weld joint design is, of course, very important, and cleanliness of the components must not be slighted. The parts to be joined often are held in fixtures to aid in accurate matching. This is especially important for butt joints where mismatch has been found to be a frequent cause of premature failure of joints. Mismatch causes stress concentration which may exceed the cohesive strength of the metal and cause fracture before localized plastic flow can bring about a redistribution of stress. When the fixtured parts are tack welded, very close attention must be given to these welds. Because of their temporary nature, tack welds sometimes are made without all the safeguards planned for the actual welds. This is a dangerous practice in view of evidence that defects which originated in tack welds can persist and ultimately cause failure. Tack welds improperly made are prone to cracking because cooling is very rapid and localized stresses are high. Porosity is more apt to occur because of the interrupted shielding during the frequent starting and stopping. All considered, tack welds can present more of a metallurgical problem than long welds made under steady-state conditions, which, in fact, often use starting tabs and run off tabs.

Much of the fusion joining of the heat-treatable steels is performed with the gas tungsten-arc process. This process often is used in preference to metal-arc welding because of the limited availability of electrodes which deposit weld metal of the highly alloyed steel compositions. Even though the gas tungsten-arc operation is more expensive, it is favored because of the close control that can be exercised over weld composition and the sound, clean weld metal that can be deposited. Excellent control is maintained over bead penetration and deposit contour. Generally, a welding rod having a composition similar to the base metal is employed for filler metal. However, it is not unusual to note that the welding rod is made with carbon and alloying element levels on the low side of the permissible ranges, and the residual phosphorus and sulfur levels are quite low to minimize cracking tendencies. A much repeated warning that deserves renewed emphasis for the heat-treatable alloy steels is that hydrogen pickup should be avoided. The necessity for this precaution varies, of course, with the nature of the steel and the preheat and interpass temperatures employed in the welding procedure. With a preheat and interpass temperature of 400 F or higher, it would seem reasonable that any hydrogen picked up would have ample opportunity to diffuse and thus would never reach a concentration in the heat-affected zone that would aggravate any tendency for the metal to crack. Yet, hydrogen has been so deceptive in its role as a promoter of cracking that any step to avoid hydrogen is additional assurance against this kind of difficulty. Therefore, the hydrogen-free welding conditions of the gas tungsten-arc process is further reason for its preferred usage.

Joint design in the heat-treatable alloy steels is usually dictated by the thickness of the base metal. For the most part, butt joints with complete penetration (no unfused abutting root faces) are strongly favored. Even fillet welds often are designed to fill bevel preparations that result in a completely penetrated joint. Double-bevel joints are used for base metal above approximately ¼-inch thickness whenever possible to minimize angular distortion.

The composition of the weld metal in gas tungsten-arc welded joints is controlled to a large degree by joint design. Very little filler metal is added to square-butt joints. Consequently, the weld metal composition is very close to that of the base metal. In beveled joints, the composition of the filler metal assumes greater importance in controlling composition. Because the shielding gas must be either argon or helium, or mixtures thereof (principally for protecting the tungsten electrode), the final composition of the weld metal is practically unchanged by oxidation. In addition to this effective shielding of the weld pool, it is common practice to provide a protective gas backing for the underside of root beads. The gas often employed is argon, and its purpose is to assist in forming a clean, defect-free surface on the underbead.

Deposition of filler metal in the joint usually is accomplished with a relatively low heat input inasmuch as high heat input tends to produce large heat-affected zones, enlarges grain size in the base metal immediately adjacent to the weld, and increases the likelihood of hot cracking both in the weld metal and in the base metal heat-affected zones. Automatic welding is greatly preferred over manual welding for straightline joints, or simple circumferential points. The automatic operation helps minimize stops and starts which frequently give rise to defects. Automatic welding also produces more uniform welds with fewer defects. It is extremely important that all materials involved in the welding operation be scrupulously clean. This includes base metal, welding rod or electrodes, and fixtures. For example, a problem with porosity and nonmetallic inclusions in a weld joint in heat treatable alloy steel was traced to abrasive grit which was not removed from the carefully ground surfaces of the prepared joint.

Some shielded metal-arc welding is performed on the heat-treatable alloy steels. Where a joint with nearly homogeneous properties is wanted, covered electrodes which deposit heat treatable weld metal are available. In most cases, these filler metals (as illustrated earlier in Table 45) do not have the same composition as the base metal for which they were intended. For example, one manufacturer of a "4340" covered electrode designed his product to deposit weld metal of the following composition:

C	Mn	Si	Cr	Ni	Mo
0.30	0.80	0.25	0.20	1.65	0.25

Note that the carbon and chromium contents are significantly lower than in wrought AISI 4340 steel. Naturally, this leaner composition reduces the level of strength obtainable in the heat treated weld metal, unless heavy dilution raises the alloy content of the deposit in the joint. However, this weld metal composition would display improved resistance to hot cracking and to cold cracking.

A special high silicon electrode is intended for welding 300-M steel, the composition of which was shown earlier in Table 85.
This electrode deposits weld metal of the following composition:

C	Mn	Si	Cr	Ni	Mo
0.40	1.20	1.95	0.75	1.75	0.35

Welding 300-M base metal with this electrode is customarily carried out with a preheat of 450 F, and a minimum interpass temperature of about the same level.

The general procedures employed in welding heat-treatable steels by the shielded metal-arc process using covered electrodes of similar alloy steel composition are approximately the same as described for the gas tungsten-arc process.

Some welding is performed on the heat-treatable alloy steels with dissimilar filler metal. The latter may be an austenitic stainless steel filler metal, or an austenitic-like nickel-base alloy. The common reasons for employing this kind of filler metal is to avoid cracking in the base metal heat-affected zones when the welding must be done with little or no preheat, and to secure a tougher weld metal (albeit of lower strength). The reasons for the excellent performance of these austenitic filler metals in avoiding underbead cracking were touched upon in Chapter 13. The low-hydrogen conditions which exist with the mineral-covered high-alloy electrodes play an important part. The danger of interface cracking in the diffusion zone between the austenitic weld metal and the base metal when hydrogen is present was illustrated in Fig. 199. Of course, the use of an austenitic filler metal still creates a hardened zone in the base metal, even though it may leave the zone uncracked. The hardness, however, can be lowered by making a multipass weld and applying a tempering bead, or by postweld temper heat treatment. As explained in Chapter 10 when discussing the matter of dissimilar metal weld joints, the question of dilution must be given close attention in joining a carbon steel or an alloy steel with a high-alloy filler metal. Ordinarily, the weld beads deposited are of uniform composition and microstructure; that is, the lower-alloy base metal which is melted finds its way into the weld melt where it is vigorously stirred by electromagnetic action to form a homogeneous alloy. However, certain conditions in welding have been noted to encourage heterogeneity, particularly deposition of the weld beads at high travel speed.

Electron beam welding has been applied to the heat-treatable steels, and this process appears capable of making sound welds *without pre-heating*. Steels designated as H-11, D6AC, X200, 300-M, 4335, 4335-V, 4340, MBMC-1, and MX-2 were welded by one group of investigators both as simple test plates and in the form of small pressure vessels. Some of these steels were represented both as air-melted, and as vacuum-melted products. It was noticed that air-melted steel produced a vigorous outgassing in the weld pool during electron beam welding under the customary vacuum, and the solidified weld displayed a rather rough surface. Nevertheless, all welds were satisfactorily sound and free of cracking. Gas tungsten-arc welded coupons and vessels also were made in the same steels for purpose of comparison. After welding by the two processes, the specimens and vessels were subjected to hardening and tempering treatments customarily applied to fully harden the respective steels. Whereas the gas tungsten-arc welded joints tended to fail in the weld metal, or in the immediately adjacent heat-affected zone during tension testing, the electron beam welded specimens usually fractured in the base metal remote from the weld. When the pressure vessels were tested to destruction, the biaxial strength of the electron beam welded joints was substantially higher than that of the arc welded joints.

Postweld Heat Treatment

Heat treatment of the weldment is a very important operation and requires close control of temperatures, cooling rates, and furnace atmospheres. The steel in the weldment first must be austenitized by heating 50 to 100 degrees F above the Ac_3 temperature. When the carbides contained in the structure are dissolved in the austenite, the weldment is air cooled, or oil quenched depending upon the alloy content of the steel and its hardening characteristics. Those steels relatively high in alloy, like H-11 and H-13, can be air cooled in thin sections, which minimizes distortion and reduces the risk of cracking from transformation stresses. The selection of a proper cooling medium is important because the ductility and fracture toughness of the final structure can be adversely affected by unsatisfactory cooling. Usually, a cooling rate that is too slow leads to unfavorable toughness. Also, it is important that these steels be cooled to a prescribed endpoint to insure adequate completeness of the transformation to martensite. For example, if a weldment being quenched or air-cooled was arrested at a temperature of perhaps 200 F and quickly moved into the tempering furnace (ostensibly to avoid quench-cracking), the final treated weldment may fail to display the expected high hardness and strength. This deficiency is the result of failing to transform enough of the austenite to martensite during the hardening treatment. When cooling was arrested at 200 F, only 50% of the structure may have made the transformation from austenite to martensite. When the steel in this half transformed condition was elevated to the tempering temperature, the remainder of the austenite easily could have undergone transformation to a much softer microstructure than tempered martensite. As a matter of fact, some of the more highly alloyed steels under these circumstances will tend to stabilize their austenite (or at least a portion of it) and retain this relatively soft constituent right down to room temperature! What happens next is a moot question. This retained austenite may remain as such until the steel is stressed, whereupon the austenite will reduce the strength. Retained austenite has been known to transform, usually under the influence of lower temperature. Transformation, with the accompanying volume increase under these circumstances, can cause cracking in some instances. More often, the newly formed martensite, which represents a hard, highly stressed (untempered) product, acts to limit the ductility and toughness of the tempered martensite in the matrix structure.

Heat treatment brings into play many metallurgical reactions which are familiar to the welding engineer. Scaling, decarburization, dimensional changes, carburization, and distortion are just a small number of the conditions which must be controlled in the heat treating operations. The types of furnaces, atmospheres, and quenching media used will vary widely with the size, shape and number of weldments. Mention was made in Chapter 12 of *deliberate* decarburization of the surface of steel during the austenitizing treatment prior to hardening. This treatment has been used on welded rocket motor casings of high strength, heat-treatable alloy steel, and apparently with some success. The object is to markedly lower the carbon in a surface layer of the steel only about 0.005 to 0.010 in. in depth. This provides a "skin" on the weldment, which, although lower in strength, has a much greater level of ductility and toughness. Inasmuch as stress concentrations generally occur at the surface where mismatch, weld undercut, and other imperfections exist, the decarburized surface layer provides metal with a greater capacity for localized plastic flow to accommodate and adjust these concentrations. Of course, in highly loaded weldments, some consideration probably must be given to the lower over-all strength of the sections, particularly if they are relatively thin and the decarburized surface layers constitute a significant percentage of the section thickness. Fatigue strength also may be lowered by a decarburized surface on the weldment.

It is not unusual for a weldment of heat-treatable alloy steel to receive one or more intermediate heat treatments prior to final hardening and tempering. If the weldment is scheduled to undergo machining operations, the still hot weldment upon completion of all welding operations may be given an annealing treatment. This may be a full anneal, or a sub-critical anneal depending upon the particular microstructure desired for best machinability during the machining operations to be applied. Some of the heat-treatable steels benefit considerably by applying a normalizing treatment prior to final hardening and tempering. Depending upon the kind of steel, normalizing may involve heating to a temperature in the vicinity of 1700 F followed by air cooling to room temperature. One purpose of normalizing is to dissolve any large globular carbides that may exist in the microstructure, and thus produce a finer distribution of carbide particles which facilitates complete solution during the subsequent austenitizing treatment for final hardening. The hardening treatment is customarily carried out with a lower austenitizing temperature (often in the vicinity of 1575 F) in order to minimize grain coarsening, and to reduce distortion during quenching. Consequently, coarse carbide particles in the structure might not dissolve in the austenite at this lower temperature. These undissolved particles not only hold valuable carbon and alloying elements from performing their function in the matrix structure, but they also detract from the ductility and toughness of the final heat treated steel.

Research on Welding Procedures

Fabricators using the heat-treatable alloy steels in weldments cannot resist chiding the welding engineer with an all-too-familiar request; namely, how can the desirable high strength and toughness of these steels be secured at a welded joint *without* a postweld hardening treatment? The tempering treatment, they magnanimously offer to perform. After all, it does not involve distortion, oxidation, quench-cracking, and the sundry ills of the hardening treatment. With customary inquisitiveness, welding investigators have started to explore at least two possible ways of using heat-treatable steels whereby they are hardened and tempered prior to welding and a postweld hardening operation is not applied.

One group of investigators have attempted to avoid the need for postweld heat treatment by using a supplementary heat source to control the transformation of austenite in the heat-affected zones, and to temper these zones if necessary as an integral part of the welding operation. They selected AISI 4340 steel as a typical heat-treatable steel, and conducted their work with specimens pre-treated (quenched and tempered) to two different levels of hardness, namely, 44-C and 54-C Rockwell, respectively. A preliminary study was made with specimens heated in a weld heat-affected zone simulating device. These were rapidly heated to 1700 F and cooled in a carefully programmed "step-quenching" to encourage transformation to bainite rather than martensite. Transformation diagrams were constructed from dilation data obtained during cooling, and the synthetically heat-affected specimens were examined for microstructure and tested for impact toughness. Considerable information was obtained on the growth of bainite under these cooling conditions, and the amount of austenite retained in the final microstructure at room temperature. The prior condition of the base metal (whether 44-C or 54-C Rockwell) had no influence on the bainite growth curve in the simulated specimens. The amount of austenite retained at room temperature for various holding times terminated during the bainite transformation was found to pass through a maximum near the end of the rapid reaction.

When gas tungsten-arc welds were made in base metal over which an induction coil was positioned such that continuous cooling of the weld joint was interrupted at 600 F for 10 minutes, the heat-affected zone structure of the actual weld joint did not correlate with that of the simulated specimen. It was concluded that cooling rate does not of itself determine the structure which results from austenite transformation. It was felt that a system of controlled cooling to effect strong, tough heat-affected zones must take into account (1) the true shape and position of heating and cooling curves, (2) peak temperature, (3) time at peak temperature, (4) prior base metal history, and (5) factors affecting restraint. Further work is being conducted along these lines.

A different approach to the problem of avoiding the necessity for postweld retreatment is that taken by the advocates of electron beam welding. Electron beam welds show a much finer microstructure in the weld metal and a narrower heat-affected zone than found in gas tungsten-arc welded joints because the electron beam weld is made with a markedly lower heat input. The fine structure of the weld metal is credited to the fact that spacing between dendrites is proportional to the square root of the welding energy input. Because hardness traverses of electron beam welds in hardenable steels showed unusually high hardness in the fine structure of the as-welded joint, studies were undertaken to determine to what extent the degradation of properties in the heat-affected zone of pretreated steels could be minimized.

H-11 steel (both air-melted and vacuum-melted in thicknesses up to ⅛ inch) has been welded by the electron beam process in a single pass with the usual square-butt type of joint. The base metal was hardened and tempered to a strength level of 300 ksi UTS, and was welded in this condition without preheating. Transverse tensile specimens fractured in the coarser-grained region of the heat-affected zone immediately adjacent to the fused zone. Tensile failures occurred at strength levels of 250 to 280 ksi UTS, even for wide welds (0.320 inch) made with higher heat input. No cracking or distortion occurred. Fusion zone impact values for the air-melted and vacuum-melted steels were equal to those of the heat treated base metals.

"MARAGING" ALLOY STEELS

In 1959, a series of new high-strength alloy steels were introduced under the designation *Maraging Steels;* which would suggest that they are martensitic in structure, and are able to gain strength through aging. In commenting on ambiguity in trade names in Chapter 1, the maraging steels were singled out as being neither martensitic, nor age-hardenable in the strict sense of the terms. Since the metallurgical behavior of these steels must be clearly understood in order to analyze their weldability, let us examine their true character.

Originally, the maraging steels consisted of three basic compositions containing 18%, 20% and 25% nickel, respectively, along with other alloying elements to act as hardening agents. Carbon, manganese and silicon were not among the deliberately-added alloying elements; in fact, they were limited, much in the same manner as undesirable residual elements, to maxima of 0.03% for carbon, and 0.10% for manganese and for silicon. Therefore, these maraging steels, technically speaking, are *irons* rather than steels.

After a period of introductory experience, the 18% nickel maraging steel has been singled out as the most promising of the series because it is the simplest to heat treat to gain the desired mechanical properties, and the strength and toughness are more consistent after hardening. Although the 20% nickel and 25% nickel steels offer a broader variety of mechanical properties at various stages of heat treatment which might be helpful in fabricating operations, little use has been made of these higher nickel steels. The original maraging steels are listed in Table 86-A

Table 86-A — MARAGING STEELS

(High-Strength Alloy Irons of the Precipitation Hardening Type)

Common nickel-base designation	CHEMICAL ANALYSES (ILLUSTRATIVE)										TYPICAL MECHANICAL PROPERTIES IN HARDENED CONDITION[a]			
	C	Mn	Si	Cr	Ni	Mo	Co	Ti	Al	Others	UTS ksi	YS ksi	Hardness Rockwell	Charpy V-Notch ft-lbs.
25% Ni	0.02	0.08	0.08	...	25.0	...	...	1.5	0.2	Cb 0.4	260	240	52-C	...
20% Ni	0.02	0.08	0.08	...	20.0	...	...	1.5	0.2	Cb 0.4	260	240	52-C	18
18% Ni(200)	0.02	0.08	0.08	...	18.0	3.2	8.5	0.2	0.1	B 0.003 Zr 0.01	210	200	47-C	60
18% Ni(250)	0.02	0.08	0.08	...	18.0	5.0	7.5	0.4	0.1	B 0.003 Zr 0.01	265	250	52-C	22
18% Ni(300)	0.02	0.08	0.08	...	18.0	5.0	9.0	0.6	0.1	B 0.003 Zr 0.01	300	290	57-C	15
12% Ni-1	0.02	0.06	0.06	5.0	12.0	3.0	...	0.20	0.22	B 0.005 Zr 0.01	175	169	40-C	75
12% Ni-2	0.02	0.07	0.09	5.0	12.0	3.0	...	0.25	0.35	...	190	184	41-C	45

[a] Properties after precipitation hardening by treatments prescribed for each alloy.

Table 86-B — *MARAGING STEELS*

Specification for 18 Percent Nickel Precipitation Hardening (Maraging) Alloy Steel Plates for Pressure Vessels (abstracted from ASTM A538-65)

	Grade A	Grade B	Grade C
Chemical requirements, percent by weight, ladle analysis			
Carbon, max	0.03	0.03	0.03
Nickel	17.0 –19.0	17.0 –19.0	18.0 –19.0
Cobalt	7.0 – 8.5	7.0 – 8.5	8.0 – 9.5
Molybdenum	4.0 – 4.5	4.6 – 5.1	4.6 – 5.2
Titanium	0.10– 0.25	0.30– 0.50	0.55– 0.80
Silicon, max	0.10	0.10	0.10
Manganese, max	0.10	0.10	0.10
Sulfur, max	0.010	0.010	0.010
Phosphorus, max	0.010	0.010	0.010
Aluminum	0.05– 0.15	0.05– 0.15	0.05– 0.15
The following elements in the amount specified shall be added to the steel			
Boron	0.003	0.003	0.003
Zirconium	0.02	0.02	0.02
Calcium	0.05	0.05	0.05
Mechanical property requirements — solution treated 1500/1750F — AC or WQ			
Hardness, max	34 Rc	34 Rc	34 Rc
	321 Bhn	321 Bhn	321 Bhn
Mechanical property requirements — precipitation hardened 900F (± 25F) — 4 hrs.			
Tensile strength, min, ksi	210	240	280
Yield strength 0.2% offset, ksi	200–235	230–260	275–305
Elongation, % in 2 in., min	8	6	6
Reduction of area, % min, round cross section specimens	40	35	30
Rectangular cross section specimens	35	30	25

along with typical mechanical properties which they offer in the hardened condition. It is important to note that the 18% nickel steel is produced with varying amounts of supplementary alloying elements which result in steels offering three progressively higher levels of strength. These three steels are differentiated in Table 86-A by a suffix on the designation which indicates their typical yield strengths. Also shown in Table 86-A are two recently introduced 12% nickel maraging steels which offer somewhat lower strength, but which possess a high level of toughness. The manufacture of the 18% nickel maraging steels was started by a number of producers, each of whom offered three steels of different strength capability. However, each producer had a little different idea of the strength levels wanted, and each applied a different trade name to their products. In late 1965, the ASTM issued a standard specification for 18% nickel maraging steel plates for pressure vessel usage. This specification, ASTM A538, is outlined in Table 86-B. Three 18% nickel steels identified as Grades A, B and C are defined by this specification. These grades are distinguished by differences in chemical composition and in strength in the hardened condition. The multiplicity of 18% nickel maraging steels of different strength capability can lead to misapplication problems that cannot be remedied through heat treatment, and will be discussed further during a review of chemical composition.

The maraging steels are based upon the behavior of a matrix structure which contains very high short-range stresses and elastic strain, and which holds dissolved elements or compounds at a level of supersaturation. This kind of matrix will readily produce a highly dispersed precipitate when heated to proper temperature for diffusion of the solute to precipitation sites in the strained lattice. This is *precipitation hardening,* of course, and it is unfortunate that some naive purchasers of maraging steels have been misled by the name *maraging* into thinking that sections would harden by *aging* at ambient temperature in due time. More important, however, the reader must not be misled in gaining a true concept of these "steels." Although most literature discusses the microstructures which form in the alloys under the various conditions of temperature and time as "austenite" and "martensite," it is important to recognize that the phases present are more accurately described as the "gamma" and the "alpha$_2$" phases of the iron–nickel alloy system. The alpha$_2$ phase is the body-centered cubic crystallographic lattice which forms through the shear type reaction (martensite-like transformation) rather than by nucleation and growth. The crystal structure of this iron–nickel alloy "martensite" is identical to that of iron–nickel alloy "ferrite" except that the martensite-like structure contains an extremely large number of dislocations. Despite the very low level of carbon in the martensite of the maraging steel, the presence of only 0.02% of this element appears to have a significant influence upon strength and hardness. Whereas the yield strength of a carbon-free, iron–nickel martensite would be estimated to be approximately 42 ksi, the maraging steels in the freshly-formed martensitic condition display at least 95 ksi yield strength. Of course, this is substantially lower than the strength of higher-carbon martensite found in the heat-treatable alloy steels. It is important, therefore, that the various phases in the maraging steels be reappraised for their actual properties because they are quite different from their counterparts in conventional steels. So, if all preconceived notions will be put aside, let us see how the maraging steels are treated to increase their hardness, and the manner in which they must be welded and postweld heat treated to obtain useful properties.

25% NICKEL MARAGING STEEL

The 25% nickel alloy is probably the most complex of the maraging steels, and an explanation of its metallurgical behavior provides an excellent basis on which to further discuss the steels of lower nickel content. Surely the reader will recall that nickel has been described as an alloying element in iron and in steel which has a profound effect in promoting the face-centered cubic crystal structure (gamma phase or austenite), and in encouraging the retention of this kind of lattice structure to lower transformation temperatures. The latter remark is a reminder that nickel depresses the M_s temperature, and, in fact, lowers the entire martensite transformation range. When added as an alloying element in iron, nickel makes transformations quite sluggish, especially those expected to occur at moderate temperatures and below. The presence of so large an amount of nickel as 25% in this first maraging steel actually lowers the martensite transformation range below room temperature. The M_s temperature of the 25% nickel maraging steel usually is about 50 F. Consequently, when the 25% nickel maraging steel is austenitized at a high temperature (let us say at 1500 F, because the Ac_1 temperature is approximately 1100 F) and is air cooled, the steel remains essentially austenitic when it arrives at room temperature! It is quite soft in this condition, about Rockwell C-10, and although the other alloying elements, such as titanium and aluminum, are in solid solution, this austenitic matrix is not amenable to significant hardening upon aging, or even to precipitation hardening when heated. However, if this austenite can be made to transform by some means at a relatively low temperature through the martensite-like or shear-type reaction, then a highly suitable matrix structure will be provided for subsequent precipitation hardening. As illustrated in Fig. 242, the 25% nickel maraging steel after annealing at 1500 F and cooling to room temperature, can be transformed from austenite to martensite by either (a) heating to about 1300 F to precipitate elements whose loss from the matrix raises its M_s temperature to about 160 F upon cooling from this "ausaging" treatment, or (b) cold working the metastable austenite with at least 25% reduction to produce sufficient transformation to martensite.

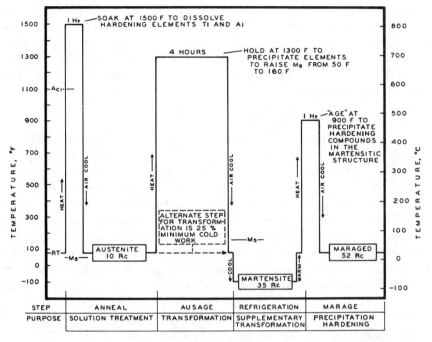

Fig. 242 — Heat treating sequence for 25% Nickel Maraging Steel.

Critical step in the procedure is to ensure transformation during the ausaging and the refrigeration treatments to an essentially martensitic structure to provide a matrix amenable to precipitation hardening.

When the matrix of the 25% Ni steel transforms to martensite, as it is certain to do upon being cooled substantially below 160 F after ausaging, or upon being cold worked, not only does it contain the internal stress and strain that aids in dispersing the precipitate, but a much higher degree of supersaturation develops because of the lower solubility for the titanium and aluminum previously held in the austenite. In this intermediate condition, that is, martensite with a supersaturation of other alloys in solid solution, the hardness of the steel may range from about Rockwell C-30 to C-40, depending upon the method by which the transformation was accomplished and the degree of completion. Usually, a small amount of retained austenite is present in the otherwise martensitic structure.

As the final step for hardening, the supersaturated martensite is heated to a temperature within the range of about 750–900 F, whereupon extremely fine, complex compounds of nickel, titanium and aluminum are precipitated. Thus the martensite is precipitation hardened, or in the vernacular of the orginators of these steels, it is "mar-aged." As a result of this final treatment, the hardness is increased substantially. The level of hardness will depend, of course, upon the temperature and time to which the martensite was exposed.

The ability of the 25% nickel maraging steel to accomplish transformation from austenite to martensite upon cooling from the 1300 F ausaging treatment is controlled to a large degree by the titanium content. When the titanium is about 1.5% or above, the transformation to martensite is nearly completed by air cooling and holding about 12 hours at room temperature. When titanium is less than about 1.5%, however, refrigeration must be applied after ausaging to complete the transformation. With the lower titanium content, less nickel is removed from solution in the austenite (through the formation of Ni_3Ti) during the 1300 F treatment.

If the titanium content of the steel happens to be on the low side of the permissible range, the maraging or precipitation hardening step (4) sometimes is carried out at a lower temperature and for a longer period of time, for example, four hours at 800 F instead of one hour at 900 F. Although *over aging* is commonly practised with other precipitation hardening alloys, the maraging steels do not enjoy this liberty. Overaging is the application of a higher than normal temperature to reduce the strength and hardness a little below the maximum obtainable through precipitation. By allowing slightly larger particles of the precipitate to agglomerate, not only is the hardness lowered, but the fracture toughness and ductility are improved. The maraging steels, however, are handicapped by a relatively low Ac_1 temperature. Consequently, if the final precipitation hardening or maraging temperature is raised above the 900 F level, the martensite starts to undergo reversion to austenite. In fact, if the martensite is held too long at temperatures in the vicinity of 900 F the reversion to austenite will commence. The presence of the austenite will reduce strength and hardness, and will impair fracture toughness of the maraged structure. Repeating the maraging treatment at a lower temperature will not alleviate the effect of the reformed austenite because this structure is not amenable to precipitation hardening.

Before proceeding to other maraging steels, certain facts regarding the microstructural phases and their transformation characteristics should be pointed out. Because the martensite ($alpha_2$) which forms is very low in carbon content, the crystallographic form is body-centered *cubic* rather than body-centered *tetragonal*. Therefore, less expansion occurs during the formation of the martensite. The transformation proceeds isothermally as well as athermally. Because the body-centered cubic lattice is not strained in the manner of the tetragonal lattice of conventional martensite, the product is relatively soft. Altogether, the likelihood of cracking after transformation has taken place is greatly reduced.

A remarkable fact about welding the maraging steels, and this is particularly true of the 25% Ni steel, is that the heat-affected zones adjacent to the weld are *softened* rather than *hardened* by the heating and cooling. If, for example, base metal of the 25% Ni steel had been hardened to Rockwell C-52 *prior* to welding, the as-welded heat-affected zones would be returned to the austenitic condition and would display a hardness of about Rockwell C-10. This metallurgical behavior permits welding without preheating. However, to restore the strength and hardness of the heat-affected zones to that of the original hardened condition, both the 1300 F ausaging treatment (and possibly the refrigeration step) and the maraging treatment at 900 F are required.

Initially, the 25% nickel maraging steel was looked upon with favor as a sheet steel because its low hardness and low work hardening rate in the annealed condition were very satisfactory for cold rolling or cold forming operations. However, the rather complicated hardening treatment, and difficulties in securing satisfactory ductility and toughness in the hardened condition have shifted attention to other maraging steels.

20% NICKEL MARAGING STEEL

The 20% Ni steel, although not presently being produced in any significant quantity, demonstrates how the metallurgical behavior of these steels changes as the nickel content is lowered. The schematic heat treating sequence chart in Fig. 243 shows that upon cooling from a 1500 F annealing temperature, the alloy content of this steel is not high enough to sustain an austenitic structure at room temperature, as did the 25% Ni steel. Instead, the solution-treated austenite reaches a M_s temperature at about 250 F and transformation to martensite proceeds as cooling continues to room temperature. While at room temperature, retained austenite continues to transform (isothermally) to martensite with time. However, if the nickel content is at the high side of the permissible range, the amount of austenite which is retained, and which will not transform isothermally at room temperature, may be large enough to hamper subsequent precipitation hardening to the expected strength level. Steel of this character will require refrigeration, perhaps to about –100 F, to encourage the retained austenite to transform to martensite. After the structure has been transformed to martensite, precipitation hardening is carried out in the same manner as the 25% Ni steel by maraging treatment at about 900 F.

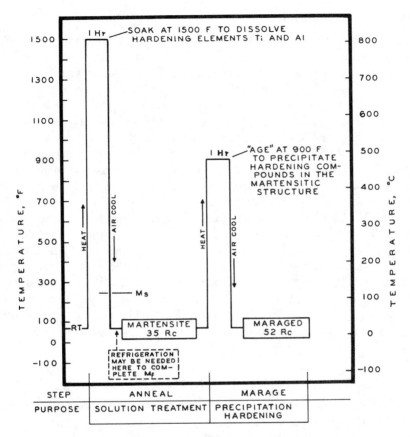

Fig. 243 — The 20% Nickel Maraging Steel requires a less-complicated heat treating sequence.

Note that martensite structure is formed upon cooling from the 1500 F annealing temperature providing cooling is carried far enough below the M_s temperature (250 F). Sometimes refrigeration may be necessary to secure adequate transformation to martensite.

Welding can be performed on the 20% nickel maraging steel without preheat because the heat effect of welding again will produce a reasonably soft microstructure immediately adjacent to the weld. In this case, essentially a low-carbon martensite (with some retained austenite) will form in the base metal heat-affected zones. In the heat-affected area immediately-adjacent to the weld, the precipitation hardening alloying elements will be in solid solution. In the regions of the heat-affected zones farther away from the weld, other important changes occur that will be discussed in detail under the 18% nickel maraging steels.

18% NICKEL MARAGING STEELS

The welding engineer who has reason to plunge into a thorough study of the maraging steels probably will be amazed at the large volume of work already reported in the literature on the metallurgy and welding of these steels. The maraging steels have been of great interest because of certain military and aerospace hardware which require a steel of high strength, good toughness, good weldability, and particularly which would not require postweld heat treatment that involved high temperatures and rapid cooling. The latter requirement is quite important because of the great size of some weldments, such as submarine hulls and giant rocket casings. The maraging steels appeared to offer the possibility of requiring at most only a 900 F maraging treatment, and this perhaps could be applied locally to the joint. The maraging steels (speaking mainly of the 18% Ni types) continue to look attractive for these applications despite some difficulties. They hold real promise of being welded without requiring preheat in either the annealed, or the fully-hardened (maraged) conditions. However, it is not unexpected that problems would be encountered with this new, unique kind of steel. The welding engineer who works with a maraging steel must be ready to cope with an imposing number of new metallurgical phenomena that control the soundness, strength, and toughness of weld joints.

Chemical Composition of the 18% Ni Maraging Steels

The 18% nickel maraging steels are quite similar to the 20% Ni steel inasmuch as the same simple sequence of treatments is employed for annealing and hardening, Fig. 244. Both the 20% Ni and the 18% Ni types are essentially martensitic after annealing, and generally require only the maraging treatment at about 900 F to produce precipitation hardening. However, differences in the remainder of their alloy compositions cause a number of changes in metallurgical characteristics and impart somewhat different mehanical properties. Molybdenum and cobalt in the 18% nickel steels were thought at first to be helpful as solid solution alloying elements. They were believed to assist in maintaining toughness at low temperatures, and in retaining useful strength at elevated temperatures. However, as the structures of the maraged steels were studied closely, molybdenum was found to enter directly into particles which precipitation hardened the matrix. On the other hand, cobalt appears to promote a faster precipitation hardening response, but does not in itself produce appreciable hardening. Of course, these alloying elements also affect the transformation of austenite upon cooling from the annealing temperature. The M_s temperature of the 18% Ni (250) steel is about 400 F, while that for 18% Ni (300) steel is 325 F. The temperature at which the austenite to martensite transformation stops (essentially the M_f point) is approximately 200 F. Transformation proceeds to martensite over a wide range of cooling rates, from as slow as 4 degrees per minute, to as rapidly as 275 degrees per minute.

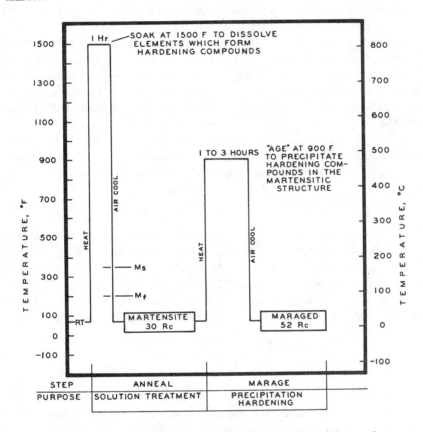

Fig. 244 — Sequence of heat treating steps for the 18% nickel maraging steels.

Originally, three types of 18% nickel maraging steel were proposed: These were Ni–Mo–Co–Ti–Al containing irons which were capable of attaining three progressively higher levels of tensile strength, and so the steels were identified as 18%Ni (200), 18% Ni(250) and 18% Ni(300). The number in parentheses indicates the UTS in ksi normally obtained after maraging. These differences in strength are secured principally by adjusting the molybdenum, titanium and aluminum contents of the steels. Because these steels do not lend themselves easily to overaging or underaging to obtain other levels of strength, additional types of 18% Ni steel soon appeared which were intended to provide specific strength capability along with a degree of fracture toughness judged adequate for the intended application. These additional types represent modifications of the hardening elements in the composition, and have been dubbed 18% Ni (160), 18% Ni (280), and so forth. Roughly speaking, fracture toughness increases with lower levels of strength. Therefore, relatively heavy weldments may demand greater consideration for toughness and call for a steel of lower strength capability. Usually, the steels of higher strength are given consideration for weldments of thinner sections where demands for fracture toughness are not as severe, and where fracture toughness can be measured with greater confidence.

The need to foretell the strength capabilty of a maraging steel from its chemical composition has prompted investigators to develop equations for this purpose. One proposed equation for the 18% Ni steels is as follows:

$$\text{Yield Strength, ksi} = 38.1 + 8.8\,(\%\,\text{Co}) + 22.6\,(\%\,\text{Mo}) + 87.7\,(\%\,\text{Ti})$$

This equation, incidently, does not consider aluminum as a hardener; yet, work with the 18% Ni (200) steel has shown that aluminum is equal to titanium in strengthening effect. If the above equation is applied to the composition requirements for the three original maraging steels, the permissible composition limits would appear to allow the steels to vary over the following ranges of yield strength in the maraged condition:

18% Ni (200)   –   30 ksi
18% Ni (250)   –   44 ksi
18% Ni (300)   –   48 ksi

Residual elements in the maraging steels play unusual roles in controlling strength, fracture toughness, and cracking susceptibility. Because of the unique chemical composition of the maraging steels, experience with residual elements in conventional alloy steels is of little assistance in anticipating effects. Sulfur is very damaging in the maraging steels because it forms platelets of titanium sulfide (TiS) which are flattened into thin, large-area films during hot rolling. These non-metallics are detrimental to fracture toughness. Carbon above the 0.03% level also is harmful to fracture toughness because it forms both coarse titanium carbonitride particles which appear in the ingot structure, and fine particles which subsequently precipitate and redissolve in grain boundaries during heat treatment. Small

Table 86-C — *MARAGING STEELS*

Effects of Alloying and Residual Elements in 18% Nickel Steel

Element	Approx. Range, %	Level Present	Effect in Base Metal	Effect in Weld Metal
Nickel	17–19	Too low	Lowers strength.	Lowers strength. Cracking susceptibility increases.
		Too high	Promotes retention of austenite, lowers strength, and reduces toughness.	Promotes reversion to austenite in segregated pools which reduces strength and toughness.
Cobalt	7.0–9.5	Too low	Lowers strength.	Lowers strength. Cracking susceptibility increases.
		Too high	Increases strength, but reduces toughness.	Reduces strength and toughness.
Molybdenum	3.0–5.2	Too low	Lowers strength.	Lowers strength. Increases cracking susceptibility.
		Too high	Increases strength. Lowers toughness.	Reduces strength and toughness.
Titanium	0.10–0.80	Too low	Lowers strength.	Increases porosity. Lowers strength.
		Too high	Reduces toughness.	Forms low-melting sulfides. Promotes austenite segregation.
Silicon	0.10 max	Too high	Reduces toughness.	Increases hot cracking susceptibility. Reduces toughness.
Manganese	0.30 max	Too high	Reduces toughness.	Reduces toughness.
Carbon	0.03 max	Too high	Reduces strength.	Markedly reduces toughness.
Sulfur	0.010 max	Too high	Reduces toughness.	Markedly increases hot cracking susceptibility, and reduces toughness.
Aluminum	0.05–0.15	Too high	Increases strength. Reduces toughness.	Increases strength. Reduces toughness.
Boron	Very small addition		Improves toughness.	Increases cracking susceptibility and reduces toughness.
Zirconium	Very small addition		Improves toughness.	Increases cracking susceptibility and reduces toughness.
Hydrogen	Residual			Increases cracking susceptibility.
Oxygen	Residual			Reduces toughness.
Nitrogen	Residual		Forms TiN and TiCN particles which reduce toughness.	Reduces toughness by formation of TiN and TiCN particles.
Calcium	Deoxidizer			

amounts of boron and zirconium are added during manufacture to retard carbide agglomeration at grain boundaries as in nickel-base alloys. A small addition of calcium (0.05%) often is added as a deoxidizer in heats of maraging steel melted in air to reduce the residual oxygen content as low as possible. Nitrogen also is regarded as a very undesirable residual element. Even though nitrogen is firmly tied up as titanium nitride and titanium carbonitride, strong evidence has been obtained that these compounds lower fracture toughness. Particles of TiN and TiCN have been found concentrated on the faces of brittle fractures. Although silicon and manganese are widely used as alloying elements in many steels, they are undesirable in the maraging steels. Silicon impairs fracture toughness when present in amounts exceeding about 0.1%. Manganese in amounts up to about 0.3% does not appear to be harmful. A summary of available information regarding the effects of alloying and residual elements upon the properties of 18% Ni maraging steels is presented in Table 86-C.

Nature of Microstructure Hardened by Maraging

Electron microscopy using thin sections of 18% Ni hardened maraging steel has revealed that a high density of fine precipitated particles is formed in the martensitic structure in two distinct modes of distribution. Ribbons of a precipitate identified as Ni_3Mo intermetallic compound are formed along dislocation lines and martensite sub-boundaries. Tiny individual spherical particles, tentatively identified as Ni_3Ti, are distributed throughout the matrix. The particles range in size from 100 to 500 A, and are distributed in the matrix with an interparticle spacing of about 500 A. The particles exhibit some coherency with the lattice of the matrix.

The 18% Ni steels increase in hardness with increasing maraging time. Surprisingly, the lower maraging temperatures produce higher peak hardness levels, but the times required are considerably longer. It is important to note that significantly lower fracture toughness is found when a higher level of strength and hardness is secured by a lower-temperature, longer-time maraging treatment. Consequently, most maraging is performed at 900 F for one to four hours.

When an attempt is made to overage the precipitation hardened structure and improve fracture toughness by coarsening the precipitated particles, the maraging steels respond in a manner that is quite different from other precipitation hardening alloys. As the temperature is increased, and if the time at the maraging temperature is lengthened clusters of precipitated particles redissolve locally in the matrix to form small patches of austenite. These patches are sufficiently enriched with Ni, Mo and Ti to remain stable upon cooling from the maraging temperature. Cobalt appears to help minimize this reversion to austenite during the maraging treatment. When small pools of stable austenite are formed in the microstructure, particularly by heating in the temperature range of about 1000 to 1200 F, considerable difficulty will be experienced in regaining composition homogeneity so that the area represented by the pools will again transform to martensite. As will be shown shortly, stable austenite formed by reversion from martensite presents a problem in the heat-affected zones of both weld metal and base metal.

Banding and Anisotropy

Strong directionality in properties has appeared in rolled plate of the maraging steels which is traceable to banding in the microstructure. The condition appears to stem from chemical heterogeneity which develops during the solidification of ingots. This condition persists in the wrought product as layers of retained austenite running parallel to the rolling direction in the martensitic matrix. The fracture toughness of hardened sections exhibiting this structural condition is very poor when stressed transverse to the rolling direction. Even if a plate has been cross-rolled, the toughness through the short-transverse direction can be very poor. This matter of banding is regarded as a major problem in the maraging steels produced from cast ingots, and it becomes more acute with increasing section thickness. Consumable-electrode vacuum melting is effective in minimizing the problem.

A homogenizing treatment at very high temperature (2100 to 2300 F) for fifteen to twenty hours has been reported to eliminate banding, but the treatment seldom is practicable. Also, even though the banding may be eliminated, the steel so treated usually displays somewhat low fracture toughness in all directions after hardening. This deterioration of toughness is suspected to be caused by a condition known as *thermal embrittlement.* Considerable grain coarsening occurs during the treatment at the very high temperature, and there is evidence that some phase (not yet identified, but suspected to be titanium carbide) segregates in the boundaries of these coarse grains. This phase appears as an almost continuous film, and it remains in the microstructure despite subsequent recrystallization into finer grains. Maraging steel which contains this film will fracture with very low energy absorption. The path of fracture will be principally along the prior austenite grain boundaries which contained the film, and plastic deformation will be extremely localized. Some evidence has been found that nonmetallic inclusions, principally sulfides, tend to segregate in the bands of austenite in the heavy sections. Of course, high-temperature heat treatment will not disperse these concentrations of nonmetallics. Investigators have found these nonmetallics intimately associated with brittle fractures in heavy sections.

Directionality in mechanical behavior also can develop from preferred-orientation effects which develop in the grain structure of the maraging steels. These effects are not as firmly entrenched as the chemical heterogeneity which causes banding. Anisotropy caused by orientation can be eliminated by double annealing, which involves a first anneal at 1650 F, followed by a second anneal from the customary 1500 F.

Corrosion Resistance

An undesirable characteristic of the maraging steels which does not concern the welding engineer directly, but which easily might play an important part in the service performance of a weldment is the rather high susceptibility to stress-corrosion cracking when in the maraged condition. These steels will fail in a brittle manner when stressed and exposed to corrosive aqueous solutions such as salt water, tap water, and even distilled water. The stress-corrosion cracking type of failure also will develop when the steel is exposed to corrosive industrial atmospheres, marine atmospheres, and trichloroethylene for long periods of time. Time-to-failure generally decreases as the strength of the steel increases. Welded joints appear susceptible to failure in the heat-affected zones. It is important that the welding engineer keep in mind that regardless of their high alloy content, the maraging steels are not corrosion-resisting alloys.

Welding the 18% Nickel Maraging Steels

Most of the commercially used welding and cutting processes which are applicable to alloy steels have been tried on the maraging steels. The literature contains much data on test joints welded by the gas tungsten-arc process. Somewhat less data is provided on joints welded by the gas metal-arc, submerged-arc, shielded metal-arc (with covered electrodes), and electron beam processes. In general, sound joints, free of cracking and porosity, and having satisfactory mechanical properties can be obtained. However, great care must be taken with all aspects of the welding procedure. Joint preparation, cleaning steps, filler metal selection, control of welding heat input, and many other conditions must be arranged with considerable skill to consistently secure satisfactory welded joints. Even then, difficulty may be encountered with conditions yet unrecognized in the character of these relatively new steels. Consequently, it is imperative for the welding engineer to obtain the most up-to-date information on the ex-

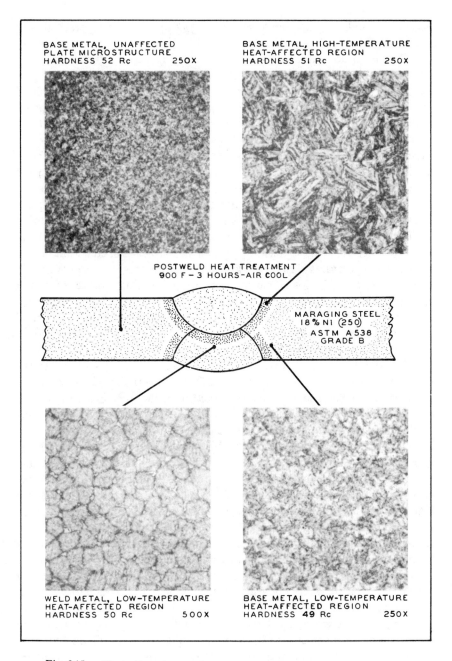

BASE METAL, UNAFFECTED
PLATE MICROSTRUCTURE
HARDNESS 52 Rc   250X

BASE METAL, HIGH-TEMPERATURE
HEAT-AFFECTED REGION
HARDNESS 51 Rc   250X

POSTWELD HEAT TREATMENT
900 F – 3 HOURS–AIR COOL

MARAGING STEEL
18% Ni (250)
ASTM A538
GRADE B

WELD METAL, LOW-TEMPERATURE
HEAT-AFFECTED REGION
HARDNESS 50 Rc   500X

BASE METAL, LOW-TEMPERATURE
HEAT-AFFECTED REGION
HARDNESS 49 Rc   250X

Fig. 245 — Heat-affected zones in 18% Nickel Maraging Steel showing
(schematically) the regions of varying hardening response to postweld
precipitation hardening treatment.

pected weldability of the actual sections being joined, and to proceed with a carefully planned program to make and test the required weldment.

The most attractive feature of the maraging steels, which has stimulated so much welding research in their direction, is their ability to regain almost full strength at weld joints by heating the weldment to about 900 F for approximately one to three hours. Or, just the joint area can be heated to 900 F if the base metal was maraged prior to welding. Notice that the claim is made for regaining *almost* full strength. This qualification is necessitated by the metallurgical behavior of the microstructure in the weld heat-affected zone. For the moment, let us examine the heat-affected zone of the *base metal*. The 18% nickel maraging steels have two narrow regions in the heat-affected zone which do not respond completely to subsequent maraging treatment. These regions which do not fully precipitation harden are (1) the grain-coarsened region immediately adjacent to the weld metal, and (2) a region in the outermost portion of the heat-affected zone where the peak temperatures during welding were in the range of approximately 1100 to 1200 F. The lower hardness found in the grain-coarsened region after the maraging treatment is only slightly below that of the unaffected base metal; the difference being perhaps only one or two Rockwell-C hardness points. The region exposed to 1100 to 1200 F during the weld thermal cycle is more noticeably affected, and after a maraging treatment may be found to register two to four Rockwell-C hardness points below the normal base metal. This region of 1100 to 1200 F peak temperature contains the stable austenite which reverted from the preexisting martensite when the region was heated during welding. The manner in which this stable austenite forms in localized patches was described earlier in discussing attempts to over-age the 18% Ni maraging steels. In the weld heat-affected zone, the distribution of the stable austenite phase is extremely fine, and often requires electron microscopy at about 10,000 magnification to reveal the minute patches. Despite their small size, the austenite patches which do not respond to the maraging treatment can be present in sufficient number to detract from the strength and hardness in this region. Fig. 245 shows schematically the region of impaired properties which is located just beyond the high-temperature annealed (solution treated) region which lies immediately adjacent to the weld metal. The lower temperature region, in which reversion to stable austenite occurs, is observed as a narrow, light-etching band in a metallographic specimen. Although this region is not as strong after re-maraging as is the remainder of the weldment, it may be tougher. Nevertheless, the maximum joint strength obtainable in a weldment hardened only by postweld maraging appears to be limited by the precipitation hardening capability of this austenite-containing region.

The region exists both in the heat-affected zones of the base metal, and in the weld metal. The reversion of martensite to austenite is a temperature–time controlled function in these steels. In simple heating studies, 3% austenite developed upon heating at 1000 F for five minutes. When the time was extended to thirty minutes, the amount of austenite increased to 6%. Heating to 1200 F for one hour produced 50% austenite. Because a region of intermediate temperature exposure (about 1100 to 1200 F) is inescapable during the localized heating from welding, attempts have been made to minimize the amount of stable austenite which develops in the microstructure by restricting heat input and accelerating cooling. As will be shown shortly, the maraging steels are best welded with procedures something like those described for the quenched and tempered alloy steels.

Table 87 — *TYPICAL MECHANICAL PROPERTIES OF WELDED JOINTS IN 18% Ni (250) MARAGING STEEL*[a]

	UTS ksi	YS 0.2% ksi	Elong. in 1 in, %	Red. of area, %	Weld metal hardness Rc	Charpy-V at 70F
Unwelded base metal						
Annealed[c]	158	122	15	63	...	...
Maraged[d]	276	272	9	42	(52)	...
Shielded metal-arc[b]						
As-welded	160	130	5	35	35	25
Maraged[d]	242	225	6	26	50	10
Gas metal-arc[b]						
As-welded	154	134	5	40	37	39
Maraged[d]	235	220	7	30	50	15
Submerged-arc[b]						
As-welded	155	130	6	24	32	33
Maraged[d]	235	220	6	25	49	10

[a] Typical properties with ½ in. thick plate.
[b] All welded specimens fractured in the HAZ.
[c] Annealed at 1500 F.
[d] Maraged at 900 F for 3 hours.

Weld metal as-deposited usually shows pools of retained austenite in a cellular microstructure because of the micro-coring type of segregation which regularly appears in high-alloy steel weld metals. Additional austenite may form by reversion when the weld metal is subjected to intermediate temperatures (1100 to 1200 F) by the heating from multipass welding. The strength of weld metal seldom is equal to that of wrought base metal after postweld maraging, as is shown in Table 87. Consequently, transverse tensile specimens of uniform cross section (weld bead reinforcement removed) usually fracture in the weld metal even though a softened zone produced by reversion to austenite also exists in the base metal heat-affected zone. The strength of weld joints which have been postweld maraged may be 5 to 15% lower than that of the maraged base metal depending upon many conditions, such as base metal thickness, and weld heat input. High heat input usually creates a weaker area in the base metal heat-affected zone, and therefore tensile specimens are likely to fracture in the soft region of the base metal. Relatively low weld heat input usually results in the weld metal being the weaker of the two regions. Of course, if a convex reinforcement is left on the weld metal, the tensile fracture probably will occur in the base metal.

When weldments are postweld annealed at 1500 F prior to being subjected to the 900 F maraging treatment, the joint areas usually harden uniformly. However, it is not uncommon to find the weld metal slightly lower in strength and hardness; particularly if the weld metal composition has not been properly adjusted. In fact, there is not complete agreement among investigators as to whether maraging steel weld metal after any manner of postweld heat treatment will consistently achieve the higher strengths obtainable in base metal. Nevertheless, if the reduced strength (5 to 15%) commonly found in weld metal after only postweld maraging cannot be tolerated, annealing prior to maraging is recommended.

Fracture Toughness of Welded Joints

Although the maraging steels often display a significantly higher fracture toughness than conventional heat treatable alloy steels at a comparable strength level, the toughness of weld joints has been of concern to many investigators. The fracture toughness of both weld metal and the base metal in the heat-affected zones of some weldments had been found to be much lower than that of the unaffected maraged base metal, sometimes as much as 25 to 50% lower. Because weld joints comprise the area where discontinuities and high localized stress are most apt to occur, here is where the lowered fracture toughness can be least tolerated. For example, a study of welded joints in ½-inch thick plate, which were to sustain stress in the order of 200 ksi, revealed by fracture-toughness measurements that the critical crack size would be only 0.02 to 0.03 in. in depth. Small flaws like this are difficult to detect in nondestructive testing, and therefore inspection will assume a role of considerable importance in manufacture of the weldment. Many of the initial reports on the welding of maraging steels singled out this disturbing lack of fracture toughness in the weld metal and the heat-affected zones of joints made by all of the applicable processes (from submerged-arc to electron beam), and pointed out that the deficiency was present despite wide variations in welding conditions with a given process. One group of investigators reported that even when the weldments were postweld annealed at 1500 F prior to maraging some impairment of the fracture toughness remained. Another study which dealt with gas tungsten-arc welded joints in ½-inch plate using vacuum-melted weld rod made use of a specially notched slow-bend test specimen to evaluate fracture toughness. Both single and double maraging treatments were applied to the specimens. K_{Ic} values calculated from the test data ranged from 73 to 93 ksi $\sqrt{}$ inches for the maraged base metal, from 46 to 63 ksi $\sqrt{}$ inches for the weld metal, and intermediate values for the heat-affected zone of the base metal.

According to the most recent reports, the impairment of fracture toughness at the weld joints can be largely avoided by careful control of procedure, particularly heat input, during the welding operation. However, in any evaluation of the maraging steels for toughness or ductility, it is necessary to recognize that these steels have an unusually low work-hardening rate. Consequently, plastic deformation prior to ductile fracture tends to be highly localized. For example, when a section is broken in tension, very little uniform elongation occurs. Instead, the section begins to neck down at some point as soon as the yield stress is reached. Characteristically, tension tests produce high reduction of area values, low total elongation, and high yield strength-to-tensile strength ratios.

The maraging steels also are characterized by Charpy V-notch energy–temperature curves which have only a modest plateau energy level. The steel does not display a marked ductile-to-brittle impact transition as the temperature is lowered — even to temperature as low as –200 F. Energy absorption, however, steadily decreases as the temperature is lowered, and at –200 F the impact energy value is usually less than 20 ft-lbs for the higher-strength maraging steels.

Welding Procedures

Remarkably little difficulty with cracking and microfissures has been experienced in welding the maraging steels, considering the high level of strength, and that welding generally is performed without preheating. Lehigh test specimens (described in Chapter 16) have been welded with full restraint in the test plate and no cracking has occurred. Preheating is avoided, of course, because of its influence toward increasing the width of the heat-affected regions and reducing their cooling rate. A maximum interpass temperature of 250 F usually is held in multipass welding operations. Increasing attention is being given to multipass welding of maraging steels with very small beads — even to the extent of making a final "fillerless" pass with a gas tungsten-arc torch on the last deposited bead using a very low heat input. Some evidence has been reported that high heat input can result in heat-affected zone cracking. This finding comes from an investigation of the failure of a 260-in. diameter solid-propellant rocket motor case constructed of 18% Ni (250) maraging steel plate joined by submerged-arc welding as reported in NASA TM X-1194, January 1966. Failure occurred during proof pressure testing by catastrophic fracture which initiated at a crack defect in the base metal heat-affected zone of a longitudinal weld joint in the cylindrical shell. This area also had undergone some repair welding by the gas tungsten-arc process. The defect at which fracture initiated was 1.4-in. long by 0.10-in. wide, and had remained undetected by nondestructive testing because of its size, orientation and location. Similar cracks were found in the weld heat-affected zone elsewhere in the motor case during post-failure examination. The fracture toughness of the submerged arc welds was judged not adequate to tolerate defects of the size mentioned. Fracture toughness of welded test plates was approximately 55 ksi $\sqrt{}$ in. (K_{Ic}) at yield strengths of 215 to 220 ksi.

The selection of filler metal for welds made by fusion joining in the maraging steels demands close attention, although many of the intricate problems of composition adjustment are handled in advance by the welding rod or electrode manufacturer. It is important that the weld metal closely match the hardening capability of the base metal. Weld metal with over-matching strength after heat treatment is likely to impose undue stress on the heat-affected zones of the base metal, and will not have toughness comparable to the base metal. Weld metal of under-matching strength may be suitable for fillet welded joints, but it seldom is satisfactory for butt joints. Inasmuch as strength in the finally maraged condition is controlled mainly by alloy composition, a deliberate calculation should be made of the weld composition that is likely to be found in the actual joint. This calculation requires consideration of filler metal composition, base metal composition, percent dilution expected, and so forth. In general, the nickel and cobalt contents may be the same as the base metal, but the molybdenum content usually is reduced a little to decrease tendencies for the segregation of alloying elements in the areas of precipitates, and the reversion to austenite which results in lower strength and fracture toughness.

Thorough deoxidation of the weld pool is required to avoid porosity. Consequently, the titanium and aluminum present serve both as alloying (hardening) elements and as deoxidizers. This situation has led to some difficulty when over generous amounts of titanium and aluminum were added for the purpose of deoxidation. The maraged weld deposits were too hard and brittle for service conditions. The amount of titanium and aluminum required for deoxidation will depend, of course, upon the welding process being used. For example, a welding filler metal containing about 0.5% titanium has been reported to serve satisfactorily in gas tungsten-arc welding, but has deposited unsound (porosity-containing) weld metal in gas metal-arc and submerged-arc welding. Some work is being done with auxiliary gas shielding around the gas metal-arc torch to reduce the need for large amounts of deoxidizer in the electrode. Electrodes for submerged-arc welding have been produced which contain as much as 2.5% titanium to insure thorough deoxidation. At the moment, there appears to be much confusion about the optimum amounts of titanium and aluminum desired in electrodes or rods for the various fusion joining processes.

Evidence is mounting that the elements carbon, manganese, silicon, sulfur, oxygen, nitrogen and hydrogen should be held to very low levels. Carbon must be held low in the weld metal because it forms titanium carbide and carbonitride, perhaps with more harmful effect than in the case of base metal. Manganese and silicon appear to have a detrimental influence on the fracture toughness of the weld metal just as they do in base metal. Even when an electrode with very low manganese and silicon is employed, keeping these elements at a low level in a submerged-arc deposit requires the use of a special flux formulated for the maraging steels. Ordinary submerged-arc welding fluxes have ingredients that contribute large amounts of manganese and silicon to the deposit. Sulfur is virtually *poison* in maraging steel weld metal because it strongly promotes hot cracking susceptibility. The very low level of sulfur desired makes it necessary to use only the best raw materials in preparing fluxes for coverings on electrodes, or for submeged-arc welding. The role of nitrogen in weld metal is not well understood. Some investigators believe that nitrogen should be held to less than 0.005%; particularly when the titanium content of the weld metal is high. High nitrogen appears to promote hot cracking and to adversely affect fracture toughness. Electron microscopy has shown that titanium nitride often is present in significant amount in pools of retained austenite on the surfaces of brittle fractures.

Hydrogen also is suspected of adverse influences, although its hazards have not been established firmly by tests. Hydrogen is believed to cause underbead cracking if an excessive amount enters the heat-affected zones of the base metal via the weld metal. Therefore, welding operations are conducted with low-hydrogen conditions as a precaution. Some investigators feel that a low level of hydrogen is very important in the weld metal, and they strongly recommend the use of a vacuum-melted welding rod or electrode in gas-shielded arc welding operations. They prefer to see the weld metal hydrogen content well below 5 ppm. In spite of the underbead

cracking which is suspected to be promoted by hydrogen, the maraging
steels do not appear to be highly susceptible to hydrogen embrittlement
and delayed fracture (static fatigue) as are many other very high strength
steels. Even when cathodically charged with hydrogen, the maraging steels
are more resistant to hydrogen embrittlement than AISI 4340 steel, for

Table 88 — *TYPICAL FILLER METAL COMPOSITIONS FOR JOINING
THE 18% NICKEL (250) MARAGING STEEL*

Elements	Welding rod for gas tungsten-arc process, %	Electrode for gas metal-arc process, %
Carbon	0.025 max	0.025 max
Manganese	0.10 max	0.10 max
Phosphorus	0.010 max	0.010 max
Sulfur	0.010 max	0.010 max
Silicon	0.10 max	0.10 max
Chromium	0.50 max	0.50 max
Nickel	17.5–18.5	17.5–18.5
Cobalt	9.0–10.5	9.0–10.5
Molybdenum	4.0–5.0	4.0–5.0
Titanium	0.40–0.60	0.90–1.25
Aluminum	0.05–0.15	0.05–0.15
Zirconium	0.005 max	0.005 max
Calcium	0.05 max	0.05 max
Boron	0.003 max	0.003 max
Nitrogen	25 ppm max	25 ppm max
Oxygen	50 ppm max	50 ppm max
Hydrogen	5 ppm max	5 ppm max

example. Tests have shown that 18% Ni (300) steel in the maraged condition requires 6 to 12 hours of cathodic charging in a 4% sulfuric acid
solution before it reaches the same degree of hydrogen embrittlement as
will 4340 steel in only 5 minutes of similar charging. Also, maraging steel
recovers ductility more rapidly and effectively upon baking at 300 F. In
delayed, brittle fracture testing, the maraging steel has demonstrated greater
resistance to static fatigue when charged with more than 5 ppm of hydro-

gen. It has been postulated that the maraging steels may "trap" hydrogen within the fine structure of the lattice in some yet unrecognized manner. This hydrogen is pictured as being *not* readily diffusible because it is not in solid solution — and therefore, it is innocuous.

These findings on the influences of alloying and residual elements in maraging steel weld metal have had the expected effect upon manufacturing specifications for welding rods and electrodes. Table 88 lists typical requirements for two forms of filler metal currently being produced for use on 18% Ni (250) maraging steel.

Because electron beam welding offers the opportunity to weld butt joints with the lowest possible heat input, some attention has been given to applying this process to the maraging steels. Several investigating groups have conducted studies, the results of one being shown in Table 89. These results with electron beam welding have not been particularly promising to date because of low ductility and fracture toughness. In fact, no real advantage has been shown over the gas tungsten-arc process. Metallographic examinations have shown highly segregated and preferentially-oriented grains in the weld metal of electron beam welded joints.

Table 89 — *MECHANICAL PROPERTIES OF ELECTRON BEAM WELDED JOINTS IN 18% Ni (280) MARAGING STEEL*[a]

	SEQUENCE OF HEAT TREATING AND WELDING[b]				
	1 Annealed 2 Maraged (Unwelded)	1 Annealed 2 Maraged 3 Welded (As-welded)	1 Annealed 2 Maraged 3 Welded 4 Re-maraged	1 Annealed 2 Welded 3 Maraged	1 Annealed 2 Welded 3 Annealed 4 Maraged
Ult. tens. str., ksi	266	243	266	267	274
Yield strength, ksi	263	243	262	266	270
Elongation, % in 1-in. gage in 2-in. gage	14.0 8.0	3.5 1.5	5.5 . . .	3.5 2.5	5.0 3.0

[a] Values are averages from quadruplicate tests on 0.3-in. thick plate.
[b] Annealed at 1500 F for one hour and air cooled. Maraged at 925 F for 3¾ hours.

(Data from Kohn and Schaper)

Thermal cutting operations on the maraging steels deserve as much metallurgical scrutiny as does welding. When thermal cutting is performed with a very high temperature heat source, such as a plasma-jet torch, heavy sections may display internal fine cracking a short distance behind the cut edge. The location of these microfissures appears to coincide with the demarcation between the high-temperature zone immediately adjacent to the cut edge which undergoes complete austenization, and the next zone where only partial reversion to austenite takes place. The fissures usually propagate along paths perpendicular to the edge, and generally are located about mid-thickness where the stresses are highest. The fissures are particularly prone to occur if the steel contains any of the film-like phase associated with thermal embrittlement.

12% NICKEL MARAGING STEELS

The most recently developed maraging steels contain only 12% nickel. As shown in Table 86A, cobalt has been eliminated from the alloy composition, and approximately 5% chromium has been added. These experimental 12% Ni steels are being studied for possible use at a yield strength level of 160 to 180 ksi where they are expected to display greater fracture toughness. In welding studies to date, the behavior of the microstructure in the heat-affected zones of the 12% Ni steels was found to be quite similar to that of the 18% Ni steels. When joints welded by the gas tungsten-arc and gas metal-arc processes were postweld maraged, a decrease of approximately 5% was found in the yield strength of the base metal region which experienced the 1100 to 1200 F intermediate temperature exposure.

ALLOY STEELS IN HIGH-TEMPERATURE SERVICE

The manufacture of weldments for service at "high temperatures" (usually taken to mean above about 500 F) has become a specialized area of fabrication. To accommodate the effects of temperature, *per se,* and thermal cycling, a new segment of technology has been developed to guide the design, selection of material, and the construction of these weldments. We will concern ourselves, of course, chiefly with the general character of the alloy steels which are commonly employed in this service; however, a number of metallurgical aspects of design, construction and operation can play a vital role in weldment performance and will be pointed out in passing.

Higher operating temperatures often demand that weldments be made of alloy steel because of two property limitations of iron (and carbon steel) which grow more acute as temperature rises, namely, strength decreases, and corrosion accelerates. Loss of strength was shown in Chapter 6 to be measurable in a number of ways. The kind of weldment and its intended service will determine whether hot tensile strength, creep rate, or stress–rupture criteria should be used to judge the suitability of a steel for the application. The usual corrosion threat is oxidation, inasmuch as most oxidizing media become more active with increasing temperature. The corrosion problem at high temperatures may be complicated by other phenomena, such as localized stress-oxidation failure, chemical reaction with sulfurous gases, and attack by hot hydrogen. The use of alloy steel is not always the most effective means of controlling weldment deterioration. Sometimes, steps must be taken to lower the metal temperature, or to eliminate a corrosive agent from the environment. When the article to be exposed to a high temperature is a *weldment,* there will be added reasons for double-checking possible effects of service conditions upon performance.

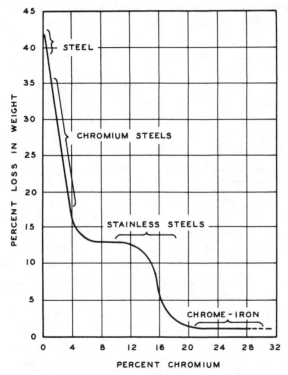

Fig. 246 — Influence of chromium content of steel upon oxidation resistance at high temperature.

Loss of weight for ½-Inch cubes after 48 hours exposure at 1835 F.
(MacQuigg)

A survey of the alloy steels commonly employed in high-temperature service will show chromium and molybdenum as the two most frequently used alloying elements. Molybdenum is effective for increasing strength at higher temperatures. Chromium increases strength, and improves oxidation resistance. Fig. 246 shows the improvement which takes place in the oxidation resistance of iron as chromium is added. Note the remarkable increase which occurs starting with the initial addition. This greater resistance to oxidation is credited to the affinity which chromium has for oxygen and the kind of protective oxide film or scale which forms on the surface of the chromium-containing steels. When the chromium content exceeds about 10 or 12%, a remarkable degree of oxidation resistance is achieved. Another marked improvement occurs as the chromium content is raised above about 17%. The test conditions represented in Fig. 246 for evaluating oxidation resistance are quite severe, so this would explain why a chromium level of about 10% marks the start of the stainless and heat-resisting steels. Nevertheless, the improvement imparted by lesser amounts of chromium can be useful in steels exposed to lower temperatures or milder environments.

The efficacy of chromium and molybdenum in aiding strength and oxidation resistance is so outstanding that the chromium–molybdenum alloy steels dominate the high-temperature weldment field as materials of construction. Table 90 lists representative alloy steels often used in weldments for high-temperature service as selected from ASTM material standards. This listing starts with a steel containing only an addition of ½% molybdenum, mainly for increased strength, and progresses through steels of increasing chromium content up to a level of 9% chromium. Many high-temperature or heat-resisting steels lie beyond this chromium level, but they are considered "high-alloy" steels and are not included in this present volume. Many other steels, most of them of proprietary composition, could be added to the list in Table 90, but these would represent modifications of the basic compositions. They usually contain small additions of vanadium, tungsten and nickel to gain added creep strength or stress-rupture life. The most important point to keep in mind is that alloying elements, such as chromium, molybdenum, vanadium, etc., although added to bolster strength or oxidation resistance at high temperatures, also are *hardenability* promoters. Therefore, welding procedures must be designed to accommodate these materials as hardenable steels. Close attention must be paid to the carbon content of the base metal and weld metal, since this is the first important factor in determining the extent of precautions to be incorporated in the welding procedure. It will be noted that all of the steels listed in Table 90 are relatively low in carbon content. However, the design engineer sometimes is tempted to select one of the available steels of higher carbon content— forgetting for the moment that a welding problem could arise. The steels listed in Table 90 seldom are used at service temperatures above about 1050 F because of inadequacies in strength or corrosion resistance.

Weld metal for joining the high-temperature steels usually has an

Table 90 — *REPRESENTATIVE ALLOY STEELS USED IN WELDMENTS FOR HIGH-TEMPERATURE SERVICE*

Common designation	ASTM specification reference	CHEMICAL COMPOSITION — PERCENT					Tensile Properties	
		C	Mn	Si	Cr	Mo	UTS, ksi	Yld. Str., ksi
C–Mo	Grade T1 A 209	0.10– 0.20	0.30– 0.80	0.10– 0.50	...	0.44– 0.65	55 min	30 min
C–Mo	Grade T1b A 209	0.14 max	0.30– 0.80	0.10– 0.50	...	0.44– 0.65	53 min	30 min
½ Cr – ½ Mo	Grade P2 A 335	0.10– 0.20	0.30– 0.61	0.10– 0.30	0.50– 0.81	0.44– 0.65	55 min	30 min
1 Cr – ½ Mo	Grade B A 387	0.17 max	0.40– 0.65	0.15– 0.30	0.80– 1.15	0.45– 0.65	60 – 82	35 min
1¼ Cr – ½ Mo	Grace C A 387	0.17 max	0.40– 0.65	0.50– 1.00	1.00– 1.50	0.45– 0.65	60 – 85	35 min
2¼ Cr – 1 Mo	Grade D A 387	0.15 max	0.30– 0.60	0.50 max	2.00– 2.50	0.90– 1.10	60 – 85	30 min
3 Cr – 1 Mo	Grade E A 387	0.15 max	0.30– 0.60	0.50 max	2.75– 3.75	0.90– 1.10	60 – 85	30 min
5 Cr – ½ Mo	Grade P5 A 335	0.15 max	0.30– 0.60	0.50 max	4.00– 6.00	0.45– 0.65	60 min	30 min
5 Cr – ½ Mo (High Si)	Grade P5b A 335	0.15 max	0.30– 0.60	1.00– 2.00	4.00– 6.00	0.45– 0.65	60 min	30 min
5 Cr – ½ Mo (Ti or Cb)[a]	Grade P5c A 335	0.12 max	0.30– 0.60	0.50 max	4.00– 6.00	0.45– 0.65	60 min	30 min
7 Cr – ½ Mo	Grade P7 A 335	0.15 max	0.30– 0.60	0.50– 1.00	6.00– 8.00	0.44– 0.65	60 min	30 min
9 Cr – 1 Mo	Grade P9 A 335	0.15 max	0.30– 0.60	0.25– 1.00	8.00– 10.0	0.90– 1.10	60 min	30 min

[a] Ti 4 × C min., 0.70 max., or Cb 8 × C min. and 10 × C max.

alloy composition similar to the base metal. Electrodes for shielded metal-arc welding the steels which contain up to about 2½% chromium can be selected from the standard AWS-ASTM chromium–molybdenum classes shown in Table 45. Electrodes for welding the steels containing 5% and 7% chromium were shown in Table 51. A number of electrodes of chromium–molybdenum composition are available as proprietary brands. Alloy steel electrodes of the more popular Cr–Mo compositions are available for gas metal-arc, and submerged-arc welding. Alloyed fluxes for use with carbon steel electrodes also are available for submerged-arc welding. Weld metals of these Cr–Mo compositions, as might be expected, have limited toughness in the as-welded condition. Preheating is widely used to keep the deposits from cracking, and postweld stress-relief heat treatment ordinarily is applied to improve the tough-

ness of the weld metal and the base metal heat-affected zones. Sometimes for weldments where postweld heat treatment cannot be applied, a
weld metal possessing more suitable mechanical properties in the as-
welded condition may be employed. An austenitic Cr–Ni stainless steel,
or a nickel-base alloy filler metal generally is selected, as examples,
E309 or E310 stainless steels. While these dissimilar weld metals possess
good strength and toughness, their use does not eliminate hardening of
the weld heat-affected zones, and further deliberating must be done to
decide whether this structural condition will affect performance in service.
Also, certain of the austenitic weld metals have thermal expansivity
coefficients which are considerably greater than those of the C–Mo or
Cr–Mo base metals. Differences in thermal expansivity between the base
and weld metals can lead to the generation of high stresses which tend
to concentrate at the toe of the weld. These stresses can be particularly
harmful if the joint is subjected to cyclic temperature changes. They can
induce localized stress-oxidation failure at the base–weld metal interface,
or can produce a thermal-fatigue type of fracture. Welding with austenitic
filler metal is more widely practiced in equipment for the petroleum industry where units operate under more-or-less steady-state conditions,
rather than in the steam-power generation field where demand variation
causes cycling of temperature and pressure.

Among the precautions to be taken in fabricating weldments for
high-temperature service is the oft-stated rule of avoiding crevices and
notches at weld joints. The presence of these stress raisers is not likely to
lead to a dramatic, brittle failure as has been described for weldments in
service at room temperature and below, but their presence can be very
damaging in the long run. In addition to concentrating stress, which
possibly could lead to a stress-rupture failure, crevices and notches also
may trap foreign material which in time can cause corrosion damage.
Welding slag, particularly that which is high in fluoride content, has been
pointed out in Chapter 13 as being undesirable as a residue on equipment entering high-temperature service. Solid particles from the process
stream of the operation can be trapped in crevices. Low-melting compounds, such as oxides of vanadium, sodium, and zinc, can be very
harmful if they act to flux away the protective chromium oxide scale
which should form on the surface of the steel.

An important application in which alloy steel weldments are subjected to high-temperature service is the refining and reforming equipment
of the petroleum industry. Many of the reactor units and piping in refining
plants operate at high temperatures and strong demands are made for
strength, corrosion resistance, trouble-free performance, and longevity.

Two unusual problems have been encountered in catalytic reformers and the associated piping which are not brought on by welding, but it is imperative that the welding engineer be aware of their occurrence. Catalytic reformers operate in the temperature range of 850 to 1050 F at pressures greater than 250 psi handling a flow of hydrogen-rich gas mixtures. When hydrogen sulfide is present in the stream to the extent

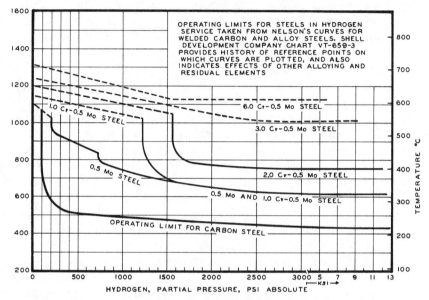

Fig. 247 — Guide to the selection of steels for service in hydrogen under high temperature and high pressure. (Nelson)

of about 1½% and higher, the steel process equipment can suffer serious general corrosive attack. Sulfur penetrates the steel intergranularly and converts the metal into iron sulfide. The rate of attack is controlled principally by temperature and the hydrogen sulfide concentration. Carbon steels and low-chromium steels are equally susceptible to attack, and the only recourses are to lower the operating temperature, or scrub the hydrogen sulfide out of the process stream. Steels containing 10 to 17% chromium show moderate improvement to hydrogen sulfide attack, while the austenitic Cr–Ni stainless steels have good resistance.

A second problem in catalytic reformers arises from a unique form of attack by the hot hydrogen gas on the steel. Ordinary decarburization is not a particularly damaging reaction when it occurs on the surface of a steel weldment in high-temperature service; however, when decarburization occurs in an atmosphere of hot hydrogen under high pressure the attack can be cause for great concern. Under these conditions, hydrogen can reduce iron carbide particles and other nonmetallics in the steel. The reaction can be accompanied by blistering and cracking from the pressure of the hydrocarbon gases formed internally in the steel. Minute voids are formed where the solid secondary phases and particles are removed by the hydrogen. Because chromium carbides are more resistant to reduction by hydrogen, the chromium–molybdenum steels offer greatly improved resistance to attack. The curves shown in Fig. 247 are widely used as a guide in selecting steels for service based upon these process conditions. As indicated by the Nelson curves, the severity of attack by hydrogen increases with higher temperatures and with greater partial pressures. Hydrogen appears to act physically as well as chemically upon the steel. Attack proceeds in three stages: (1) diffusion of atomic hydrogen into the steel, (2) decarburization by hydrogen reduction, and (3) intergranular fissuring. When conditions of temperature and pressure encourage attack upon a steel of given composition, decarburization starts at the surface and in time may proceed completely through the wall of a vessel or piping system. Fissuring starts in the most highly stressed areas and proceeds until a major crack propagates through the wall and relieves internal pressure. The influence of temperature, as indicated in Fig. 247, is greater than that of pressure in promoting attack. Actual deterioration of the steel by decarburization and fissuring is preceded by an incubation period during which the maximum charging with hydrogen occurs. If, during this period, the hydrogen atmosphere is removed, the contained hydrogen will effuse out of the steel as dictated by the temperature of the material. When maximum charging with hydrogen occurs at high temperature, this point appears to mark the beginning of a transition period where the metal suffers permanent loss of ductility and toughness. However, no evidence appears in the microstructure which is related to this damage. The period of toughness deterioration is followed by decarburization. The carbon content may be reduced to as low as 0.01%, in the decarburized region with commensurate loss of strength. Stress is an important factor in producing the fissuring. This unsoundness may develop in areas which are not necessarily the most severely decarburized. Decarburization proceeds more rapidly at grain boundaries, along dendrite axes, and in cold worked zones, and therefore does not always progress through a steel section as a uniform frontal attack.

Welded joints in carbon steel have been found through experience to suffer from hydrogen attack somewhat earlier than wrought base metal. The reason for this greater susceptibility has not been established. Furthermore, hydrogen attack has occurred unexpectedly on weld metal in

Cr–Mo steel weldments— not because weld metal is more susceptible to this form of attack, but because the weld metal *did not contain* the proper chromium and molybdenum contents. Several major petroleum refining companies have conducted investigations of the alloy compositions of weld metal in the joints of operating equipment and have been disturbed to find a substantial number of cases of inadequate alloy content. For example, it appeared that too little attention had been paid to filler metal identification and that 2½ Cr–1 Mo base metal had been joined with ½ Cr–½ Mo filler metal. The point to be emphasized is that an error of this kind is not likely to become apparent immediately. The strength of the lower-alloy weld metal would be about the same as if a 2¼ Cr–1 Mo filler metal were deposited. Even the stress-rupture strength possibly would be adequate. Only after some period of service will the hot hydrogen atmosphere lead to decarburization and fissuring of the lower alloy weld metal and possibly cause a catastrophic failure. Obviously, good control must be exercised over identification of materials of construction and check analyses should be made to insure weld metal of proper chemical composition.

ALLOY STEELS IN CRYOGENIC SERVICE

The fact that iron and many steels lose toughness as temperature is lowered, sometimes to a startling degree over a narrow transition range, has been previously emphasized many times. Information also has been provided in appropriate earlier chapters on the kinds of steel which display improved toughness and which have lower fracture-transition temperatures. In the main, the ability of a steel to retain adequate toughness at the lowest temperature expected during service determines its suitability for cryogenic usage. Only those steels which have sufficient toughness at the lowest temperature to accommodate the propagation of discontinuities by the energy-absorbing shear type of fracture are truly safe to employ. While it may seem superfluous to again bring these steels up for discussion, there is good reason to look into the technology of fabricating them into weldments for cryogenic service. Stronger demands are being made for strength, toughness, and assurance against brittle fracture as service temperatures move downward toward absolute zero. The construction of weldments for cryogenic service has become as much a specialized industrial science as is the making of weldments for high-temperature service.

An attempt will be made here to summarize the important facets of steel selection, joint design, welding procedure, and testing and inspection techniques when constructing a weldment for cryogenic service.

Since the term *cryogenic* does not connote any particular temperature range, we shall consider those applications which involve service temperatures below –50 F. This will avoid repeating much of the information presented earlier on certain steels of the high-strength, low-alloy type which have improved fracture toughness at low temperatures. We also will skip over the quenched and tempered high-strength alloy steels to avoid repetition; even though these steels have admirable fracture toughness at low temperatures. We will concentrate on steels which have been designed to have especially good fracture toughness at *very low* temperatures. It should be understood, however, that many other steels are used in cryogenic service, at least in the temperature range of –50 down to –100 F.

STEELS FOR VERY LOW TEMPERATURE SERVICE

Steelmaking has been shown to play a very important part in securing good fracture toughness at low temperatures. The following features are particularly helpful in lowering the fracture-toughness transition temperature: (a) minimal use of carbon as an alloying element, (b) thorough deoxidation (killed steel), (c) fine grain size, (d) heat treated microstructure (normalized, or quenched and tempered), and (e) alloying with nickel. Each of these features when embodied in a steel increases its cost. Heat treatment and alloying with nickel are the more costly. Consequently, various combinations of these features are found in steels tailored to be serviceable down to specific low temperature levels. It is clear, however, that a particularly effective way of achieving very low temperature serviceability is to alloy the steel with a substantial amount of nickel. Fig. 248 shows in a general way that ordinary hot rolled carbon steel (containing about 0.25% carbon) at best is notch tough only to about 0 F. Heat treatment can improve fracture toughness, of course, and extend its range of usefulness down to at least –50 F, and possibly as low as –75 F. By adding nickel in substantial amounts, the range of applicability can be extended as follows:

Steel Composition	Lowest Service Temperature
2¼ % Nickel	–75 F
3½ % Nickel	–150 F
5% Nickel	–200 F
9% Nickel	–320 F

The service temperature limits listed above are based upon having a minimum Charpy (keyhole or U-notch) impact strength of at least 15 ft-lbs. These temperatures are recognized for all but the 5% nickel steel in ASTM A300. There has been much debate over claims that 15 ft-lbs keyhole or U-notch Charpy as required by ASTM A300 *does not* provide assurance of adequate toughness, and that the Charpy V-notch specimen should be used in testing for serviceability. This thinking is embodied in a new ASTM standard (A553) issued for 9% nickel steel plate which has been heat treated by quenching and tempering for pressure vessel usage. Here, a 25 ft-lb minimum Charpy V-notch requirement is set for longitudinal specimens.

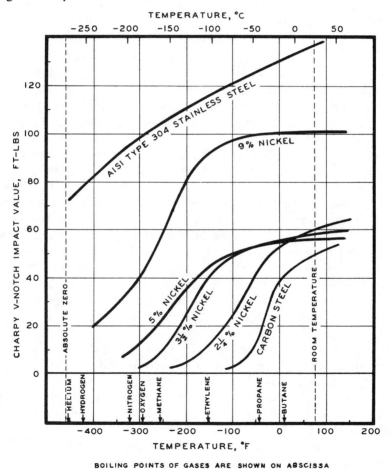

Fig. 248 — Impact properties of steels over a wide range of temperature, showing the benefit of nickel in lowering toughness-transition temperature, and superiority of austenitic stainless steel at all temperatures.

One group of investigators has proposed more rigorous Charpy V-notch requirements for other steels to establish the lowest safe service temperature — at least for steels employed in welded pressure vessels. A summation of this more conservative thinking is as follows:

	Minimum Energy, Ft-Lbs, Charpy V-Notch	
Type of Steel	To Prevent Fracture Initiation	To Prevent Fracture Propagation
Rimmed and Semikilled	10	15
Fully Killed Fine Grain	15	25
High Strength Steel (50 ksi Min. Yld.)	25	35
Quenched and Tempered	30	45

The composition limits for 2¼, 3½ and 9% nickel steel were shown earlier in Table 78. The 5% nickel steel is widely used in Europe, but not in the USA; presumably because it does not offer sufficient advantage over the 3½% nickel steel to justify its higher cost. It must be appreciated that the Charpy-V energy-absorption curves shown in Fig. 248 represent "normal expectancy" for properly manufactured and heat treated steel. Many conditions can cause scatter, and sometimes marked deviations occur from the predicted normal values. The condition of heat treatment is very influential, as is shown in Fig. 249 for the 3½% nickel steel. In the hot rolled or as-forged condition, the impact strength would be very unpredictable. Normalizing lowers the transition temperature principally through grain refinement. Quenching and tempering is more effective in lowering transition temperature because it produces a fine grain size plus a more favorable distribution of carbide particles in the alloyed matrix. Despite the efficacy of these steelmaking and heat treating practices, even the best of the alloy steels (e.g., 9% nickel) decreases to an undesirably low level of notch toughness as temperature drops below about –375 F. Hence, the use of 9% nickel steel is sanctioned only down to –320 F. Also included in Fig. 248 is the curve for Type 304 austenitic chromium–nickel stainless steel. Note that this steel does not exhibit a toughness transition, and maintains a superior level of energy absorption down to the lowest obtainable testing temperature (–452 F). This exemplary performance is attributable, of course, to the face-centered cubic crystalline structure of the steel.

A number of additional conditions that adversely influence fracture toughness, particularly at very low temperatures may bear re-emphasis here. Although steel should be fully killed and fine grained for best toughness, residual aluminum content in excess of about 0.05% is unfavorable. Sulfur and phosphorus are influential, and both elements

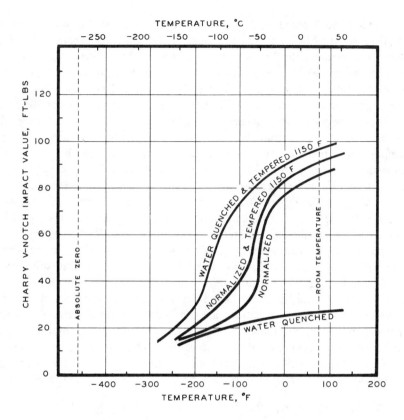

Fig. 249 — Effect of condition or heat treatment on impact properties of 3½% nickel alloy steel.

should be held to lower levels than found in steels for service at ordinary
temperatures. Carbon content is very important, as should be realized by
now. While the widely used ASTM specifications which cover the nickel
alloy steels for cryogenic service limit the carbon contents to relatively
low levels, it is prudent to use as little carbon as possible as a strengthening element without jeopardizing compliance with the specified strength
levels. Impact values obtained from specimens oriented transversely to the
primary direction of rolling in a plate will be lower in some degree than
those from longitudinally oriented specimens. Thicker plates tend to give
lower impact values. Cold working, as would be produced during forming,
ordinarily does not seriously affect toughness if limited to about 3%.
However, if the steel is sensitive to strain hardening, or to strain aging
upon subsequent heating, the fracture toughness may be affected detrimentally.

Other mechanical and physical properties must be considered in addition to toughness in selecting a steel for cryogenic service. Strength often is a prime consideration because it is a determining factor in the cost of the material required for the weldment. Strength–weight ratio can be the deciding factor where the weight of the finished weldment is all important. Incidentally, Type 304 stainless steel frequently is handicapped by its relatively low yield strength at room temperature. Even though the strength of the steel may be substantially higher at the actual service temperature, this ordinarily cannot be used to advantage by raising the allowable design stresses. Fatigue strength can be a factor if the applied stresses are dynamic because of frequent temperature cycling or load fluctuations. Although physical characteristics like thermal conductivity, and linear expansion and contraction, regularly receive close scrutiny when comparing different materials of construction (for example, when comparing alloy steel with austenitic stainless steel), there is relatively little variation in these and many other properties and characteristics across the breadth of the carbon and alloy steels. Demands for corrosion resistance in the material of construction are lessened in cryogenic weldments because most chemical reactions are markedly decreased in rate at lower temperatures. The welding engineer cannot afford to be inattentive on the matter of corrosion resistance, however, because product purity, attack on the weldment while at ambient temperature, and other conditions encountered in regular operation may be important corrosion-wise.

WELDMENT AND JOINT DESIGN

There is an old adage which goes, "Only a fool prods the sleeping bear to see how quickly he will awake!" This is essentially the philosophy followed in designing and fabricating weldments for cryogenic service. Fabricators wisely avoid every possible condition that might represent a challenge to the toughness of the metal. Although the material of construction is predicted to have a toughness transition temperature comfortably below the service temperature, and therefore should be capable of adjusting to localized over stress at discontinuities, the question remains whether the full-size structure will behave like the laboratory test specimen which predicted tough behavior. As will be explained in Chapter 16, we have not reached a stage of proficiency in laboratory testing where results can be obtained to accurately foretell the performance of a weldment in service. The test results will be very useful in comparing the toughness of different steels, and in rough measurements of the influence of variable metallurgical and environmental conditions on toughness. However, much judgment must be exercised in relating these results to the probable behavior of an actual weldment, where size, design, fabrication procedures, residual stresses, and other factors also influence behavior.

The majority of weldments constructed for cryogenic service are in the form of pressure vessels, piping systems, pumps, valves and tanks. The need for these articles arises from the tremendous increase in activities involving the use of liquefied gases. The very low boiling points of such useful gases as methane, oxygen, nitrogen and hydrogen account for the use of cryogenics in the liquefaction and transportation of these gases. The rules followed for the design, fabrication and operation of pressurized equipment usually are those of the ASME Boiler and Pressure Vessel Code. Most of the tanks used for storing and transporting the liquefied gases hold their contents at atmospheric or low pressures. Loss of the contents is minimized through insulation to reduce "boil-off." Many of the vessels are double-wall construction with a vacuum jacket, or with a highly effective insulator such as perlite (volcanic lava) between the shells. This double-wall construction can introduce problems in fabrication with regard to support of the inner shell. Joints in cryogenic weldments are of the butt-type whenever possible, and with complete penetration or fusion to avoid notch effect.

WELDING PROCEDURES

In planning a welding procedure for any of the nickel alloy steels, the welding engineer must arrange for a high degree of integrity both in geometric form and in metallurgical character. Joints must be virtually free of design faults or workmanship defects that would promote unnecessary stress concentration. Unfused root faces, or severe undercutting are typical examples of "triggers" for brittle fractures in cryogenic service. Furthermore, the procedure must include control over welding conditions that would promote underbead cracking, and must provide a notch-tough metallurgical structure in the weld metal and heat-affected zones of the final weldment. In general, these requirements call for the following procedural features:

(1) Preheating, *per se*, is not required; however, base metal temperature must not be too low for the plate composition, thickness, and degree of restraint.

(2) Low-hydrogen electrodes, or a hydrogen-free welding process must be employed.

(3) Filler metal must be carefully selected to assure both the required strength and the minimum impact properties specified for the lowest test temperature.

(4) Welding technique must not involve excessive heat input that would produce coarse-grained weld deposits and detract from the toughness of the heat-affected zones. Stress-relief heat treatment may be required for certain of the nickel alloy steels to restore toughness, or may be required by the ruling code.

(5) Welding operations should be performed in the downhand or horizontal positions if possible because vertical and overhead deposition of weld metal detracts from its impact properties, and are more likely to produce a joint with discontinuities and defects.

Welding 2¼% Nickel Steel

ASTM A203 covers 2¼% nickel steel. Although Grade B was given as an example in Table 78, the specification provides two grades with carbon maxima regulated in each grade by plate thickness. For plates (a) up to 2 inches, (b) over 2 to 4 inches, and (c) over 4 to 6 inches maximum, Grade A may contain maximum carbon contents of 0.17, 0.20, and 0.23%, respectively. Whereas Grade B may contain 0.21, 0.24, and 0.25%, respectively. The higher carbon levels of Grade B produce somewhat higher strength levels (70 to 85 ksi UTS and 40 ksi minimum YP for Grade B, as compared to 65 to 77 ksi UTS and 37 ksi minimum YP for Grade A). Obviously, greater care may be required in welding the Grade B steel if the steelmaker actually has made use of the higher permissible carbon limits in his product. Both grades are expected to display a 15 ft-lb minimum Charpy keyhole or U-notch impact strength at –75 F when ordered to ASTM A300. Ordinarily, a normalizing treatment consisting of heating to 1650F followed by air cooling is used to obtain the required mechanical properties.

The 2¼% nickel steels are widely used for handling liquid propane (–44 F) and other applications down to the lowest permissible service temperature of –75 F. Large cargo tanks of 2¼% nickel steel have been built into ocean-going ships to transport liquefied butane (–26 F) and propane. These tanks carry the gas at atmospheric pressure. Insulation slows down boil-off. The evaporating cargo gas is piped to the ship's boilers to generate steam for propulsion. The tanks are of rectangular design, but with coved corners. They are shop fabricated and installed aboard ship. The selection of a steel for these tanks usually is guided by a regulatory specification which calls for a maximum NDT of –65 F. The NDT for 2¼% nickel steel plate commonly is in the vicinity of –100 F.

The 2¼% nickel steels fall into P-Number 4 of the classification system outlined in Table 62 of Chapter 12. This category indicated that a preheat of 300 F and a postweld stress relief heat treatment often would

be necessary for such a steel. In shop practice today, joints in 2¼%
nickel steel seldom are welded at room temperature, but more often
are preheated to 200 to 250 F. A 300 F minimum preheat may be advisable
if the carbon level is 0.20% and above, or if restraint on the joint is particularly high. Stress-relief heat treatment at about 1150 F often is applied
to 2¼% nickel steel welded pressure vessels and pressure piping for
cryogenic service because the treatment is required by a ruling code or
specification. Some non-code weldments have been postweld stress-relief
heat treated simply because it appeared to be good practice to lower the
residual stresses and to temper the heat-affected zones prior to exposure
under service conditions at a very low temperature. However, studies of
the behavior of welded joints and actual pressure vessels of certain nickel
alloy steels, including the 2¼% nickel type, have shown that even in
the as-welded condition adequate fracture toughness usually is maintained
to comply with test requirements, and with expected service conditions.
This good as-welded performance is predicated on the base metal having
been placed in a condition of optimum toughness by normalizing and tempering, or by quenching and tempering. Nevertheless, the 2¼% nickel
steel has not been allowed exceptions to the requirements of paragraph
UCS-67 of the ASME Code as has the 9% nickel steel.

Shielded metal-arc welding of the 2¼% nickel steels usually is performed with covered electrodes of the E80XX-C1 classification. The necessity of maintaining low-hydrogen conditions during welding limits electrode selection to the –15, –16 and –18 types of coverings. As shown
earlier in Tables 45 and 47, these electrodes produce all-weld-metal deposits containing approximately 2½% nickel which extends the 15 ft-lb
Charpy-V impact transition to a temperature in the vicinity of –80 F. Similar tests on joints in 2¼% nickel steel plate as heavy as 1-inch thick
found the 15 ft-lb transition temperature for specimens notched at the
fusion line and at various locations in the base metal heat-affected zone
to be in the vicinity of –130 F.

Welding 3½% Nickel Steel

Steels containing 3½% nickel for service at temperatures as low as
–150 F are identified as Grades D and E in ASTM A203 (and A300).
Carbon maxima again are regulated by plate thickness. For plates (a)
up to 2 inches, and (b) over 2 to 4 inches, Grade D may contain maximum carbon contents of 0.17 and 0.20%, respectively. Whereas Grade
E may contain 0.20 and 0.23% maximum, respectively. The strength requirements for the low-carbon and the higher-carbon varieties of 3½%
nickel steel are identical to those of the 2¼% nickel steel. Consequently,

the maximum allowable design stresses vary with carbon content rather than nickel content. Heat treatment of the 3½% nickel steels ordinarily consists of normalizing from about 1600 F, since this is the specified treatment in ASTM A 300. However, improved toughness can be obtained by applying normalizing at 1650 F and tempering at 1175 F, or by quenching from 1650 F followed by tempering at 1175 F.

The 3½% nickel steels fall into P-Number 9 of Table 62, which suggests that greater consideration must be given to preheating and postweld heat treatment. Yet, in shop practice, the need for preheating the 3½% nickel steels for welding appears about the same as described for the 2¼% nickel steels. However, because the additional nickel in the 3½% nickel steel aids in gaining the required strength, the steelmaker can be more conservative in his use of carbon as an alloying element. Therefore, the need for preheating may be somewhat less critical with the 3½% nickel steels. Nevertheless, this steel has high hardenability, and if the carbon content is above about 0.20%, or if restraint upon the joint is high, preheating in the range of about 200 to 250 F may be advisable.

Shielded metal-arc welding of the 3½% nickel steels is performed with electrodes of the E80XX-C2 classification which bear low-hydrogen types of coverings. Table 45 and 47 show that weld metal deposits contain about 3¼% nickel, and have a 15 ft-lb Charpy-V transition temperature of −80 F and lower. As shown in Fig. 250, the energy transition is at a lower temperature if the keyhole specimen is used. The performance of weld metal in the impact test will vary with different lots of electrodes, and with welding conditions. Consequently, a certain amount of testing and very close attention to welding procedure is required to insure specified impact properties. Low temperature impact properties sufficient for most applications can be obtained at temperatures down to −150 F. Most manufacturers of E80XX-C2 electrodes report typical Charpy-V impact values of about 35 ft-lbs at this temperature. As also shown in Fig. 250, postweld stress-relief heat treatment does not always improve the impact properties of weld metal. In fact, a slight impairment of properties more often occurs. Much research effort has been directed toward the 3½% nickel steel weld metal to eliminate some of the variation in impact strength, and to lower the toughness transition temperature. Just a small downward shift in weld metal transition temperature would permit the 3½% nickel steel filler metal to be used in additional important applications. For example, liquefied ethylene, with a boiling point of −155 F, is being handled in increasing amounts for use in many industries, such as the manufacturing of plastics. The toughness transition temperature of 3½% nickel steel plate can be shifted below this temperature by resorting to a quenching and

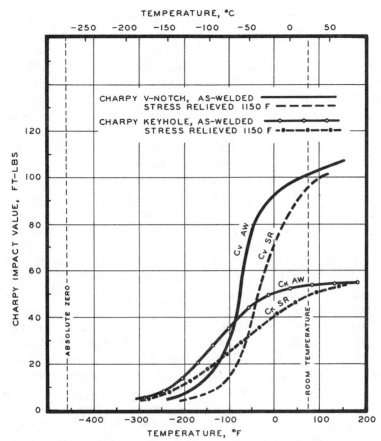

Fig. 250 — Typical impact properties of 3½% nickel steel weld metal as affected by temperature. Charpy V-notch and keyhole specimens from all-weld-metal deposits.

tempering heat treatment. However, the problem remains of securing a weld filler metal of comparable cost which will display adequate toughness at temperatures below –155 F. At the moment, the regular E80XX-C2 class of electrode does not offer real promise of consistently meeting the impact requirements.

Some experimental work conducted in the USA with a covered electrode prepared from a 3½% nickel steel core electrode (rather than the regular rimmed steel core electrode and an alloy-containing flux covering) suggested that such an electrode would deposit weld metal with improved low-temperature fracture toughness. At –150 F, the alloy-steel core electrode produced about 50 ft-lbs Charpy-V, which indicates that this weld metal might be suitable for service at somewhat lower temperatures. However, continued tests with additional lots of this type of electrode have not produced equally satisfactory results.

Work conducted more recently in Great Britain on 3½% nickel steel weld metal from covered electrodes confirmed that commercial electrodes do indeed produce weld deposits of unpredictable, and sometimes unsatisfactory impact strength at –150 F. A laboratory study which involved the making of electrodes to cover a wide range of weld metal compositions showed that a substantial improvement could be made in low-temperature toughness by closer control of residual phosphorus and sulfur levels. When heats of steel core wire were melted from high-purity raw materials, which resulted in a total phosphorus and sulfur content of less than 0.010%, the weld deposits in 3½% nickel steel joints exceeded 100 ft-lbs Charpy-V at –150 F. Variations in carbon content over the range of 0.05 to 0.08% appeared to have no influence upon toughness. Nitrogen was suspected to exert a detrimental effect, but no results were obtained on this element. Molybdenum in amounts up to 0.35% appeared helpful in maintaining low-temperature toughness in the stress-relief heat treated condition; however, an increase in molybdenum to 0.60% brought about a marked reduction in toughness. Although a specially-made covered electrode of 3½% nickel steel for weldments to serve at –150 F or below has not yet appeared on the commercial market to date, the findings of this investigation seem to be reflected in the development of an experimental 12% nickel steel filler metal to be described shortly for use in joining 9% nickel steel.

At the present time, it appears that service temperatures lower than –150 F will call for a departure from alloy steel weld metal having a "ferritic" (bcc) type of crystallographic structure. Weld metal deposited by electrodes of austenitic stainless steel (E309 or E310), or of austenitic-like nickel-base alloys certainly would be satisfactory for welding 3½% nickel steel for service at temperatures just below –150 F, although these dissimilar weld metals would be costly. Of course, the relatively high coefficient of expansion of the austenitic stainless steels would have to be taken into consideration if employed in a 3½% nickel steel weldment destined to undergo thermal cycling in service.

Submerged-arc welding of 3½% nickel steels had been handicapped for some time by the lack of suitable electrodes. Recently, both alloy steel electrodes and combinations of carbon steel electrode and alloyed flux have appeared on the market for joining these steels, and also may be used for the 2¼% nickel steels. These filler metals are designed to deposit weld metal containing about 3% nickel. In some cases, to help reduce weld metal cracking tendencies, the manganese content is increased to about 1% in the weld metal. Some electrodes contain approximately ¼% molybdenum, and approximately 0.15% aluminum for deoxidation purposes, but these elements have not been clearly shown to play a part in improving the impact properties of the weld metal. A very important part of the submerged-arc welding technique to insure good impact properties at low temperatures is to employ multipass deposition. At temperatures in the vicinity of –100 to –150 F, the highest impact values for both the as-welded and the stress-relief heat treated conditions have been obtained on those joints welded with the greatest number of passes.

Gas metal-arc welding of 3½% nickel steel is becoming increasingly popular now that several alloy steel electrodes are available commercially. The composition of these electrodes are much like the 3½%Ni—1%Mn—¼%Mo electrodes described for submerged-arc welding; however, in an effort to avoid weld metal cracking susceptibility, an aluminum content of about 0.5%, and sharply restricted phosphorus and sulfur contents in the electrodes have been found helpful. Higher aluminum contents exerted a harmful effect upon weld metal impact values.

Weldments of 3½% nickel steel constructed to the ASME Code often are required to be postweld stress-relief heat treated. A temperature not exceeding 1175 F usually is employed to avoid loss of strength in the material. British practice with vessels of 3½% nickel steel for service at temperatures down to –150 F is to permit use as-welded providing the steel and the joints meet a 15 ft-lb Charpy-V impact requirement.

Welding 5% Nickel Steel

Economic reasons have been cited for the very limited use of 5% nickel steel in the USA. There also is a metallurgical reason. Initial attempts to join 5% nickel steel with a steel filler metal containing approximately 5% nickel encountered serious difficulty with cracking in the weld metal. When no solution to this problem appeared to be at hand with a 5% nickel steel filler metal, fabricators turned to the use of austenitic stainless steel, and nickel-base alloy weld metals. Possibly, the lower yield strength of these weld metals at room temperature, and their greater cost also tended to discourage the use of 5% nickel steel.

Welding 9% Nickel Steel

Undismayed by the experience in welding 5% nickel steel, metallurgists were attracted by the better low-temperature toughness of a 9%

nickel steel. For some additional cost, this higher nickel content provided fracture toughness capability for service down to –320 F. The 9% nickel steel also provided higher strength, even in its softest condition, which could be used to advantage to reduce the wall thickness of pressure vessels and piping. This greater strength was recognized by the ASME in setting the allowable design stresses for 9% nickel steel.

ASTM Standard A353 covers 9% nickel steel. Requirements for plates to be used in pressure vessels or piping at low temperature are provided in A300. Although ASME Code vessels and piping for cryogenic service ordinarily would require postweld stress-relief heat treatment because of the provisions of Paragraph UCS-67, a modification was made in this requirement through the medium of Code Case 1308. This case permits fabrication of 9% nickel steel weldments and their use in service *as-welded* at temperatures as low as –320 F when: (1) the thickness of shells, heads and other pressure-containing parts are from 3/16 to 2 inches (forgings 3 inches maximum), (2) cold forming strains are less than 3%, (3) the thickness of the base metal *at weld joints* does not exceed 1½ inches, and (4) the material has been heat treated by prescribed quench and temper, or by double normalize and temper heat treatments to produce specified mechanical properties.

The quenching and tempering treatment of Code Case 1308 (also a requirement of the newly-issued ASTM A553) requires austenitizing at 1475 F and a water quench. Reheating to the range of 1050 to 1125 F is required for tempering, and the material must be cooled from the tempering temperature at a rate *not less than* 300 degrees F per hour. The double normalized and tempered treatment requires an initial austenitizing at 1650 F followed by air cooling, a second austenitizing at 1450 F followed by air cooling, and tempering in the range of 1050 to 1125 F. Optimum toughness develops in the 9% nickel steel when tempered in the 1050 to 1125 F temperature range because of an unusual microstructural change, namely, the formation of austenite at tempering temperature. In this respect, the behavior of the 9% nickel steel is somewhat like the maraging steels which were described earlier. When 9% nickel steel is heated for tempering, a significant amount of austenite begins to form at temperatures above about 800 F. In this sense, the steel has a rather low Ac_1 temperature; if such a critical temperature actually exists. The temperature at which most of the carbide present goes into solution in the austenite is above approximately 1125 F. The Ac_3 temperature is believed to be approximately 1300 F. Upon cooling solution-treated austenite, transformation may proceed to microstructures of (1) martensite, (2) bainite, and (3) proeutectoid ferrite. Quenching in water or oil produces essentially a martensitic structure containing less than 1% retained austenite (M_s point about 650 F). Air cooling tends to encounter a rapid bainite formation at a temperature level of about 900 F. Slower cooling results in proeutectoid ferrite formation over the temperature range of about 900 to 1250 F. Slow cooling does not affect strength noticeably, but it does have an adverse effect upon toughness, particularly at low temperatures. When the quench-hardened structure (Rockwell C-41) is heated for tempering, austenite again starts to reform upon reaching temperatures in excess of about 800 F. The stability of this austenite is dependent upon composition changes during its formation. Relatively short heating times at the lower tempering temperatures produces the most stable austenite as evidenced by ability to resist transformation at temperatures as low as –320 F. It is assumed that the austenite initially has a relatively high carbon content, but that the carbon content diminishes with time at temperature. As much as 15% austenite can be formed by tempering at about 1100 F, and about half of this is retained after exposure to –320 F. The impact strength of 9% nickel steel can be correlated closely with the amount of reformed or reverted austenite, its composition, and its stability at the lowest temperature of exposure following tempering. Optimum toughness is secured in a 9% nickel steel by tempering in the range of 1050 to 1125 F for a sufficient length of time to produce stable austenite. Reheating to a temperature below 1000 F, for example, 800 F, reduces fracture toughness at lower temperatures. The cooling rate from the tempering temperature is important because slow cooling has the same effect as reheating to a lower temperature. The phenomenon involved here is believed to be temper embrittlement. Briefly, the fracture toughness is believed to be controlled by the usual tempering phenomena observed in a hardened alloy steel, but with austenite reversion playing a significant role.

The composition and properties of 9% nickel steel are outlined in Table 91. A steel of this alloy composition falls into classification P-number 10 (Table 62), which also suggests need for a preheat temperature of 300 F, and the application of a postweld stress-relief heat treatment. However, the rather low actual carbon content of 9% nickel steel and the toughness of its particular microstructure alleviates the need for these features in the welding procedure. Welding on cold base metal is to be avoided on general principles. However, much welding of plate in thicknesses up to 2 inches has been carried out at room temperature. As plate thickness increases, and/or joint restraint becomes more severe, many fabricators feel that preheat to some convenient temperature in the range of 200 to 400 F is good assurance against cracking. There is some evidence that preheat improves the impact properties of the weld metal.

Table 91 — REQUIREMENTS AND PROPERTIES OF 9% NICKEL ALLOY STEEL

CHEMICAL COMPOSITION (ASTM A 353) [a]

	Grade A Required	Grade A Typical	Grade B Required	Grade B Typical
Carbon, max	0.13	0.10	0.13	0.10
Manganese, max	0.80	0.50	0.90	0.65
Phosphorus, max	0.035	< 0.02	0.035	< 0.02
Sulfur, max	0.040	< 0.02	0.040	< 0.02
Silicon	0.15–0.30	0.25	0.15–0.30	0.25
Nickel	8.50–9.50	9.0	8.50–9.50	9.0

[a] Also see ASTM A553, a new standard for 9% nickel steel plates in the quenched and tempered condition for use in pressure vessels.

MECHANICAL PROPERTIES REQUIRED OF PLATE

	Tensile properties UTS, ksi min	Tensile properties YS, ksi, min	Impact properties Ft-lbs, min, at test temperature of –320 F
Grade A	90	60	15 [b]
Grade B	95	65	15 [b]
Case 1308	100–120	75	25 [c]

[b] When ordered to ASTM A 300, Charpy keyhole or U-notch.
[c] Charpy V-notch. Requirement is for double-normalized and tempered condition; quenched and tempered condition requires 30 ft-lbs.

PROPERTIES TYPICAL OF BUTT-WELDED JOINTS IN PLATE (AS-WELDED)

Welding process	UTS, ksi	YS, ksi	Location of tensile fracture	Charpy V-Notch impact strength ft-lbs at –320 F Base metal HAZ	Charpy V-Notch impact strength ft-lbs at –320 F Weld metal
Manual shielded metal-arc with covered electrode [d]	100	60	Weld metal	75	65
Gas metal-arc (spray-transfer) [e]	100	55	Weld metal	50	50
Gas metal-arc (shorting-arc transfer) [e]	97	60	Weld metal	60	90
Submerged arc [f]	98	60	Weld metal	52	95

[d] Ni–Cr–Fe–Mn–Cb or Ni–Cr–Fe–Mo Alloy Covered Electrode, such as ENi Cr Fe–3 or ENi Cr Fe–2, as shown in Table 54.
[e] Ni–Cr–Mn–Cb or Ni–Cr–Fe–Ti Alloy Electrode, such as ERNi Cr–3 or ERNi Cr Fe–6, as shown in Table 55.
[f] 65%Ni–27%Mo electrode and special low-silica granulated submerged arc welding flux.

Shielded metal-arc welding, when first applied to the 9% nickel steel using electrodes of similar metal composition, encountered the same difficulty as mentioned earlier for the 5% nickel steel, namely, severe weld metal cracking. Also, the weld metal, when sound, did not have adequate fracture toughness at low temperatures. Charpy-V values of the 9% nickel steel weld metal at –320 F was less than 5 ft-lbs. To circumvent these problems, the welding engineer turned to the use of austenitic stainless steel weld metal. Electrodes of the E310 (25 Cr–20 Ni) gave excellent results except that the tensile strength of the dissimilar metal weld did not quite meet the minimum tensile requirements for the base metal. The search for a stronger weld metal then moved to the nickel-base alloy electrodes of the "Inconel-type" as listed earlier in Table 54 and 55. These provided a weld metal which achieved a slightly higher tensile strength, almost equal to that of the base metal, but which had a yield strength which barely exceeded 55 ksi. However, this kind of weld metal had excellent low-temperature impact properties, and no difficulties were encountered in qualifying these electrodes for ASME Code weldments. The nickel-base alloy electrodes continue to be the more widely used on 9% nickel steel weldments today. Because the weld metal deposited by these electrodes has approximately 95% joint strength efficiency, the ASME allowable design stress is reduced for the 9% nickel steels in welded construction. Both the stainless steel and the nickel-base alloy electrodes bear low-hydrogen coverings, which is in keeping with the welding of an alloy steel that forms martensite in its heat-affected zones during welding.

Gas metal-arc welding can be performed on 9% nickel steel using electrodes of the same general nickel-base alloy compositions. Of course, the designations are different for the bare electrode and small modifications may appear in alloying elements when compared with deposit compositions for covered electrodes. Table 55 shows two nickel-base alloy electrodes identified as ERNi Cr-3 and ERNi Cr Fe-6 which are used for gas metal-arc welding the 9% nickel steel. Because of its lower strength and greater coefficient of thermal expansion, austenitic stainless steel weld metal has not been employed on 9% nickel steel to any significant extent. The shorting-arc form of gas metal-arc welding has been highly recommended for joining 9% nickel steel. The lower current and voltage is claimed to reduce a problem with arc-blow to be described shortly. Of the various gases employed for shielding, a mixture of 90% helium and 10% argon has proved most satisfactory with the nickel-base alloy electrode. This electrode ordinarily produces a viscous molten weld metal, but the helium-rich gas mixture improves the fluidity of the molten weld pool. The mechanical properties of gas metal-arc welded joints in 9% nickel steel are equally satisfactory as those made with covered arc-welding electrodes, and, as shown in Table 91, will pass the requirements of ASME Section IX and Code Case 1308.

No significant use has been made of the submerged-arc welding process of 9% nickel steel because of generally poor impact test results encountered with regular combinations of electrodes and flux applied; including the Ni–Cr–Fe types of electrodes and the special fluxes designed to protect them in submerged-arc welding. The greater dilution usually encountered with this process makes duplication of successful weld compositions (as in the shielded metal-arc, and gas metal-arc processes) rather difficult. To date, no submerged-arc procedure for 9% nickel steel has successfully qualified under applicable ASME code rules for a vessel intended for cryogenic service at –320 F. However, encouraging results have been obtained using an electrode of 65% Ni–27% Mo and a special low-silica flux. On heavy plate, where the joint preparation holds dilution to a relatively low percentage, the properties of the joint are like those listed in Table 91. On a square-butt, two-pass welded joint, where dilution is significantly higher, the strength of the weld metal increases, and the impact strength decreases, perhaps to approximately 45 ft-lbs at –320 F. Nevertheless, this level of toughness is adequate to satisfy the requirements of Code Case 1308. It remains to be seen whether this costly electrode and flux will prove to be commercially useful in 9% nickel steel weldment fabrication.

When 9% nickel steel is welded by one of the arc processes, the high-temperature portion of the heat-affected zones ordinarily becomes martensitic because of the very low critical cooling rate of this alloy steel. Whereas the hardness of the heat treated (tempered) plate ranges from about C-22 to C-26 Rockwell, the hardness in the heat-affected zone rises to approximately C-38 to C-40 at a point about 1/32 inch from the weld fusion line. This is, of course, almost the maximum hardness obtainable in a martensitic structure of approximately 0.10% carbon content, which is the typical carbon content of 9% nickel steel. Despite this increase in hardness, there is no marked decrease in toughness of the heat-affected zone. In fact, a small portion of the zone where the hardness is in the vicinity of C-35 Rockwell may display improved impact test results at low temperature. Some welding engineers, particularly in Europe, view this 10 to 15 point increase in Rockwell hardness with suspicion, and maintain that a hardness of about Rockwell C-36 should not be exceeded in the heat-affected zone for service in the as-welded condition. To conform with the C-36 hardness limitation, the carbon content of the 9% nickel steel must be restricted to 0.08% maximum. Experience in the USA with 9% nickel steel weldments in the as-welded condition has not given reason to further restrict the carbon content of steel under ASTM A353 or A553.

When 9% nickel steel is welded with nickel-base alloy filler metal, the dissimilarity in mechanical properties between weld metal and base metal causes difficulty in conducting transverse bend tests on the weld joint. The lower-strength weld metal causes the specimen to bend sharply or cripple at the weld edges. For this reason, a longitudinal bend specimen is permitted under Code Case 1308.

Preparation for Welding

Scale on the surface of 9% nickel steel from hot rolling and/or heat treatment is unusually adherent. It must be removed from any area on which the nickel-base alloy electrode is to be deposited to avoid difficulty with porosity in the weld metal. Scale removal can be accomplished by flame cleaning, sandblasting, pickling, or grinding. Whatever the method used, the removal must be thorough.

Unusual incidents with "arc-blow" have arisen during the arc-welding of 9% nickel steel using direct-current. This is the wild, erratic arc behavior which is believed to be produced by unfavorable magnetic fields around the arc. This difficulty appears to be prone to occur with 9% nickel steel because the steel is easily magnetized; that is, the steel has a high magnetic remanence as compared with most constructional steels. Undesirable residual magnetism will remain in the steel after it has been subjected to a magnetic field, such as by lifting the material with a crane magnet, the magnetic flux generated by the passage of heavy direct current during welding, or by the flux from magnetic particle inspection. Residual magnetism is believed to accentuate the arc blow. Demagnetization can be accomplished by various means, such as the application of an AC coil, or by heating. Sometimes the undesirable magnetic flux during DC arc welding can be nullified by wrapping the ground cable of the welding circuit around the joint. Some fabricators avoid the problem by arranging for AC arc welding. In addition to requiring an AC power source, the electrodes must be operational on AC. Covered electrodes are readily available for AC operation, but only limited quantities of wire designed for AC gas metal-arc welding have been produced. As explained in Chapter 10, electrodes for AC operation require an emissive coating to maintain a satisfactory arc.

Research on Ferritic Filler Metal

New findings regarding the low-temperature toughness of alloy steel weld metal has encouraged research on a "ferritic" nickel steel weld metal (as contrasted with the "austenitic" stainless steel or nickel-base

Table 92 — *EXPERIMENTAL 12% NICKEL STEEL ELECTRODE FOR GAS METAL-ARC WELDING OF 9% NICKEL ALLOY STEEL*

CHEMICAL COMPOSITION OF ELECTRODES

	For shorting-arc transfer Limits	Typical	For spray-type transfer Limits	Typical
Carbon	0.03–0.07	0.05	0.03–0.07	0.05
Manganese	0.50–0.80	0.65	0.50–0.80	0.65
Phosphorus	0.005 max	0.003	0.005 max	0.003
Sulfur	0.005 max	0.004	0.005 max	0.004
Silicon	0.10 max	0.05	0.10 max	0.03
Nickel	11.5–13.5	12.5	11.5–13.5	12.5
Aluminum	0.01–0.06	0.02	0.01–0.06	0.02
Titanium	. . .	. . .	0.08–0.15	0.10
Oxygen	100 ppm max	75 ppm	100 ppm max	75 ppm
Nitrogen	100 ppm max	75 ppm	100 ppm max	75 ppm
Hydrogen	3 ppm max	1.5 ppm	3 ppm max	1.5 ppm

MECHANICAL PROPERTIES TYPICAL OF BUTT-WELDS IN PLATE

Welding process	UTS, ksi	YS, ksi	Elong. %, 2 in.	Red. of area	Location of tensile fracture
Gas metal-arc (either spray-type or short-ing-arc trans-fer)					
Transverse specimens					
As-welded	115	92	7	63	Plate
Stress-relieved	109	90	14	68	Plate
All-weld-metal tensile specimens					
As-welded	156	106	10	32	
Stress-relieved	120	105	22	62	

CHARPY V-NOTCH IMPACT TEST SPECIMENS NOTCHED IN WELD METAL

	Typical impact values, ft-lbs Room temp.	–200 F	–320 F
As-welded	64	60	44
Stress-relieved	93	80	56

(data from Witherell and Peck)

alloy weld metals) for 9% nickel steel weldments. Encouraging results have been obtained, but at a level of approximately 12% nickel rather than at 9% nickel. Chemical composition of the most promising 12% nickel steel filler metals are shown in Table 92 along with typical mechanical properties of weld metal deposited by the gas metal-arc process. Although this electrode has not yet achieved commercial status, the information gathered during its development represents a substantial contribution on the metallurgy of welding alloy steels for cryogenic service.

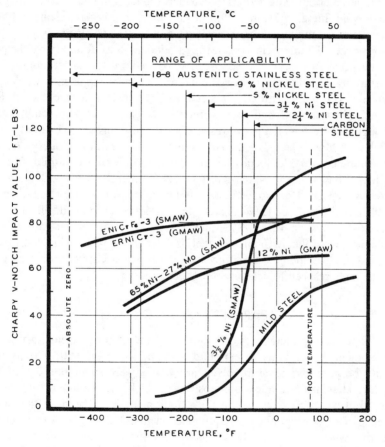

Fig. 251 — Typical impact properties of weld metals in as-deposited condition as affected by temperature.

The 12% nickel steel electrode shown in Table 92 evolved from a lengthy study which covered compositions ranging in nickel content from approximately 8 to 14%. It was learned that the silicon content must be kept very low in weld metal of these nickel steels to avoid a high susceptibility to weld metal hot cracking. Raising the nickel content from 9 to 12% appeared to improve toughness by increasing the amount of retained stable austenite in the low-carbon martensitic matrix. However, increasing the nickel content above 13% caused severe weld metal hot cracking. The addition of ¼% molybdenum reduced hot cracking tendency, but decreased toughness; so no use was made of this alloying element. Aluminum was found to improve weld metal toughness when in the range of about 0.02 to 0.04%. Much higher aluminum contents promoted weld metal cracking. Phosporus and sulfur were clearly shown to accentuate any cracking tendency, and detracted from impact test performance. Titanium in a controlled amount was found very helpful in preventing porosity in weld metal deposited by the shorting-arc type of transfer. Significant improvement in toughness appeared when the electrode was manufactured by steelmaking practices that obtained low oxygen, nitrogen and hydrogen contents. To show the appreciable gain in toughness at low temperatures achieved with this experimental 12% nickel steel filler metal, Fig. 251 contains Charpy-V impact energy curves for a number of weld metals ranging in composition from mild steel to the nickel-base alloys. Note that the 3½% nickel steel weld metal as presently deposited has inadequate toughness at temperatures below about –150F, and that the 12% nickel steel weld metal would fill the gap that exists between the 3½% nickel steel and the nickel-base alloys. Attempts to use the 12% nickel steel as filler metal in the shielded metal-arc and the submerged-arc processes have produced very discouraging results with respect to fracture toughness to date.

NUCLEAR SERVICE ALLOY STEELS

The welding metallurgy of alloy steels used for nuclear service, at the moment, is the same as expounded in the foregoing text. This is true simply because the steels involved are a relatively small number of the regular, standardized alloy compositions which are commercially available. However, this may not be the situation for long, because the safety aspects of operating nuclear equipment demand a degree of structural integrity which is not easily attained with presently-available materials, and the effect of radiation leads to a variety of problems with the materials of construction. These shortcomings encourage research, and research begets change for the better. Reams of literature already are available on the problems which arise with the metal components of a nuclear power system. In general, the following troublesome changes occur, the rate of development being dependent mainly upon the amount of irradiation:

(1) All ferritic steels regardless of alloy composition undergo a change in mechanical properties. Hardness, tensile strength, and yield strength increase substantially. Ductility is reduced. Fracture toughness is adversely affected. The toughness transition temperature is raised markedly — sometimes as much as *several hundred* degrees. This is the change of greatest technological importance.

(2) Austenitic stainless steels are not as severely affected by irradiation from the standpoint of fracture toughness. Irradiation introduces a yield-point phenomenon in the stress-strain behavior of these steels. High-temperature ductility may be adversely affected.

(3) Corrosive attack on the metals in the system usually is accelerated under the pressurized environment common to most nuclear systems. Elements in the corrosion products become radioactive and their transport throughout the system causes much difficulty in maintaining radiation-safe operating conditions, and in maintenance. Elements which form nuclides with relatively long half-lives, such as cobalt, manganese, tantalum, and chromium, are particularly objectionable.

Welded joints, *per se,* have not been singled out as being especially prone to the above troublesome changes. At the present time, a properly made weld will perform as well as the base metal. No difficulty has been encountered with galvanic, selective, or accelerated attack in or near properly welded joints. Of course, to insure that the weld is properly made, the metallurgy of the welding operations must be mastered to the highest degree — just as is the design of the equipment, the control of material quality, and the execution of fabricating operations. There appears to be no need to repeat here the aspects of welding metallurgy which are important and which could bear reemphasis in connection with weldments for nuclear service. Instead, some remarks about future trends may prove more helpful over the long run.

Changes in the properties of metals subjected to irradiation have been described in Chapter 6 to be attributable to the formation of defects in their crystal lattice. The degree of change depends upon the quantity and kind of radiation, and the temperature of the metal during exposure. Whenever a neutron having sufficient energy (above about 350 eV) impacts a lattice atom, the atom is imparted enough energy to enable it to break away from its normal position. Below about 500 F, high neutron dosages are particularly damaging to fracture toughness. Above about 500 F, property changes are not as great because thermal agitation allows dislocations to migrate within the lattice and either annihilate each other or to form relatively innocuous clusters. Annealing at temperatures above 500 F acts to remove radiation damage. A guiding philosophy in selecting a steel for nuclear service is to favor the steel with the lowest toughness transition temperature, because irradiation in service is certain to raise this temperature. Alloy steels are often selected for nuclear service because they usually have lower toughness transition temperatures. Also, the design requirements of the newer, larger reactors would call for plates of carbon steel to be of impractical thickness; for example, a nuclear reactor vessel might require a wall thickness of 12 inches if constructed of carbon steel. The stronger alloy steels permit a reduction in wall thickness to a more practical dimension.

Phenomena other than radiation effects also encourage the selection of an alloy steel. Reactors which operate with liquid sodium at 1000 to 1200 F for heat transfer have been troubled by decarburization. Work on the $2\frac{1}{4}\%$ Cr–1% Mo steels (favored for their good high-temperature creep strength) already has shown that a modified Cr–Mo steel which also contains $\frac{1}{2}\%$ V and 0.1% Cb should give improved service. No manner of alloying employed in steels to date has been truly successful in forestalling the deleterious effects of irradiation. There is, however, considerable variation in the amount of change which occurs in different steels with a given dose of radiation. These variations in damage sometimes are found associated with surprisingly small differences in steel composition. A little information has evolved on objectionable alloying. For example, materials containing boron when subjected to thermal neutrons may experience transmutation of the boron and the formation of helium. This change causes both embrittlement and changes in the volume of the steel. We must keep in mind that metallurgists have just begun to research the problem of damage by irradiation and it would be technical cowardice to believe that no improvement can be made to overcome this failing. Speculation on the matter suggests that alloy steels of the future for nuclear service will be quite different from the presently used steels. The question with which we should concern ourselves is, "Will the welding metallurgist and welding engineer be ready with processes and procedures to make welded joints in these new alloy steels that will perform equally as well as the base metal?"

Here are some very early indications of the nature of alloy steels of the future for nuclear service, and the properties and characteristics which must be (1) preserved in the base metal heat-affected zones, and (2) produced in the weld metal zone. The new steels probably will be made extremely fine grained because the harmful effects of irradiation are lessened as grain size becomes smaller. Elements which are presently employed in steel for purposes of deoxidation, or as a strengthening alloying element, such as manganese, may be taboo because the formation of radioactive nuclides from these elements are highly objectionable during operations and in carrying out maintenance on nuclear systems. Strengthening and hardening of the new alloy steels may be accomplished by dispersion hardening (see Chapter 7) rather than the customary mechanisms because the presence of certain kinds of dispersoids has been shown to alleviate the harmful effects of irradiation. It appears probable that to produce a dispersoid of similar composition, size and interparticle spacing in the weld metal will be a very difficult task. Lastly, but not least, alloy steels of the future for nuclear service will be as defect free, as uniform in properties, and as close to specified targets for composition, structure and properties as the most advanced steelmaking operations will permit. Whether this will be accomplished with present steelmaking facilities, including vacuum degassing, continuous casting, and so forth, remains to be seen. Possibly the electron beam melting furnace, or an entirely new steelmaking process will provide the desired material. The question of equal importance is, "Will sufficient progress be made in welding to provide joints which also are defect free, and which have properties comparable to the nuclear-quality base metals?"

In closing this discussion of alloy steel weldments for nuclear service, mention can be made of Section III of the ASME Boiler and Pressure Vessel Code which covers Nuclear Vessels. The vessels covered by Section III of the Code are classified in three categories which can be roughly described as follows:

Class A Vessels — Reactor vessels, or chambers of vessels that are involved in the primary nuclear system.

Class B Vessels — Containment vessels.

Class C Vessels — Nuclear-related vessels.

Just as is Section VIII for Unfired Pressure Vessels frequently cited as guidance for good practice in fabricating weldments for all kinds of ordinary usage, so is Section III held in high esteem for the experience and wisdom which it encompasses with regard to pressure vessels for nuclear service.

ELECTRICAL STEELS

The welding of electrical steels is a classic illustration of art preceding science. Slowly, but surely, manufacturers of electrical apparatus, such as transformers, motors, and electronic devices, have been turning to welding as a means of holding together stacks of laminations and fixing the ends of wound cores of the thin gage steel that make up the heart of many pieces of electrical equipment. Of course, much welding is performed on electrical steel sheet and strip as it is processed by the steel producer. However, this welding is virtually an integral part of the steelmaking operations, and the weld joint often benefits from subsequent operations, such as rolling and annealing. Welding operations carried out in the manufacture of electrical hardware encounter many more conditions which are unfavorable to the making of a satisfactory weld. Much of the welding being performed in this area appears to be based upon trial and error approach to finding successful procedures.

What are electrical steels? A more fitting name on the basis of their composition would be "electrical irons," or "iron–silicon alloys," because these steels make no use whatsoever of carbon as an alloying element. In fact, carbon is an undesirable residual element and is regularly held to very low limits. In light of our earlier admonitions on the role played by carbon in governing the weldability of steel, it may seem that the welding of the very low-carbon electrical steels will present no particular problem — certainly no difficulty will be experienced with hardening from martensite formation in heat-affected zones. Nevertheless, electrical steels can present the welding engineer with a metallurgical nightmare. Instead of hardening problems, these alloy steels present inescapable situations involving excessive grain growth, contamination, toughness-transition, and other unfavorable phenomena, the likes of which have not been seen in other alloy steels.

Electrical steels are not ordinarily supplied to chemical composition limits because the user is primarily interested in their electrical and magnetic properties. The all important properties, such as volume electrical resistivity, magnetic permeability, hysteresis loss, eddy current loss, and interlaminar loss are controlled not only by composition, but by the processing steps employed in producing the flat rolled finished material. Electrical steels were only recently classified by the AISI. The designations assigned to the various types consist of the prefix letter "M," which stands for *magnetic* material, and a number which originally indicated the core loss (hysteresis loss and eddy current loss in watts per pound). However, improvements in making electrical steels have reduced core loss so that the numerical portion of the designation no longer pinpoints the guarantee on core loss. Table 93 lists representative electrical steels of the various general classes which have developed. Many additional steels, both standard AISI types and proprietary compositions, are being used. In addition to having substantial differences in chemical composition, the electrical steels display wide variations in the nature of their micro-structure and magnetic properties. The term "oriented" refers to the magnetic and crystallographic directional properties of the steels. Oriented steels possess magnetic properties which are strongly enhanced with respect to the direction of rolling. This characteristic is determined by the crystallographic structure and the degree of preferred orientation embodied therein. In non-oriented steels, the magnetic properties are far less directional.

Table 93 — *REPRESENTATIVE ELECTRICAL STEELS*

Material description	Applicable AISI designation	TYPICAL CHEMICAL COMPOSITION [a]						MECHANICAL PROPERTIES		
		C	Mn	P	S	Si	UTS ksi	YS ksi	Elong. %, 2 in.	Hardness Rock.-B
Non-oriented low-silicon[b]	M-45	0.01	0.3	0.01	0.02	1.0	52	32	31	60
Non-oriented low-silicon[b]	M-43	0.01	0.3	0.01	0.02	1.5	62	42	33	70
Non-oriented medium-silicon[b]	M-19	0.01	0.1	0.01	0.01	3.0	72	56	18	88
Non-oriented high-silicon	M-14	0.02	0.1	0.01	0.002	4.5	75	68	4	89
Oriented silicon	M-5	0.002	0.1	0.01	0.002	3.2	60	48	17	81

[a] These compositions are merely illustrative because electrical and magnetic properties rather than chemical specifications are specified to control the quality of most electrical steels.
[b] These steels usually contain some aluminum (0.3) to aid the silicon in enhancing the magnetic properties.

Silicon is used as a major alloying element in electrical steels because it increases the volume electrical resistivity of iron and it aids in the production of crystal structures of desirable shape and size for low hysteresis loss and good permeability. As the silicon content of the iron–silicon alloy is increased, the ferrite-forming influence of silicon restricts the formation of austenite (gamma phase) upon heating. Beyond approximately 2½% silicon, the low-carbon electrical alloys retain the ferritic microstructure at all temperatures up to the melting point. This structural characteristic allows the steel to grow large grains when annealed at high temperatures, which improves magnetic properties. In oriented silicon steel, the grain size may be so coarse as to have single grains extend through the entire thickness of a lamination section. Silicon above approximately 5% makes an alloy which is too brittle at room temperature for most commercial use. Electrical steels of the grain-oriented type usually have a silicon content of about 3%. In the non-oriented steels, the silicon may range from 0.5 to 5%, and usually is used in combination with a small amount of aluminum, inasmuch as aluminum also is a ferrite-forming alloying element in iron and produces other metal-lurgical benefits. Except for a small amount of manganese, other elements in electrical steels are kept to a minimum practical amount.

WELDABILITY OF ELECTRICAL STEELS

Electrical steels which possess a single phase (ferritic) micro-structure at all temperatures present a fundamental welding problem. The rapid grain growth which occurs upon heating and the absence of a grain-refining allotropic transformation may be fine for securing desirable mag-netic properties, but this is not a favorable behavior for welding oper-ations. As illustrated in Fig. 252, an arc weld made across a stack of

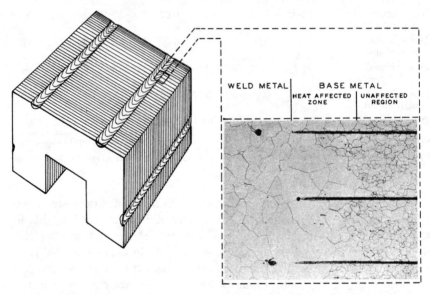

Fig. 252 — Microstructure of gas tungsten-arc welded joint across laminations of M-36 electrical steel bearing a C-4 core plate.

Note grain-coarsening in base metal heat-affected zone and coarse-grained weld metal. Etchant-Nital Mag. 100X

electrical steel laminations produces considerable grain coarsening in the heat-affected zones, and forms a very coarse-grained weld deposit. Con-sequently, the base metal heat-affected zones and the weld metal have lower ductility and toughness than the unaffected base metal, which, incidently, are not at a comfortable level before welding.

Welding procedures for electrical steels generally are based upon minimum heat input to avoid excessive grain size in the weld metal and heat-affected zones. Cooling rate cannot be accelerated by low base metal temperature because the ferritic types undergo a marked decrease in toughness as temperature is lowered. Indeed, the toughness transition may be located in the vicinity of room temperature. Most welding is performed, therefore, at room temperature, or with moderate preheat (up to about 250 F). Care must be taken to avoid high restraint upon weld joints, particularly as the weldment cools to room temperature. Ordinarily, the weld metal and the base metal heat-affected zones are not susceptible to hot cracking. However, stress raisers can easily initiate cold cracking because of the limited fracture toughness of the steel in the vicinity of room temperature.

An important feature of electrical steels may escape the attention of the welding engineer during initial planning of welding operations. This feature is the unusual surface coatings commonly applied to the flat rolled stock for the purpose of reducing interlaminar loss, and in some cases to enhance punchability. The importance of these insulating coatings is magnified when welding across laminations because *many* surfaces are presented to the weld proper. For example, the electrical steel may be employed as strip 0.014-in. thick. When punched laminations from this strip are stacked, more than one hundred forty surfaces per inch are intersected by a fusion weld pass. If the surface bears some kind of foreign material, the pickup by the weld metal is substantial. The coatings employed for insulation, called "core plating" by the trade, range from thin oxide films to rather heavy ceramic or glass coatings applied by various processing techniques. Surface insulation is such an important part of electrical steel strip that the AISI also has standardized a number of the regularly used core plates and has assigned identification as shown in Table 94. These core plates can give rise to various kinds of weld metal defects, including porosity, slag inclusions, and cracking, as indicated by the remarks in Table 94 regarding welding behavior.

Despite the problems which harass the welding of electrical steels, manufacturers have been finding welding to be a satisfactory method of making efficient electrical equipment. Welding is looked upon with favor as a low cost way of joining laminations into stacks for transformer cores. In view of the nature of steel composition, microstructure, and surface conditions which are peculiar to electrical steels, the welding engineer obviously must be intimately familiar with the material employed, and must rationalize on the effect each feature of the steel is likely to have

Table 94 — TYPES OF INSULATION OR CORE PLATES APPLIED TO FLAT-ROLLED ELECTRICAL STEEL

AISI Identification	Description of insulation	Behavior of steel in welding
C-0	Oxide film formed by hot rolling, annealing, or steam-bluing. Resistance ordinarily is low, but can be increased by use of controlled atmosphere during annealing.	Weldability usually not adversely affected. Silicon in base metal acts as deoxidizer to overcome any tendency for oxide film to cause porosity.
C-1	Enamel or varnish coating applied by dipping or spraying to required thickness. Limited resistance to heat.	Problem with weld metal porosity usually arises because coating generates gases (mostly hydrogen) under welding heat.
C-2	Inorganic ceramic insulation consisting of a glass-like film which is usually formed by applying a magnesia coating and annealing at a high temperature in hydrogen. Reaction between coating and silicates in surface forms the core plate.	Ceramic film melts during fushion welding to form a slag on weld pool. Amount of slag depends upon film thickness. Welding flux may be required to control slag.
C-3	Enamel or varnish coating applied by dipping or spraying to required thickness. Withstands higher temperatures than C-1 coating, but cannot be stress-relief annealed.	Problem with weld metal porosity usually arises because coating generates gases (mostly hydrogen) under welding heat.
C-4	Insulating surface film formed by chemical treatment, such as phosphating. Withstands temperatures up to about 1475 F.	When phosphates are employed as core plate, fusion weld metal may pick up substantial increase in phosphorous content and become crack susceptible.
C-5	Inorganic insulating film of high resistance formed by chemical treatment similar to that of C-4, but with the addition of inorganic filler like the magnesia of C-2 to enhance resistance. Withstands temperatures up to about 1475 F.	Problems may arise in fusion welding with slag formed by the magnesia filler, and with phosphorous pickup in weld metal.

upon the overall welding operation. For example, if some form of resistance welding is attempted on electrical steel bearing a core plate with a high insulation value, the operation may be thwarted by the surface condition. Some form of gas tungsten-arc, or gas metal-arc spot welding may provide a solution to the problem. Gas tungsten-arc welding is widely used on electrical steels, but a variety of problems can arise if the procedure is not tailored for (a) the type of steel, (b) the gage or thickness, (c) the kind of core plate, and (d) the design of the joint and part. As illustrated in Fig. 253, the joining of laminations in a stack may be accomplished by a number of techniques. The choice is guided

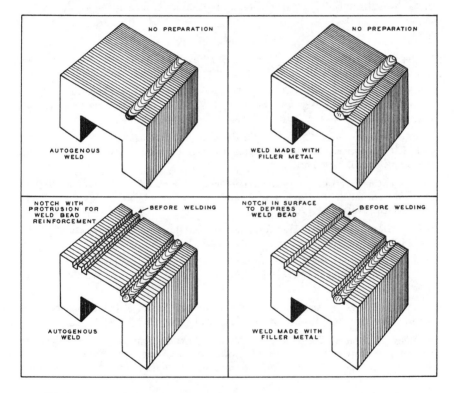

Fig. 253 — Examples of weld joint designs for assembly of stacks of electrical steel laminations.

by such questions as: (1) Will the design permit a convex weld bead reinforcement to protrude beyond the edge of the stack? (2) Will the fused base metal form satisfactory weld metal, or is a dissimilar filler metal needed? (3) Will an objectionable slag form on the molten weld metal that will interfere with its flow, or that might affect subsequent machining operations if hard particles of slag adhere to the weld surface? and (4) Will undesirable elements be picked up by the weld metal from the core plate that might cause weld unsoundness? One technique for securing a finer-grain, tougher weld metal is to employ a low-carbon rimmed steel filler metal and avoid excessive pickup during deposition. A small amount of the high-silicon base metal pickup in the weld metal will serve nicely as a deoxidizer. With reasonably low silicon content in the weld metal (i.e., below 2%), the grain-refining benefit from the austenite to ferrite transformation is obtained and the toughness of the weld metal is substantially greater than a high-silicon ferritic weld deposit.

Suggested Reading

"Higher-Strength Steels for Welded Structures," by R. D. Stout, 1960 Adams Lecture, The Welding Journal, v 39, no. 7, Research Suppl. pp 273s-283s, July 1960.

"Utilization of Quenching and Tempering for Improvement in Properties of Low-Alloy Steels in Heavy Sections," by R. E. Lorentz, Jr., 1962 Adams Lecture, Ibid, v 41, no. 10, pp 433s-447s, October, 1962.

"Factors Which Affect Low-Alloy Weld Metal Notch-Toughness," by S. S. Sagan and H. C. Campbell, Welding Research Council Bulletin Series, No. 59, Welding Research Council, New York, 1960.

"Fracture Characteristics of Some High-Strength, Weldable, Structural Steels," by E. T. Wessel and L. E. Hays, The Welding Journal, v 42, no. 11, Research Suppl. pp 512s-528s, November 1963.

I–T Diagrams, (Isothermal Transformation of Austenite in a Wide Variety of Steels), Third Edition, U.S. Steel Corporation, Pittsburgh, Pa., 1963.

"Welding Ferrous Materials for Nuclear Power Piping," A Committee Report, AWS Committee on Piping and Tubing, AWS D 10.5-59, American Welding Society, New York.

"Radiation Effects in Steel," by L. F. Porter, Special Technical Publication No. 276, American Society for Testing Materials, Philadelphia, Pa., 1959.

Welding and Brazing Techniques for Nuclear Reactor Components, by Gerald M. Slaughter, Prepared under the direction of American Society for Metals for United States Atomic Energy Commission, Rowman and Littlefield, Inc., New York, 1964.

Chapter 16

WELDING TESTS

The role played by the welding engineer varies considerably from one project to another in the fields of steel construction and manufacturing. Often, he may be called into consultation with design, procurement and manufacturing personnel during the initial stages of planning the production of a new weldment. The weldment, as we are well aware, may be anything from a steel bridge to a display rack. The purpose of this concluding chapter is to point out the depth to which the welding engineer sometimes must probe to be certain that his recommendations on joining are completely in order, and to describe sources of information which are at hand to guide the engineer in analyzing proposed weldments. We will continue to concentrate upon metallurgical information which the engineer should seek to support his recommendations.

When confronted with a new weldment, the welding engineer usually first makes a quick appraisal of three general questions:

(1) Is the article of unusual design or size?

(2) Is the steel one on which there is welding experience, or is it a new type?

(3) What are the service conditions, and will they demand special joint properties?

Too frequently, the engineer is given only enough time to use knowledge accumulated from study and experience to plan the joining operations. It is not unusual to find that circumstances will not permit fabrication of a prototype or even a scale model, to prove the suitability of suggested assembly methods. As the engineer commences his review of the article to be joined, he may find that conditions of design, material, and service are not exactly like any previous case on which he can find information. Under these circumstances, he depends heavily upon information gained from *tests of welds,* and from *welding tests.* The two terms are not synonymous, as will be explained shortly.

WELDMENT DESIGN

The design of the article, that is, the over-all size and thickness of its sections ordinarily is given an initial sweeping review to see if any of the welding, brazing and soldering processes are not applicable because of physical limitations. In describing the processes in Chapter 3, some mention was made of the thickness of base metal for which each process was best suited. As examples, the thick shell of a high-pressure vessel would not be welded by the laser process, nor would the thin face sheet of a honeycomb panel be welded by the submerged arc process. Next, attention is directed to the anticipated service conditions, since these indicate the strength required of the joints. Here again, many of the processes can be eliminated from consideration. For example, the wheel of an automobile would not be soldered because of inadequate strength at the joint. Of course, many other aspects of the service conditions must be taken into consideration. Those conditions calling for good joint toughness, like low temperatures or impact loading, require special consideration in selecting the welding process and devising the welding procedure. Sometimes the design of the article restricts the kind of joints that can be made in the article. If one side of the base metal section is inaccessible, a number of the welding processes will not be applicable. Naturally, the selection of a joining process also is guided by the number of units to be produced, production rate required, allowable joining cost, joint appearance required, equipment available, and many other factors involved in planning the production and sale of the article. However, these factors are not metallurgical in nature, so they will not be treated in any detail here. Also, it is important for the welding engineer to keep in mind that properly planned weldments employ welded joints only where circumstances warrant their use. The engineer must not be so impressed with the efficacy of his processes that he overlooks cases where welding can be avoided. For example, if the welding engineer could point out that a simple change in forming practice would eliminate the need for a weld joint, this certainly would be to his credit in the final analysis. A major responsibility of the welding engineer, however, is to be certain that the article is *designed as a weldment.* Too often, articles are designed only on the basis of function, readily-available steel sections, and other miscellaneous considerations, and the matter of assembly by welding is an afterthought, or is taken for granted as a trouble-free final operation not requiring any particular attention. It is not unusual in this weld-pioneering period that a welding engineer must literally fight for the following principles in design and fabrication:

(1) The article design, that is, the shapes of the component pieces, should facilitate as much as possible the welding process selected for joining.

(2) Weld joints must not be located where they will exert undue notch-effect or stress-concentration through their heat-affected zones or their geometry.

(3) In the fabrication of the article, welding must not be used as an all-powerful, saving operation which is assumed to be capable of overcoming poor fit-up between components, and not requiring any further finishing operation that ordinarily would be applied to a casting or a forging of the same shape.

TYPES OF STEEL AND WELDMENT PERFORMANCE

The second question which the welding engineer must review concerns the steel employed in the welded article. Is the steel a familiar type on which welding experience has been accumulated, or is it a new composition? In this era of rapid technological advancement, new steels frequently are introduced as the material of construction for a weldment. Here is where the welding engineer clearly demonstrates his ability to use different sources of information to develop recommendations on welding procedures. Unless he has had previous experience with a closely comparable type of steel, he must find the answer to a number of pertinent questions. Will any of the currently used joining processes be applicable? If filler metal is needed, shall it be of the same general composition as the base metal? Is weld metal of this type likely to develop a harmful degree of porosity? Will the weld be susceptible to hot or cold cracking? What will be the nature of the weld–base metal interface? Will the heat-affected zone of the base metal undergo any significant changes in microstructure or mechanical properties, and will this zone be susceptible to any particular form of cracking? The answers to these questions are most easily developed by using the groundwork of metallurgical information presented in earlier chapters and securing specific details from test data.

As the engineer probes deeper into the welding behavior of a steel base metal, he cannot avoid the question of weld joint performance in service. Even though he provides a procedure for efficiently joining the steel components, he also must be certain that the welded joints are capable of withstanding subsequent conditions to which the weldment might be subjected. He must appraise the weld joint as a whole, that is, the weld metal and the heat-affected base metal, to determine whether these areas possess the properties required, not only for service, but also for additional fabricating operations which sometimes are performed to complete the weldment. For example, it is not uncommon to roll a piece of steel sheet into a band or a cylinder, join the abutting ends by welding, and then subject this weldment to many kinds of hot or cold working operations to form the final required article. The weld, in addition to having strength comparable to that of the base metal, also must have the ductility or capacity for deformation. A wide variety of tests have been devised to assist him in finding the answer to many of his questions.

TESTS OF WELDS

Information on both the behavior of a steel in welding, and the capability of its weld joints in service can be secured by applying a number of familiar, frequently-used mechanical tests or examination methods to a weld joint of the kind and size under consideration. Table 95 lists typical *tests of welds* and indicates the kind of information obtained from each test and how this information can be used. These tests sometimes are regarded as *indirect* tests of the suitability of a material for welding and for service in the form of a weldment. Many of these tests are destructive tests; that is, they usually require that the metal be deformed in some way to secure information. This precludes application of the tests to the actual weldment intended for use. However, a few nondestructive methods of inspection are listed that can be applied to sample welds or joints in the finished weldment. If a welded joint were subjected to the entire gamut of tests, the results would provide a reasonably complete appraisal of its soundness, its capability for plastic deformation, and its engineering properties (strength, hardness, toughness, etc.). However, suitability of the joint for service would have to be estimated from the test values. Because the weld joint in actual service is not pulled apart in simple uniaxial tension, or bent 180 degrees, or subjected to a measured impact load at a notch of prescribed shape as performed in the test of the weld, these test data do not provide a *direct* measure of the suitability of the joint for service. Sometimes, considerable effort is expended in establishing a correlation between certain properties of a weld and its service performance. Unfortunately, these relationships hold true only as long as all of the conditions under which the work was conducted are unchanged.

As soon as plate thickness, joint design, temperature, or any one of the many significant conditions are changed, generally the correlation no longer exists.

Much can be said about each of the mechanical tests in Table 95, particularly with regard to the modified forms which have been developed as investigators attempted to improve their effectiveness in evaluating welded joints. Tensile specimens, for example, have been prepared transversely and longitudinally from weld joints, and have ranged in size from small, slender machined sections to large plates 40-inches wide and 15 feet in length containing a centrally-located weld joint. The purpose of the latter specimen was to determine whether the residual stresses associated with the weld joint would detract from load-carrying ability. Incidently, this work with large tensile tests led to the deliberate inclusion of reproducible defects in the weld joint (small slots made with a jeweler's saw), and thus evolved a new form of specimen for research on the brittle fracture of mild steel. This specimen is known as the *wide, notched and welded plate test.*

Standardized tensile specimens for testing joints in plate, sheet and pipe may be found in a number of documents, such as the AWS *Standard Qualification Procedure* (B3.0), Section IX of the *ASME Boiler and Pressure Vessel Code,* and the AWS *Welding Handbook,* Section 1.

Bend tests on weld joints ordinarily are intended to reveal defects, or to provide a measure of joint ductility. Although seemingly a simple test, the bend specimen may be difficult to interpret, and many times difficulty is encountered in performing the test because of non-uniformity of mechanical properties across the joint. Specimens may be bent by several methods: (a) free-bend, (b) guided bending in a jig, and (c) roller-die forming. With the first two methods, weld metal of overmatching strength can result in non-uniform elongation across some areas of the weld joint. Greater deformation may occur in zones of lower strength, such as the base metal heat-affected zones, and fracture may occur solely by exhausting elongation locally rather than by fracture initiation at a defect. The severity of a bend test increases as specimen thickness and width are increased, and as the bend radius becomes smaller. Special bend specimens containing notches, or precracked areas will be described later.

Notched-bar impact testing in the USA usually implies use of either Charpy or Izod specimens. Earlier discussion pointed out that although the Charpy specimen originally made use of a keyhole notch, or a U-notch (both of which terminate in an 0.079-inch diameter round notch), the current trend in impact testing is to make use of the V-notch, which is 0.079-inch deep, has a 45° included angle, and terminates at an 0.010-inch

Table 95 — TESTS OF WELDED JOINTS

Type of Test	Kind of Information Obtained	Typical Uses of Information
Tension	Tensile strength, proportional limit, yield points, modulus of elasticity, tensile elongation, and reduction of area at fracture.	Comparison with base metal properties indicates joint efficiency.
Hardness	Resistance to deformation or penetration.	Hardness is a rough indication of strength, also resistance to wear and abrasion.
Bend	Elongation of outer fibers, bend angle, minimum bend radius, occurrence of fissures or cracks.	Gives rough measure of toughness and plastic deformation capability. Also reveals fissures.
Notched-Bar Impact	Energy absorption of standard specimen in foot-pounds, energy transition temperature, fracture transition temperature, lateral contraction at notch, and lateral expansion behind notch.	Gives measurements of toughness which correlate roughly with service performance of weldments.
Fatigue	Endurance limit, finite fatigue strength, fatigue life.	Fatigue data guides the allowable stresses in dynamically loaded weldments.
Torsion	Torsional elastic limit, yield strength, and apparent ultimate shear stress.	Data can be used to design proper strength and stiffness in parts subjected to torsional stresses.
Notched-Tension	Cohesive strength of metal under varying degrees of multiaxiality of tension stresses depending upon notch design.	Relationship between notch and unnotched tensile strength is another indication of toughness.
Pre-Cracked Tension	Cohesive strength of metal under conditions of maximum notch acuity (i.e., a crack), G_c value and K_{Ic} value.	Fracture-toughness evaluation.
Nick-Fracture	Examination of fracture faces reveals entrapped slag, porosity, and gives rough indication of grain size and toughness.	Examination for soundness. Sometimes can indicate whether fine or coarse grain.
Stress-Rupture	Tensile-type test specimen is heated to prescribed elevated temperature and loaded. Strain rate is appreciable and rupture of specimen usually occurs in time.	To determine number of hours the weld joint will carry the prescribed load at elevated temperature before complete failure occurs. Stress-rupture data usually is reported as the stress to produce failure in 100, 1000, 10,000, and 100,000 hours.

Test	Description	Application
Creep	Tensile-type specimen is heated to prescribed elevated temperature and loaded. The amount of load is less than a stress-rupture test. Creep specimens ordinarily are subjected to no more than about 0.5% total strain. Stress-strain at temperature is plotted to calculate stress producing a creep rate of 1% for 10,000 hours, or 1% in 100,000 hours.	To determine stress permitted in welded members which will be heated to elevated temperatures in service where weldment must not stretch excessively, albeit slowly.
Macro Etch	Reveals macro defects, like slag, porosity, and cracks. Also shows outline of weld metal in base metal.	Establishes soundness of weld. Permits calculation of dilution.
Metallographic Examination	Microstructure of weld metal, base metal and heat-affected zones. Also micro-cleanliness and microscopic defects, like fissures and minute porosity.	Very useful information for estimating properties and diagnosing abnormalities.
Dye-Penetrant Inspection	Reveals defects which are open to surface.	Useful for detecting cracks, small blowholes and slag pockets which extend to surface.
Magnetic Particle Inspection	Reveals surface or sub-surface discontinuities.	Useful for detecting cracks, seams, and other defects which are in the surface or just below the surface of the metal.
Radiographic Inspection	Provides "shadowgraph" of object in which any condition representing a decrease or an increase in the density of the metal will be recorded by virtue of change in absorption of the X-rays or gamma rays.	Nondestructive method of examination for defects that represent unsoundness, as well as entrapment of high-density particles, like tungsten.
Ultrasonic Inspection	Detects any internal condition that provides an "internal surface" able to reflect ultrasonic sound waves.	Can determine size and location of internal defects, like cracks, inclusion, porosity and high-density particles. Also can indicate very large grain size.
X-Ray Diffraction Inspection	Determines residual stresses in metal sections with reasonable accuracy.	Establishes whether residual stresses have been reduced to proper low level by postweld heat treatment.
Eddy Current Testing	Reveals surface or sub-surface discontinuities.	Useful for continuous inspection of moving product, such as tubing, to detect cracking or incomplete fusion along weld seam.

radius apex. Another type of notched-bar impact specimen, not often used in the USA, is the Schnadt atopy-coheracy test specimen which contains a hard metal pin in a hole parallel to and behind the notch to replace the material normally under compression in the Charpy or Izod test specimens. Schnadt specimens are made in a series of varying notch acuity ranging from no notch to a sharp knife impression. The latest Schnadt testing procedure also involves testing at different levels of loading velocity.

In discussing the many measurements which can be made with notched-bar impact specimens (Chapter 6), mention was made of the deformation which occurs in the fractured cross-section. Lateral contraction at the root of the notch was pointed out as a measure of initial ductility which could be used as a sensitive indicator of transition from ductile to brittle fracture-initiation. Current thinking on the impact testing of certain high-strength steels (quenched and tempered variety) places emphasis on the *lateral expansion* in the Charpy V-notch specimen *opposite* the notch. It has been proposed that a more meaningful criterion of satisfactory fracture-toughness is to have a minimum lateral expansion opposite the notch of 0.015 inch, rather than to require a minimum energy absorption.

An interesting modification of Charpy V-notch impact testing is the use of partly precracked specimens (the partial cracking having been accomplished by low-blow technique, or by fatigue). The ductile-to-brittle transition which occurs in the precracked Charpy energy–temperature curve coincides, temperaturewise, with the fracture-appearance transition. Also, the energy loss when divided by the broken area (called W/A which is expressed as in-lbs/in^2) matches closely G_c crack-toughness values. The philosophy of using a precracked Charpy test specimen is that by having a fracture already present the energy absorption associated with fracture initiation in a V-notch specimen is eliminated. Accordingly, the energy absorption measured is mainly that required for fracture propagation in the material. The precrack technique supposedly circumvents the biggest objection to heeding the energy absorption value from Charpy notched-bar testing; namely, that the regular Charpy ft-lb value represents an integration of crack initiation energy, fracture propagation energy, and various minor energy losses. Some investigators feel that this regular Charpy value can be misleading in fracture-toughness analysis because the crack initiation energy is the largest factor in the total result. Since cracks may be already present in a welded structure, it is felt that resistance to fracture propagation, rather than crack initiation is the material property to be measured and evaluated.

Notched tensile tests have been used for many years, but the usefulness of this kind of specimen took on new significance with the recent application of linear-elastic fracture mechanics (Chapters 6 and 13). This concept combines the knowledge of the metallurgist with that of the stress analyst, and provides a tool which can be used to assist in material selection, design and inspection. In the conventional tensile test, the stress is approximately uniformly distributed over the cross-section and it can be characterized by the load divided by the area. When a sharp notch or a crack is introduced into the section under load, an intensified stress field develops in the material ahead of the crack terminus. The stress normal to the crack diminishes as the inverse square root of the distance. Because this relationship holds for any elastically bound tensile crack, the amplitude of the stress field ahead of the crack is defined by the following equation:

$$K = \sigma y \sqrt{2 \pi r}$$

where σy is the component of stress normal to the plane of the crack at a distance r ahead of the terminus. In ordinary tensile testing, we often characterize the behavior of the material by the onset of yielding under the uniformly applied stress. However, a new response of the material to the applied stress-field parameter K has been selected to characterize *fracture* behavior in a notched or precracked tensile test. This response is the K level at which the notch or crack becomes a running fracture. This K level is designated K_c, which is the plane-stress critical stress intensity factor. Because K_c is dependent upon testing conditions, such as specimen thickness and width, the stress K concept has been carried a step farther to predict K under conditions of full constraint in the direction parallel to the crack front. The limiting value which applies to a section of infinite thickness containing a crack has been identified as K_{Ic}, or the *plane-strain* critical stress which produces running fracture. This factor is intended to serve as a primary index of the fracture toughness of a material at a given temperature.

A number of forms of tensile specimens have been developed for determining K_{Ic}. The preferred design is one in which there is a minimum of plastic deformation in the zone at the terminus of the notch or crack under stress conditions that produce the running fracture. Most investigators agree that a machined notch should be terminated or extended by a real crack. The specimen as a whole, therefore, must be large relative to the size of the plastic zone surrounding the crack tip. During tensile loading it is necessary to know the size of the advancing slow-growth crack versus load up to the point of running fracture. While an ink-staining method was mentioned in earlier discussion, the use of various kinds of *compliance gages* for continuously measuring crack extension during loading to fracture has become the preferred technique.

The load–deflection curve of a fracture-toughness tensile test obtained with a compliance gage is very much like the familiar stress–strain curve of a regular tensile test. The early portion is a straight line representing elastic strain within the gage length. The start of slow crack growth is indicated by a slight deviation from the straight line, although development of a small plastic zone at the crack tip may contribute to this initial deviation from the curve. At some point in loading, an abrupt change occurs in the curve because of substantial crack development (running fracture) at constant load. This point in referred to as "pop-in," and is marked by an audible click or pop. Acoustical systems have been devised for accurately recording the precise moment of pop-in because the load at this point is employed in calculating the plane-strain critical stress intensity factor, K_{Ic}.

Tougher steels, which more readily undergo plastic flow at the tip of a crack, require very large specimens to secure sufficient constraint. Crack instability must be achieved before yielding occurs in the crack process zone in order to determine a critical stress intensity factor that is truly a measure of fracture toughness. Sometimes it is more practical to prepare and test large precracked bend specimens. While several disadvantages arise in bend testing, K_{Ic} can be calculated from the displacement–load data. In the case of lower-strength, tough steels, the value of K_c may be so large as to be indeterminable.

Fracture-toughness testing has been receiving considerable attention by ASTM and much effort has been directed toward developing test specimens and procedures that produce significant results. However, the determination of K_c under plane-stress conditions and the calculation of the plane-strain fracture-toughness factor, K_{Ic}, still is the subject of vigorous research and debate. Three types of specimens appear to be receiving greatest attention: (1) notched round tensile test, (2) partial through thickness precracked tensile test, and (3) slow notched bend test. Table 96 lists a number of test specimens currently being studied and the equations employed for K_{Ic} calculation. In applying this new fracture-toughness testing technique to weld joints, the specimens are prepared so that the notch, or the pre-crack is located in the weld metal, or in the heat-affected zone of the base metal as desired by the investigator.

It is an expensive, time-consuming task to prepare a sample weld joint similar to those to be incorporated in a weldment and to subject this joint to many of the destructive tests listed in Table 95. As mentioned earlier, the engineer seldom is given time to conduct any appreciable

Table 96 — *THEORETICAL FORMULAS FOR PLANE-STRAIN FRACTURE TOUGHNESS, K_{Ic}*

Test and investigator	Formulas for general case
Notch Round —Irwin	$\sigma_N\sqrt{D}\left[2\left(\dfrac{d}{D}\right)^4\left\{1-\dfrac{d}{D}+0.364\left(\dfrac{D}{d}\right)\left(1-\dfrac{d}{D}\right)^2\right\}\right]^{1/2}$
Single Edge Notch —Paris	$\sigma_N\sqrt{D}\left[\pi\left(\dfrac{d}{D}\right)^2\left(1-\dfrac{d}{D}\right)\left\{1+\left(1-\dfrac{d}{D}\right)^2\left[6\cosh^{-1}\left(\dfrac{1}{1-\dfrac{d}{D}}\right)-\dfrac{1}{2}\right]\right\}\right]^{1/2}$
Slow Notch-Bend Shallow Notch —Wundt	$\sigma_N\sqrt{D}\left[\pi\left(\dfrac{a}{D}\right)\left(1-\dfrac{a}{D}\right)^3\right]^{1/2}$
Intermediate Notch —Bueckner	$\sigma_N\sqrt{D}\left[0.40\left\{\left(\dfrac{a}{D}\right)^{1/2}+\pi\left(\dfrac{a}{D}\right)\left(1-\dfrac{a}{D}\right)^{3/2}\right\}\right]^{1/2}$
Deep Notch —Wundt	$\sigma_N\sqrt{D}\left[0.521\ \left(\dfrac{d}{D}\right)\right]^{1/2}$
Center Notch "Pop-In" —Krafft	$\sigma_N\sqrt{D}\left[\left(\dfrac{d}{D}\right)^2\tan\left\{\dfrac{\pi}{2}\left(1-\dfrac{d}{D}\right)\right\}\right]^{1/2}$
Partical Through Crack —Irwin	$\sigma_0\sqrt{a}\left[\dfrac{3.77}{\phi^2-0.212\,(\sigma_0/\sigma_{ys})^2}\right]^{1/2}$

(After Gerberich)

number of tests — to say nothing of seeking a correlation between some of the test data and performance of the weld under service conditions. Little wonder, then, that the welding engineer seeks to develop a simple, rapidly conducted welding test which provides quantitative information on a quality of the steel known as *weldability*.

We frequently use this term *weldability* because it is extremely convenient to express the practicability of welding a material. The term is convenient to use, but quite difficult to define. Even today, we have no general agreement on a carefully worded precise meaning. In a broad sense, weldability might be taken as the relative ease by which a metal can be welded to produce satisfactory joints. It will take very little thought to see the myriad of descriptive and restrictive clauses which can stem from this simple definition. For example, by what welding process is the ease of welding to be judged, and what system will be used to express the evaluation? Some steels are more rapidly welded by a particular process. Therefore, what process is to be accepted as a reference standard in conducting the welding test? What type of joint shall be embodied in the test specimen and what will constitute a satisfactory welded joint? Obviously, a satisfactory joint is one which performs in a suitable manner in service, but what service properties are to be measured in the welded test specimen? On this point we could continue for many pages, for the relative importance of service properties, like strength, ductility, and soundness, may vary considerably with the particular application.

Much work has been done on the problem of evaluating the weldability of specific groups of steels, as examples: ordinary mild steel, armor plate compositions, and the alloy hardenable steels. Despite the complexity of the problem of evaluating weldability, considerable progress has been made. The remainder of this Chapter is devoted to a description of welding tests (or *weldability* tests) which have been developed and applied to steels. It appears fitting to include a description of these tests in this book, because in creating these tests the metallurgist and welding engineer have given much consideration to the metallurgical changes which occur though the heat effect of welding.

WELDING TESTS

A welding test may incorporate an actual welding operation in its method or procedure, or it may only simulate the significant effects of welding. Regardless whether welding is actually performed, or merely simulated, the test commonly is called a *welding test,* and is intended to measure weldability. None of the tests devised to date will evaluate with equal efficacy (a) the ability of the base metal and any filler metal to be fabricated by welding, and (b) the suitability of the welded joints for service.

The majority of weldability tests developed thus far are designed to measure the fabricability of the metals under test. This aspect of welding has received greater attention simply because the first task is to join the metal into a weldment. Only recently has proper emphasis been placed on developing tests which evaluate the suitability of the welded steel for service. The common objectives for which investigators strive in developing a weldability test can be described as:

1. Simplicity in specimen design and test procedure.

2. Minimum equipment and instrumentation.

3. No uncontrolled variables to adversely affect reproducibility.

4. Must be sensitive to the effects of welding upon the weld metal and the base metal, and must properly emphasize those conditions which are truly significant in actual welding operations.

5. Should produce numerical data for convenience and accuracy in recording, plotting and comparing.

6. A relatively small number of tests should permit extrapolation or interpolation over a wide range of conditions as might be encountered in the fabricating procedures and the service requirements of a wide variety of weldments.

None of the currently used welding tests provide data which are applicable to a wide range of weldments. One major stumbling block is the great differences in metallurgical conditions imposed by the various welding processes. For example, it is not possible to assess the suitability of a steel for a weldment to be joined by the gas welding process from data secured with a welding test which employs metal-arc welding. About the only similarity between the two processes is that both produce a localized heat-affected zone in the base metal, but even here the rates of heating and cooling are quite different. Attempts have been made to find a "common denominator" weldability test by devising apparatus which simulates the effects of welding. These efforts also have been prompted by the desire to obtain more closely and consistently controlled conditions from test-to-test than appeared possible with actual welding. Synthetic welding tests have achieved some success. At least, they are able to reproduce the thermal cycle of welding in sections of base metal. While this provides some unusual advantages in research studies on welding problems, it does not appear likely to lead to the universal test. Possibly an all-purpose test never will be achieved. The situation appears analogous to the machinability testing problem where no single test will closely predict the performance of a metal in all kinds of machining operations, like drilling, turning, milling and broaching. This is the case despite efforts to measure and analyze the basic forces required to cut metals in each particular operation. Likewise, the behavior of a metal when exposed to the fundamental conditions of welding can be evaluated, but these data do not enable us to accurately predict performance with any appreciable number of the welding processes available today. The development of a simple test to predict service behavior would seem to be an even greater problem — in view of the infinite variations in service conditions to which weldments are exposed. Yet, surprising progress has been made here, as will be shown shortly. Note that *toughness* has been singled out as a fundamental quality which is of major importance in virtually all weld joints. Therefore, many welding tests which propose to evaluate the suitability of the welded metal for service are designed to measure toughness in some manner.

The number of welding tests now in use or under serious study exceeds that which could be completely reviewed here, so let us discuss examples of the various types to show how the welding engineer obtains guidance on the weldability of steels. The descriptions of tests which follow are not necessarily complete, because our attention should be centered upon the metallurgical principles of interest in each test. However, sufficient information is provided in each case, or is included in the list of suggested reading, so that complete details for proper execution of the test may be secured.

JOMINY HARDNESS-BEND DUCTILITY WELDABILITY SYSTEM

In 1943, a novel system was proposed for measuring the weldability of carbon and alloy steels *without actually welding*. Time has proved the system to be incapable of closely evaluating the service capability of weld joints — the principal objective for which it was designed. However, some of the metallurgical concepts incorporated in this system are so unique that it merits at least a brief description here. A complete description can be found in a booklet entitled *Guide to the Weldability of Steels* as listed under Suggested Reading.

The aims of the Jominy Hardness-Bend Ductility System were to predict the effect of a specified arc-welding procedure upon (1) the likelihood of cracking and (2) the service capability of the heat-affected base metal adjacent to a weld in the steel under test. Briefly, the system attempted these predictions through use of a Jominy hardenability test conducted on the steel under standard conditions except that an austenitizing temperature of 2100 F is employed, and through a series of slow, notched-bend coupons bearing a 1/8-in. radius notch. These bend coupons also were austenitized at 2100 F and various cooling rates were employed (air, oil, water quench) to reproduce the hardness levels found along the length of the Jominy bar. An austenitizing temperature of 2100 F was used because this appeared to cause approximately the same degree of grain coarsening as observed in the base metal heat-affected zone of actual welds.

The system demonstrated first, that a weld joint of given design and size, at a specific temperature, and welded with a particular heat input (joules per inch) always displayed the same cooling rate in the weld

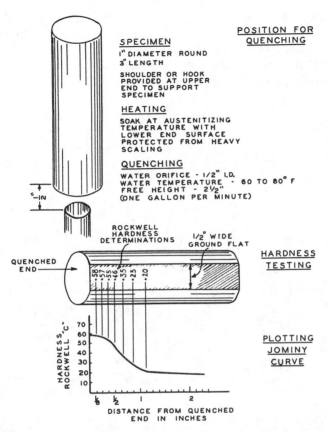

SPECIMEN
1" DIAMETER ROUND
3" LENGTH

SHOULDER OR HOOK
PROVIDED AT UPPER
END TO SUPPORT
SPECIMEN

HEATING
SOAK AT AUSTENITIZING
TEMPERATURE WITH
LOWER END SURFACE
PROTECTED FROM HEAVY
SCALING

QUENCHING
WATER ORIFICE - 1/2" I.D.
WATER TEMPERATURE - 60 TO 80° F
FREE HEIGHT - 2½"
(ONE GALLON PER MINUTE)

POSITION FOR QUENCHING

ROCKWELL
HARDNESS
DETERMINATIONS

1/2" WIDE
GROUND FLAT

QUENCHED END

HARDNESS TESTING

PLOTTING JOMINY CURVE

DISTANCE FROM QUENCHED END IN INCHES

Fig. 254 — Jominy End-Quench Hardenability Test Bar as used in *Guide to Weldability of Steels.*

heat-affected zone. Tables were published in the guidebook, which gave the cooling rate for many different combinations of weld joint design and size, preheat temperature, and heat input. These tables were based on the work of three investigating laboratories, each of which used a different method of determination to arrive at practically the same cooling rates. The first laboratory used a piece of electrical equipment called a *Heat-Mass-Flow Analyzer* and predicted cooling rates by electrical analogy. The second actually measured with a recording pyrometer the cooling rates experienced in a variety of standard weld joints using many combinations of preheat temperature and welding heat input. The third measured the hardness of the weld heat-affected zone and then referred to the specially treated end-quench hardenability test bar, Fig. 254, for the same steel where the cooling rate could be ascertained for any particular hardness merely by noting the position on the bar at which the hardness occurred. The use of this Jominy bar was found to be so convenient, that the bar positions, that is, the distances from the quenched end in sixteenths of an inch, were used in the tables in place of cooling rate figures, because they represent essentially the same information.

Jominy Hardening Factor, $^1/_{16}$ In.	Welding Speeds, In./Min.							
	2	3	4	6	8	10	12	18
2	0.90	1.50	1.80	2.70	3.60	4.5	5.4	8.1
2.5	1.5	2.1	2.7	4.2	5.7	6.9	8.4	12.6
3	2.1	3.0	3.9	6.0	7.8	9.9	11.7	17.7
3.5	2.4	3.6	4.8	6.9	9.3	12.0	14.1	21
4	2.7	4.2	5.4	8.1	10.8	13.5	16.2	24.3
4.5	3.3	4.8	6.3	9.6	12.6	15.9	18.9	28.5
5	3.6	5.4	7.2	10.8	14.4	18.0	21.6	32.4
6	4.5	6.7	9.0	13.5	18.0	22.5	27	41
7	5.1	7.8	10.2	15.3	20.4	25.5	30.6	46
8	5.7	8.7	11.4	17.1	22.8	28.5	34.2	51
9	6.3	6.4	12.9	19.3	25.8	32.1	39	57
10	7.2	10.8	14.4	21.6	28.8	36	43.2	65
12	8.4	12.6	16.8	25.2	33.6	42	51	75
14	9.6	14.4	19.2	28.8	39	48	57	87
16	10.8	16.2	21.6	32.4	43.2	54	65	97
18	11.7	17.4	23.1	35	46	58	69	105
20	12.3	18.6	24.6	37	49	61.5	75	111
22	13.2	19.8	26.4	40	53	66	79	119
24	13.8	20.7	27.6	41.4	55	69	83	124

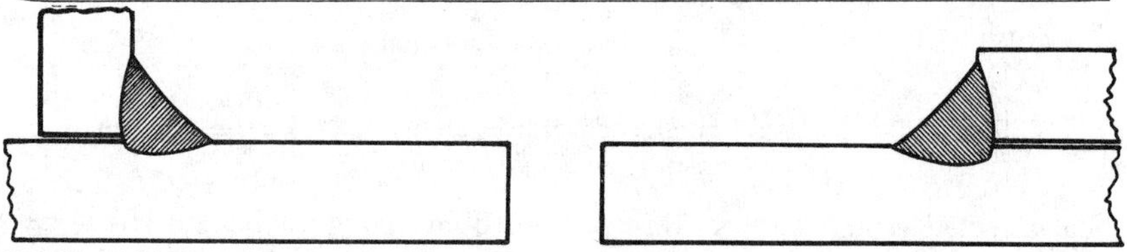

FIRST PASS FILLET WELDED T-JOINT   SINGLE PASS WELDED LAP JOINT

Fig. 255 — Volt-ampere factors (kw) for first pass fillet welds in 1-in. thick plate at room temperature.

To put this system to use, the conditions under which a weld is to be made must be fixed; i.e., the joint design, plate thickness, preheat temperature, and heat input per lineal inch of weld must be known. From these, the tables in the Guidebook are used to find the cooling rate of the base metal heat-affected zone immediately adjacent to the weld. This rate, as mentioned earlier, is expressed as a location on the Jominy bar. Let us assume that we are planning to deposit a fillet weld between pieces of plate 1-in. thick at room temperature (75 F). The welding will be performed at a speed of 6 in. per minute, using 300 amperes of current and a closed circuit voltage of 20. This amounts to 6.0 kw of power, or 60,000 joules (or 60 kilojoules) per inch. The proper table in the guidebook for our imaginary joint is shown in Fig. 255. Here we find that these welding conditions would produce a cooling rate equivalent to that found at 3 sixteenths on the Jominy bar. Next, the Jominy hardenability curve for the particular lot of steel we are to weld must be secured. From this curve we can learn the hardness obtained at the three-sixteenths position. Accordingly, this will be the hardness of the metal in the heat-affected zone of our proposed weld. Incidentally, the size and kind of electrode is reported to have a negligible effect on the hardness. Correction factors to compensate for changes in cooling rate at the start and end of a weld depending upon the proximity of the plate edge also are provided for the system. Further examination of the table in Fig. 255 will show that any increase in heat input would result in a greater distance on the Jominy bar; that is, a slower cooling rate, which is in complete agreement with the fundamentals discussed in Chapter 4.

As the remaining step in this system, a series of notched-bend coupons of the (unwelded) base metal are austenitized at 2100 F and different cooling media employed to span the rate or rates expected in welding. For most cases, this involves cooling in water, oil, moving air, still air, and sand. After making a hardness determination on each coupon, the slow bend test is conducted at room temperature to determine the maximum bend angle before failure. Naturally, specimens cooled at a faster rate possess higher hardness and lower bend capability. By plotting hardness versus bend angle, a curve can be established to permit interpolation of the bend angle (ductility) of metal having the same hardness as that expected in the heat-affected zone. For the example being studied, this is the hardness at the three-sixteenths position on the Jominy bar. Data on a number of steels obtained with this system suggested that a bend angle of 20 degrees or more gives assurance of ample ductility for most kinds of service. If the weldment is scheduled to be stress-relief heat treated (which would be likely to produce a bend angle substantially greater than 20 degrees), then a minimum bend angle of 10 degrees is needed for avoidance of cracking in the heat-affected zone in the as-welded condition until the treatment can be applied. If the weldment is joined with austenitic stainless steel electrodes, minimum bend angles of 6 degrees to avoid cracking and 12 degrees to assure satisfactory service as welded, are required because of the benefits which regularly accompany the use of this kind of weld deposit.

The weaknesses of this Jominy hardness-bend ductility system are pinpointed by more recent findings on cracking susceptibility and fracture toughness in service. We know, for example, that the kind of electrode covering (cellulosic versus low-hydrogen) has a powerful influence on the occurrence of cracking in the heat-affected zone. Therefore, the 10 degree notched-bend angle is not always a useful criterion. For judging service capability, we now know that toughness in weldments should be measured as *crack* initiation and propagation characteristics, and that rapid loading and controlled temperature also should be included as part of the test procedure. Finally, the heating of a Jominy bar to 2100 F for 30 minutes is a far cry from the actual peak of the thermal cycle in the base metal zone heat-affected by welding. The maximum temperature reached by the base metal undoubtedly is higher and the time at any given temperature obviously is much shorter. These factors have been given further consideration in more recently developed weldability tests.

SYNTHETIC WELDING TESTS

Apparatus for simulating the heat-effect of welding, and thus creating a synthetic weldability test, are available in two general types: (1) a unit which heats and cools a metal specimen over a thermal cycle exactly like that found in a particular weld, and (2) a unit which not only heats and cools the specimen over the "weld" thermal cycle, but which also can apply a controlled tension load to the specimen at any time during the cycle.

The first type of unit, which subjects a specimen to the same heat-effect endured by the base metal adjacent to a weld, usually heats the test portion of the specimen by electrical resistance heating. The current may be induced by a surrounding induction coil or applied by direct contact. The most popular technique is to heat a round bar specimen directly by electrical resistance. A thermocouple is attached to the surface of the specimen to measure its temperature and feed a signal to an electrical power input control. The system also includes a device which varies the power input in order to have the specimen temperature follow the weld thermal cycle. Where the cooling rate of the specimen must be faster than the rate obtained in air, a water spray or a stream of nitrogen gas may be directed at the specimen to accelerate the cooling. However, the specimen temperature during cooling still may be regulated by a small input of power to balance excessive heat removal by the quenching medium.

This unit for producing synthetic "weld heat-affected" base metal offers the opportunity to secure a specimen of sufficient size to perform almost any kind of mechanical test or metallurgical examination. In contrast to the all-weld-metal specimens mentioned in Chapter 10, we now can make test specimens which are uniformly heat-affected base metal (or weld metal) as found at any particular spot in or near a weld. We merely need to determine the thermal cycle which the metal undergoes in the actual weld. This cycle is set in the machine as a reference or guideline, and the specimen is heated and cooled accordingly.

The microstructure and hardness found in synthetically weld-treated specimens are remarkably close to those observed at the actual spot being simulated in the weld joint. Much work has been done with tensile testing of synthetically weld heat-affected specimens in attempting to correlate tensile ductility with important factors in weldability, like weld joint toughness and underbead cracking susceptibility. While the correlation is sufficiently close in some cases to provide a test method of limited usefulness, deviations are not uncommon when a number of steels are reviewed. The absence of residual and reaction stresses, hydrogen pickup, and other conditions imposed upon the actual weld heat-affected zone tends to produce erroneously favorable results with synthetically treated specimens.

The second type of unit which subjects a specimen to both thermal cycle and to tension loading comes closer to duplicating the conditions in the heat-affected zone of a weld. One popular machine of this kind consists of a high-speed time-temperature control device coupled with a high-speed tensile-testing apparatus. The machine contains an electrical power transformer for heating a specimen by resistance and also a loading system for applying tension loads over a wide range of speed at any given time. Therefore, the machine can be used to study the effect of any given thermal cycle on the mechanical properties or the microstructure of a metal. Stress may be applied to the steel specimen to simulate the reaction stresses anticipated in the welding operation, or sufficient stress may be applied to rupture the specimen at any designated point in the thermal cycle to measure its strength and ductility. Ductility usually is evaluated by the reduction in area of the specimen at the break. The great advantage offered by the machine is that a steel specimen of appreciable size may be subjected to the thermal and stress conditions expected *at any particular location* in the base metal heat-affected zone next to a weld. After this exposure to the simulated thermal and stress cycle of welding, the specimen can be subjected to any of the mechanical tests or metallurgical examinations to assess the properties expected at this particular spot in the base metal heat-affected zone. Often, the actual base metal heat-affected zone will display a particular microstructure only in a very limited area, and considerable difficulty is experienced in attempting to gain knowledge of the properties of the metal in this area. A number of papers have appeared in the literature which explain how the response of a steel to welding can be analyzed bit by bit to gain a highly detailed account of the properties in the joint area at any given moment during the weld cycle.

BEAD-ON-PLATE WELD TESTS

The bead-on-plate welded specimen represents the simplest form of welding test, and yet it has far-reaching possibilities for evaluating weldability. Almost any combination of base metal, weld metal, welding process, and welding conditions can be employed to prepare a specimen. A weld bead is deposited on a piece of plate, for example, as shown in Fig. 256, or perhaps a torch may be used to merely fuse a path on the surface of the plate. The procedure for preparing the bead-on-plate test can be altered to secure wide variations in thermal changes and stress conditions. Increasing the thickness and width of the plate for a given weld bead size will increase the restraining effect of the plate and create higher stresses in the specimen. Plate sections of greater mass will also produce faster cooling rates at the weld. On the other hand, preheating can be applied conveniently to decrease the cooling rate. Refrigerating the plate before welding, of course, will increase the cooling rate. The weld may be made manually, automatically by a welding machine, or can be deposited by a covered metal-arc electrode laid on the surface of the plate to produce a self-depositing or *firecracker* weld. The heat input as determined by welding current and speed of travel are also important in determining the weld cooling rate as we discussed in Chapter 4.

The examination of the bead-on-plate specimen after welding will depend upon the nature of the base and weld metals, and the defects or conditions to which the materials are suspected of being susceptible. A general examination, such as made when new or unfamiliar materials are being tested, would include the preparation of marcroetched sections to determine if porosity, cracking, gross segregation, etc., exist in or near the weld, and the preparation of a metallographic sample so that the microstructure of the unaffected base metal, the weld heat-affected zone, and the weld metal itself can be studied. If the base metal or weld metal is a hardenable steel, a transverse section may be removed from the plate and ground for hardness testing. A traverse of Rockwell, Vickers, or microhardness impressions can be made across the weld metal and heat-affected zones.

Alloy steels of high hardenability are frequently subjected to a bead-on-plate test as a first step to determining the properties of the weld heat-affected zone and the likelihood of cracking occurring there during welding. With a minimum amount of machining, the bead-on-plate specimen

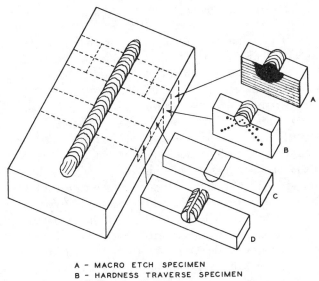

A - MACRO ETCH SPECIMEN
B - HARDNESS TRAVERSE SPECIMEN
C - BEND SPECIMEN
D - NOTCHED-BEND SPECIMEN

Fig. 256 — Simple bead-on-plate weld test specimen.

can be subjected to bending, impact, or other mechanical tests. The practice of notching specimens prior to bending started many years ago with bead-on-plate specimens. Investigators experimented with a variety of shapes and sizes of notches cut in the surface of the test piece. In one case, the notch was a hack-saw cut placed longitudinally through the center of the weld bead with the bottom of the notch at the weld fusion line. The purpose of the notch was to concentrate the bending stress on the most critical portion of the base metal heat-affected zone. Another purpose of a notch in a bead-on-plate specimen was to impose multiaxial stresses upon the metal as it deformed in bending so that the ability of the metal to flow under these conditions could be determined. The severity of the test was increased by altering the following conditions for the bending operation: (1) decreasing the temperature of the specimen, (2) increasing the rate of bending, and (3) intensifying the multiaxial stress condition by increasing the sharpness or the depth of the notch.

Kommerell Test

One of the first slow-bend test procedures applied to a longitudinal bead-on-plate specimen was that proposed by Kommerell and Bierett of Germany in 1938. A test specimen 75 mm wide by 350 mm in length is prepared from the base metal by depositing a weld bead in a shallow groove in the center of the plate section. For plate 50 mm thick, a mandrel having a round nose of 90 mm diameter is used to attempt a 180° bend with the weld on the outer surface of the bend. Ordinarily, the bending operation is conducted at room temperature, although a more recently introduced procedure involves testing additional specimens at lower temperatures to cover expected service conditions. The bend angle at crack initiation, and the bend angle at fracture are employed as criteria of performance. The location of the crack initiation, whether weld metal, or base metal heat-affected zones, is noted. It has been reported that the bend angle at crack initiation is not affected by temperature, while the bend angle at fracture will show a decrease with lower temperatures. The difference between the two temperature transition curves for crack initiation and for fracture is assumed to indicate the resistance of the steel to propagation of the initiated crack. The Kommerell test has received little attention in the USA. An Austrian Standard 3052 has been written to cover the Kommerell test. It proposes a surface elongation of 23% on the outer fibers of the bend as the safe minimum for crack initiation. This corresponds to a bend angle of at least 55° in a specimen of approximately 25 mm thickness.

FRACTURE-TOUGHNESS TESTS OF WELDED SPECIMENS

Fracture-toughness testing had its beginning on unwelded sections of metal. For example, the *Robertson Crack Arrest Test* utilized a section of plate which was drastically cooled from one edge and modestly heated from the opposite edge. After applying a uniform tensile stress to the plate section parallel to these edges, a crack was initiated in the cold edge and allowed to propagate across the plate toward the heated edge. Propagation continued until the steel was sufficiently tough to arrest the fracture. The temperature at the point of arrest when plotted against the stress applied usually showed that brittle fracture was very difficult above a characteristic temperature for each particular material. However, the importance of resistance to fracture in welded structures, where heat-affected zones, weld metal, and residual stresses might well play a role in brittle cracking, soon goaded investigators into somehow incorporating a weld joint, or at least a weld area, in their test specimens. The principal objective of this new generation of specimens has been, of course, to predict the behavior of a full-scale weldment, regardless of size, from the performance of a relatively small, simple laboratory test piece. Surprising progress has been made in gleaming information from these specimens that indicates the merits of materials, joint designs, and fabricating procedures for real weldments.

Kinzel Test

One of the early test methods developed for fracture-toughness testing, which received considerable attention in the USA, is a longitudinal-bead, slow notched-bend test called the Kinzel test. A bead-on-plate specimen is prepared into which a special notch (same as used in the Charpy-V specimen) is cut into the base metal normal to the weld axis as shown in Fig. 257. Deposition of the longitudinal bead, or the heat-effect of a weld made by fusion joining produces a heat-affected zone in the base metal which contains a variety of microstructures. Replicate specimens are prepared to permit testing over a range of temperature. The bend coupons are progressively loaded with the notched face in tension until the load reaches a maximum and falls back to about one-half this value. The test data recorded for each specimen includes bend angle at maximum load, total energy absorbed, maximum load, and the mode of fracture if it occurs. However, the observation of greatest significance appears to be the percent reduction in specimen width that occurs just below the apex of the notch. This decrease in width is termed *lateral contraction,* and appears to be the most sensitive index of performance. The notch in the Kinzel specimen is intended to leave a portion of weld metal below the root.

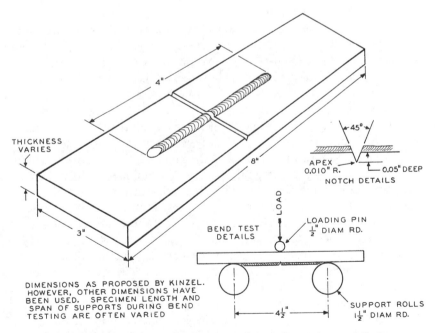

Fig. 257 — Longitudinal bead-on-plate weld converted to notched-bend specimen (Kinzel Test).

Therefore, all of the microstructures in and adjacent to the weld bead are exposed to the concentration of stress and restraint which accompanies a notch. Two distinct transitions appear to occur with the Kinzel specimens as the test temperature is lowered: (1) a transition in ductility (as measured by lateral contraction), and (2) a transition in fracture appearance. The ductility transition appears to be determined by brittle fracture initiation in the specimen and seems to be affected somewhat by the stress pattern developed through specimen dimensions and other conditions that intensify initial stress. Fracture mode transition appears to be determined by the resistance of the steel to the propagation of a running crack (cleavage fracture) and is not sensitive to specimen dimensions or to initial stress raisers. Some investigators who have used the Kinzel test claim that the ductility transition temperature is of greater significance in considering service capability than is the fracture transition. Usually, the temperature cited as the ductility transition is that point at which lateral contraction drops to one percent. Examination of the fractured ends of broken Kinzel specimens can reveal helpful information on the locus of fracture initiation and the area of fracture arrest if it occurs.

Fracture Mechanics in the Kinzel Test

The ductility and fracture transitions indicated by the Kinzel specimens for a particular steel are controlled by the ease with which fracture is initiated and the resistance of the base metal to fracture propagation as the temperature is lowered. Notched-bend specimens which do not contain a weld or weld heat-affected zone display higher than 1 percent lateral contraction down to a relatively low temperature. When the ductility transition temperature (at which 1 percent lateral contraction occurs) is finally reached, it is observed that early cleavage initiates from the shear crack which first forms in the apex of the notch. Welding raises the transition temperature by producing microstructural conditions in the weld metal, and particularly in the heat-affected base metal, which more readily initiate and propagate cleavage or running fractures. Brittle (cleavage) fracture often initiates in the coarse grained region of heat-affected base metal immediately adjacent to the weld. This region may consist of hard pearlite or martensite with limited ferrite in the grain boundaries. These microstructural conditions decrease fracture toughness. The next region of the heat-affected zone, a little farther away from the weld, normally displays grain refinement and consequently is inclined to display better toughness. This region sometimes arrests fractures which initiated in the coarse grained region; that is, until the testing temperature is lowered to the ductility transition temperature. The next region, moving away from the weld, is the zone heated between the A_3 and A_1 temperatures of the steel. Here, the microstructure will consist of clusters or patches of pearlite because only partial transformation to austenite occurred during the weld thermal cycle. This region generally will display a lower fracture toughness than the grain refined region. Thus when the grain refined zone effectively arrests a cleavage crack or converts it to a shear (ductile) failure, the inter-critical region may reactivate a running fracture when the crack reaches this portion of the heat-affected zone.

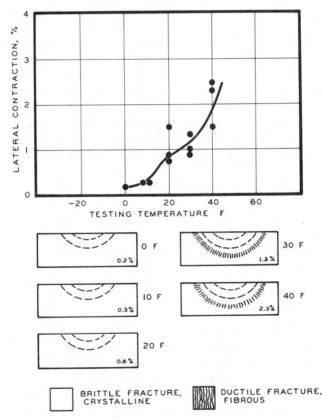

Fig. 258 — Example of ductility transition behavior and fracture patterns in a series of Kinzel specimens on 1-inch thick ASTM A212 steel. (after Stout)

Rectangles represent fractured ends of specimens. Dotted lines indicate weld metal and heat-affected zones. Open areas indicate cleavage (brittle) fracture. Cross-hatching indicates shear (ductile) fracture.

Figure 258 shows the ductility transition and fracture patterns observed in a series of Kinzel specimens prepared in carbon steel plate 1-in. thick. Note that even though a cleavage crack initiated in the weld and heat-affected zones the unaffected base metal was able to arrest the brittle fracture — until the test temperature was lowered to 20 F. At this level and below, the cleavage crack propagated through the entire specimen and the low lateral contraction value (less than 1 percent) was produced. Brittle failure occurs in the Kinzel test whenever two conditions coexist at a given temperature: (1) a zone must be able to initiate a cleavage or running crack, and (2) the remaining steel section must be able to propagate the running fracture. To improve the performance of the welded steel temperature-wise, the resistance to cleavage fracture propagation of either the weld heat-affected zone or the base metal must be improved. Postheating increases the toughness of the heat-affected zone, while heat treatment of the plate before welding helps the unaffected base metal. Preheating and controlled weld heat input influence the transition temperature by altering the susceptibility to cleavage crack initiation in the heat-affected zone. Different steels vary considerably in the way preheat and weld heat input affects the crack-initiation susceptibility of the heat-affected zone.

Explosion Bulge Test

The explosion bulge test makes use of a large plate specimen that incorporates novel features in its preparation and testing procedure. Knowledge gained from the explosion bulge test has led to the development of another test (drop-weight) which is presently receiving much attention. The explosion bulge test was devised in the U.S. Naval Research Laboratory (NRL) to study the problem of brittle fracture in structural steels used in welded ship hulls. Fig. 259 shows that a 20-in. square of ship plate (usually of 1-in. thickness) is provided with a unique "crack-starter." The latter feature is a short bead of very hard, brittle weld metal which is notched in a manner to insure the initiation of a cleavage crack as soon as the base metal is subjected to any bending. The specimen, with the welded face down, is placed upon the circular supporting die and a standardized charge of explosive is detonated at a fixed position above the specimen. During the extremely rapid loading of the test plate, a cleavage crack is initiated at the root of the notch in the weld metal and is presented to the base metal as a running crack. The behavior of the test plate depends upon the ability of the base metal to arrest the running crack and to deform while permitting only a high-energy absorbing, shear-type fracture to propagate. If the steel is not capable of arresting the

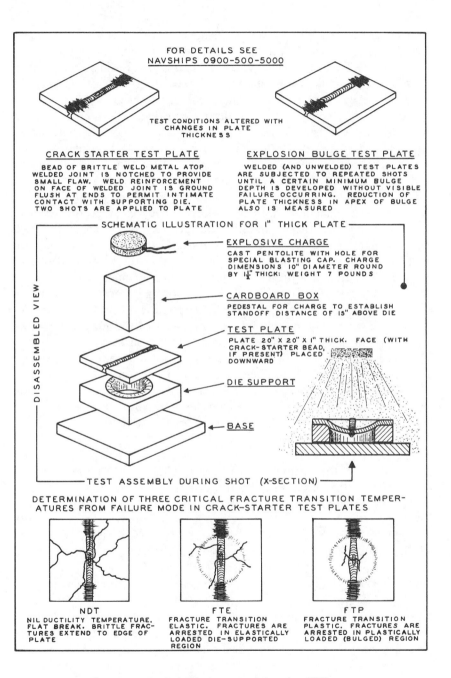

FOR DETAILS SEE
NAVSHIPS 0900-500-5000

TEST CONDITIONS ALTERED WITH
CHANGES IN PLATE
THICKNESS

CRACK STARTER TEST PLATE

BEAD OF BRITTLE WELD METAL ATOP
WELDED JOINT IS NOTCHED TO PROVIDE
SMALL FLAW. WELD REINFORCEMENT
ON FACE OF WELDED JOINT IS GROUND
FLUSH AT ENDS TO PERMIT INTIMATE
CONTACT WITH SUPPORTING DIE.
TWO SHOTS ARE APPLIED TO PLATE

EXPLOSION BULGE TEST PLATE

WELDED (AND UNWELDED) TEST PLATES
ARE SUBJECTED TO REPEATED SHOTS
UNTIL A CERTAIN MINIMUM BULGE
DEPTH IS DEVELOPED WITHOUT VISIBLE
FAILURE OCCURRING. REDUCTION OF
PLATE THICKNESS IN APEX OF BULGE
ALSO IS MEASURED

SCHEMATIC ILLUSTRATION FOR 1" THICK PLATE

DISASSEMBLED VIEW

EXPLOSIVE CHARGE
CAST PENTOLITE WITH HOLE FOR
SPECIAL BLASTING CAP. CHARGE
DIMENSIONS 10" DIAMETER ROUND
BY 1½" THICK: WEIGHT 7 POUNDS

CARDBOARD BOX
PEDESTAL FOR CHARGE TO ESTABLISH
STANDOFF DISTANCE OF 15" ABOVE DIE

TEST PLATE
PLATE 20" X 20" X 1" THICK. FACE (WITH
CRACK-STARTER BEAD, IF PRESENT) PLACED
DOWNWARD

DIE SUPPORT

BASE

TEST ASSEMBLY DURING SHOT (X-SECTION)

DETERMINATION OF THREE CRITICAL FRACTURE TRANSITION TEMPER-
ATURES FROM FAILURE MODE IN CRACK-STARTER TEST PLATES

NDT
NIL DUCTILITY TEMPERATURE.
FLAT BREAK. BRITTLE FRAC-
TURES EXTEND TO EDGE OF
PLATE

FTE
FRACTURE TRANSITION
ELASTIC. FRACTURES ARE
ARRESTED IN ELASTICALLY
LOADED DIE-SUPPORTED
REGION

FTP
FRACTURE TRANSITION
PLASTIC. FRACTURES ARE
ARRESTED IN PLASTICALLY
LOADED (BULGED) REGION

Fig. 259 — Explosion bulge test employed at NRL.

running crack, the plate develops many cleavage fractures and breaks flat; that is, little plastic forming occurs downward into the die cavity.

The stand-off explosive charge was selected for loading the specimen to insure a continuing store of energy to feed the propagating cracks. In essence, the gas pressure was maintained for sufficient duration so that stress unloading could not occur during cracking. The final, important feature of the explosion bulge test is to have a series of specimens heated or cooled to progressive temperatures over a range that encompasses the steel's suspected fracture transition point. Below this temperature, the test plates show no deformation because the weld crack is accepted by the base metal (starting at the heat-affected zone) as a brittle, running fracture and is unable to resist its propagation by cleavage fracture mechanics. Above the fracture transition temperature range, the brittle weld crack is arrested. Energy from the explosive charge is effectively utilized by the plate by deforming (bulging) into the die. Any cracking that does occur is the ductile, shear type of fracture. Much attention has been given to interpreting the finer aspects of the pattern and modes of fracture in the tested plates. Termination of cleavage fractures in the outer edges of the plate over the supporting anvil where stresses are lower can be an early sign that the brittle-to-ductile fracture transition temperature is near. The occurrence of shear lip along the plate surface on otherwise cleavage fractures also signals the coming of fracture transition to ductile failure. The fracture transition temperature range as determined by the explosion bulge test is believed to represent the temperature range above which brittle fractures cannot propagate in a weldment of the steel tested.

Drop-Weight (NDT) Test

Because brittle fracture can occur in weldments with no more energy available than the elastic strain in the structure, the investigators at NRL shifted their attention from high-energy fracture analysis (explosion bulge) to a relatively low-energy fracture study. This approach probably was more in keeping with the residual stresses found in weldments and service loading conditions imposed upon conventional structures. They again elected to use a specimen containing a preplaced crack on the premise that many weldments contain small flaws or imperfections that may act like a sharp crack. They decided to load the specimen by means of a free-falling weight to simulate the velocity associated with impact loading, and to limit the stress to the yield point since this represents the approximate amount of elastic energy often available in a weldment in the area of a weld. Finally, in view of the strong dependence of fracture mechanism upon temperature, they decided to arbitrarily fix factors like flaw size and imposed stress, and vary the temperature to determine the level at which a steel would lose its ability to develop even a minute amount of plastic deformation in the presence of a crack-like notch. This temperature, at which the NRL drop-weight specimen first initiates a major cleavage or running crack in the base metal is called the *nil-ductility transition temperature;* or "NDT" temperature, as it is now widely known.

Figure 260 provides the essential details of the bead-on-plate specimen with the "crack-starter" weld, and the procedure which is employed to test a series of specimens over a range of progressive temperatures to determine the NDT for a steel base metal. The drop-weight test was devised for testing relatively heavy structural sections, and is not recommended for base metal pieces less than ½-in. thick. A complete description of the standardized method for conducting the NRL Drop-Weight Test is presented in ASTM E208, while a description of the original work can be found in NRL Report 5831. The test is surprisingly reproducible, and requires only 6 to 8 specimens to establish the temperature (NDT) below which a weldment of the steel in question is susceptible to brittle failure. Of course, a weldment in service below its NDT is not doomed to inevitable failure. This new criterion simply indicates that catastrophic cracking is a distinct possibility if circumstances require the metal to dissipate energy by plastic flow at the tip of a crack. Below the NDT, the steel is likely to permit the crack front to propagate at high-speed by the cleavage mechanism with little or no dissipation of the energy.

The drop-weight test is intended to be principally a test of the base plate. However, the surfacing weld bead does produce a heat-affected microstructure in the base metal, albeit small. In many steels, the NDT value is not influenced by the small volume of heat-affected metal at the root of the weld crack; at least, this is true if the heat-affected zone has a crack initiation sensitivity equal to or greater than that of the unaffected plate material. Of course, some steels, like the quenched and tempered alloy steels which are treated to a high hardness may produce a tougher microstructure when exposed to the thermal cycle of welding, and in a case like this their heat-affected zone may resist initiation and propagation and thus lead to deceptively low NDT. For this reason, some consideration has been given to depositing the crack-starter bead prior to the heat treatment of the plate of certain steels. However, the tempering temperature must be limited to about 600F to avoid softening the crack-starter bead and thereby affect its cleavage cracking propensity. The test probably should not be performed on cold worked steel because of possible recrystallization in the heat-affected zone. Nevertheless, all of these steels are welded, and may be used in the as-welded condition. Perhaps an evaluation of the as-welded drop-weight specimen "come what may" is a realistic approach.

The simplicity of the drop-weight specimen, the apparatus for applying load and the interpretation of results has encouraged wide use of this test. The specimens may be oxygen-cut from a parent plate, but at least

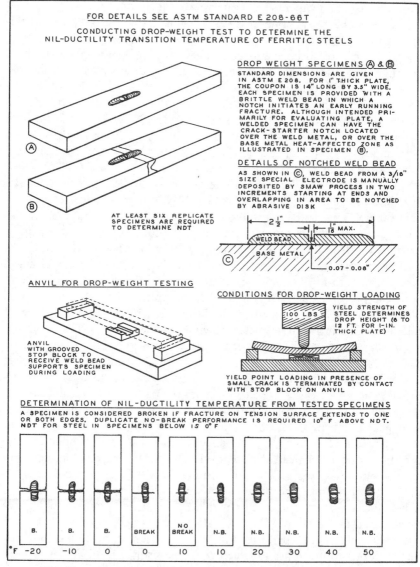

Fig. 260 — NRL drop-weight test for determination of nil-ductility transition (NDT) temperature.

1 in. of metal should be removed from the side edges by a cold sawing or machining operation. When thinner specimens are prepared from a very thick plate, the original rolled surface is to be employed on the welded (tension) face of the specimen. Weld crack-starter beads are notched by a thin abrasive disk. It will be noted that the stress applied to the specimen during the impact loading is limited to the yield point by a stopping block attached to the anvil below the specimen. This is the practical device for evaluating the ability of the steel to withstand yield point loading in the presence of a small flaw. When the tup strikes the back of the specimen, the very earliest bending generates a sharp, cleavage crack which initiates in the root of the weld notch and runs to the weld fusion line. As bending continues and the imposed stress in the outer fibers rises to the yield point, the steel either (1) accepts initiation of a cleavage crack which "runs" completely through the section and results in a broken specimen, or (2) initiation of cleavage fracture is resisted and the specimen bends the small, additional amount permitted by the anvil stop without complete fracturing. The general practice is to temperature-condition a prepared specimen at a test temperature estimated to be a little above the expected NDT temperature. If this first specimen does not break,

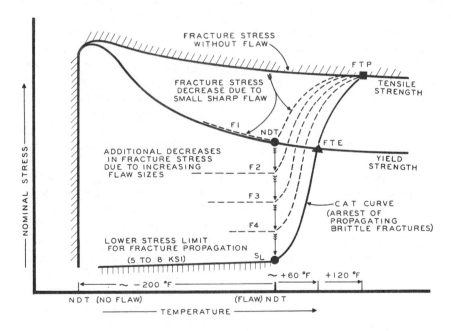

Fig. 261 — Transition temperature features of steels. (After Pellini and Puzak)

other specimens are tested at lower temperatures in 40 degrees F steps until a broken specimen is obtained. A test is then conducted at a temperature between the broken and unbroken specimen levels to narrow the determination to within 20 degrees F, and then again between the broken and unbroken specimen levels to narrow the fix to within 10 degrees F. At this point, a second test is made at the lowest temperature level of an unbroken specimen. The NDT is defined as the temperature 10 degrees F above which duplicate specimens exhibit no-break performance.

Much work has been done to utilize the NDT concept in a procedure for evaluating the brittle-fracture safety of weldments of structural steels. Figure 261 is a fracture analysis diagram offered by the originators of the drop-weight test. This diagram is intended to illustrate the relationships that exist between the fracture strength of a steel, temperature, and flaws of varying size. Data from a number of different crack-starter tests were employed in constructing this diagram. Steel without a flaw is shown to increase gradually in strength with decreasing temperature. The yield strength rises at a faster rate than does the tensile strength so that at some low temperature they coincide and fracture takes place here with essentially no plastic flow. This temperature level may be considered the "NDT" in the *absence* of any flaw. When a small, sharp flaw is present, like the cleavage crack in the weld of the drop-weight specimen, the fracture stress is decreased over a transition range as indicated by the curve labeled "fracture stress decrease due to small, sharp flaw." The NDT then is defined as the highest temperature at which the decreasing fracture stress for fracture initiation due to the small flaw becomes contiguous with the yield strength curve of the steel. Below NDT, the fracture stress follows the yield strength curve (F1). However, increasing flaw size results in lowered fracture stresses as suggested by curves F2, F3 and F4. The approximate fracture stress is inversely proportional to the square root of the flaw size. A most important fact depicted by the family of fracture stress curves is that a substantial increase occurs in the stress required to initiate fracture as the temperature rises above the NDT temperature.

Also shown on the diagram in Fig. 261 is a curve identified as CAT. This is the *crack arrest temperature;* meaning, the temperature at which even a propagating cleavage fracture will be arrested at particular levels of applied stress. Furthermore on this curve, the crack arrest temperature for an applied stress equal to the yield strength is defined as "FTE," meaning *fracture transition elastic.* Similarly, "FTP" marks *fracture transition plastic;* that is, the temperature above which fractures occur entirely by shear. Consequently, above this point the fracture stress approximates the tensile strength of the steel despite the presence of a flaw. The lower shelf labeled "S$_L$," approximately 5 to 8 ksi, is the lower stress limit for initiating and propagating a fracture from a major flaw. Propagation is not possible below this level because the minimum small amount of elastic strain energy is not available for continuation of the cleavage mechanism at the tip of the flaw. Note that the FTE temperature is 60 F above NDT, while the FTP temperature is 120 F above NDT in the generalized fracture-analysis diagram. Although there is complete agreement on the fact that the toughness of steel increases with rising temperature, considerable debate has arisen on whether these fracture transition phenomena can be predicted to occur at specific temperature increments above NDT. The originators of the fracture analysis diagram in Fig. 261 based the FTE and FTP points upon data from various tests and case histories of fracture occurrence in service.

NDT as determined by the drop-weight test is regarded as the most important reference point on the fracture analysis diagram because of the simplicity with which it is determined, and because a steel is characterized by a single NDT. While anomalous NDT results have been secured with drop-weight tests on some steels, the fracture analysis system holds considerable promise for guiding engineering deign and selection of steel for fracture-safe weldments. The literature is becoming heavily documented with accounts of the significance of NDT in terms of service failures and successful performance. Of course, the NDT concept is quite conservative because it presumes that crack-like flaws will be present in the load-carrying joints and members of the weldment. While this may not be true of certain specially fabricated and inspected weldments, it may be prudent to proceed on this assumption with most other weldments.

Drop-Weight Tear-Test (DWTT)

A relatively new fracture-toughness test, developed in an attempt to predict the possibility of brittle fracture in full-scale steel pipelines, is known as the *Battelle Drop-Weight Tear-Test* (BDWTT). This test holds promise of being applicable to a broader range of steels than those used in pipelines, and has the advantage over the NDT test of being able to use base metal of less than ½-inch thickness. The DWTT specimens are also easily prepared, are low in cost, and the tested specimens are readily evaluated. As illustrated in Fig. 262, the DWTT specimen consists of a 3-inch by 12-inch coupon cut from the full plate thickness. It has a 45° included angle notch pressed with a very sharp chisel into the center of one edge to a depth of 0.200 inch. The root radius of this notch is held to less than 0.001 inch by periodic sharpening of the chisel. The specimen is broken under impact loading using a pendulum or a drop-weight tup.

The specimen is supported on its notched edge by anvils 10 inches apart, and the impact load is applied to the opposite edge much in the same manner as a Charpy impact test bar. Large amounts of energy are required to break DWTT specimens of substantial thickness in tough steels. The drop-weight units initially used were of 1,300 ft-lb capacity. Pendulum machines of 5,000 ft-lb capacity and greater have been constructed to break DWTT specimens.

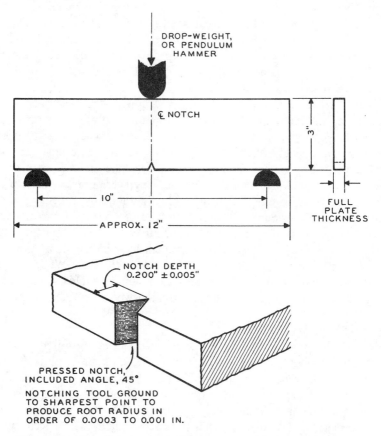

Fig. 262 — Battelle drop-weight tear-test specimen and testing procedure.

Examination of a series of DWTT specimens of a particular steel broken over a wide range of temperature will show that although a cleavage fracture initiates from the sharp notch in the specimen edge, the mode of fracture changes over a relatively narrow range of temperature from cleavage to shear as testing progresses to higher temperatures. In

Fig. 263, a typical group of DWTT specimens cut from ¾-inch plate of A36 steel has been broken. The fractured faces of each specimen have been examined to determine the amount of shear fracture which developed at the various test temperature. It will be noted that starting at the

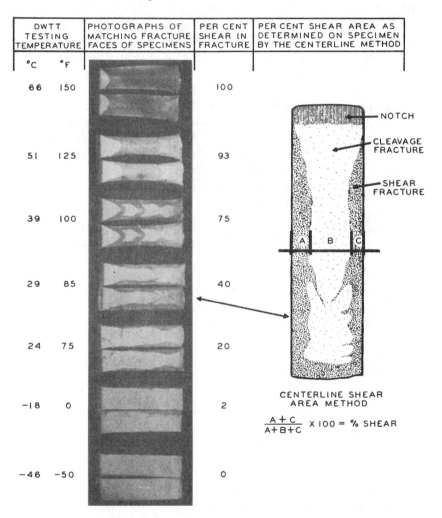

DWTT TESTING TEMPERATURE		PHOTOGRAPHS OF MATCHING FRACTURE FACES OF SPECIMENS	PER CENT SHEAR IN FRACTURE	PER CENT SHEAR AREA AS DETERMINED ON SPECIMEN BY THE CENTERLINE METHOD
°C	°F			
66	150		100	
51	125		93	
39	100		75	
29	85		40	
24	75		20	
-18	0		2	
-46	-50		0	

NOTCH

CLEAVAGE FRACTURE

SHEAR FRACTURE

A B C

CENTERLINE SHEAR AREA METHOD

$$\frac{A+C}{A+B+C} \times 100 = \% \text{ SHEAR}$$

Fig. 263 — Appearance of fractured faces of typical drop-weight tear-test specimens broken over a wide temperature range.

Test specimens prepared from ¾-inch thick plate of ASTM A36 steel. One method of measuring per cent shear fracture exhibited by specimen is illustrated on the test piece which was broken at 85 F.

lowest testing temperature (−50 F), the fracture mode was 100% cleavage. As the testing temperature was increased, a small amount of shear fracture appeared as shear lips along the edges of the fractured face at the plate surfaces. The amount of shear lip grew slowly as testing temperature increased until a very rapid change from cleavage to shear occurred over the temperature range of approximately 75 to 100 F. The amount of shear area on the fracture faces of each specimen can be measured by either of two simple techniques. In the first method, one sample thickness of material is neglected immediately beneath the notch and at the opposite edge. This eliminates the initiation effects and cold work produced by the impact tup or pendulum hammer. The percent shear on the remaining fractured surface then is estimated visually. In the second method, called "centerline shear area method," the percent shear is determined at a single point; namely, the midpoint of the fractured face. This is done by measuring the thickness of the shear lips and dividing by the total specimen thickness. The two methods give similar results in determining the percent shear in the fracture.

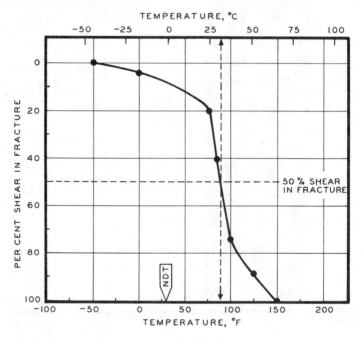

Fig. 264 — Curve plotted from drop-weight tear-test (DWTT) data depicts transition from tough (shear) fracture to brittle (cleavage) fracture. The 50%-shear temperature is employed as the significant value to mark the fracture-toughness capability of the steel.

If the amounts of shear fracture which developed in the DWTT specimens of Fig. 263 are plotted against temperature, a characteristic curve for the steel as shown in Fig. 264 is obtained. Because of the rapid fracture-mode transition, the temperature at which 50% shear fracture occurs seems to be a convenient way of expressing the performance of a steel in the drop-weight tear-test. The 50%-shear temperature for the steel represented in Figures 263 and 264 is 90 F as noted on the diagram. Incidently, this same A36 steel was tested by the NDT drop-weight test, and the NDT established was 30 F as shown in Fig. 264.

The procedure used in drop-weight tear-testing has continued to be studied to improve the test, even though the width of the transition region usually is only 10 to 15 degrees F. It has been established that neither the velocity of the impact blow (as affected by the height of a drop-weight), nor the excess energy in ft-lbs employed during the breaking of the specimens appears to influence fracture behavior. Notch depth does not appear critical; however, an increase in the root radius of the notch causes greater scatter of determinations in the transition area and a more gradual change in fracture mode.

In view of our interest in the fracture toughness of weldments, it can be mentioned that the DWTT specimen might easily contain a weld joint across the 3-inch width at the center, and that the sharp notch could be pressed into the weld metal, or into various locations of the base metal heat-affected zones. Work of this kind is now underway in a number of laboratories and soon the welding engineer will be exposed to a new outpouring of fracture-toughness data expressed in terms of 50%-shear temperature.

Correlation of Results from Fracture-Toughness Tests

On numerous occasions, investigators have compared results from the many different fracture-toughness tests, including those which can be applied to welded specimens. One usual objective is to see how well the various tests agree on the ranking of a number of steels known to differ in toughness. For the most part, a reasonably close general agreement exists, as shown in Fig. 265, and the trend of results adds emphasis to the need for good fracture toughness in most weldments.

Another purpose of correlation studies is to determine if any basic parameter of fracture toughness is suggested that comes closer to predicting the behavior of real engineering structures under stipulated service conditions. Considerable time is required to study the specific characteristics measured by each type of test specimen, and careful discrimination between these characteristics is necessary to gain an understanding of possible

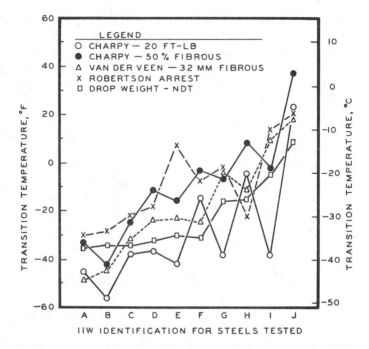

Fig. 265 — Relative behavior of ten structural steels when tested by four different fracture-toughness tests. (International Institute of Welding, Doc. IX-114-58)

relationships between the different types of tests.

A comparison of fracture-toughness data from several different kinds of tests has been made in Figures 266, 267, and 268 for A36 hot-rolled carbon steel, A212 - Grade B (A300) normalized carbon steel, and XV-60 high-strength, low-alloy vanadium-containing steel of 60 ksi minimum yield strength, respectively. For each steel, the data plotted include (a) DWTT shear fracture, (b) NDT, (c) Charpy-V energy absorption, (d) Charpy-V shear fracture, and (e) Charpy-V lateral expansion opposite notch. Note that in each case, NDT is approximately 60 degrees F below the 50%-shear fracture temperature of DWTT. Thus, the DWTT 50%-shear fracture point corresponds with FTE on the fracture analysis diagram shown earlier in Fig. 261. Furthermore, the minimum temperature at which each steel fractures in DWTT with 100% shear is approximately 120 degrees F above its NDT — which lends support to FTP in Fig. 261. The midpoint of the Charpy-V fracture transition from ductile to brittle failure occurs at a temperature which corresponds reasonably well with 50%-shear in DWTT and with FTE. Studies have been made in Charpy-

V impact testing using a technique for measuring the dynamic load on the specimen during the complete course of fracturing the specimen. A most important observation from this work is that the initial impact load normally is almost equal to the yield strength for mild steel specimens. This fact seems to help explain why the 50%-shear fracture temperatures in the Charpy-V impact and the DWTT specimens agree closely with FTE in the fracture analysis diagram. The lateral expansion opposite the notch in Charpy-V testing does not appear to undergo a marked transition as testing temperature is varied. Of course, these correlations do not necessarily hold for all steels, but are pointed out to show some of the stronger relationships which can be observed in fracture-toughness specimen behavior.

The latest thinking regarding the question of safe toughness performance, guided by the NDT + 60 degree F (FTE) concept, is that the minimum Charpy-V energy absorption might well be 15 ft-lbs if the

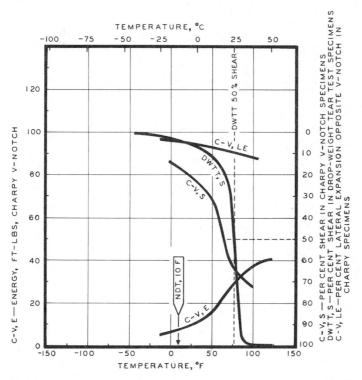

Fig. 266 — Comparison of data from Charpy-V, DWTT, and NDT tests for hot-rolled A36 carbon steel tested over a range of temperature.

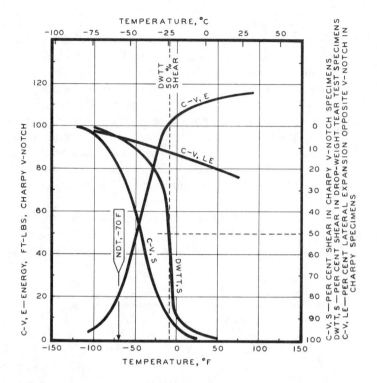

Fig. 267 — Comparison of data from Charpy-V, DWTT, and NDT Tests for A212 — Grade B (A300) normalized carbon steel tested over a range of temperature.

steel has a yield strength of 30 ksi or lower. However, with steels of greater strength, a higher minimum level of Charpy-V energy absorption may be in order. For steels of 30 to 45 ksi yield strength, a minimum Charpy-V of 20 ft-lbs has been suggested, whereas for steels of 45 to 75 ksi yield strength a minimum Charpy-V value of 35 ft-lbs has been proposed.

FILLET WELD TEE-BEND TEST

Attempts have been made to develop a welding test for predicting service performance using a specimen that employs fillet weld beads. These efforts were prompted by the thought that fillet welded joints are widely used in structures, and that the test specimen configuration should be more in keeping with the actual joints under consideration. Study of fillet-joint welding tests has diminished to a very low ebb at the present time, but one popular test originated some years ago was called the *guided tee-bend test*.

As illustrated in Fig. 269, a test assembly consisting of two plates foming a Tee-joint was fillet welded under arbitrarily fixed conditions. The welded assembly was sectioned transversely into Tee sections 1¼-in. wide. These Tee sections are bent in a guiding jig as shown in Fig. 269 until the angle of bending is 120 degrees or until the specimen has fractured. An evaluation of weldability is based upon both the change in hardness that takes place in the base metal heat-affected zone as compared with the unaffected plate metal, and the ductility exhibited by the weld joints in the bend test. Any fractures which occur in the specimens are to be classified as follows:

The guided tee-bend test has not proved very useful except for a very rough comparison of the ductility and toughness of such joints in

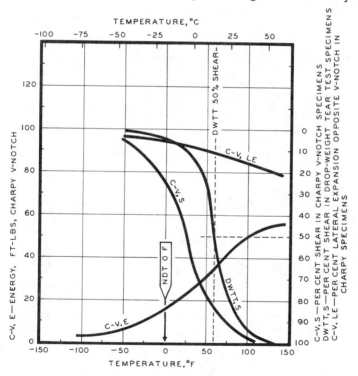

Fig. 268 — Comparison of data from Charpy-V, DWTT, and NDT tests for XV-60 high-strength, low-alloy vanadium-containing steel tested over a range of temperature. Composition of steel included 0.18% C, 1.24% Mn, 0.04% Si and 0.06% V.

structural steels. More recently acquired knowledge would call for a number of changes in the specimen and test procedure to reduce uncontrolled variables. The most obvious source of variability is the nature of the toe of the weld bead where the various classes of cracking initiates. Differences in the geometry of the weld bead and the amount of undercutting as determined by the welding technique would produce varying degrees of stress concentration at the toe. Consequently, differences in bend angle would be a reflection of the welder's skill in addition to the weldability of the steel under test.

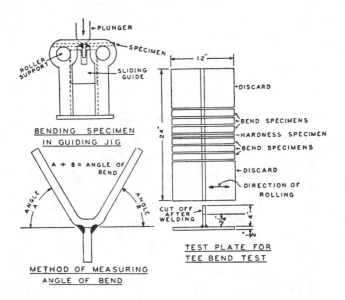

Fig. 269 — Fillet weld guided tee-bend weld test.

Type 0 — The specimen bends to 120 degrees without fracture or tear of any kind.

Type 1 — A crack which starts in the bond zone at the toe of the fillet and follows the fusion zone under the weld, but does not turn into the plate metal.

Type 2 — A slowly progressing crack which starts at the toe of the fillet and extends either directly into the plate metal or follows the fusion zone for a short distance and then turns into the plate metal, but does not continue entirely across the plate metal.

Type 3 — A sudden or sharp crack which generally starts at the toe of the fillet and extends into and entirely across the plate metal.

RESTRAINED-JOINT WELDING TESTS

A number of welding tests have been developed using base metal sections of varying size and shape to form a butt joint. The joint is held under considerable restraint during welding either by virtue of the size and assembly of the base metal pieces, or by welding the base metal pieces themselves to a massive backing plate. A specimen with a butt joint was desired, in contrast to the bead-on-plate or fillet-weld specimens described earlier, because the butt weld represented the kind of joint anticipated in weldments of the steel under test, and because tests of the weld area could be more readily conducted. Restrained-joint welding tests often are designed to provide information for a particular application, as can be seen from the examples to follow; however, most of the tests of welds listed in Table 95 are more easily prepared from a butt joint. The principal purpose of the restraint upon the joint during welding is, of course, to determine whether any cracking susceptibility will appear under the more-or-less fixed restraint of the test. The degree of restraint in the test specimen usually is intended to equal or exceed that anticipated in weldments.

U.S. Navy Torture Plate Weld Test

This test, which originated as part of U.S. Navy Specification 46E4, has been used by the Bureau of Ships to determine the suitability of alloy steel (STS) as homogeneous armor plate, and of austenitic Cr–Ni stainless steel armor welding electrodes. The test plate, as shown in Fig. 270, was believed to represent conditions of restraint, cooling, and so forth, found in the welding of joints in the armor plating of warships. After welding, the test is subjected to a searching examination for soundness and tensile testing to measure strength and ductility of the weld joint. The considerable restraint afforded by the heavy backing member, to which the base metal test plate is fillet welded, was quick to reveal susceptibility to underbead cracking in the base metal, and microfissures or hot cracking in the weld metal.

U.S. Army "H" Plate Weld Test

The Ordnance group has successfully employed a welded test plate in which three butt joints formed the letter "H." This specimen is used for evaluating (1) the fabricability of armor steel, (2) the suitability of filler metals and welding procedures, (3) the performance or service capabilities of the armor and the weld joints, and (4) the projectiles themselves which the actual weldments were expected to withstand. An assembly of four pieces of heavy armor plate as shown in Fig. 271 is welded with

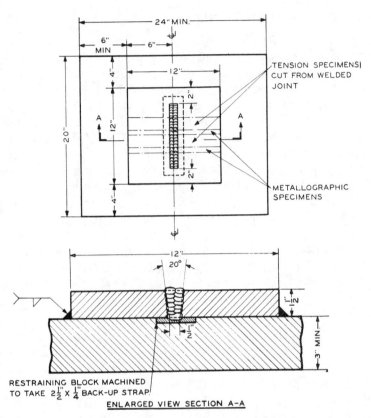

Fig. 270 — U.S. Navy "torture" test plate.

armor welding electrodes. The most critical weld joint is the cross-bar of the "H," marked with a No. 3, which is welded after the two parallel side or leg joints marked No. 1 and No. 2 are completely welded. The degree of restraint imposed upon the cross-bar joint during welding is considerable. If radiographic examination shows the armor plate and the welding electrode to be capable of producing a sound joint in the "H" plate, the entire assembly is taken to the firing range and shot at with various types of missiles under carefully controlled conditions. Any number of tests of welds can be made in the butt joints to gather supplementary data to explain ballistic performance.

CRACK-SUSCEPTIBILITY WELDING TESTS

A number of welding tests have been developed in which the sole aim is to evaluate the tendency of a weld joint to develop cracking; that is, either cracking in the weld metal or cracking in the base metal heat-affected zone. The matter of ductility in the heat-affected zone is not considered, usually because multi-pass welds are to be deposited in which each subsequent bead tempers the heat-affected zone of the preceding bead, or perhaps the weld joint is to be heat treated afterward to secure particular mechanical properties. Naturally, we are anxious to know if cracking will occur during or immediately after welding because any heat treating operation to restore ductility or improve mechanical properties will not rid the joint of crack defects. The specimen design need not be one to permit mechanical tests of the weld. Ordinarily, a searching examination is made by nondestructive and destructive methods of testing for cracking.

The main feature of crack-susceptibility test specimens is the very high degree of restraint imposed upon the base metal pieces. The high

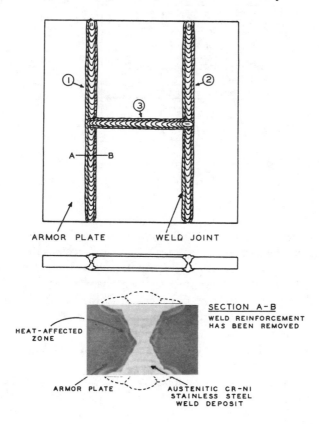

ARMOR PLATE   WELD JOINT

SECTION A-B
WELD REINFORCEMENT
HAS BEEN REMOVED

HEAT-AFFECTED
ZONE

ARMOR PLATE   AUSTENITIC CR-NI
STAINLESS STEEL
WELD DEPOSIT

Fig. 271 — U.S. Army Ordnance "H" test plate.

degree of restraint generates high stresss in the weld area during cooling and tests the ability of metal to endure these stresses without cracking. The restraint is achieved in various ways, and in some cases is varied during the test, as will be seen in the examples that follow.

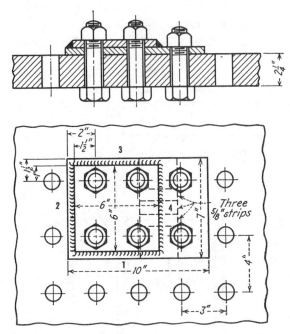

Fig. 272 — Reeve test for cracking in base metal heat-affected zone.

Reeve Cracking Test

The Reeve test, Fig. 272, was developed in England. Restraint is imposed upon the 6-in. square and 7 by 10-in. rectangular base metal pieces by bolting them to a massive bedplate. The four fillet weld beads are deposited around the four sides of the square plate in the prescribed sequence. The highest stresses are generated in the fourth fillet weld area. After the weld has cooled to room temperature for a stated period of time, the weldment is unbolted and two sections, as indicated in Fig. 272, are removed from the fourth fillet weld and examined metallographically for cracking.

The Reeve test has lost popularity because of the variable restraint offered by the bolting. This variability can be reduced by using a measured torque to tighten the bolts and by precision fit or body-bound bolts. However, experience has shown that the restraint required in a cracking test can be easily secured through specimen design and restraining welds, and with less variation in restraint than by bolting the base metal sections.

Controlled Thermal Severity (CTS) Test

The controlled thermal severity cracking test was proposed for evaluating the susceptibility of carbon and alloy steels to underbead cracking in the hardened base metal heat-affected zone of an arc-weld. The specimen shown in Fig. 273 is assembled by bolting the two base metal pieces together and depositing the anchor welds. The bolt is not considered to play a part in governing the restraint upon the test welds. After deposition of the anchor welds, the specimen is cooled to room temperature before the bithermal weld, and before the trithermal weld is deposited. The extent of heat-affected zone cracking is determined metallographically, and is believed to be dependent upon the cooling rate of the base metal immediately adjacent to the weld as it drops below the temperature level of about 575 F. The thickness of the base metal sections (T and B) are varied to alter the thermal severity (cooling rate). In con-

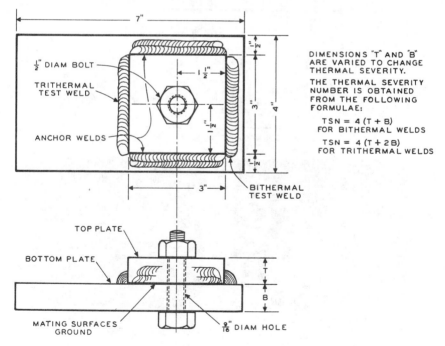

DIMENSIONS "T" AND "B" ARE VARIED TO CHANGE THERMAL SEVERITY.

THE THERMAL SEVERITY NUMBER IS OBTAINED FROM THE FOLLOWING FORMULAE:

$TSN = 4 (T + B)$ FOR BITHERMAL WELDS

$TSN = 4 (T + 2B)$ FOR TRITHERMAL WELDS

Fig. 273 — Controlled thermal severity (CTS) cracking-susceptibility test. (Cottrell)

ducting the CTS test, at least several specimens are prepared with progressive increases in base metal thickness in an attempt to determine the critical cooling rate for a given electrode and base metal combination that produces underbead cracking. It is important, of course, to maintain fixed heat input (joules per inch) from test to test if the base metal thickness is to properly indicate changes in cooling rate.

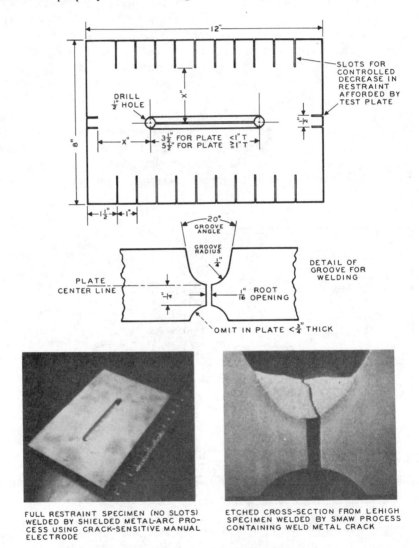

FULL RESTRAINT SPECIMEN (NO SLOTS) WELDED BY SHIELDED METAL-ARC PROCESS USING CRACK-SENSITIVE MANUAL ELECTRODE

ETCHED CROSS-SECTION FROM LEHIGH SPECIMEN WELDED BY SMAW PROCESS CONTAINING WELD METAL CRACK

Fig. 274 — Lehigh restraint cracking test (Doan and Associates)

Lehigh Restraint Cracking Test

The Lehigh restraint test was one of the earliest to incorporate a design feature that permitted quantitative evaluation of the degree of restraint at which cracking would occur in a weld upon cooling. The specimen, illustrated in Fig. 274, consists of a piece of plate with a special weld groove in the center. Slots are cut in the sides and ends of the plate to control the degree of restraint offered by the plate upon the weld. For each electrode or base metal to be tested, a series of plates usually are prepared. The length of slots in the plate are progressively varied from one specimen to another in order to have a gradation in the degree of restraint. The amount of restraint embodied in a particular specimen can be expressed numerically by the width of the specimen between the terminus of the slots, or twice the dimension "X" in Fig. 274. The threshold degree of restraint for causing cracking is determined by first welding a specimen under full restraint (no saw cuts). If any specimen displays cracking, another which imposes less restraint (deeper saw cuts) is prepared until finally a restraint level is reached at which no cracking occurs. The specimen with least restraint that displays cracking is considered the threshold specimen, and the width of this specimen (slot-to-slot dimension) can be used to express the cracking susceptibility of the particular electrode and plate combination. As this number (width dimension) decreases, the cracking susceptibility increases. Tests are conducted with welding conditions fixed; however, replicate series of tests may be prepared using different levels of heat input during welding.

The Lehigh restraint test has been found to be very useful for measuring the cracking susceptibility of the weld metal deposit. The test appears to be sufficiently sensitive to not only differentiate between the various classes of electrodes, but to evaluate the influence of different base metals upon weld metal cracking (via dilution), and to detect differences in performance in various lots of electrodes within a particular class. While most of the work reported in the literature on the Lehigh test is centered upon use of the shielded metal-arc welding process, submerged-arc and gas metal-arc also can be used to weld the Lehigh specimen.

The cracking which occurs in the weld metal in the Lehigh specimen usually can be observed on the top or bottom surfaces. Of course, cracking on the root surface may be more difficult to detect because it ordinarily initiates at the junction between weld and base metals. Some investigators measure the cracking severity in each specimen by noting the percent of the bead length which appears to be cracked. However, experience has shown that internal cracking may have occurred, and this is best detected by metallographic examination. Usually, five or six cross-sections are prepared at equal increments along the weld to establish the amount of cracking present. Metallographic examination also has revealed cracking in the base metal heat-affected zones of certain high-strength steels in the Lehigh specimen. This cracking usually initiates at one of the weld metal–base metal junctions at the root, and it propagates for some distance in the base metal heat-affected zone parallel to the fusion line. This cracking also has been observed to abruptly change its course and propagate through the weld metal. When the weld metal is readily cracked in the test, no cracking ordinarily is found in the base metal heat-affected zones even though the base metal has a cracking susceptibility. Obviously, the stress-relief which results from the weld cracking reduces the severity of conditions imposed upon the base metal zones. Therefore, to properly subject the base metal to the Lehigh test, a specimen must be prepared with a satisfactory (uncracked) weld deposit.

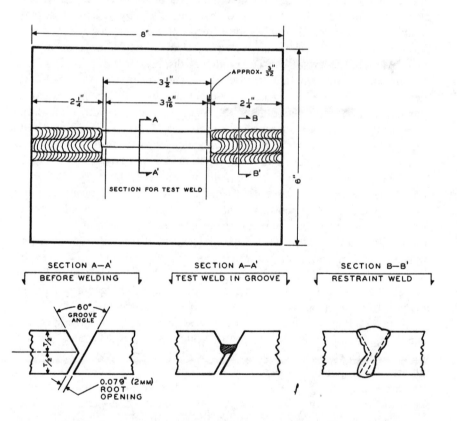

Fig. 275 — Tekken Y-groove restraint weld cracking specimen.

Tekken Restraint Test

An interesting variation of the Lehigh-type specimen has been proposed by Japanese investigators. The Tekken specimen is characterized by an oblique root gap at the base of a partial V-groove as shown in Fig. 275. The specimen is easily prepared by simple torch beveling or machining, and smaller sections of plate can be employed. The originators report that they found the Tekken specimen to be somewhat more sensitive than the Lehigh specimen in detecting base metal cracking susceptibility, whereas the Lehigh specimen appeared to be better suited for cracking tests of electrodes. They found that although cracking behavior was influenced by the shape of the groove and position of the root gap, virtually all of the cracking initiated from the root of the weld in both the Tekken and the Lehigh specimens.

Houldcroft Crack-Susceptibility Test

The Houldcroft crack-susceptibility test was developed for evaluating quantitatively the weld metal hot-cracking tendency of sheet material during gas tungsten-arc welding. A unique feature of the Houldcroft specimen, shown in Fig. 276, is the gradation of restraint in the individual specimen by slots of varying length in the edges of the sheet. The test is conducted by starting a weld made by fusion joining at the unslotted end of the specimen. If the sheet material is weld-crack sensitive, a crack will initiate and will propagate along the weld until the degree of restraint is insufficient to continue the cracking. The length of the crack can be used as a measure of hot cracking susceptibility; that is, the longer the crack the greater the sensitivity to cracking. The Houldcroft specimen ordinarily is not clamped during welding, and welding conditions are carefully standardized and held constant. Complete penetration must be secured and the weld width must not vary. In general, wider weld width and faster weld travel speed tend to increase the likelihood of cracking. Therefore, these two welding conditions can be adjusted to produce weld cracking just at the start of a specimen of almost any sheet material and rely upon the decreasing restraint along the specimen length to provide an index of cracking sensitivity for the particular welding conditions.

A mathematical analysis was made of the Houldcroft hot cracking test to determine the thermal strains developed during its execution. The thermal strains were assumed to vary along the length of the weld by virtue of the slots cut into the sides. However, users of the test were not certain that the hot cracking susceptibility of a material was proportional to the crack length. By adding an integral run-on-tab to the starting position, as

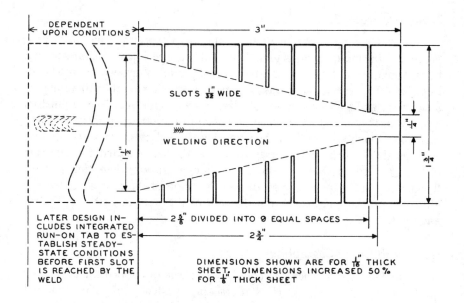

Fig. 276 — Houldcroft crack-susceptibility test.

shown in Fig. 276, steady-state thermal distribution is more nearly established in the critical early portion of the test, and this helps reduce scatter
in test data. Cracking susceptibility does not appear to be proportional to
the crack length in the original specimen design; however, a crack susceptibility factor can be computed which will facilitate a comparison of
the inherent cracking sensitivities of different steels.

Cruciform Test for Plate-Cracking Susceptibility

The cruciform specimen is a double-tee fillet welded assembly (Fig.
277) which offers progressively higher degrees of restraint on the four fillet
welds made in the unit. The test was developed principally for evaluating
the susceptibility of a steel to underbead cracking in the heat-affected
zone of hardenable base metals, like the quenched and tempered alloy
steels. Much testing of armor plate has been conducted with the cruciform
test, and the experience has indicated that all conditions in the welding
and testing procedure must be closely controlled to obtain reproducible
results concerning the cracking susceptibility of the base metal used.

The cruciform specimen is welded with the assembly at a specified
temperature prior to the deposition of each fillet bead. The beads are
deposited in the sequence shown using carefully regulated welding conditions to insure that the increasing degree of restraint on each successive

fillet bead will be the only variable. After completion of the fourth weld, the specimen is held at room temperature for 48 hours and then stress relief heat treated at 1150 F for 2 hours (heating and cooling from 1150 F

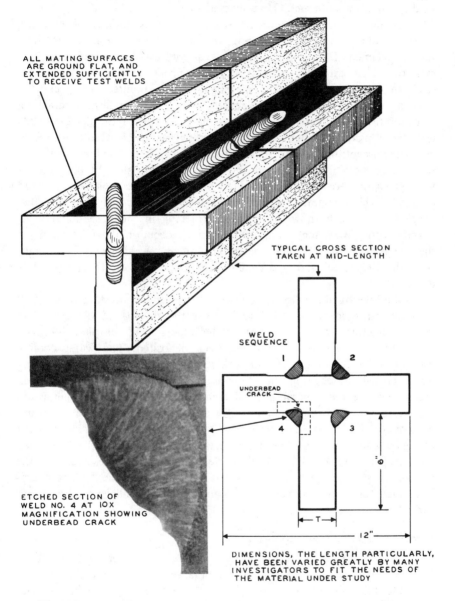

ALL MATING SURFACES
ARE GROUND FLAT, AND
EXTENDED SUFFICIENTLY
TO RECEIVE TEST WELDS

TYPICAL CROSS SECTION
TAKEN AT MID-LENGTH

WELD
SEQUENCE

UNDERBEAD
CRACK

ETCHED SECTION OF
WELD NO. 4 AT 10X
MAGNIFICATION SHOWING
UNDERBEAD CRACK

DIMENSIONS, THE LENGTH PARTICULARLY,
HAVE BEEN VARIED GREATLY BY MANY
INVESTIGATORS TO FIT THE NEEDS OF
THE MATERIAL UNDER STUDY

Fig. 277 — Cruciform test for plate-cracking susceptibility. (Poteat and Warner)

at the rate of 100 degrees F per hour). The specimen is inspected for external signs of cracking, and then is sliced into cross-sections for metallographic examination to determine whether cracking has occurred in the weld metal or the base metal heat-affected zones.

A number of recent reports describing investigations of cracking during welding under restraint refer to the cruciform test as the most severe specimen of the static type; that is, as contrasted to a weld test specimen to which external stress is applied *during* welding to accentuate strain in the weld area. Various investigators have pointed out specifically that the cruciform test is more severe in detecting underbead cracking susceptibility in the base metal than is the CTS test, or the bead-on-plate test. Even plate as thin as ½ inch displays as much ability to reveal cracking susceptibility as does plate 1-inch thick. The cruciform test is so severe that welding a quenched and tempered alloy steel of the 100 ksi yield strength variety by the shielded metal-arc process using a covered electrode which contains a slightly high moisture content in the flux (0.25%) has been shown to produce cracking in the base metal heat-affected zone. Weld metal cracking also may occur in the fillet beads of the cruciform test specimen, particularly if the weld metal is a high-strength, alloy steel and hydrogen is not maintained at the proper low level.

One investigator, who was studying the effect of moisture in E11018 class electrode coverings, tried to increase the severity of the cruciform test by directing streams of water on the underside of the plates between which the previous weld bead had been deposited. The water cooling was applied a few minutes after welding. Surprisingly, the rapid cooling was reported to result in the elimination of cracking in both the weld metal and the base metal heat-affected zones even when the moisture content of the covering was as high as 0.50%. However, a moisture content of 2.5% in the electrode covering caused a small amount of underbead cracking. The base metal being tested was a quenched and tempered (100 ksi YS) alloy steel. It was hypothesized that the cooling must have been at a favorable rate at which the hydrogen embrittlement cracking mechanism is hampered by insufficient diffusion of hydrogen.

Circular-Groove Welding Tests

Welded test plates incorporating a circular groove or weld joint have been employed to test a number of combinations of plate and sheet materials, and filler metals, because of the unusual severity obtainable with this weld configuration. The specimen is unique because it subjects the fusion zone and base metal heat-affected zone to far greater stress than would ordinarily be encountered with a more conventional type of joint consisting of roughly the same mass of material. The particular form of the circular-groove test plate to be used here for illustrative purposes is shown in Fig. 278 (a). A simple circular groove with tapering faces and a rounded bottom has been cut into the face of a square piece of plate. The rounded solid bottom is desirable as it eliminates the notches that are found at the bottom of a groove prepared completely through the plate and fitted with a back-up strip. These notches may cause difficulty in weld metal which tends to be highly crack-susceptible.

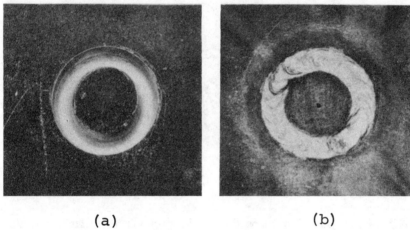

(a) **(b)**

Fig. 278 — Circular-groove weld test plate.

(Left Hand) (a) — Circular groove with tapering sides and rounded root machined in face of 12-in. square plate 1½-in. thick.

(Right Hand) (b) — Completely welded test plate. Hole in center of core is for thermocouple to measure interpass temperature.

The circular groove is filled with a convenient number of weld layers. The initial temperature and interpass temperature can, of course, be varied at will, and depend upon the nature of the materials being tested. Figure 278 (b) illustrates a complete, welded test plate. The manner in which the test plate functions so as to produce intense stresses is believed to be as follows: First, during deposition of each layer of weld metal, the central core of base metal expands at a rate greater than that of the outer plate section because of its isolated position and smaller mass. Upon solidification of the weld metal and over-all cooling of the plate, the core consequently contracts more than the surrounding plate section and stresses are set up between the core and weld metal. The stresses can be varied by changing the dimensions of the square plate. Cracking may occur in the weld metal, at the fusion line, or in the base metal heat-affected zone.

A convenient method of examining the welded circular-groove plate for cracking is to section the plate into quarters and prepare metallographic or macroetch specimens. For example, Fig. 279 shows two quarters of a circular-groove plate that consist of a highly hardenable low-alloy base metal which has been welded with austenitic Cr–Ni steel electrodes of an

Fig. 279 — Method of sectioning and examining circular-groove test plate for welding defects.

early vintage. Upon close inspection of the two polished segments in the foreground, it will be noticed that the specimen on the right-hand side contains a fusion line crack between the central core and the weld metal. The nature of this crack is illustrated in greater detail by the photomicrograph shown earlier in Fig. 199.

A number of additional welding test specimens which embody a circular weld joint or weld bead have evolved. These have been identified as (1) *Circular-Patch Weld Test,* (2) *Modified Circular Restraint Weld Test,* (3) *U. S. Navy Circular-Patch Weld Test, and* (4) *Battelle Restrained Circular Bead Weld Test.* In the circular patch weld test specimen, a round patch section with a double bevel preparation is placed within a circular hole in the center of a plate 12-in. square (sheet specimens 5-in. square also have been tried). In the case of the plate, decreasing the diameter of the circular weld groove (decreasing the patch diameter) acts to increase the degree of restraint and increase the heating of the patch or core area. It has been determined that residual stresses in the order of the base metal yield strength will be present after welding when the patch diameter/plate-width ratio is 0.5 or lower (i.e., 6-in. diameter patch or smaller in a 12-in. square plate).

The modified circular restraint weld test specimen is cut into quarters prior to welding. The mating edges of these four blocks are surface ground to secure a precision fit. The blocks are then re-assembled into a circular-groove plate and tack welded. The purpose of having a tight butt joint intersect the circular groove is to also determine whether the weld metal is susceptible to propagation of a crack from the joint in the base metal.

The Battelle restrained circular-bead weld test was developed to evaluate sheet material. It is conducted with a specimen 2-in. square which is sandwiched between two copper cooling plates which have a circular opening in the center. These plates greatly increase the heat sink capacity of the base metal. A circular weld bead is deposited on the surface of the plate within the round opening in the top copper platen. In the original development work, the test welds formed a 1-in. diameter circle, and the welded specimen was quickly quenched in ice water to increase the severity of the test. However, depending upon the nature of the base metal and the welding process to be employed, the circular bead cracking-susceptibility test can be modified in many ways. The specimen even can be adapted to the gas torch welding process on sheet steel when proper consideration is given to heat input.

Suggested Reading

Guide to the Weldability of Steels, American Welding Society, New York, 1943.

Weldability of Steels, R. D. Stout and W. D. Doty, Welding Research Council, New York, 1953.

Standard Methods for Mechanical Testing of Welds, American Welding Society, A4.0-42, and 1945 Supplement.

Establishment of a Standard Test for Brazed Joints, American Welding Society, C3.1-63.

"Comparison and Analysis of Notch Toughness Tests for Steels in Welded Structures," by H. H. Johnson and R. D. Stout, Welding Research Council Bulletin No. 62, July 1960.

"Methods of Evaluating Welded Joints," by M. D. Randall, R. E. Monroe and P. J. Rieppel, DMIC Report 165, Defense Metals Information Center, Battelle Memorial Institute, December 28, 1961.

"Fracture Analysis Diagram Procedures for the Fracture-Safe Engineering Design of Steel Structures," by W. S. Pellini and P. P. Puzak, Welding Research Council Bulletin No. 88, May 1963.

"Ultrasonic Inspection of Welds," by Bernard Ostrofsky, The Welding Journal, v 44, no. 3, Research Suppl. pp 97s-106s, March 1965.

"Current Trends in Testing Methods, Design and Materials for Fracture Toughness," by W. W. Gerberich, ASM Metals Engineering Quarterly, v 4, no. 4, pp 23-31, November 1964.

"Current Methods of Fracture-Toughness Testing of High-Strength Alloys with Emphasis on Plane Strain," by J. E. Campbell, DMIC Report 207, Defense Metals Information Center, Battelle Memorial Institute, August 31, 1964.

"Fracture Testing of Weldments," by J. A. Kies, H. L. Smith, H. E. Romine, and H. Bernstein, NASA Report No. CR-140, Prepared by Naval Research Laboratory, OTS, Washington, D.C., 1964.

"Fracture-Toughness Testing and its Applications," ASTM Special Technical Publication No. 381.

APPENDIXES

APPENDIX I

COMMONLY USED ABBREVIATIONS

A	Angstrom unit	EL	endurance limit
ac	alternating current (noun)	emf	electromotive force
a-c	alternating current (adjective)	esu	electrostatic unit
AC	air cooled	ev	electron volt
AISI	American Iron and Steel Institute		
amp	ampere	F	Fahrenheit, degrees
AMS	Aeronautical Material Standard, SAE	FC	furnace cool
		fcc	face-centered cubic
		fp	freezing point
ASME	American Society of Mechanical Engineers	fpm	feet per minute
		fps	feet per second
ASTM	American Society for Testing and Materials	ft-lb	foot-pound
at-%	atomic per cent		
at. wt	atomic weight	g	gram
AW	as welded	GMAW	Gas Metal-Arc Welding
AWS	American Welding Society	GTAW	Gas Tungsten-Arc Welding
bcc	body-centered cubic	hcp	hexagonal close-packed
Bhn	Brinell hardness number	hf	high frequency
BOF	basic oxygen furnace	hr	hour
bp	boiling point		
Btu	British thermal unit	ID	inside diameter
		in.	inch
C	Centigrade, degrees	ipm	inches per minute
C_v	Charpy V-notch	IPY	inches penetration per year
cal	calorie		
cu cm	cubic centimeter	j	joule
cfh	cubic feet per hour		
cm	centimeter		
coef	coefficient	K	Kelvin, degrees
cp	chemically pure	kg	kilogram
cps	cycles per second	kji	kilojoules heat input per inch
cu ft	cubic feet	ksi	thousand pounds per square inch
cu in.	cubic inches		
		kv	kilovolt
dc	direct current (noun)	kw	kilowatt
d-c	direct current (adjective)		
deg	degrees	l	liter
diam	diameter	lf	low frequency
DPH	diamond pyramid hardness	<	less than
E	Young's modulus	max	maximum
El.	elongation	M_f	martensite finish

ABBREVIATIONS (continued)

min	minimum	SAE	Society of Automotive Engineers
ml	milliliter		
mm	millimeter	SAW	Submerged Arc Welding
mμ	millimicron	sec	second
>	more than	SMAW	Shielded Metal-Arc Welding
mp	melting point	sp, SP	straight polarity
M$_s$	martensite start	sp gr	specific gravity
μ	micron	sp ht	specific heat
μ	Poisson's ratio	sq cm	square centimeters
		sq ft	square foot
OD	outside diameter	sq in.	square inch
OH	open hearth	SR	Stress Relieved
OQ	oil quenched		
		temp	temperature
pH	hydrogen ion concentration		
ppm	parts per million	USN	United States Navy
psi	pounds per square inch	UTS	ultimate tensile strength
QT	Quenched and Tempered	v	volt
RA	reduction in area	WQ	water quenched
Rc	Rockwell C scale	wt-%	weight per cent
rf	radio frequency		
rp, RP	reverse polarity	YP	yield point
RT	room temperature	YS	yield strength

GREEK ALPHABET

Readers who are not entirely familar with the Greek characters used as symbols in scientific notation will find it helpful to refer to the alphabetical listing shown below.

Alpha	= A, α = A, a		Nu	= N, ν	= N, n
Beta	= B, β = B, b		Xi	= Ξ, ξ	= X, x
Gamma	= Γ, γ = G, g		Omicron	= O, o	= O, o
Delta	= Δ, δ = D, d		Pi	= Π, π	= P, p
Epsilon	= E, ϵ = E, e		Rho	= P, ρ	= R, r
Zeta	= Z, ζ = Z, z		Sigma	= Σ, σ	= S, s
Eta	= H, η = E, e		Tau	= T, τ	= T, t
Theta	= Θ, θ = Th, th		Upsilon	= Υ, υ	= U, u
Iota	= I, ι = I, i		Phi	= Φ, ϕ	= Ph, ph
Kappa	= K, κ = K, k		Chi	= X, χ	= Ch, ch
Lambda	= Λ, λ = L, l		Psi	= Ψ, ψ	= Ps, ps
Mu	= M, μ = M, m		Omega	= Ω, ω	= O, o

TERMINOLOGY, DEFINITIONS AND WELDING SYMBOLS

For accurate communication both in metallurgy and welding the use of proper terms and symbols is unquestionably of prime importance to the engineer. However, as a review of the source material will quickly reveal, it would be quite impractical to include a listing here of such terms, definitions and symbols. For one thing, the inclusion would be far too lengthy; for another, the periodic revisions that are necessary would soon make such listing out-of-date. The reader, therefore, is referred to the sources listed below. These publications, which are readily available, are kept current through periodic revision.

AWS Definitions—Welding and Cutting, AWS A3.0 (latest edition). American Welding Society, 345 E. 47th Street, New York, N.Y. 10017.

Metals Handbook, Volume 1, Properties and Selection of Metals (latest edition). American Society for Metals, Metals Park, Novelty, Ohio.

Standard Welding Symbols, AWS A2.0 (latest edition). American Welding Society, (as above).

THE ELEMENTS

Chemical Symbols, Weights, Physical Properties

Element	Symbol	Atomic No.	Atomic Weight	Melting Point deg F	Boiling Point deg F	Thermal Conductivity (a)	Electrical Resistivity (b)	Coef of Thermal Expansion (c)
Actinium	Ac	89	227	1920	...	...	...	...
Aluminum	Al	13	26.98	1220	4442	0.53	2.7	13.1
Americium	Am	95	243	...	...	...	...	...
Antimony	Sb	51	121.76	1167	2516	0.04	39.0	4.7
Argon	Ar	18	39.94	−309	−302	0.4×10^{-4}	...	...
Arsenic	As	33	74.91	1503	1135(d)	...	33.3	2.6
Astatine	At	85	210	576	...	...	...	...
Barium	Ba	56	137.36	1317	2980	...	...	...
Berkelium	Bk	97	249	...	...	...	...	...
Beryllium	Be	4	9.01	2332	5020	0.35	4.0	6.4
Bismuth	Bi	83	209	520	2840	0.02	106.8	7.4
Boron	B	5	10.82	3690	...	...	1.8×10^{12}	4.6
Bromine	Br	35	79.92	19	136	...	...	...
Cadmium	Cd	48	112.41	610	1409	0.22	6.8	16.6
Calcium	Ca	20	40.08	1540	2625	0.30	3.9	12.4
Californium	Cf	98	249	...	...	...	...	...
Carbon	C	6	12.01	6740(d)	8730	0.06	1375.0	0.3– 2.4
Cerium	Ce	58	140.13	1479	6280	0.03	75.0	4.4
Cesium	Cs	55	132.91	84	1273	...	20.0	54.0
Chlorine	Cl	17	35.46	−150	−30	0.2×10^{-4}	...	...
Chromium	Cr	24	52.01	3407	4829	0.16	12.9	3.4
Cobalt	Co	27	58.94	2723	5250	0.16	6.2	7.7
Columbium	Cb	41	92.91	4474	8901	0.12	12.5	4.1
Copper	Cu	29	63.54	1981	4703	0.94	1.7	9.2
Curium	Cm	96	245	...	...	...	...	...
Dysprosium	Dy	66	162.51	2565	4230	0.02	57.0	5.0
Einsteinium	E	99	254	...	...	...	...	...
Erbium	Er	68	167.20	2727	4770	0.02	107.0	5.0
Europium	Eu	63	152	1519	2710	...	90.0	14.4
Fermium	Fm	100	253	...	...	...	...	...
Fluorine	F	9	19	−363	−307	...	...	...

(a) Thermal conductivity at about room temperature in cal/sq cm/cm/sec/deg C.
(b) Electrical resistivity in microhm-cm.
(c) Coefficient of linear thermal expansion at about room temperature in microin./in./deg F.
(d) Sublimes.
(e) Estimated.

THE ELEMENTS (Continued)

Element	Symbol	Atomic No.	Atomic Weight	Melting Point deg F	Boiling Point deg F	Thermal Conductivity (a)	Electrical Resistivity (b)	Coef of Thermal Expansion (c)
Francium	Fr	87	223	81(e)	...	...	...	...
Gadolinium	Gd	64	157.26	2394	4950	0.02	140.5	2.2
Gallium	Ga	31	69.72	86	4059	0.08	17.4	10.0
Germanium	Ge	32	72.60	1719	5125	0.14	46.0	3.2
Gold	Au	79	197	1945	5380	0.71	2.4	7.9
Hafnium	Hf	72	178.50	4032	9750	0.22	35.1	288.0
Helium	He	2	4	−454	−452	3.3×10^{-4}	...	...
Holmium	Ho	67	164.94	2662	4230	...	87.0	...
Hydrogen	H	1	1.01	−434	−423	4.1×10^{-4}	...	...
Indium	In	49	114.82	313	3632	0.06	8.4	18.0
Iodine	I	53	126.91	237	361	10.4×10^{-4}	1.3×10^{15}	52.0
Iridium	Ir	77	192.20	4449	9570	0.14	5.3	3.8
Iron	Fe	26	55.85	2798	5430	0.18	9.7	6.5
Krypton	Kr	36	83.80	−251	−242	0.2×10^{-4}	...	...
Lanthanum	La	57	138.92	1688	6280	0.03	57.0	2.8
Lead	Pb	82	207.21	621	3137	0.08	20.6	16.3
Lithium	Li	3	6.94	357	2426	0.17	8.6	31.0
Lutetium	Lu	71	174.99	3006	3510	...	79.0	...
Magnesium	Mg	12	24.32	1202	2025	0.37	4.4	15.0
Manganese	Mn	25	54.94	2273	3900	...	185.0	12.2
Mendelevium	Mv	101	256	...	...	...	...	...
Mercury	Hg	80	200.61	−37	675	0.02	98.4	...
Molybdenum	Mo	42	95.95	4730	10,040	0.34	5.2	2.7
Neodymium	Nd	60	144.27	1866	5756	0.03	64.0	3.3
Neon	Ne	10	20.18	−416	−411	0.0001	...	...
Neptunium	Np	93	237	1179	...	...	...	...
Nickel	Ni	28	58.71	2647	4950	0.22	6.8	7.4
Nitrogen	N	7	14	−346	−320	0.6×10^{-4}	...	...
Nobelium	No	102	247	...	...	...	...	...
Osmium	Os	76	190.20	4900(e)	9950	...	9.5	2.6
Oxygen	O	8	16	−362	−297	0.6×10^{-4}	...	...
Palladium	Pd	46	106.40	2826	7200	0.17	10.8	6.5
Phosphorus	P	15	30.98	112	536	...	1×10^{17}	70.0
Platinum	Pt	78	195.09	3217	8185	0.16	10.6	4.9
Plutonium	Pu	94	242	1184	6000	0.02	141.4	30.6
Polonium	Po	84	210	489	...	...	...	...
Potassium	K	19	39.10	147	1400	0.24	6.2	46.0
Praseodymium	Pr	59	140.92	1686	5468	0.03	68.0	2.2

THE ELEMENTS *(Continued)*

Element	Symbol	Atomic No.	Atomic Weight	Melting Point deg F	Boiling Point deg F	Thermal Conduc- tivity (a)	Elec- trical Resis- tivity (b)	Coef of Thermal Expansion (c)
Promethium	Pm	61	145	1880(e)	...	...	...	...
Protactinium	Pa	91	231	2246(e)	...	...	...	...
Radium	Ra	88	226.05	1292	...	...	...	...
Radon	Rn	86	222	—96(e)	—79	...	...	...
Rhenium	Re	75	186.22	5755	10,650	0.17	19.3	3.7
Rhodium	Rh	45	102.91	3571	8130	0.21	4.5	4.6
Rubidium	Rb	37	85.48	102	1270	...	12.5	50.0
Ruthenium	Ru	44	101.10	4530	8850	...	7.6	5.1
Samarium	Sm	62	150.35	1962	2966	...	88.0	...
Scandium	Sc	21	44.96	2802	4946	...	61.0	...
Selenium	Se	34	78.96	423	1265	12×10^{-4}	12.0	21.0
Silicon	Si	14	28.09	2570	4860	0.20	10.0	2.8
Silver	Ag	47	107.88	1761	4010	1.00	1.6	10.9
Sodium	Na	11	23	208	1638	0.32	4.2	39.0
Strontium	Sr	38	87.63	1414	2520	...	23.0	...
Sulfur	S	16	32.07	246	832	6.3×10^{-4}	2×10^{23}	36.0
Tantalum	Ta	73	180.95	5425	9800	0.13	12.4	3.6
Technetium	Tc	43	99	3870(e)	...	...	...	...
Tellurium	Te	52	127.61	841	1814	0.01	436,000	9.3
Terbium	Tb	65	158.93	2472	4586	...	...	3.9
Thallium	Tl	81	204.39	577	2655	0.09	18.0	16.0
Thorium	Th	90	232.05	3182	7000	0.09	13.0	6.9
Thulium	Tm	69	168.94	2813	3130(e)	...	79.0	...
Tin	Sn	50	118.70	449	4120	0.15	11.0	13.0
Titanium	Ti	22	47.90	3035	5900	6.60	42.0	4.7
Tungsten	W	74	183.86	6170	10,706	0.40	5.6	2.6
Uranium	U	92	238.07	2070	6904	0.07	30.0	5.8
Vanadium	V	23	50.95	3450	6150	0.07	25.4	4.6
Xenon	Xe	54	131.30	—169	—162	1.2×10^{-4}	...	...
Ytterbium	Yb	70	173.04	1515	2786	...	29.0	13.9
Yttrium	Y	39	88.92	2748	5490	0.04	57.0	...
Zinc	Zn	30	65.38	787	1663	0.27	5.9	22.0
Zirconium	Zr	40	91.22	3366	6470	0.21	40.0	3.2

(a) Thermal conductivity at about room temperature in cal/sq cm/cm/sec/deg C.
(b) Electrical resistivity in microhm-cm.
(c) Coefficient of linear thermal expansion at about room temperature in microin./in./deg F.
(d) Sublimes.
(e) Estimated.

CONVERSIONS FOR FAHRENHEIT—CENTIGRADE TEMPERATURE SCALES

Enter the central (bold-face) columns with the number to be converted. If converting Fahrenheit degrees, read the Centigrade equivalent in the column headed "C". If converting Centigrade degrees, read the Fahrenheit equivalent in the column headed "F".

C		F
−273	**−459**	
−268	**−450**	
−262	**−440**	
−257	**−430**	
−251	**−420**	
−246	**−410**	
−240	**−400**	
−234	**−390**	
−229	**−380**	
−223	**−370**	
−218	**−360**	
−212	**−350**	
−207	**−340**	
−201	**−330**	
−196	**−320**	
−190	**−310**	
−184	**−300**	
−179	**−290**	
−173	**−280**	
−168	**−270**	−454
−162	**−260**	−436
−157	**−250**	−418
−151	**−240**	−400
−146	**−230**	−382
−140	**−220**	−364
−134	**−210**	−346
−129	**−200**	−328
−123	**−190**	−310
−118	**−180**	−292
−112	**−170**	−274
−107	**−160**	−256
−101	**−150**	−238
− 96	**−140**	−220
− 90	**−130**	−202
− 84	**−120**	−184
− 79	**−110**	−166
− 73	**−100**	−148
− 68	**− 90**	−130
− 62	**− 80**	−112
− 57	**− 70**	− 94
− 51	**− 60**	− 76
− 46	**− 50**	− 58
−40	**−40**	−40
−34	**−30**	−22
−29	**−20**	− 4
−23	**−10**	14
−17.8	**0**	32
−16.7	**2**	35.6
−15.6	**4**	39.2
−14.4	**6**	42.8
−13.3	**8**	46.4
−12.2	**10**	50.0
−11.1	**12**	53.6
−10.0	**14**	57.2
− 8.9	**16**	60.8
− 7.8	**18**	64.4
− 6.7	**20**	68.0
− 5.6	**22**	71.6
− 4.4	**24**	75.2
− 3.3	**26**	78.8
− 2.2	**28**	82.4
− 1.1	**30**	86.0
0.0	**32**	89.6
1.1	**34**	93.2
2.2	**36**	96.8
3.3	**38**	100.4
4.4	**40**	104.0
5.6	**42**	107.6
6.7	**44**	111.2
7.8	**46**	114.8
8.9	**48**	118.4
10.0	**50**	122.0
11.1	**52**	125.6
12.2	**54**	129.2
13.3	**56**	132.8
14.4	**58**	136.4
15.6	**60**	140.0
16.7	**62**	143.6
17.8	**64**	147.2
18.9	**66**	150.8
20.0	**68**	154.4
21.1	**70**	158.0
22.2	**72**	161.6
23.3	**74**	165.2
24.4	**76**	168.8
25.6	**78**	172.4
26.7	**80**	176.0
27.8	**82**	179.6
28.9	**84**	183.2
30.0	**86**	186.8
31.1	**88**	190.4
32.2	**90**	194.0
33.3	**92**	197.6
34.4	**94**	201.2
35.6	**96**	204.8
36.7	**98**	208.4
37.8	**100**	212.0
43	**110**	230
49	**120**	248
54	**130**	266
60	**140**	284
66	**150**	302
71	**160**	320
77	**170**	338
82	**180**	356
88	**190**	374
93	**200**	392
99	**210**	410
100	**212**	414
104	**220**	428
110	**230**	446
116	**240**	464
121	**250**	482
127	**260**	500
132	**270**	518
138	**280**	536
143	**290**	554
149	**300**	572
154	**310**	590
160	**320**	608
166	**330**	626
171	**340**	644
177	**350**	662
182	**360**	680
188	**370**	698
193	**380**	716
199	**390**	734
204	**400**	752
210	**410**	770
216	**420**	788
221	**430**	806
227	**440**	824
232	**450**	842
238	**460**	860
243	**470**	878
249	**480**	896
254	**490**	914
260	**500**	932
266	**510**	950
271	**520**	968
277	**530**	986
282	**540**	1004
288	**550**	1022
293	**560**	1040
299	**570**	1058
304	**580**	1076
310	**590**	1094
316	**600**	1112
321	**610**	1130
327	**620**	1148
332	**630**	1166
338	**640**	1184
343	**650**	1202
349	**660**	1220
354	**670**	1238
360	**680**	1256
366	**690**	1274
371	**700**	1292
377	**710**	1310
382	**720**	1328
388	**730**	1346
393	**740**	1364
399	**750**	1382
404	**760**	1400
410	**770**	1418
416	**780**	1436
421	**790**	1454
427	**800**	1472

TEMPERATURE CONVERSION TABLE (Continued)

C	F		C	F		C	F		C	F	
432	810	1490	738	1360	2480	1043	1910	3470	1349	2460	4460
438	820	1508	743	1370	2498	1049	1920	3488	1354	2470	4478
443	830	1526	749	1380	2516	1054	1930	3506	1360	2480	4496
449	840	1544	754	1390	2534	1060	1940	3524	1366	2490	4514
454	850	1562	760	1400	2552	1066	1950	3542	1371	2500	4532
460	860	1580	766	1410	2570	1071	1960	3560	1377	2510	4550
466	870	1598	771	1420	2588	1077	1970	3578	1382	2520	4568
471	880	1616	777	1430	2606	1082	1980	3596	1388	2530	4586
477	890	1634	782	1440	2624	1088	1990	3614	1393	2540	4604
482	900	1652	788	1450	2642	1093	2000	3632	1399	2550	4622
488	910	1670	793	1460	2660	1099	2010	3650	1404	2560	4640
493	920	1688	799	1470	2678	1104	2020	3668	1410	2570	4658
499	930	1706	804	1480	2696	1110	2030	3686	1416	2580	4676
504	940	1724	810	1490	2714	1116	2040	3704	1421	2590	4694
510	950	1742	816	1500	2732	1121	2050	3722	1427	2600	4712
516	960	1760	821	1510	2750	1127	2060	3740	1432	2610	4730
521	970	1778	827	1520	2768	1132	2070	3758	1438	2620	4748
527	980	1796	832	1530	2786	1138	2080	3776	1443	2630	4766
532	990	1814	838	1540	2804	1143	2090	3794	1449	2640	4784
538	1000	1832	843	1550	2822	1149	2100	3812	1454	2650	4802
543	1010	1850	849	1560	2840	1154	2110	3830	1460	2660	4820
549	1020	1868	854	1570	2858	1160	2120	3848	1466	2670	4838
554	1030	1886	860	1580	2876	1166	2130	3866	1471	2680	4856
560	1040	1904	866	1590	2894	1171	2140	3884	1477	2690	4874
566	1050	1922	871	1600	2912	1177	2150	3902	1482	2700	4892
571	1060	1940	877	1610	2930	1182	2160	3920	1488	2710	4910
577	1070	1958	882	1620	2948	1188	2170	3938	1493	2720	4928
582	1080	1976	888	1630	2966	1193	2180	3956	1499	2730	4946
588	1090	1994	893	1640	2984	1199	2190	3974	1504	2740	4964
593	1100	2012	899	1650	3002	1204	2200	3992	1510	2750	4982
599	1110	2030	904	1660	3020	1210	2210	4010	1516	2760	5000
604	1120	2048	910	1670	3038	1216	2220	4028	1521	2770	5018
610	1130	2066	916	1680	3056	1221	2230	4046	1527	2780	5036
616	1140	2084	921	1690	3074	1227	2240	4064	1532	2790	5054
621	1150	2102	927	1700	3092	1232	2250	4082	1538	2800	5072
627	1160	2120	932	1710	3110	1238	2260	4100	1543	2810	5090
632	1170	2138	938	1720	3128	1243	2270	4118	1549	2820	5108
638	1180	2156	943	1730	3146	1249	2280	4136	1554	2830	5126
643	1190	2174	949	1740	3164	1254	2290	4154	1560	2840	5144
649	1200	2192	954	1750	3182	1260	2300	4172	1566	2850	5162
654	1210	2210	960	1760	3200	1266	2310	4190	1571	2860	5180
660	1220	2228	966	1770	3218	1271	2320	4208	1577	2870	5198
666	1230	2246	971	1780	3236	1277	2330	4226	1582	2880	5216
671	1240	2264	977	1790	3254	1282	2340	4244	1588	2890	5234
677	1250	2282	982	1800	3272	1288	2350	4262	1593	2900	5252
682	1260	2300	988	1810	3290	1293	2360	4280	1599	2910	5270
688	1270	2318	993	1820	3308	1299	2370	4298	1604	2920	5288
693	1280	2336	999	1830	3326	1304	2380	4316	1610	2930	5306
699	1290	2354	1004	1840	3344	1310	2390	4334	1616	2940	5324
704	1300	2372	1010	1850	3362	1316	2400	4352	1621	2950	5342
710	1310	2390	1016	1860	3380	1321	2410	4370	1627	2960	5360
716	1320	2408	1021	1870	3398	1327	2420	4388	1632	2970	5378
721	1330	2426	1027	1880	3416	1332	2430	4406	1638	2980	5396
727	1340	2444	1032	1890	3434	1338	2440	4424	1643	2990	5414
732	1350	2462	1038	1900	3452	1343	2450	4442	1649	3000	5432

$$C = 5/9 \ (F-32) \qquad F = 9/5 \ C + 32$$

CONVERSION FACTORS & METRIC REMINDERS

To facilitate conversion of some of the U. S. and British units used in this book to the metric and other systems, a number of conversion factors are given below. In addition. the list of metric reminders should help the reader in·recognizing a number of basic relationships. The values given may be rounded off to the practical needs of the user.

Multiply	By	To Obtain
inches	25.40	millimeters
inches	2.540	centimeters
inches	0.02540	meters
feet	0.30480	meters
square inches	645.160	square millimeters
square inches	6.45160	square centimeters
cubic inches	16.3871	cubic centimeters
cubic feet	28.316	liters
pounds (avdp)	0.45359	kilograms
pounds per square inch	0.000703	kilograms per square millimeter
atmospheres	14.7	pounds per square inch
atmospheres	760	millimeter Hg (torr)
cubic feet per hour	0.4719	liters per minute
British thermal units	1055	joules
calories	4.186	joules
watts	3.413	Btu per hour

1 meter (m) = 39.37 in.
1 centimeter (cm) = 1×10^{-2} m = 0.3937 in.
1 millimeter (mm) = 1×10^{-1} cm = 0.03937 in.
1 micron (μ) = 1×10^{-3} mm = 39.37×10^{-6} in.
1 millimicron (mμ) = 1×10^{-3} μ = 39.37×10^{-9} in.
1 Angstrom (A) = 1×10^{-7} mm = 39.37×10^{-10} in.
1 square centimeter (sq cm) = 100 square millimeters (sq mm) = 0.1550 sq in.
1 cubic centimeter (cu cm) = 1000 cubic millimeters (cu mm) = 0.0610 cu in.
1 liter (1) = 1000.03 cu cm = 1.057 liquid quarts = 61.025 cu in.
1 gram (g) = 0.001 kilogram (kg) = 0.03527 oz (avdp)
1 kilogram (kg) = 1000 g = 2.2046 lb (avdp)
1 millimeter Hg (torr) = 1000 microns Hg = 0.01934 psi

APPENDIX III

PROBLEMS

The material in this appendix may be used by the instructor in class exercises, or by the individual to measure the profit of his reading. The questions and problems are grouped according to chapters, and the information required to answer each question or to solve each problem lies within the respective chapter.

Chapter 10 — FILLER METALS FOR JOINING IRON AND STEEL

1. How much emphasis should be placed upon striving to obtain weld metal of the selfsame chemical composition as the base metal to be joined?
2. If the chemical composition of a weld metal is carefully adjusted to be the same as that of the base metal will the microstructures of the weld metal and the base metal be identical?
3. What is an "autogenous" weld?
4. Are the mechanical properties of weld metal always superior to those of the base metal?
5. What can be offered as an explanation for the higher yield strength invariably found in weld metal as compared with base metal of similar composition?
6. Describe some of the conditions which tend to make weld metal heterogeneous in alloy composition within its cross section.
7. What kind of steel wire is most widely used as the core wire in the flux-covered electrodes of mild steel, and low-alloy steel employed in shielded metal-arc welding?
8. How does the welding process employed in fusion joining affect the strength of the weld metal?
9. In what principal way does the carbon steel electrode used in gas metal-arc welding differ from the carbon steel welding rod employed for oxyacetylene welding?
10. During deposition of a weld bead by the shielded metal-arc process, what happens to the base metal which is melted from the edge preparation?
11. If a weld bead was described as having undergone 80% dilution during welding, what is known about the sources of metal for forming the bead?
12. If a steel weldment of ASTM A 537, Grade A steel intended for cryogenic service is assembled by the GMAW process, what electrode composition should be selected to produce weld metal containing a mini-

mum of 1.5% nickel, assuming that equal amounts of filler metal and base metal (melted by penetration) fill the joints?

13. What is an "emissive" electrode and in what welding process is it employed?

14. If arc welding electrodes of the E11018-G classification were purchased for shielded metal-arc welding a high-strength steel, but the welder found that a root bead could be deposited more easily by the gas tungsten-arc process, could he remove the covering from the electrode and use the core wire as a welding (filler) rod to make a satisfactory joint? Explain.

15. Are the weld metals employed in joining carbon and alloy steels normally of low-carbon content? Why?

16. What alloying elements are frequently added to weld metal to improve suitability for service at high temperatures?

17. What alloying elements are added to weld metal to improve toughness at very low temperatures?

18. Why has sulfur been overlooked as an effective alloying element for improving the machinability of weld metal?

19. If steel tubing of 80 ksi tensile strength were to be welded in constructing a heat exchanger for service at 875 F, would covered arc welding electrodes of E-8018-B4L and E8018-C1 be equally suited for the application? Explain.

20. If a steel having a tensile strength of 115 ksi minimum is welded with an electrode of the E12018-G classification, what precautions must be taken with respect to the composition of the weld metal and the final condition of the weldment?

21. Designate the AWS–ASTM specification which covers the electrode and granulated flux materials to be used in the welding of carbon steels, of alloy steels.

22. Are high-alloy steel (stainless steel) filler metals ever employed in the welding of carbon and alloy steels?

23. What happens when a high-alloy steel metal is diluted excessively in being deposited in a joint in mild steel?

24. In what fundamental respect are nickel-base alloy weld metals like the austenitic high-alloy steel weld metals?

25. Why is a slightly oxidizing flame adjustment usually used in oxy-acetylene braze welding of steel when the filler metal is a copper-base alloy containing zinc?

Chapter 11 — SHRINKAGE AND DISTORTION IN WELDMENTS

1. Explain the difference between solidification shrinkage, contraction, and distortion.
2. If a precise 1-inch cube of mild steel is heated from 70 F to a temperature of 120 F, assuming the coefficient of expansion to be 6.7×10^{-6} and Young's Modulus to be 30 million, what will be its dimensions at the higher temperature? If the 1-inch cube is completely constrained from expanding during this heating, what level of stress will develop in the metal at the higher temperature and what will be the nature of the stress?
3. Explain what happens if the cube (in question no. 2) is heated to 1700 F under complete constraint and is then cooled under complete restraint back to 70 F.
4. Give a short definition of residual stress, reaction stress, and structure stress as these stresses are related to welding.
5. How are residual stresses related to the yield strength of steel at room temperature and at elevated temperatures?
6. Briefly describe a method of measuring residual stresses in a simple bar of steel, also in the area of a welded joint in a steel plate.
7. What is a stress gradient, and what is its significance?
8. A butt weld is to be made in a vee joint between free plates $6 \times 6 \times \frac{1}{2}$ inches. Describe the distortions that occur as a result of welding. Where are the maximum tensile residual stresses located? What is the approximate level of maximum residual stress? How high are the reaction stresses?
9. What precaution might well be taken with respect to the temperature of a weldment if it is to be proof tested at a high stress level, or deliberately over stressed to "iron-out" peak residual stresses?
10. Does the presence of residual stresses in a weldment detract from its load-carrying capability in service?
11. In arc-welding a butt joint in steel plate, can an approximation be made of the overall shrinkage of the assembly normal to the longitudinal axis of the weld? of the longitudinal shrinkage parallel to the weld?
12. Does transverse shrinkage increase or decrease with greater weld cross section? Why?
13. In what way does restraint upon the workpieces transverse to the weld axis, affect transverse shrinkage? residual stresses?
14. What factor exerts principal control over angular distortion in welding, and what steps can be taken to minimize this form of distortion?
15. How does multipass welding of a vee joint in 1-inch thick plate influence transverse shrinkage? angular distortion?

16.   Describe briefly the essential steps in thermal straightening to correct bowing in a steel I beam.

17.   Of what practical value is the oft-repeated, time-tested observation regarding the localized heating of a metal section to the effect that "the *hot* side will become the *short* side."

Chapter 12 — PREHEATING AND POSTHEATING

1.   What are the principal reasons for considering the application of preheating or postheating to a weldment?

2.   How does preheating reduce the cooling rate at the weld?

3.   What possible detrimental effects or conditions may result from preheating?

4.   How does preheating prevent cold cracking in the base metal heat-affected zones of hardenable steel during welding?

5.   How can the chemical composition of steel be translated into suggested preheat temperature?

6.   Explain the mechanics by which preheating reduces residual stresses.

7.   What benefit has been shown to be gained from preheating even mild steel weldments where good fracture toughness is a requisite?

8.   Metallurgical difficulties sometimes arise when base metal at a very low temperature is arc welded. What is the nature of these difficulties and what factor in welding serves as their basic cause?

9.   If a hardenable steel workpiece has been properly preheated for arc welding is there any necessity for specifying interpass temperature conditions?

10.   When are precautions with respect to temperature and cooling practice advisable if an arc welding operation must be interrupted for a substantial period of time?

11.   Why is preheating used in thermal cutting operations, such as performed with oxygen cutting and the plasma-jet torch, and how is it applied customarily?

12.   How does preheating deepen the heat-affected zone in the base metal adjacent to a weld?

13.   Why cannot local preheating be substituted without reservation for total preheating?

14.   Does postweld stress-relief heat treatment make preheating unnecessary? Explain.

15.   Would postweld stress-relief heat treatment be advisable for a weldment which is to be machined to final close dimensions? Why?

16. What is the difference, if any, between postweld stress-relief heat treatment and a postweld annealing treatment?

17. Is a temperature of 1100 F suitable for the thermal stress relieving of all steels? Explain.

18. Has experience shown postweld stress-relief heat treatment to be of any significant value in steel pressure vessels?

Chapter 13 — DIFFICULTIES AND DEFECTS

1. What is the difference between a defect and a discontinuity?

2. Why are cracks likely to be found in the arc-strike marks left on the surface of a weldment?

3. What is the meaning of "penetration" and "dilution?" Are these terms related in any way?

4. Explain how the bubbling of an insoluble gas through a bath of molten metal will rid the bath of other dissolved gases.

5. Describe at least three possible causes of porosity in weld metal.

6. Name at least four elements or compounds which may be encountered as a contaminant in welding; the difficulty or defect which each can cause; and the mechanism by which the contaminant exerts its undesirable effect.

7. Explain how "worm holes" may be formed in weld metal.

8. Describe several causes of slag inclusions in weld metal.

9. What can be meant by the term "burning" in metals?

10. Is undercutting at the edge of a weld of any real significance? If so, what are some causes of undercutting?

11. What are the general characteristics of "cold cracking" as compared with "hot cracking?"

12. Why is the crater of a weld bead prone to display a higher susceptibility to cracking?

13. Under what circumstances is hot cracking likely to be found in heat-affected zones?

14. Where in a weld joint is cold cracking likely to occur, and what are the possible causes?

15. Describe briefly the "stress-induced diffusion" concept which appears to best explain hydrogen embrittlement.

16. What approximate level of hydrogen would be expected in the weld metal deposited by an E6010 electrode under ordinary welding conditions?

17. How might hydrogen embrittlement result in the catastrophic failure of a weldment many months after its fabrication?

18.   What are "fisheyes" in weld metal?

19.   Under what circumstances is cracking likely to occur along the interface between weld metal and base metal?

20.   What three general courses can be taken to control embrittlement induced by hydrogen?

21.   What is meant by "anisotropy" in base metal?

22.   Why are weldments prone to give more difficulty with fatigue failure? What is the most important factor in a weldment that promotes this form of fracture?

23.   What is meant by "critical crack size?"

24.   What is "chevron pattern" in a fracture, and what is its significance?

25.   Under what conditions can graphite form in a steel weldment, and what is likely to be the consequences of its formation?

Chapter 14 — WELDING CARBON STEEL

1.   What are the lowest and the highest carbon contents likely to be encountered in products commonly referred to as "carbon steels?"

2.   What factors may influence the cooling rate of a weld joint?

3.   How can the cooling rate at some particular point in a weld joint be determined indirectly from hardness measurements?

4.   Distinguish between "critical range" and "critical cooling rate."

5.   If martensite is found in the heat-affected zone of a given weld, why will changing the steel to one of lower hardenability be likely to prevent the appearance of martensite?

6.   What is the connection between the occurrence of martensite in the heat-affected zone and the cooling rate or temperature gradient?

7.   Why is great emphasis placed upon the appearance of martensite in the vicinity of a weld, despite the fact that as the cooling rate is increased gradually, the mechanical properties of the steel also change gradually?

8.   Is the hardness of martensite in steel governed by any particular element?

9.   Describe the changes that may occur in the volume of a medium-carbon steel as it is heated to 1700 F and slowly cooled to room temperature; also when quenched in water.

10.   How can the critical range for a steel be determined? Can it be calculated by any means?

11.   What is a "CCT" diagram?

12.   What kind of defect might be encountered in a gas tungsten-arc weld made in a rimmed steel?

13. Approximately what range of carbon content is likely to be found for the so-called "mild steels?"

14. What maximum levels of carbon and manganese appear to represent the practical limit for unqualified weldability in a carbon steel?

15. What are some of the first steps that can be taken to secure a carbon steel with improved fracture toughness?

16. What are the requirements of ASTM A 300 that insure good fracture toughness in steels for low-temperature service?

17. Are any alloying elements, other than carbon and manganese, ever found in significant quantities in carbon steels?

18. What advantages are offered by quenched and tempered carbon steel plates for use in weldments?

19. What considerations must be given to the selection of filler metal for use in joining quenched and tempered, high-strength carbon steels?

20. Why are the steels used in pipelines commonly evaluated for under-bead cracking susceptibility by shielded metal-arc welding with cellulosic-covered electrodes?

21. Describe the precautions which should be incorporated in procedures for arc welding a high-carbon steel (0.65% C).

22. What factor in the composition of cast iron has greatest influence upon weldability?

23. Explain the concept of "carbon equivalency" in estimating the weldability of steels.

Chapter 15 — WELDING ALLOY STEELS

1. Give a few reasons for adding alloying elements to steel.

2. Briefly describe at least four of the strengthening mechanisms which operate in alloy steels.

3. What is "synergism" in alloy steels?

4. Are alloy steels necessarily more difficult to weld than carbon steels?

5. How does the grain size of austenite influence transformation during cooling?

6. Define "hardenability" in a steel.

7. If a curve were plotted to illustrate transformation of austenite during continuous cooling, would it differ greatly from a curve plotted for iso-thermal transformation?

8. In what way do the alloying elements carbon, manganese, chromium, nickel and molybdenum affect the M_s point of steel during the transformation of austenite upon cooling?

9. What two alloying elements appear to exert greatest control over the fracture toughness of alloy steels? Are any of the alloying elements outstanding in improving fracture toughness at low temperatures?

10. What is meant by "recovery" in welding alloy steels?

11. What improved properties, in addition to higher strength, can be found in the high-strength, low-alloy steels?

12. What four properties or characteristics of a quenched and tempered alloy steel are controlled through chemical composition to obtain satisfactory weldability and to insure good service performance?

13. Why is high heat input generally to be avoided in welding quenched and tempered alloy steels?

14. What can be generally said about the fracture toughness of vanadium-alloyed weld deposits of high strength level if a postweld stress-relief heat treatment is applied?

15. Why is AISI 4340 usually referred to as a "heat-treatable alloy steel?" What precautions usually are taken in welding this steel?

16. Under what circumstances would the deliberate decarburization of the surface of an alloy steel weldment be desirable?

17. Briefly describe the general chemical composition and metallurgical behavior of the maraging steels. What fundamental behavior of the maraging steels account for their ability to be welded without the danger of cold cracking in their base metal heat-affected zones?

18. What alloying elements are most often employed in alloy steels for use in weldments intended for high temperature service?

19. What alloying element has proved very useful in steels for service at very low temperatures?

20. What is meant when a 3½% nickel steel is pointed out as a P-Number 9 steel?

21. Why are the magnetic properties of 9% nickel steel an important factor in arc welding operations?

22. What changes occur in the properties of steel under irradiation in nuclear service that are of importance to the safety of the equipment?

23. In what way is the chemical composition and the structure of the silicon-alloyed electrical steels unfavorable metallurgically during welding?

Chapter 16 — WELDING TESTS

1. Do you agree that the terms "tests of welds" and "welding tests" are synonymous?

2.   Give reasons for insisting that articles to be assembled by welding should be *designed* as a weldment.

3.   In what kind of testing are the factors "K_c" and "K_{Ic}" discussed. What do they indicate?

4.   In your own opinion, how might "weldability" be defined?

5.   Give a brief description of the Jominy Hardness-Bend Ductility System for controlling cracking and ductility in the heat-affected zone of weld joints in hardenable steels. What are the useful innovations and the poor features of this system?

6.   Describe at least two test methods for evaluating the fracture toughness of weld joints.

7.   What is the cruciform test? What is unique about it?

8.   Suggest a new, simple test for evaluating the weldability of steels.

INDEX

Volume 2

Sulfur:
- absorption during heating, 199
- hot cracking influence, 235, 431
- low-alloy steel weld metal, 67
- maraging alloy steels, 528
- segregation test method, 222

Superstrength alloy steels, 503

Surfacing:
- alloy steel filler metals, 103
- carbon steel filler metals, 102
- cast iron, filler metals, 388
- welding rods and electrodes, 100
- weld metal, 196

Synergistic effects of alloys, 450

Synthetic welding tests, 598

Tall's stress measurement method, 121

Tekken restraint welding test, 631

Temperature conversion table, 646

Temper brittleness, 71, 169
- alloy steels, 428
- vanadium influence, 488

Tempering anneal, 158

Tempering during stress relief heat treatment, 160, 167

Tensile properties, 585
- elongation, 291
- gas metal-arc weld deposits, 56
- notched specimen, 589
- weld metal, 32

Tests of welds, 584

Thermal cracking, 193

Thermal embrittlement, 531

Thermal straightening, 138

Thermal stress, 112

Tin-base solders, 19

Titania-type electrode covering, 42, 83

Titanium:
- alloy in steel, 201
- vitreous enameling steel, 345
- weld metal deoxidizer, 343

Toe cracking, 229

Torsion tests, 586

Toughness, 292
- alloy steel weldments, 423, 454, 472
- carbon steel weldments, 618
- weld metal, 10

Transformation hardening, 404

Transverse shrinkage, 130

Transverse specimens from weld joint, 369

Trithermal weld in CTS test, 627

Troostite, microstructure, 177

Tubing, carbon steels, 370

Tungsten carbide in surfacing weld, 104

Twinning in martensite, 246

Ultra high-strength steels, 498

Ultrasonic inspection, 587

Ultrasonic vibration, use, 280

Underbead cracking, 229, 633
- formula for evaluation, 393

Undercutting, 250
- brittle fracture influence, 502
- fatigue property influence, 284
- weld toe character, 218

U. S. Army H-plate weld test, 623

U. S. Navy torture plate weld test, 623

Vanadium:
- filler metal alloying, 490
- high-strength, low-alloy steels, 448
- hot cracking influence, 432
- low-alloy steel weld metal, 72, 75
- shielded metal-arc weld deposits, 75
- temper brittleness influence, 488

Volume shrinkage upon solidification, 108

W/A, crack-toughness value, 588

Wagon tracks, 214

Water of crystallization, 202